PEARSON

ALWAYS LEARNING

Elayn Martin-Gay

Beginning Algebra

MAT 0022 and MAT 0056
Revised Custom Edition for Palm Beach State College

Taken from:
Beginning Algebra, Seventh Edition
by Elayn Martin-Gay

Cover Art: Courtesy of Photodisc/Getty Images.

Taken from:

Beginning Algebra, Seventh Edition
by Elayn Martin-Gay
Copyright © 2017, 2013, 2009 by Pearson Education, Inc.
New York, New York 10013

This special edition published in cooperation with Pearson Education, Inc.

Pearson Education, Inc., 330 Hudson Street, New York, New York 10013
A Pearson Education Company
www.pearsoned.com

Printed in the United States of America

6 17

000200010272023648

JC

ISBN 10: 1-323-44124-7
ISBN 13: 978-1-323-44124-4

Contents

This book is dedicated to students everywhere—and we should all be students. After all, is there anyone among us who really knows too much? Take that hint and continue to learn something new every day of your life.

Best of wishes from a fellow student: Elayn Martin-Gay

Preface

Beginning Algebra, **Seventh Edition** was written to provide a solid foundation in algebra for students who might not have previous experience in algebra. Specific care was taken to make sure students have the most up-to-date, relevant text preparation for their next mathematics course or for nonmathematical courses that require an understanding of algebraic fundamentals. I have tried to achieve this by writing a user-friendly text that is keyed to objectives and contains many worked-out examples. As suggested by AMATYC and the NCTM Standards (plus Addenda), real-life and real-data applications, data interpretation, conceptual understanding, problem solving, writing, cooperative learning, appropriate use of technology, number sense, estimation, critical thinking, and geometric concepts are emphasized and integrated throughout the book.

The many factors that contributed to the success of the previous editions have been retained. In preparing the Seventh Edition, I considered comments and suggestions of colleagues, students, and many users of the prior edition throughout the country.

What's New in the Seventh Edition?

- **New Getting Ready for the Chapter Test** can be found before each Chapter Test. These exercises help increase student success by helping students prepare for their chapter test. The purpose of these exercises is to check students' conceptual understanding of the topics in the chapter as well as common student errors. It is suggested that students complete and check these exercises before taking a practice Chapter Test. All Getting Ready for the Test exercises are either Multiple Choice or Matching, and all answers can be found in the answer section of this text.

  Video Solutions of all exercises can be found in MyMathLab and on the Interactive DVD Lecture Series. These video solutions contain brief explanations and reminders of material in the chapter. Where applicable, incorrect choices contain explanations.

  Getting Ready for the Test exercise numbers marked in blue indicate that the question is available in **Learning Catalytics**. `lc`

- **New Learning Catalytics** is an interactive student response tool that uses students' smartphones, tablets, or laptops to engage them in more sophisticated tasks and thinking. Generate class discussion, guide your lecture, and promote peer-to-peer learning with real-time analytics. Accessible through MyMathLab, instructors can use Learning Catalytics to:

  — Pose a variety of open-ended questions that help your students develop critical thinking skills.

  — Monitor responses to find out where students are struggling.

  — Use real-time data to adjust your instructional strategy and try other ways of engaging your students during class.

  — Manage student interactions by automatically grouping students for discussion, teamwork, and peer-to-peer learning.

  For *Beginning Algebra,* Seventh Edition, new Getting Ready for the Test exercises marked in blue are available in Learning Catalytics. To search for the questions in Learning Catalytics, select **Discipline: Developmental Math,** and **Book: Martin-Gay, Beginning Algebra, 7e;** or search the question library for **MGBA7e Ch** and the chapter number. For example, search **MGBA7e Ch4** for questions from Chapter 4.

- **New Student Success Tips Videos** are 3- to 5-minute video segments designed to be daily reminders to students to continue practicing and maintaining good organizational and study habits. They are organized in three categories and are available in MyMathLab and the Interactive Lecture Series. The categories are:

    1. Success Tips that apply to any course in college in general, such as Time Management.

    2. Success Tips that apply to any mathematics course. One example is based on understanding that mathematics is a course that requires homework to be completed in a timely fashion.

    3. Section- or Content-specific Success Tips to help students avoid common mistakes or to better understand concepts that often prove challenging. One example of this type of tip is how to apply the order of operations to simplify an expression.

- **New Key Concept Activity Lab Workbook** includes Extension Exercises, Exploration Activities, Conceptual Exercises, and Group Activities. These activities are a great way to engage students in conceptual projects and exploration as well as group work.

- **The Martin-Gay MyMathLab** course has been updated and revised to provide more exercise coverage, including assignable video check questions and an expanded video program. There are section lectures videos for every section, which students can also access at the specific objective level; new Getting Ready for the Test video solutions; new Student Success Tips videos; and an increased number of watch clips at the exercise level to help students while doing homework in MathXL.

    Vocabulary, Readiness & Video Check Questions continue to be available in the text and for assignment in MyMathLab. The **Readiness** exercises center on a student's understanding of a concept that is necessary in order to continue to the exercise set. The **video check questions** are included in every section for every learning objective. These exercises are a great way to assess whether students have viewed and understood the key concepts presented in the videos.

- **Exercise Sets Revised and Updated** The text exercise sets have been carefully examined and revised. Special focus was placed on making sure that even- and odd-numbered exercises are paired and that real-life applications are updated.

Key Continuing Resources and Pedagogical Features

- **Interactive DVD Lecture Series**, featuring your text author Elayn Martin-Gay, provides students with active learning at their own pace. The videos offer the following resources and more:

    A complete lecture for each section of the text highlights key examples and exercises from the text. Pop-ups reinforce key terms, definitions, and concepts.

    An interface with menu navigation features allows students to quickly find and focus on the examples and exercises they need to review.

    Interactive Concept Check exercises measure students' understanding of key concepts and common trouble spots.

    New Student Success Tips Videos.

- **The Interactive DVD Lecture Series** also includes the following resources for test prep:

    New Getting Ready for the Chapter Test Videos

    The Chapter Test Prep Videos help students during their most teachable moment—when they are preparing for a test. This innovation provides step-by-step solutions for the exercises found in each Chapter Test. For the Seventh Edition, the chapter test prep videos are also available on YouTube™. The videos are captioned in English and Spanish.

The Practice Final Exam Videos help students prepare for an end-of-course final. Students can watch full video solutions to each exercise in the Practice Final Exam at the end of this text.

- **The Video Organizer** is designed to help students take notes and work practice exercises while watching the Interactive Lecture Series videos (available in MyMathLab and on DVD). All content in the Video Organizer is presented in the same order as it is presented in the videos, making it easy for students to create a course notebook and build good study habits.

  - Covers all of the video examples in order.
  - Provides ample space for students to write down key definitions and properties.
  - Includes Play and Pause button icons to prompt students to follow along with the author for some exercises while they try others on their own.

  The Video Organizer is available in a loose-leaf, notebook-ready format. It is also available for download in MyMathLab.

Key Pedagogical Features

The following key features have been retained and/or updated for the Seventh Edition of the text:

Problem-Solving Process   This is formally introduced in Chapter 2 with a four-step process that is integrated throughout the text. The four steps are **Understand, Translate, Solve,** and **Interpret.** The repeated use of these steps in a variety of examples shows their wide applicability. Reinforcing the steps can increase students' comfort level and confidence in tackling problems.

Exercise Sets Revised and Updated   The exercise sets have been carefully examined and extensively revised. Special focus was placed on making sure that even- and odd-numbered exercises are paired.

Examples   Detailed, step-by-step examples were added, deleted, replaced, or updated as needed. Many examples reflect real life. Additional instructional support is provided in the annotated examples.

Practice Exercises   Throughout the text, each worked-out example has a parallel Practice Exercise. These invite students to be actively involved in the learning process. Students should try each Practice Exercise after finishing the corresponding example. Learning by doing will help students grasp ideas before moving on to other concepts. Answers to the Practice Exercises are provided in the back of the text.

Helpful Hints   Helpful Hints contain practical advice on applying mathematical concepts. Strategically placed where students are most likely to need immediate reinforcement, Helpful Hints help students avoid common trouble areas and mistakes.

Concept Checks   This feature allows students to gauge their grasp of an idea as it is being presented in the text. Concept Checks stress conceptual understanding at the point of use and help suppress misconceived notions before they start. Answers appear at the bottom of the page. Exercises related to Concept Checks are included in the exercise sets.

Mixed Practice Exercises   Found in the section exercise sets, these require students to determine the problem type and strategy needed to solve it just as they would need to do on a test.

Integrated Reviews   A unique, mid-chapter exercise set that helps students assimilate new skills and concepts that they have learned separately over several sections. These reviews provide yet another opportunity for students to work with mixed exercises as they master the topics.

Vocabulary Check Provides an opportunity for students to become more familiar with the use of mathematical terms as they strengthen their verbal skills. These appear at the end of each chapter before the Chapter Highlights. Vocabulary, Readiness & Video exercises provide practice at the section level.

Chapter Highlights Found at the end of every chapter, these contain key definitions and concepts with examples to help students understand and retain what they have learned and help them organize their notes and study for tests.

Chapter Review The end of every chapter contains a comprehensive review of topics introduced in the chapter. The Chapter Review offers exercises keyed to every section in the chapter, as well as Mixed Review exercises that are not keyed to sections.

Chapter Test and Chapter Test Prep Video The Chapter Test is structured to include those problems that involve common student errors. The **Chapter Test Prep Videos** give students instant author access to a step-by-step video solution of each exercise in the Chapter Test.

Cumulative Review Follows every chapter in the text (except Chapter 1). Each odd-numbered exercise contained in the Cumulative Review is an earlier worked example in the text that is referenced in the back of the book along with the answer.

Writing Exercises \These exercises occur in almost every exercise set and require students to provide a written response to explain concepts or justify their thinking.

Applications Real-world and real-data applications have been thoroughly updated, and many new applications are included. These exercises occur in almost every exercise set, show the relevance of mathematics, and help students gradually and continuously develop their problem-solving skills.

Review Exercises These exercises occur in each exercise set (except in Chapter 1) and are keyed to earlier sections. They review concepts learned earlier in the text that will be needed in the next section or chapter.

Exercise Set Resource Icons Located at the opening of each exercise set, these icons remind students of the resources available for extra practice and support:

See Student Resource descriptions page xi for details on the individual resources available.

Exercise Icons These icons facilitate the assignment of specialized exercises and let students know what resources can support them.

- ▶ Video icon: exercise worked on the Interactive DVD Lecture Series and in MyMathLab.
- △ Triangle icon: identifies exercises involving geometric concepts.
- ＼ Pencil icon: indicates a written response is needed.
- ▦ Calculator icon: optional exercises intended to be solved using a scientific or graphing calculator.

Optional: Calculator Exploration Boxes and Calculator Exercises The optional Calculator Explorations provide keystrokes and exercises at appropriate points to give an opportunity for students to become familiar with these tools. Section exercises that are best completed by using a calculator are identified by ▦ for ease of assignment.

Student and Instructor Resources

STUDENT RESOURCES

Interactive DVD Lecture Series Videos	**Video Organizer**	**Student Solutions Manual**
Provides students with active learning at their pace. The videos offer:	Designed to help students take notes and work practice exercises while watching the Interactive Lecture Series videos.	Provides completely worked-out solutions to the odd-numbered section exercises; all exercises in the Integrated Reviews, Chapter Reviews, Chapter Tests, and Cumulative Reviews.
<ul><li>A complete lecture for each text section. The interface allows easy navigation to examples and exercises students need to review.</li><li>Interactive Concept Check exercises</li><li>Student Success Tips Videos</li><li>Practice Final Exam</li><li>Getting Ready for the Chapter Test Videos</li><li>Chapter Test Prep Videos</li></ul>	<ul><li>Covers all of the video examples in order.</li><li>Provides ample space for students to write down key definitions and rules.</li><li>Includes Play and Pause button icons to prompt students to follow along with the author for some exercises while they try others on their own.</li></ul> Available in loose-leaf, notebook-ready format and in MyMathLab.	**Key Concept Activity Lab Workbook** includes Extension Exercises, Exploration Activities, Conceptual Exercises, and Group Activities.

INSTRUCTOR RESOURCES

Annotated Instructor's Edition	**Instructor's Resource Manual with Tests and Mini-Lectures**
Contains all the content found in the student edition, plus the following: <ul><li>Classroom example paired to each example</li><li>Answers to exercises on the same text page</li><li>Teaching Tips throughout the text, placed at key points</li><li>Video Answer Section</li></ul>	<ul><li>Mini-lectures for each text section</li><li>Additional Practice worksheets for each section</li><li>Several forms of test per chapter—free response and multiple choice</li><li>Answers to all items</li></ul>**Instructor's Solutions Manual** **TestGen**® (Available for download from the IRC)
Instructor-to-Instructor Videos—available in the Instructor Resources section of the MyMathLab course.	**Online Resources** **MyMathLab**® (access code required) **MathXL**® (access code required)

Get the most out of
MyMathLab®

MyMathLab is the world's leading online resource for teaching and learning mathematics. MyMathLab helps students and instructors improve results and provides engaging experiences and personalized learning for each student so learning can happen in any environment. Plus, it offers flexible and time-saving course-management features to allow instructors to easily manage their classes while remaining in complete control, regardless of course format.

Personalized Support for Students

- MyMathLab comes with many learning resources–eText, animations, videos, and more–all designed to support your students as they progress through their course.

- The Adaptive Study Plan acts as a personal tutor, updating in real time based on student performance to provide personalized recommendations on what to work on next. With the new Companion Study Plan assignments, instructors can now assign the Study Plan as a prerequisite to a test or quiz, helping to guide students through concepts they need to master.

- Personalized Homework allows instructors to create homework assignments tailored to each student's specific needs by focusing on just the topics they have not yet mastered.

Used by nearly 4 million students each year, the MyMathLab and MyStatLab family of products delivers consistent, measurable gains in student learning outcomes, retention, and subsequent course success.

Acknowledgments

Many people helped me develop this text, and I will attempt to thank some of them here. Cindy Trimble was *invaluable* for contributing to the overall accuracy of the text. Dawn Nuttall, Emily Keaton and Suellen Robinson were *invaluable* for their many suggestions and contributions during the development and writing of this Seventh Edition. Chakira Lane, Patty Bergin, and Lauren Morse provided guidance throughout the production process.

A very special thank you goes to my editor, Mary Beckwith, for being there 24/7/365, as my students say. Last, my thanks to the staff at Pearson for all their support: Michael Hirsch, Rachel Ross, Heather Scott, Michelle Renda, Chris Hoag, and Paul Corey.

I would like to thank the following reviewers for their input and suggestions:

Sheila Anderson, *Housatonic Community College*
Tom Blackburn, *Northeastern Illinois University*
Gail Burkett, *Palm Beach State College*
James Butterbach, *Joliet Junior College*
Laura Dyer, *Southwestern Illinois College*
Sharon Edgemon, *Bakersfield College*
Hope Essien, *Olive-Harvey College*
Randa Kress, *Idaho State University*
Ted Lai, *Hudson Community College*
Nicole Lang, *North Hennepin Community College*
Lee LaRue, *Paris Junior College*
Jeri Lee, *Des Moines Area Community College*
Jean McArthur, *Joliet Junior College*
Michael Montano, *Riverside Community College*
Lisa J. Music, *Big Sandy Community and Technical College*
Linda Padilla, *Joliet Junior College*
Scott Perkins, *Lake Sumter Community College*
Marilyn Platt, *Gaston College*
Sandy Spears, *Jefferson Community College*
Ping Charlene Tintera, *Texas A & M University*
Jane Wampler, *Housatonic Community College*
Peter Zimmer, *West Chester University*

I would also like to thank the following dedicated group of instructors who participated in our focus groups, Martin-Gay Summits, and our design review for the series. Their feedback and insights have helped to strengthen this edition of the text. These instructors include:

Billie Anderson, *Tyler Junior College*
Cedric Atkins, *Mott Community College*
Andrea Barnett, *Tri-County Technical College*
Lois Beardon, *Schoolcraft College*
Michelle Beerman, *Pasco Hernando Community College*
Laurel Berry, *Bryant & Stratton College*
John Beyers, *University of Maryland*
Bob Brown, *Community College of Baltimore County–Essex*
Lisa Brown, *Community College of Baltimore County–Essex*
NeKeith Brown, *Richland College*
Sue Brown, *Guilford Technical Community College*
Gail Burkett, *Palm Beach State College*
Cheryl Cantwell, *Seminole Community College*
Jackie Cohen, *Augusta State College*
Julie Dewan, *Mohawk Valley Community College*
Janice Ervin, *Central Piedmont Community College*
Richard Fielding, *Southwestern College*

Cindy Gaddis, *Tyler Junior College*
Nita Graham, *St. Louis Community College*
Pauline Hall, *Iowa State College*
Elizabeth Hamman, *Cypress College*
Pat Hussey, *Triton College*
Dorothy Johnson, *Lorain County Community College*
Sonya Johnson, *Central Piedmont Community College*
Irene Jones, *Fullerton College*
Paul Jones, *University of Cincinnati*
Kathy Kopelousos, *Lewis and Clark Community College*
Nancy Lange, *Inver Hills Community College*
Judy Langer, *Westchester Community College*
Lisa Lindloff, *McLinnan Community College*
Sandy Lofstock, *St. Petersburg College*
Kathy Lovelle, *Westchester Community College*
Jamie Malek, *Florida State College*
Jean McArthur, *Joliet Junior College*
Kevin McCandless, *Evergreen Valley College*
Daniel Miller, *Niagara County Community College*
Marica Molle, *Metropolitan Community College*
Carol Murphy, *San Diego Miramar College*
Greg Nguyen, *Fullerton College*
Eric Ollila, *Jackson Community College*
Linda Padilla, *Joliet Junior College*
Davidson Pierre, *State College of Florida*
Marilyn Platt, *Gaston College*
Susan Poss, *Spartanburg Community College*
Natalie Rivera, *Estrella Mountain Community College*
Judy Roane, *Pearl River Community College*
Claudinna Rowley, *Montgomery Community College, Rockville*
Ena Salter, *Manatee Community College*
Carole Shapero, *Oakton Community College*
Janet Sibol, *Hillsborough Community College*
Anne Smallen, *Mohawk Valley Community College*
Barbara Stoner, *Reading Area Community College*
Jennifer Strehler, *Oakton Community College*
Ellen Stutes, *Louisiana State University Eunice*
Tanomo Taguchi, *Fullerton College*
MaryAnn Tuerk, *Elsin Community College*
Gwen Turbeville, *J. Sargeant Reynolds Community College*
Walter Wang, *Baruch College*
Leigh Ann Wheeler, *Greenville Technical Community College*
Valerie Wright, *Central Piedmont Community College*

A special thank you to those students who participated in our design review: Katherine Browne, Mike Bulfin, Nancy Canipe, Ashley Carpenter, Jeff Chojnachi, Roxanne Davis, Mike Dieter, Amy Dombrowski, Kay Herring, Todd Jaycox, Kaleena Levan, Matt Montgomery, Tony Plese, Abigail Polkinghorn, Harley Price, Eli Robinson, Avery Rosen, Robyn Schott, Cynthia Thomas, and Sherry Ward.

Elayn Martin-Gay

About the Author

Elayn Martin-Gay has taught mathematics at the University of New Orleans for more than 25 years. Her numerous teaching awards include the local University Alumni Association's Award for Excellence in Teaching, and Outstanding Developmental Educator at University of New Orleans, presented by the Louisiana Association of Developmental Educators.

Prior to writing textbooks, Elayn Martin-Gay developed an acclaimed series of lecture videos to support developmental mathematics students in their quest for success. These highly successful videos originally served as the foundation material for her texts. Today, the videos are specific to each book in the Martin-Gay series. The author has also created Chapter Test Prep videos to help students during their most "teachable moment"—as they prepare for a test—along with Instructor-to-Instructor videos that provide teaching tips, hints, and suggestions for each developmental mathematics course, including basic mathematics, prealgebra, beginning algebra, and intermediate algebra. Her most recent innovations are the Algebra Prep Apps for the iPhone and iPod Touch. These Apps embrace the different learning styles, schedules, and paces of students and provide them with quality math tutoring.

Elayn is the author of 12 published textbooks as well as multimedia interactive mathematics, all specializing in developmental mathematics courses. She has participated as an author across the broadest range of educational materials: textbooks, videos, tutorial software, and courseware. This offers an opportunity of various combinations for an integrated teaching and learning package offering great consistency for the student.

Applications Index

Review of Real Numbers

CHECK YOUR PROGRESS

In this chapter, we review the basic symbols and words—the language—of arithmetic and introduce using variables in place of numbers. This is our starting place in the study of algebra.

A Selection of Resources for Success in this Mathematics Course

Textbook

Instructor

MyMathLab and MathXL

Video Organizer

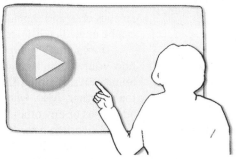

Interactive Lecture Series

For more information about the resources illustrated above, read Section 1.1.

1.1 Study Skill Tips for Success in Mathematics

OBJECTIVES

1 Get Ready for This Course.

2 Understand Some General Tips for Success.

3 Know How to Use This Text.

4 Know How to Use Text Resources.

5 Get Help as Soon as You Need It.

6 Learn How to Prepare for and Take an Exam.

7 Develop Good Time Management.

Before reading Section 1.1, you might want to ask yourself a few questions.

1. When you took your last math course, were you organized? Were your notes and materials from that course easy to find, or were they disorganized and hard to find—if you saved them at all?

2. Were you satisfied—really satisfied—with your performance in that course? In other words, do you feel that your outcome represented your best effort?

If the answer is "no" to these questions, then it is time to make a change. Changing to or resuming good study skill habits is not a process you can start and stop as you please. It is something that you must remember and practice each and every day. To begin, continue reading this section.

OBJECTIVE

1 Getting Ready for This Course

Now that you have decided to take this course, remember that a *positive attitude* will make all the difference in the world. Your belief that you can succeed is just as important as your commitment to this course. Make sure you are ready for this course by having the time and positive attitude that it takes to succeed.

Make sure that you are familiar with the way that this course is being taught. Is it a traditional course, in which you have a printed textbook and meet with an instructor? Is it taught totally online, and your textbook is electronic and you e-mail your instructor? Or is your course structured somewhere in between these two methods? (Not all of the tips that follow will apply to all forms of instruction.)

Also make sure that you have scheduled your math course for a time that will give you the best chance for success. For example, if you are also working, you may want to check with your employer to make sure that your work hours will not conflict with your course schedule.

On the day of your first class period, double-check your schedule and allow yourself extra time to arrive on time in case of traffic problems or difficulty locating your classroom. Make sure that you are aware of and bring all necessary class materials.

OBJECTIVE

2 General Tips for Success

Below are some general tips that will increase your chance for success in a mathematics class. Many of these tips will also help you in other courses you may be taking.

Most important! Organize your class materials. In the next couple pages, many ideas will be presented to help you organize your class materials—notes, any handouts, completed homework, previous tests, etc. In general, you MUST have these materials organized. All of them will be valuable references throughout your course and when studying for upcoming tests and the final exam. One way to make sure you can locate these materials when you need them is to use a three-ring binder. This binder should be used solely for your mathematics class and should be brought to each and every class or lab. This way, any material can be immediately inserted in a section of this binder and will be there when you need it.

Form study groups and/or exchange names and e-mail addresses. Depending on how your course is taught, you may want to keep in contact with your fellow students. Some ways of doing this are to form a study group—whether in person or through the Internet. Also, you may want to ask if anyone is interested in exchanging e-mail addresses or any other form of contact.

Choose to attend all class periods. If possible, sit near the front of the classroom. This way, you will see and hear the presentation better. It may also be easier for you to participate in classroom activities.

Do your homework. You've probably heard the phrase "practice makes perfect" in relation to music and sports. It also applies to mathematics. You will find that the more time you spend solving mathematics exercises, the easier the process becomes. Be sure to schedule enough time to complete your assignments before the due date assigned by your instructor.

Helpful Hint

MyMathLab® and MathXL®
When assignments are turned in online, keep a hard copy of your complete written work. You will need to refer to your written work to be able to ask questions and to study for tests later.

Helpful Hint

MyMathLab® and MathXL®
If you are doing your homework online, you can work and re-work those exercises that you struggle with until you master them. Try working through all the assigned exercises twice before the due date.

Check your work. Review the steps you took while working a problem. Learn to check your answers in the original exercises. You may also compare your answers with the "Answers to Selected Exercises" section in the back of the book. If you have made a mistake, try to figure out what went wrong. Then correct your mistake. If you can't find what went wrong, **don't** erase your work or throw it away. Show your work to your instructor, a tutor in a math lab, or a classmate. It is easier for someone to find where you had trouble if he or she looks at your original work.

Learn from your mistakes and be patient with yourself. Everyone, even your instructor, makes mistakes. (That definitely includes me—Elayn Martin-Gay.) Use your errors to learn and to become a better math student. The key is finding and understanding your errors.

Was your mistake a careless one, or did you make it because you can't read your own math writing? If so, try to work more slowly or write more neatly and make a conscious effort to carefully check your work.

Did you make a mistake because you don't understand a concept? Take the time to review the concept or ask questions to better understand it.

Did you skip too many steps? Skipping steps or trying to do too many steps mentally may lead to preventable mistakes.

Know how to get help if you need it. It's all right to ask for help. In fact, it's a good idea to ask for help whenever there is something that you don't understand. Make sure you know when your instructor has office hours and how to find his or her office. Find out whether math tutoring services are available on your campus. Check on the hours, location, and requirements of the tutoring service.

Don't be afraid to ask questions. You are not the only person in class with questions. Other students are normally grateful that someone has spoken up.

Turn in assignments on time. This way, you can be sure that you will not lose points for being late. Show every step of a problem and be neat and organized. Also be sure that you understand which problems are assigned for homework. If allowed, you can always double-check the assignment with another student in your class.

OBJECTIVE
3   Knowing and Using Your Text

Flip through the pages of this text or view the e-text pages on a computer screen. Start noticing examples, exercise sets, end-of-chapter material, and so on. Every text is organized in some manner. Learn the way this text is organized by reading about and then finding an example in your text of each type of resource listed below. Finding and using these resources throughout your course will increase your chance of success.

- *Practice Exercises.* Each example in every section has a parallel Practice exercise. As you read a section, try each Practice exercise after you've finished the corresponding example. This "learn-by-doing" approach will help you grasp ideas before you move on to other concepts. Answers are at the back of the text.
- *Symbols at the Beginning of an Exercise Set.* If you need help with a particular section, the symbols listed at the beginning of each exercise set will remind you of the numerous resources available.
- *Objectives.* The main section of exercises in each exercise set is referenced by an example(s). There is also often a section of exercises entitled "Mixed Practice," which is referenced by two or more examples or sections. These are mixed exercises written to prepare you for your next exam. Use all of this referencing if you have trouble completing an assignment from the exercise set.
- *Icons (Symbols).* Make sure that you understand the meaning of the icons that are beside many exercises. ▶ tells you that the corresponding exercise may be viewed on the video segment that corresponds to that section. ╲ tells you that this exercise is a writing exercise in which you should answer in complete sentences. △ tells you that the exercise involves geometry. ▦ tells you that this exercise is worked more efficiently with the aid of a calculator. Also, a feature called Graphing Calculator Explorations may be found before select exercise sets.

- *Integrated Reviews.* Found in the middle of each chapter, these reviews offer you a chance to practice—in one place—the many concepts that you have learned separately over several sections.
- *End-of-Chapter Opportunities.* There are many opportunities at the end of each chapter to help you understand the concepts of the chapter.

  Vocabulary Checks contain key vocabulary terms introduced in the chapter.

  Chapter Highlights contain chapter summaries and examples.

  Chapter Reviews contain review exercises. The first part is organized section by section and the second part contains a set of mixed exercises.

  Getting Ready for the Tests contain conceptual exercises written to prepare students for chapter test directions as well as mixed sections of exercises.

  Chapter Tests are sample tests to help you prepare for an exam. The Chapter Test Prep Videos found in the Interactive Lecture Series, MyMathLab, and YouTube provide the video solution to each question on each Chapter Test.

  Cumulative Reviews start at Chapter 2 and are reviews consisting of material from the beginning of the book to the end of that particular chapter.
- *Student Resources in Your Textbook.* You will find a **Student Resources** section at the back of this textbook. It contains the following to help you study and prepare for tests:

  Study Skills Builders contain study skills advice. To increase your chance for success in the course, read these study tips and answer the questions.

  Bigger Picture—Study Guide Outline provides you with a study guide outline of the course, with examples.

  Practice Final provides you with a Practice Final Exam to help you prepare for a final. The video solutions to each question are provided in the Interactive DVD Lecture Series and within MyMathLab®.
- *Resources to Check Your Work.* The **Answers to Selected Exercises** section provides answers to all odd-numbered section exercises and all integrated review and chapter test exercises.

OBJECTIVE

4 Knowing and Using Video and Notebook Organizer Resources

Video Resources

Below is a list of video resources that are all made by me—the author of your text, Elayn Martin-Gay. By making these videos, I can be sure that the methods presented are consistent with those in the text.

- *Interactive DVD Lecture Series.* Exercises marked with a ▶ are fully worked out by the author on the DVDs and within MyMathLab. The lecture series provides approximately 20 minutes of instruction per section and is organized by Objective.
- *Chapter Test Prep Videos.* These videos provide solutions to all of the Chapter Test exercises worked out by the author. They can be found in MyMathLab, the Interactive Lecture series, and YouTube. This supplement is very helpful before a test or exam.
- *Student Success Tips.* These video segments are about 3 minutes long and are daily reminders to help you continue practicing and maintaining good organizational and study habits.
- *Final Exam Videos.* These video segments provide solutions to each question. These videos can be found within MyMathLab and the Interactive Lecture Series.

Notebook Organizer Resource

This resource is in three-ring notebook ready form. It is to be inserted in a three-ring binder and completed. This resource is numbered according to the sections in your text to which they refer.

- *Video Organizer.* This organizer is closely tied to the Interactive Lecture (Video) Series. Each section should be completed while watching a lecture video on the same section. Once completed, you will have a set of notes to accompany the Lecture (Video) Series section by section.

OBJECTIVE
5   Getting Help

If you have trouble completing assignments or understanding the mathematics, get help as soon as you need it! This tip is presented as an objective on its own because it is so important. In mathematics, usually the material presented in one section builds on your understanding of the previous section. This means that if you don't understand the concepts covered during a class period, there is a good chance that you will not understand the concepts covered during the next class period. If this happens to you, get help as soon as you can.

Where can you get help? Many suggestions have been made in this section on where to get help, and now it is up to you to get it. Try your instructor, a tutoring center, or a math lab, or you may want to form a study group with fellow classmates. If you do decide to see your instructor or go to a tutoring center, make sure that you have a neat notebook and are ready with your questions.

OBJECTIVE
6   Preparing for and Taking an Exam

Make sure that you allow yourself plenty of time to prepare for a test. If you think that you are a little "math anxious," it may be that you are not preparing for a test in a way that will ensure success. The way that you prepare for a test in mathematics is important. To prepare for a test:

1. Review your previous homework assignments.
2. Review any notes from class and section-level quizzes you have taken. (If this is a final exam, also review chapter tests you have taken.)
3. Review concepts and definitions by reading the Chapter Highlights at the end of each chapter.
4. Practice working out exercises by completing the Chapter Review found at the end of each chapter. (If this is a final exam, go through a Cumulative Review. There is one found at the end of each chapter except Chapter 1. Choose the review found at the end of the latest chapter that you have covered in your course.) *Don't stop here!*
5. It is important that you place yourself in conditions similar to test conditions to find out how you will perform. In other words, as soon as you feel that you know the material, get a few blank sheets of paper and take a sample test. There is a Chapter Test available at the end of each chapter, or you can work selected problems from the Chapter Review. Your instructor may also provide you with a review sheet. During this sample test, do not use your notes or your textbook. Then check your sample test. If your sample test is the Chapter Test in the text, don't forget that the video solutions are in MyMathLab, the Interactive Lecture Series, and YouTube. If you are not satisfied with the results, study the areas that you are weak in and try again.
6. On the day of the test, allow yourself plenty of time to arrive where you will be taking your exam.

When taking your test:

1. Read the directions on the test carefully.
2. Read each problem carefully as you take the test. Make sure that you answer the question asked.
3. Watch your time and pace yourself so that you can attempt each problem on your test.
4. If you have time, check your work and answers.
5. Do not turn your test in early. If you have extra time, spend it double-checking your work.

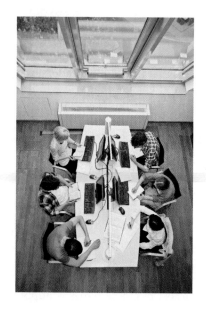

OBJECTIVE

7 Managing Your Time

As a college student, you know the demands that classes, homework, work, and family place on your time. Some days you probably wonder how you'll ever get everything done. One key to managing your time is developing a schedule. Here are some hints for making a schedule:

1. Make a list of all your weekly commitments for the term. Include classes, work, regular meetings, extracurricular activities, etc. You may also find it helpful to list such things as laundry, regular workouts, grocery shopping, etc.

2. Next, estimate the time needed for each item on the list. Also make a note of how often you will need to do each item. Don't forget to include time estimates for the reading, studying, and homework you do outside of your classes. You may want to ask your instructor for help estimating the time needed.

3. In the exercise set that follows, you are asked to block out a typical week on the schedule grid given. Start with items with fixed time slots like classes and work.

4. Next, include the items on your list with flexible time slots. Think carefully about how best to schedule items such as study time.

5. Don't fill up every time slot on the schedule. Remember that you need to allow time for eating, sleeping, and relaxing! You should also allow a little extra time in case some items take longer than planned.

6. If you find that your weekly schedule is too full for you to handle, you may need to make some changes in your workload, classload, or other areas of your life. You may want to talk to your advisor, manager or supervisor at work, or someone in your college's academic counseling center for help with such decisions.

1.1 Exercise Set MyMathLab® ▶

1. What is your instructor's name?

2. What are your instructor's office location and office hours?

3. What is the best way to contact your instructor?

4. Do you have the name and contact information of at least one other student in class?

5. Will your instructor allow you to use a calculator in this class?

6. Why is it important that you write step-by-step solutions to homework exercises and keep a hard copy of all work submitted?

7. Is there a tutoring service available on campus? If so, what are its hours? What services are available?

8. Have you attempted this course before? If so, write down ways that you might improve your chances of success during this next attempt.

9. List some steps that you can take if you begin having trouble understanding the material or completing an assignment. If you are completing your homework in MyMathLab® and MathXL®, list the resources you can use for help.

10. How many hours of studying does your instructor advise for each hour of instruction?

11. What does the ＼ icon in this text mean?

12. What does the △ icon in this text mean?

13. What does the ▶ icon in this text mean?

14. What are Practice exercises?

15. When might be the best time to work a Practice exercise?

16. Where are the answers to Practice exercises?

17. What answers are contained in this text and where are they?

18. What are Study Skills Builders and where are they?

19. What and where are Integrated Reviews?

20. How many times is it suggested that you work through the homework exercises in MathXL® before the submission deadline?

21. How far in advance of the assigned due date is it suggested that homework be submitted online? Why?

22. Chapter Highlights are found at the end of each chapter. Find the Chapter 1 Highlights and explain how you might use it and how it might be helpful.

23. Chapter Reviews are found at the end of each chapter. Find the Chapter 1 Review and explain how you might use it and how it might be useful.

24. Chapter Tests are at the end of each chapter. Find the Chapter 1 Test and explain how you might use it and how it might be helpful when preparing for an exam on Chapter 1. Include how the Chapter Test Prep Videos may help. If you are working in MyMathLab® and MathXL®, how can you use previous homework assignments to study?

25. What is the Video Organizer? Explain the contents and how it might be used.

26. Explain how the Video Organizer can help you when watching a lecture video.

27. Read or reread Objective 7 and fill out the schedule grid below.

	Monday	*Tuesday*	*Wednesday*	*Thursday*	*Friday*	*Saturday*	*Sunday*
1:00 a.m.							
2:00 a.m.							
3:00 a.m.							
4:00 a.m.							
5:00 a.m.							
6:00 a.m.							
7:00 a.m.							
8:00 a.m.							
9:00 a.m.							
10:00 a.m.							
11:00 a.m.							
Noon							
1:00 p.m.							
2:00 p.m.							
3:00 p.m.							
4:00 p.m.							
5:00 p.m.							
6:00 p.m.							
7:00 p.m.							
8:00 p.m.							
9:00 p.m.							
10:00 p.m.							
11:00 p.m.							
Midnight							

1.2 Symbols and Sets of Numbers

OBJECTIVES

1 Use a Number Line to Order Numbers.

2 Translate Sentences into Mathematical Statements.

3 Identify Natural Numbers, Whole Numbers, Integers, Rational Numbers, Irrational Numbers, and Real Numbers.

4 Find the Absolute Value of a Real Number.

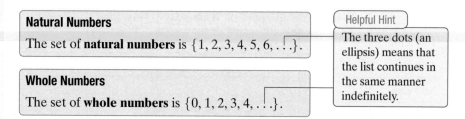

OBJECTIVE

1 Using a Number Line to Order Numbers

We begin with a review of the set of natural numbers and the set of whole numbers and how we use symbols to compare these numbers. A **set** is a collection of objects, each of which is called a **member** or **element** of the set. A pair of brace symbols { } encloses the list of elements and is translated as "the set of" or "the set containing."

Natural Numbers

The set of **natural numbers** is $\{1, 2, 3, 4, 5, 6, \ldots\}$.

Whole Numbers

The set of **whole numbers** is $\{0, 1, 2, 3, 4, \ldots\}$.

> **Helpful Hint**
> The three dots (an ellipsis) means that the list continues in the same manner indefinitely.

These numbers can be pictured on a **number line.** We will use number lines often to help us visualize distance and relationships between numbers.

To draw a number line, first draw a line. Choose a point on the line and label it 0. To the right of 0, label any other point 1. Being careful to use the same distance as from 0 to 1, mark off equally spaced distances. Label these points 2, 3, 4, 5, and so on. Since the whole numbers continue indefinitely, it is not possible to show every whole number on this number line. The arrow at the right end of the line indicates that the pattern continues indefinitely.

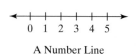

A Number Line

Picturing whole numbers on a number line helps us see the order of the numbers. Symbols can be used to describe concisely in writing the order that we see.

The **equal symbol** $=$ means "is equal to."

The symbol $\neq$ means "is not equal to."

These symbols may be used to form a **mathematical statement.** The statement might be true or it might be false. The two statements below are both true.

$2 = 2$ states that "two is equal to two."

$2 \neq 6$ states that "two is not equal to six."

If two numbers are not equal, one number is larger than the other.
The symbol $>$ means "is greater than."
The symbol $<$ means "is less than." For example,

$3 < 5$ states that "three is less than five."

$2 > 0$ states that "two is greater than zero."

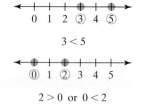

$3 < 5$

$2 > 0$ or $0 < 2$

On a number line, we see that a number **to the right of** another number is **larger.** Similarly, a number **to the left of** another number is smaller. For example, 3 is to the left of 5 on a number line, which means that 3 is less than 5, or $3 < 5$. Similarly, 2 is to the right of 0 on a number line, which means 2 is greater than 0, or $2 > 0$. Since 0 is to the left of 2, we can also say that 0 is less than 2, or $0 < 2$.

The symbols $\neq$, $<$, and $>$ are called **inequality symbols.**

> **Helpful Hint**
>
> Notice that $2 > 0$ has exactly the same meaning as $0 < 2$. Switching the order of the numbers and reversing the direction of the inequality symbol does not change the meaning of the statement.
>
> $3 < 5$ has the same meaning as $5 > 3$.
>
> Also notice that, when the statement is true, the inequality arrow points to the smaller number.

EXAMPLE 1   Insert $<$, $>$, or $=$ in the space between each pair of numbers to make each statement true

   a. 2   3   **b.** 7   4   **c.** 72   27

Solution

   a. $2 < 3$ since 2 is to the left of 3 on a number line.

   b. $7 > 4$ since 7 is to the right of 4 on a number line.

   c. $72 > 27$ since 72 is to the right of 27 on a number line.   □

PRACTICE
1   Insert $<$, $>$, or $=$ in the space between each pair of numbers to make each statement true.

   a. 5   8   **b.** 6   4   **c.** 16   82   ■

Two other symbols are used to compare numbers.
The symbol $\leq$ means "is less than or equal to."
The symbol $\geq$ means "is greater than or equal to." For example,

$$7 \leq 10 \text{ states that "seven is less than or equal to ten."}$$

This statement is true since $7 < 10$ is true. If either $7 < 10$ or $7 = 10$ is true, then $7 \leq 10$ is true.

$$3 \geq 3 \text{ states that "three is greater than or equal to three."}$$

This statement is true since $3 = 3$ is true. If either $3 > 3$ or $3 = 3$ is true, then $3 \geq 3$ is true.

The statement $6 \geq 10$ is false since neither $6 > 10$ nor $6 = 10$ is true. The symbols $\leq$ and $\geq$ are also called **inequality symbols.**

EXAMPLE 2   Tell whether each statement is true or false.

   a. $8 \geq 8$ **b.** $8 \leq 8$ **c.** $23 \leq 0$ **d.** $23 \geq 0$

Solution

   a. True. Since $8 = 8$ is true, then $8 \geq 8$ is true.

   b. True. Since $8 = 8$ is true, then $8 \leq 8$ is true.

   c. False. Since neither $23 < 0$ nor $23 = 0$ is true, then $23 \leq 0$ is false.

   d. True. Since $23 > 0$ is true, then $23 \geq 0$ is true.   □

PRACTICE
2   Tell whether each statement is true or false.

   a. $9 \geq 3$ **b.** $3 \geq 8$ **c.** $25 \leq 25$ **d.** $4 \leq 14$ ■

OBJECTIVE
2 **Translating Sentences** ▶

Now, let's use the symbols discussed to translate sentences into mathematical statements.

EXAMPLE 3   Translate each sentence into a mathematical statement.

   a. Nine is less than or equal to eleven.

   b. Eight is greater than one.

   c. Three is not equal to four.

Solution

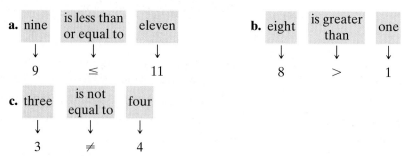

a.

nine	is less than or equal to	eleven
↓	↓	↓
9	≤	11

b.

eight	is greater than	one
↓	↓	↓
8	>	1

c.

three	is not equal to	four
↓	↓	↓
3	≠	4

PRACTICE
3   Translate each sentence into a mathematical statement.
   a. Three is less than eight.
   b. Fifteen is greater than or equal to nine.
   c. Six is not equal to seven.

OBJECTIVE
3   Identifying Common Sets of Numbers

Whole numbers are not sufficient to describe many situations in the real world. For example, quantities less than zero must sometimes be represented, such as temperatures less than 0 degrees.

Numbers Less Than Zero on a Number Line

Zero

−5 −4 −3 −2 −1   0   1   2   3   4   5

Numbers less than 0 are to the left of 0 and are labeled −1, −2, −3, and so on. A − sign, such as the one in −1, tells us that the number is to the left of 0 on a number line. In words, −1 is read "negative one." A + sign or no sign tells us that a number lies to the right of 0 on a number line. For example, 3 and +3 both mean positive three.

The numbers we have pictured are called the set of **integers.** Integers to the left of 0 are called **negative integers;** integers to the right of 0 are called **positive integers.** The integer **0 is neither positive nor negative.**

negative integers ┊ positive integers

−5 −4 −3 −2 −1   0   1   2   3   4   5

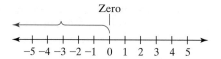

Integers

The set of **integers** is $\{ \ldots, -3, -2, -1, 0, 1, 2, 3, \ldots \}$.

> The ellipses (three dots) to the left and to the right indicate that the positive integers and the negative integers continue indefinitely.

EXAMPLE 4   Use an integer to express the number in the following. "Pole of Inaccessibility, Antarctica, is the coldest location in the world, with an average annual temperature of 72 degrees below zero." (_Source: The Guinness Book of Records_)

Solution   The integer −72 represents 72 degrees below zero.

PRACTICE
4   Use an integer to express the number in the following. The elevation of Laguna Salada in Mexico is 10 meters below sea level. (_Source: The World Almanac_)

A problem with integers in real-life settings arises when quantities are smaller than some integer but greater than the next smallest integer. On a number line, these quantities may be visualized by points between integers. Some of these quantities between integers can be represented as a quotient of integers. For example,

The point on a number line halfway between 0 and 1 can be represented by $\frac{1}{2}$, a quotient of integers.

The point on a number line halfway between 0 and -1 can be represented by $-\frac{1}{2}$. Other quotients of integers and their graphs are shown to the left.

These numbers, each of which can be represented as a quotient of integers, are examples of **rational numbers.** It's not possible to list the set of rational numbers using the notation that we have been using. For this reason, we will use a different notation.

Rational Numbers

$$\left\{ \frac{a}{b} \,\middle|\, a \text{ and } b \text{ are integers and } b \neq 0 \right\}$$

We read this set as "the set of all numbers $\frac{a}{b}$ such that a and b are integers and **b is not equal to 0.**" Notice that every integer is also a rational number since each integer can be expressed as a quotient of integers. For example, the integer 5 is also a rational number since $5 = \frac{5}{1}$.

The number line also contains points that cannot be expressed as quotients of integers. These numbers are called **irrational numbers** because they cannot be represented by rational numbers. For example, $\sqrt{2}$ and π are irrational numbers.

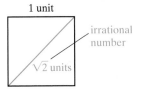

1 unit

irrational number

$\sqrt{2}$ units

Irrational Numbers

The set of **irrational numbers** is

{Nonrational numbers that correspond to points on a number line}.

That is, an irrational number is a number that cannot be expressed as a quotient of integers.

Both rational numbers and irrational numbers can be written as decimal numbers. The decimal equivalent of a rational number will either terminate or repeat in a pattern. For example, upon dividing we find that

$$\text{Rational Numbers} \begin{cases} \dfrac{3}{4} = 0.75 \,(\text{decimal number terminates or ends}) \\ \dfrac{2}{3} = 0.66666\ldots \,(\text{decimal number repeats in a pattern}) \end{cases}$$

The decimal representation of an irrational number will neither terminate nor repeat. For example, the decimal representations of irrational numbers $\sqrt{2}$ and π are

$$\text{Irrational Numbers} \begin{cases} \sqrt{2} = 1.414213562\ldots \,(\text{decimal number does not terminate or repeat in a pattern}) \\ \pi = 3.141592653\ldots \,(\text{decimal number does not terminate or repeat in a pattern}) \end{cases}$$

(For further review of decimals, see the Appendix.)

Combining the rational numbers with the irrational numbers gives the set of **real numbers.** One and only one point on a number line corresponds to each real number.

Real Numbers

The set of **real numbers** is

{All numbers that correspond to points on a number line}

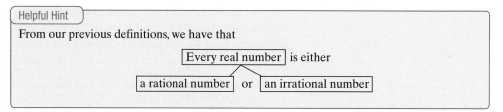

On the following number line, we see that real numbers can be positive, negative, or 0. Numbers to the left of 0 are called **negative numbers;** numbers to the right of 0 are called **positive numbers.** Positive and negative numbers are also called **signed numbers.**

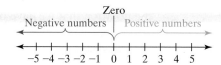

Several different sets of numbers have been discussed in this section. The following diagram shows the relationships among these sets of real numbers.

Common Sets of Numbers

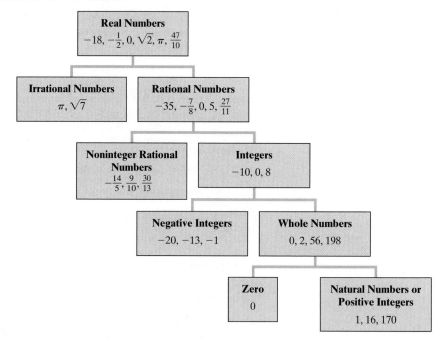

EXAMPLE 5 Given the set $\left\{-2, 0, \dfrac{1}{4}, -1.5, 112, -3, 11, \sqrt{2}\right\}$, list the numbers in this set that belong to the set of:

   a. Natural numbers   **b.** Whole numbers

   c. Integers   **d.** Rational numbers

   e. Irrational numbers   **f.** Real numbers

Solution

   a. The natural numbers are 11 and 112.

   b. The whole numbers are 0, 11, and 112.

   c. The integers are $-3, -2, 0, 11,$ and 112.

   d. Recall that integers are rational numbers also. The rational numbers are $-3, -2, -1.5, 0, \dfrac{1}{4}, 11,$ and 112.

   e. The irrational number is $\sqrt{2}$.

   f. The real numbers are all numbers in the given set. □

PRACTICE
5   Given the set $\left\{25, \dfrac{7}{3}, -15, -\dfrac{3}{4}, \sqrt{5}, -3.7, 8.8, -99\right\}$, list the numbers in this set that belong to the set of:

a. Natural numbers   **b.** Whole numbers

c. Integers   **d.** Rational numbers

e. Irrational numbers   **f.** Real numbers

We now extend the meaning and use of inequality symbols such as $<$ and $>$ to all real numbers.

Order Property for Real Numbers

For any two real numbers a and b, a is less than b if a is to the left of b on a number line.

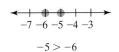

$a < b$ or also $b > a$

EXAMPLE 6 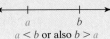   Insert $<$, $>$, or $=$ in the appropriate space to make each statement true.

a. $-1 \quad 0$ **b.** $7 \quad \dfrac{14}{2}$ **c.** $-5 \quad -6$

Solution

a. $-1 < 0$ since -1 is to the left of 0 on a number line.

$-1 < 0$

b. $7 = \dfrac{14}{2}$ since $\dfrac{14}{2}$ simplifies to 7.

c. $-5 > -6$ since -5 is to the right of -6 on a number line.

$-5 > -6$

PRACTICE
6   Insert $<$, $>$, or $=$ in the appropriate space to make each statement true.

a. $0 \quad 3$ **b.** $15 \quad -5$ **c.** $3 \quad \dfrac{12}{4}$

OBJECTIVE
4   Finding the Absolute Value of a Real Number

A number line also helps us visualize the distance between numbers. The distance between a real number a and 0 is given a special name called the **absolute value** of a. "The absolute value of a" is written in symbols as $|a|$.

Absolute Value

The absolute value of a real number a, denoted by $|a|$, is the distance between a and 0 on a number line.

For example, $|3| = 3$ and $|-3| = 3$ since both 3 and -3 are a distance of 3 units from 0 on a number line.

> **Helpful Hint**
>
> Since $|a|$ is a distance, $|a|$ is always either positive or 0, never negative. That is, **for any real number** a, $|a| \geq 0$.

EXAMPLE 7   Find the absolute value of each number.

a. $|4|$ b. $|-5|$ c. $|0|$ d. $\left|-\dfrac{1}{2}\right|$ e. $|5.6|$

Solution

a. $|4| = 4$ since 4 is 4 units from 0 on a number line.

b. $|-5| = 5$ since -5 is 5 units from 0 on a number line.

c. $|0| = 0$ since 0 is 0 units from 0 on a number line.

d. $\left|-\dfrac{1}{2}\right| = \dfrac{1}{2}$ since $-\dfrac{1}{2}$ is $\dfrac{1}{2}$ unit from 0 on a number line.

e. $|5.6| = 5.6$ since 5.6 is 5.6 units from 0 on a number line.   □

PRACTICE

7   Find the absolute value of each number.

a. $|-8|$ b. $|9|$ c. $|-2.5|$ d. $\left|\dfrac{5}{11}\right|$ e. $|\sqrt{3}|$ ■

EXAMPLE 8   Insert $<$, $>$, or $=$ in the appropriate space to make each statement true.

a. $|0|$ 2   b. $|-5|$ 5   c. $|-3|$ $|-2|$ d. $|5|$ $|6|$ e. $|-7|$ $|6|$

Solution

a. $|0| < 2$ since $|0| = 0$ and $0 < 2$.   b. $|-5| = 5$ since $5 = 5$.

c. $|-3| > |-2|$ since $3 > 2$.   d. $|5| < |6|$ since $5 < 6$.

e. $|-7| > |6|$ since $7 > 6$.   □

PRACTICE

8   Insert $<$, $>$, or $=$ in the appropriate space to make each statement true.

a. $|8|$ $|-8|$ b. $|-3|$ 0   c. $|-7|$ $|-11|$ d. $|3|$ $|2|$ e. $|0|$ $|-4|$ ■

✓ **Vocabulary, Readiness & Video Check**

Use the choices below to fill in each blank.

real	natural	whole	irrational
$|b|$	inequality	integers	rational

1. The _____ numbers are $\{0, 1, 2, 3, 4, \ldots\}$.

2. The _____ numbers are $\{1, 2, 3, 4, 5, \ldots\}$.

3. The symbols $\neq$, $\leq$, and $>$ are called _____ symbols.

4. The _____ are $\{\ldots, -3, -2, -1, 0, 1, 2, 3, \ldots\}$.

5. The _____ numbers are {all numbers that correspond to points on a number line}.

6. The _____ numbers are $\left\{\dfrac{a}{b} \,\middle|\, a \text{ and } b \text{ are integers}, b \neq 0\right\}$.

7. The _____ numbers are {nonrational numbers that correspond to points on a number line}.

8. The distance between a number b and 0 on a number line is _____.

Martin-Gay Interactive Videos

See Video 1.2

Watch the section lecture video and answer the following questions.

OBJECTIVE
1

9. In Example 2, why is the symbol $<$ inserted between the two numbers?

OBJECTIVE
2

10. Write the sentence given in Example 4 and translate it to a mathematical statement, using symbols.

OBJECTIVE
3

11. Which sets of numbers does the number in Example 6 belong to? Why is this number not an irrational number?

OBJECTIVE
4

12. Complete this statement based on the lecture given before Example 8. The _____ of a real number a, denoted by $|a|$, is the distance between a and 0 on a number line.

1.2   Exercise Set   MyMathLab

Insert $<$, $>$, or $=$ in the appropriate space to make the statement true. See Example 1.

1. 7   3

2. 9   15

3. 6.26   6.26

4. 2.13   1.13

5. 0   7

6. 20   0

7. −2   2

8. −4   −6

9. The freezing point of water is 32° Fahrenheit. The boiling point of water is 212° Fahrenheit. Write an inequality statement using $<$ or $>$ comparing the numbers 32 and 212.

10. The freezing point of water is 0° Celsius. The boiling point of water is 100° Celsius. Write an inequality statement using $<$ or $>$ comparing the numbers 0 and 100.

△ **11.** An angle measuring 30° is shown and an angle measuring 45° is shown. Use the inequality symbol ≤ or ≥ to write a statement comparing the numbers 30 and 45.

△ **12.** The sum of the measures of the angles of a triangle is 180°. The sum of the measures of the angles of a parallelogram is 360°. Use the inequality symbol ≤ or ≥ to write a statement comparing the numbers 360 and 180.

Are the following statements true or false? See Examples 2 and 6.

13. $11 \le 11$

14. $4 \ge 7$

15. $10 > 11$

16. $17 > 16$

17. $3 + 8 \ge 3(8)$

18. $8 \cdot 8 \le 8 \cdot 7$

19. $9 > 0$

20. $4 < 7$

21. $-6 > -2$

22. $0 < -15$

TRANSLATING

Write each sentence as a mathematical statement. See Example 3.

23. Eight is less than twelve.

24. Fifteen is greater than five.

25. Five is greater than or equal to four.

26. Negative ten is less than or equal to thirty-seven.

27. Fifteen is not equal to negative two.

28. Negative seven is not equal to seven.

Use integers to represent the values in each statement. See Example 4.

29. The highest elevation in California is Mt. Whitney, with an altitude of 14,494 feet. The lowest elevation in California is Death Valley, with an altitude of 282 feet below sea level. (*Source:* U.S. Geological Survey)

30. Driskill Mountain, in Louisiana, has an altitude of 535 feet. New Orleans, Louisiana, lies 8 feet below sea level. (*Source:* U.S. Geological Survey)

31. The number of graduate students at the University of Texas at Austin is 28,000 fewer than the number of undergraduate students. (*Source:* University of Texas at Austin)

32. The number of students admitted to the class of 2014 at UCLA is 80,784 fewer students than the number that had applied. (*Source:* UCLA)

33. Aaron Miller deposited $350 in his savings account. He later withdrew $126.

34. Aris Peña was deep-sea diving. During her dive, she ascended 30 feet and later descended 50 feet.

Tell which set or sets each number belongs to: natural numbers, whole numbers, integers, rational numbers, irrational numbers, and real numbers. See Example 5.

35. 0

36. $\dfrac{1}{4}$

37. −2

38. $-\dfrac{1}{2}$

39. 6

40. 5

41. $\dfrac{2}{3}$

42. $\sqrt{3}$

43. $-\sqrt{5}$

44. $-1\dfrac{5}{9}$

Tell whether each statement is true or false.

45. Every rational number is also an integer.

46. Every negative number is also a rational number.

47. Every natural number is positive.

48. Every rational number is also a real number.

49. 0 is a real number.

50. Every real number is also a rational number.

51. Every whole number is an integer.

52. $\dfrac{1}{2}$ is an integer.

53. A number can be both rational and irrational.

54. Every whole number is positive.

Insert $<, >,$ or $=$ in the appropriate space to make a true statement. See Examples 6 through 8.

55. -10 -100

56. -200 -20

57. 32 5.2

58. 7.1 -7

59. $\dfrac{18}{3}$ $\dfrac{24}{3}$

60. $\dfrac{8}{2}$ $\dfrac{12}{3}$

61. -51 -50

62. $|-20|$ -200

63. $|-5|$ -4

64. 0 $|0|$

65. $|-1|$ $|1|$

66. $\left|\dfrac{2}{5}\right|$ $\left|-\dfrac{2}{5}\right|$

67. $|-2|$ $|-3|$

68. -500 $|-50|$

69. $|0|$ $|-8|$

70. $|-12|$ $\dfrac{24}{2}$

CONCEPT EXTENSIONS

The graph below is called a bar graph. This particular bar graph shows cranberry production from the top five cranberry-producing states.

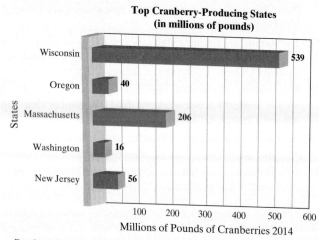

Top Cranberry-Producing States
(in millions of pounds)

Wisconsin 539
Oregon 40
Massachusetts 206
Washington 16
New Jersey 56

Millions of Pounds of Cranberries 2014

States

Data from National Agricultural Statistics Service

71. Write an inequality comparing the 2014 cranberry production in Oregon with the 2014 cranberry production in Washington.

72. Write an inequality comparing the 2014 cranberry production in Massachusetts with the 2014 cranberry production in Wisconsin.

73. Determine the difference between the 2014 cranberry production in Washington and the 2014 cranberry production in New Jersey.

74. According to the bar graph, which two states were the closest in terms of millions of pounds in 2014 cranberry crops?

This bar graph shows the number of people admitted into the Baseball Hall of Fame since its founding. Each bar represents a decade, and the height of the bar represents the number of Hall of Famers admitted in that decade.

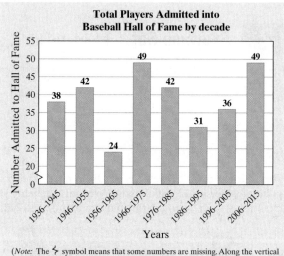

Total Players Admitted into
Baseball Hall of Fame by decade

Number Admitted to Hall of Fame

1936–1945 38
1946–1955 42
1956–1965 24
1966–1975 49
1976–1985 42
1986–1995 31
1996–2005 36
2006–2015 49

Years

(*Note:* The ⚡ symbol means that some numbers are missing. Along the vertical data line, notice the numbers between 0 and 20 are missing or not shown.)

Source: BASEBALL-Reference.com

75. In which decade(s) was the number of players admitted the greatest?

76. What was the greatest number of players admitted shown?

77. In which decade(s) was the number of players admitted greater than 40?

78. In which decade(s) was the number of players admitted fewer than 30?

79. Write an inequality statement comparing the number of players admitted in 1936–1945 and in 1966–1975.

80. Do you notice any trends shown by this bar graph?

The apparent magnitude of a star is the measure of its brightness as seen by someone on Earth. The smaller the apparent magnitude, the brighter the star. Use the apparent magnitudes in the table on page 17 to answer Exercises 81 through 86.

81. The apparent magnitude of the Sun is -26.7. The apparent magnitude of the star Arcturus is -0.04. Write an inequality statement comparing the numbers -0.04 and -26.7.

Star	*Apparent Magnitude*	*Star*	*Apparent Magnitude*
Arcturus	−0.04	Spica	0.98
Sirius	−1.46	Rigel	0.12
Vega	0.03	Regulus	1.35
Antares	0.96	Canopus	−0.72
Sun	−26.7	Hadar	0.61

(Data from *Norton's Star Atlas and Reference Handbook*, 20th Edition, edited by Ian Ridpath. © 2004 Pearson Education, Inc.)

82. The apparent magnitude of Antares is 0.96. The apparent magnitude of Spica is 0.98. Write an inequality statement comparing the numbers 0.96 and 0.98.

83. Which is brighter, the Sun or Arcturus?

84. Which is dimmer, Antares or Spica?

85. Which star listed is the brightest?

86. Which star listed is the dimmest?

Rewrite the following inequalities so that the inequality symbol points in the opposite direction and the resulting statement has the same meaning as the given one.

87. $25 \geq 20$

88. $-13 \leq 13$

89. $0 < 6$

90. $75 > 73$

91. $-10 > -12$

92. $-4 < -2$

93. In your own words, explain how to find the absolute value of a number.

94. Give an example of a real-life situation that can be described with integers but not with whole numbers.

1.3 Fractions and Mixed Numbers

OBJECTIVES

1 Write Fractions in Simplest Form.

2 Multiply and Divide Fractions.

3 Add and Subtract Fractions.

4 Perform Operations on Mixed Numbers.

OBJECTIVE

1 Writing Fractions in Simplest Form

A quotient of two numbers such as $\frac{2}{9}$ is called a **fraction.** The parts of a fraction are:

Fraction bar $\rightarrow \dfrac{2 \leftarrow \text{Numerator}}{9 \leftarrow \text{Denominator}}$

$\frac{2}{9}$ of the circle
is shaded.

A fraction may be used to refer to part of a whole. For example, $\frac{2}{9}$ of the circle above is shaded. The denominator 9 tells us how many equal parts the whole circle is divided into, and the numerator 2 tells us how many equal parts are shaded.

To simplify fractions, we can factor the numerator and the denominator. In the statement $3 \cdot 5 = 15$, 3 and 5 are called **factors** and 15 is the **product.** (The raised dot symbol indicates multiplication.)

$$
\begin{array}{ccccc}
3 & \cdot & 5 & = & 15 \\
\uparrow & & \uparrow & & \uparrow \\
\text{factor} & & \text{factor} & & \text{product}
\end{array}
$$

To **factor** 15 means to write it as a product. The number 15 can be factored as $3 \cdot 5$ or as $1 \cdot 15$.

A fraction is said to be **simplified** or in **lowest terms** when the numerator and the denominator have no factors in common other than 1. For example, the fraction $\frac{5}{11}$ is in lowest terms since 5 and 11 have no common factors other than 1.

To help us simplify fractions, we write the numerator and the denominator as products of **prime numbers.**

Prime Number and Composite Number

A **prime number** is a natural number, other than 1, whose only factors are 1 and itself. The first few prime numbers are

$$2, 3, 5, 7, 11, 13, 17, 19, 23, 29, \text{ and so on.}$$

A natural number, other than 1, that is not a prime number is called a **composite number.**

Helpful Hint

The natural number 1 is neither prime nor composite.

Every composite number can be written as a product of prime numbers. We call this product of prime numbers the **prime factorization** of the composite number.

EXAMPLE 1 Write each of the following numbers as a product of primes.

    a. 40   **b.** 63

Solution

a. First, write 40 as the product of any two whole numbers other than 1.

$$40 = 4 \cdot 10$$

Next, factor each of these numbers. Continue this process until all of the factors are prime numbers.

$$40 = 4 \quad \cdot \quad 10$$
$$= 2 \cdot 2 \cdot 2 \cdot 5$$

All the factors are now prime numbers. Then 40 written as a product of primes is

$$40 = 2 \cdot 2 \cdot 2 \cdot 5$$

b. $63 = 9 \quad \cdot \quad 7$
$$= 3 \cdot 3 \cdot 7$$

    □

PRACTICE

  1 Write each of the following numbers as a product of primes.

    a. 36   **b.** 200   ■

To use prime factors to write a fraction in lowest terms (or simplified form), apply the fundamental principle of fractions.

Fundamental Principle of Fractions

If $\dfrac{a}{b}$ is a fraction and c is a nonzero real number, then

$$\frac{a \cdot c}{b \cdot c} = \frac{a}{b}$$

To understand why this is true, we use the fact that since c is not zero, $\dfrac{c}{c} = 1$.

$$\frac{a \cdot c}{b \cdot c} = \frac{a}{b} \cdot \frac{c}{c} = \frac{a}{b} \cdot 1 = \frac{a}{b}$$

We will call this process dividing out the common factor of c.

EXAMPLE 2 Simplify each fraction (write it in lowest terms).

    a. $\dfrac{42}{49}$ **b.** $\dfrac{11}{27}$ **c.** $\dfrac{88}{20}$

Solution

a. Write the numerator and the denominator as products of primes; then apply the fundamental principle to the common factor 7.

$$\frac{42}{49} = \frac{2 \cdot 3 \cdot 7}{7 \cdot 7} = \frac{2 \cdot 3}{7} \cdot \frac{7}{7} = \frac{2 \cdot 3}{7} = \frac{6}{7}$$

b. $\dfrac{11}{27} = \dfrac{11}{3 \cdot 3 \cdot 3}$

There are no common factors other than 1, so $\dfrac{11}{27}$ is already in simplest form.

c. $\dfrac{88}{20} = \dfrac{2 \cdot 2 \cdot 2 \cdot 11}{2 \cdot 2 \cdot 5} = \dfrac{2}{2} \cdot \dfrac{2}{2} \cdot \dfrac{2 \cdot 11}{5} = \dfrac{22}{5}$ □

PRACTICE
2   Write each fraction in lowest terms.

a. $\dfrac{63}{72}$ **b.** $\dfrac{64}{12}$ **c.** $\dfrac{7}{25}$ ■

✔ **CONCEPT CHECK**

Explain the error in the following steps.

a. $\dfrac{15}{55} = \dfrac{1\!\!\!\diagup 5}{5\!\!\!\diagup 5} = \dfrac{1}{5}$ **b.** $\dfrac{6}{7} = \dfrac{5+1}{5+2} = \dfrac{1}{2}$

OBJECTIVE
2   **Multiplying and Dividing Fractions**

To multiply two fractions, multiply numerator times numerator to obtain the numerator of the product; multiply denominator times denominator to obtain the denominator of the product.

Multiplying Fractions

$$\frac{a}{b} \cdot \frac{c}{d} = \frac{a \cdot c}{b \cdot d} \qquad \text{if } b \neq 0 \text{ and } d \neq 0$$

EXAMPLE 3   Multiply $\dfrac{2}{15}$ and $\dfrac{5}{13}$. Simplify the product if possible.

Solution $\dfrac{2}{15} \cdot \dfrac{5}{13} = \dfrac{2 \cdot 5}{15 \cdot 13}$ Multiply numerators.
Multiply denominators.

Next, simplify the product by dividing the numerator and the denominator by any common factors.

$$= \frac{2 \cdot \overset{1}{\cancel{5}}}{3 \cdot \underset{1}{\cancel{5}} \cdot 13}$$

$$= \frac{2}{39}$$ □

PRACTICE
3   Multiply $\dfrac{3}{8}$ and $\dfrac{7}{9}$. Simplify the product if possible.   ■

Before dividing fractions, we first define **reciprocals.** Two fractions are reciprocals of each other if their product is 1.

For example:

The reciprocal of $\dfrac{2}{3}$ is $\dfrac{3}{2}$ because $\dfrac{2}{3} \cdot \dfrac{3}{2} = \dfrac{6}{6} = 1$.

The reciprocal of 5 is $\dfrac{1}{5}$ because $5 \cdot \dfrac{1}{5} = \dfrac{5}{1} \cdot \dfrac{1}{5} = \dfrac{5}{5} = 1$.

To divide fractions, multiply the first fraction by the reciprocal of the second fraction.

Dividing Fractions

$$\frac{a}{b} \div \frac{c}{d} = \frac{a}{b} \cdot \frac{d}{c}, \qquad \text{if } b \neq 0, d \neq 0, \text{ and } c \neq 0$$

EXAMPLE 4 Divide. Simplify all quotients if possible.

a. $\dfrac{4}{5} \div \dfrac{5}{16}$
b. $\dfrac{7}{10} \div 14$
c. $\dfrac{3}{8} \div \dfrac{3}{10}$

Solution

a. $\dfrac{4}{5} \div \dfrac{5}{16} = \dfrac{4}{5} \cdot \dfrac{16}{5} = \dfrac{4 \cdot 16}{5 \cdot 5} = \dfrac{64}{25}$ ⟵ The numerator and denominator have no common factors.

b. $\dfrac{7}{10} \div 14 = \dfrac{7}{10} \div \dfrac{14}{1} = \dfrac{7}{10} \cdot \dfrac{1}{14} = \dfrac{\overset{1}{\cancel{7}} \cdot 1}{2 \cdot 5 \cdot 2 \cdot \underset{1}{\cancel{7}}} = \dfrac{1}{20}$

c. $\dfrac{3}{8} \div \dfrac{3}{10} = \dfrac{3}{8} \cdot \dfrac{10}{3} = \dfrac{\overset{1}{\cancel{3}} \cdot \overset{1}{\cancel{2}} \cdot 5}{\underset{1}{\cancel{2}} \cdot 2 \cdot 2 \cdot \underset{1}{\cancel{3}}} = \dfrac{5}{4}$ ☐

PRACTICE
4 Divide. Simplify all quotients if possible.

a. $\dfrac{3}{4} \div \dfrac{4}{9}$
b. $\dfrac{5}{12} \div 15$
c. $\dfrac{7}{6} \div \dfrac{7}{15}$ ■

OBJECTIVE
3 Adding and Subtracting Fractions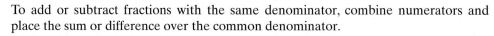

To add or subtract fractions with the same denominator, combine numerators and place the sum or difference over the common denominator.

Adding and Subtracting Fractions with the Same Denominator

$$\frac{a}{b} + \frac{c}{b} = \frac{a + c}{b}, \qquad \text{if } b \neq 0$$

$$\frac{a}{b} - \frac{c}{b} = \frac{a - c}{b}, \qquad \text{if } b \neq 0$$

EXAMPLE 5 Add or subtract as indicated. Simplify each result if possible.

a. $\dfrac{2}{7} + \dfrac{4}{7}$
b. $\dfrac{3}{10} + \dfrac{2}{10}$
c. $\dfrac{9}{7} - \dfrac{2}{7}$
d. $\dfrac{5}{3} - \dfrac{1}{3}$

Solution

a. $\dfrac{2}{7} + \dfrac{4}{7} = \dfrac{2 + 4}{7} = \dfrac{6}{7}$
b. $\dfrac{3}{10} + \dfrac{2}{10} = \dfrac{3 + 2}{10} = \dfrac{5}{10} = \dfrac{\overset{1}{\cancel{5}}}{2 \cdot \underset{1}{\cancel{5}}} = \dfrac{1}{2}$

c. $\dfrac{9}{7} - \dfrac{2}{7} = \dfrac{9 - 2}{7} = \dfrac{7}{7} = 1$
d. $\dfrac{5}{3} - \dfrac{1}{3} = \dfrac{5 - 1}{3} = \dfrac{4}{3}$ ☐

PRACTICE
5 Add or subtract as indicated. Simplify each result if possible.

a. $\dfrac{8}{5} - \dfrac{3}{5}$ **b.** $\dfrac{8}{5} - \dfrac{2}{5}$ **c.** $\dfrac{3}{5} + \dfrac{1}{5}$ **d.** $\dfrac{5}{12} + \dfrac{1}{12}$

To add or subtract fractions without the same denominator, first write the fractions as equivalent fractions with a common denominator. **Equivalent fractions** are fractions that represent the same quantity. For example,

$$\frac{3}{4} \text{ and } \frac{12}{16} \text{ are equivalent fractions}$$

since they represent the same portion of a whole, as the diagram shows. Count the larger squares, and the shaded portion is $\dfrac{3}{4}$. Count the smaller squares, and the shaded portion is $\dfrac{12}{16}$. Thus, $\dfrac{3}{4} = \dfrac{12}{16}$.

We can write equivalent fractions by multiplying a given fraction by 1, as shown in the next example. Multiplying a fraction by 1 does not change the value of the fraction.

Whole

$$\frac{3}{4} = \frac{12}{16}$$

EXAMPLE 6 Write $\dfrac{2}{5}$ as an equivalent fraction with a denominator of 20.

Solution Since $5 \cdot 4 = 20$, multiply the fraction by $\dfrac{4}{4}$. Multiplying by $\dfrac{4}{4} = 1$ does not change the value of the fraction.

$$\frac{2}{5} = \frac{2}{5} \cdot \frac{4}{4} = \frac{2 \cdot 4}{2 \cdot 4} = \frac{8}{20}$$

Multiply by $\dfrac{4}{4}$ or 1.

Thus, $\dfrac{2}{5} = \dfrac{8}{20}$.

PRACTICE
6 Write $\dfrac{2}{3}$ as an equivalent fraction with a denominator of 21.

To add or subtract with different denominators, we first write the fractions as **equivalent fractions** with the same denominator. We use the smallest or **least common denominator,** or **LCD.** (The LCD is the same as the least common multiple of the denominators.)

EXAMPLE 7 Add or subtract as indicated. Write each answer in simplest form.

a. $\dfrac{2}{5} + \dfrac{1}{4}$ **b.** $\dfrac{19}{6} - \dfrac{23}{12}$ **c.** $\dfrac{1}{2} + \dfrac{17}{22} - \dfrac{2}{11}$

Solution

a. Fractions must have a common denominator before they can be added or subtracted. Since 20 is the smallest number that both 5 and 4 divide into evenly, 20 is the **least common denominator** (LCD). Write both fractions as equivalent fractions with denominators of 20. Since

$$\frac{2}{5} \cdot \frac{4}{4} = \frac{2 \cdot 4}{5 \cdot 4} = \frac{8}{20} \quad \text{and} \quad \frac{1}{4} \cdot \frac{5}{5} = \frac{1 \cdot 5}{4 \cdot 5} = \frac{5}{20}$$

then

$$\frac{2}{5} + \frac{1}{4} = \frac{8}{20} + \frac{5}{20} = \frac{13}{20}$$

b. The LCD is 12. We write both fractions as equivalent fractions with denominators of 12.

$$\frac{19}{6} - \frac{23}{12} = \frac{38}{12} - \frac{23}{12}$$

$$= \frac{15}{12} = \frac{\overset{1}{\cancel{3}} \cdot 5}{2 \cdot 2 \cdot \underset{1}{\cancel{3}}} = \frac{5}{4}$$

c. The LCD for denominators 2, 22, and 11 is 22. First, write each fraction as an equivalent fraction with a denominator of 22. Then add or subtract from left to right.

$$\frac{1}{2} = \frac{1}{2} \cdot \frac{11}{11} = \frac{11}{22}, \quad \frac{17}{22} = \frac{17}{22}, \quad \text{and} \quad \frac{2}{11} = \frac{2}{11} \cdot \frac{2}{2} = \frac{4}{22}$$

Then

$$\frac{1}{2} + \frac{17}{22} - \frac{2}{11} = \frac{11}{22} + \frac{17}{22} - \frac{4}{22} = \frac{24}{22} = \frac{12}{11}$$

□

PRACTICE
7   Add or subtract as indicated. Write answers in simplest form.

a. $\dfrac{5}{11} + \dfrac{1}{7}$ **b.** $\dfrac{5}{21} - \dfrac{1}{6}$ **c.** $\dfrac{1}{3} + \dfrac{29}{30} - \dfrac{4}{5}$ ■

OBJECTIVE
4   Performing Operations on Mixed Numbers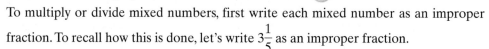

To multiply or divide mixed numbers, first write each mixed number as an improper fraction. To recall how this is done, let's write $3\frac{1}{5}$ as an improper fraction.

$$3\frac{1}{5} = 3 + \frac{1}{5} = \frac{15}{5} + \frac{1}{5} = \frac{16}{5}$$

Because of the steps above, notice that we can use a shortcut process for writing a mixed number as an improper fraction.

$$3\frac{1}{5} = \frac{5 \cdot 3 + 1}{5} = \frac{16}{5}$$

EXAMPLE 8   Divide: $2\frac{1}{8} \div 1\frac{2}{3}$

Solution   First write each mixed number as an improper fraction.

$$2\frac{1}{8} = \frac{8 \cdot 2 + 1}{8} = \frac{17}{8}; \quad 1\frac{2}{3} = \frac{3 \cdot 1 + 2}{3} = \frac{5}{3}$$

Now divide as usual.

$$2\frac{1}{8} \div 1\frac{2}{3} = \frac{17}{8} \div \frac{5}{3} = \frac{17}{8} \cdot \frac{3}{5} = \frac{51}{40}$$

The fraction $\dfrac{51}{40}$ is improper. To write it as an equivalent mixed number, remember that the fraction bar means division and divide.

$$\begin{array}{r} 1\frac{11}{40} \\ 40\overline{)51} \\ -40 \\ \hline 11 \end{array}$$

Thus, the quotient is $\dfrac{51}{40}$ or $1\dfrac{11}{40}$.

□

PRACTICE
8   Multiply: $5\frac{1}{6} \cdot 4\frac{2}{5}$ ■

As a general rule, if the original exercise contains mixed numbers, write the result as a mixed number if possible.

When adding or subtracting mixed numbers, you might want to use the following method.

EXAMPLE 9   Subtract: $50\dfrac{1}{6} - 38\dfrac{1}{3}$

Solution

$$50\dfrac{1}{6} = \quad 50\dfrac{1}{6} = \quad 49\dfrac{7}{6} \qquad 50\dfrac{1}{6} = 49 + 1 + \dfrac{1}{6} = 49\dfrac{7}{6}$$

$$\dfrac{-38\dfrac{1}{3} = -38\dfrac{2}{6} = -38\dfrac{2}{6}}{11\dfrac{5}{6}}$$

PRACTICE
9   Subtract: $76\dfrac{1}{12} - 35\dfrac{1}{4}$

✔ Vocabulary, Readiness & Video Check

Use the choices below to fill in each blank. Some choices may be used more than once.

simplified	reciprocals	equivalent	denominator
product	factors	fraction	numerator

1. A quotient of two numbers, such as $\dfrac{5}{8}$, is called a(n) _____.

2. In the fraction $\dfrac{3}{11}$, the number 3 is called the _____ and the number 11 is called the _____.

3. To factor a number means to write it as a(n) _____.

4. A fraction is said to be _____ when the numerator and the denominator have no common factors other than 1.

5. In $7 \cdot 3 = 21$, the numbers 7 and 3 are called _____ and the number 21 is called the _____.

6. The fractions $\dfrac{2}{9}$ and $\dfrac{9}{2}$ are called _____.

7. Fractions that represent the same quantity are called _____ fractions.

Martin-Gay Interactive Videos

See Video 1.3 🎥

Watch the section lecture video and answer the following questions.

OBJECTIVE 1
8. What is the common factor in the numerator and denominator of 🎬 Example 1? What principle is used to simplify this fraction?

OBJECTIVE 2
9. During the solving of 🎬 Example 3, what two things change in the first step?

OBJECTIVE 3
10. What is the first step needed in order to subtract the fractions in 🎬 Example 6 and why?

OBJECTIVE 4
11. For 🎬 Example 7, why is the sum not left as $4\dfrac{7}{6}$?

1.3   Exercise Set   MyMathLab®

Represent the shaded part of each geometric figure by a fraction.

1.

2.

3.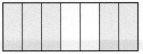

4.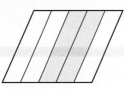

Write each number as a product of primes. See Example 1.

5. 33   **6.** 60   **7.** 98

8. 27   **9.** 20   **10.** 56

11. 75   **12.** 32   **13.** 45

14. 24

Write the fraction in lowest terms. See Example 2.

15. $\dfrac{2}{4}$ **16.** $\dfrac{3}{6}$ **17.** $\dfrac{10}{15}$

18. $\dfrac{15}{20}$ **19.** $\dfrac{3}{7}$ **20.** $\dfrac{5}{9}$

21. $\dfrac{18}{30}$ **22.** $\dfrac{42}{45}$ **23.** $\dfrac{120}{244}$

24. $\dfrac{360}{700}$

Multiply or divide as indicated. Simplify the answer if possible. See Examples 3 and 4.

25. $\dfrac{1}{2} \cdot \dfrac{3}{4}$ **26.** $\dfrac{7}{11} \cdot \dfrac{3}{5}$ **27.** $\dfrac{2}{3} \cdot \dfrac{3}{4}$

28. $\dfrac{7}{8} \cdot \dfrac{3}{21}$ **29.** $\dfrac{1}{2} \div \dfrac{7}{12}$ **30.** $\dfrac{7}{12} \div \dfrac{1}{2}$

31. $\dfrac{3}{4} \div \dfrac{1}{20}$ **32.** $\dfrac{3}{5} \div \dfrac{9}{10}$ **33.** $\dfrac{7}{10} \cdot \dfrac{5}{21}$

34. $\dfrac{3}{35} \cdot \dfrac{10}{63}$ **35.** $\dfrac{25}{9} \cdot \dfrac{1}{3}$ **36.** $\dfrac{1}{4} \cdot \dfrac{19}{6}$

The area of a plane figure is a measure of the amount of surface of the figure. Find the area of each figure below. (The area of a rectangle is the product of its length and width. The area of a triangle is $\dfrac{1}{2}$ the product of its base and height.)

△ 37.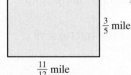

△ 38.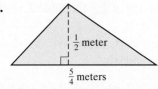

△ 39.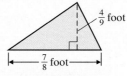

△ 40.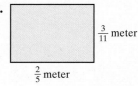

Add or subtract as indicated. Write the answer in lowest terms. See Example 5.

41. $\dfrac{4}{5} - \dfrac{1}{5}$ **42.** $\dfrac{6}{7} - \dfrac{1}{7}$

43. $\dfrac{4}{5} + \dfrac{1}{5}$ **44.** $\dfrac{6}{7} + \dfrac{1}{7}$

45. $\dfrac{17}{21} - \dfrac{10}{21}$ **46.** $\dfrac{18}{35} - \dfrac{11}{35}$

47. $\dfrac{23}{105} + \dfrac{4}{105}$ **48.** $\dfrac{13}{132} + \dfrac{35}{132}$

Write each fraction as an equivalent fraction with the given denominator. See Example 6.

49. $\dfrac{7}{10}$ with a denominator of 30

50. $\dfrac{2}{3}$ with a denominator of 9

51. $\dfrac{2}{9}$ with a denominator of 18

52. $\dfrac{8}{7}$ with a denominator of 56

53. $\dfrac{4}{5}$ with a denominator of 20

54. $\dfrac{4}{5}$ with a denominator of 25

Add or subtract as indicated. Write the answer in simplest form. See Example 7.

55. $\dfrac{2}{3} + \dfrac{3}{7}$ **56.** $\dfrac{3}{4} + \dfrac{1}{6}$

57. $\dfrac{4}{15} - \dfrac{1}{12}$ **58.** $\dfrac{11}{12} - \dfrac{1}{16}$

59. $\dfrac{5}{22} - \dfrac{5}{33}$ **60.** $\dfrac{7}{10} - \dfrac{8}{15}$

61. $\dfrac{12}{5} - 1$ **62.** $2 - \dfrac{3}{8}$

Each circle in Exercises 63–68 represents a whole, or 1. Use subtraction to determine the unknown part of the circle.

63.

64.

65.

66.

67.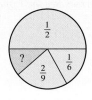

68.

Perform the indicated operations. See Examples 8 and 9.

69. $5\dfrac{1}{9} \cdot 3\dfrac{2}{3}$

70. $2\dfrac{3}{4} \cdot 1\dfrac{7}{8}$

71. $8\dfrac{3}{5} \div 2\dfrac{9}{10}$

72. $1\dfrac{7}{8} \div 3\dfrac{8}{9}$

73. $17\dfrac{2}{5} + 30\dfrac{2}{3}$

74. $26\dfrac{11}{20} + 40\dfrac{7}{10}$

75. $8\dfrac{11}{12} - 1\dfrac{5}{6}$

76. $4\dfrac{7}{8} - 2\dfrac{3}{16}$

MIXED PRACTICE

Perform the following operations. Write answers in simplest form.

77. $\dfrac{10}{21} + \dfrac{5}{21}$

78. $\dfrac{11}{35} + \dfrac{3}{35}$

79. $\dfrac{10}{3} - \dfrac{5}{21}$

80. $\dfrac{11}{7} - \dfrac{3}{35}$

81. $\dfrac{2}{3} \cdot \dfrac{3}{5}$

82. $\dfrac{3}{4} \cdot \dfrac{7}{12}$

83. $\dfrac{2}{3} \div \dfrac{3}{5}$

84. $\dfrac{3}{4} \div \dfrac{7}{12}$

85. $5 + \dfrac{2}{3}$

86. $7 + \dfrac{1}{10}$

87. $7\dfrac{2}{5} \div \dfrac{1}{5}$

88. $9\dfrac{5}{6} \div \dfrac{1}{6}$

89. $\dfrac{1}{2} - \dfrac{14}{33}$

90. $\dfrac{7}{15} - \dfrac{7}{25}$

91. $\dfrac{23}{105} - \dfrac{2}{105}$

92. $\dfrac{57}{132} - \dfrac{13}{132}$

93. $1\dfrac{1}{2} + 3\dfrac{2}{3}$

94. $2\dfrac{3}{5} + 4\dfrac{7}{10}$

95. $\dfrac{2}{3} - \dfrac{5}{9} + \dfrac{5}{6}$

96. $\dfrac{8}{11} - \dfrac{1}{4} + \dfrac{1}{2}$

The perimeter of a plane figure is the total distance around the figure. Find the perimeter of each figure in Exercises 97 and 98.

△ **97.**

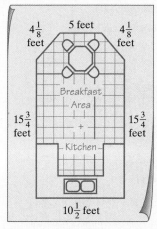

△ **98.**

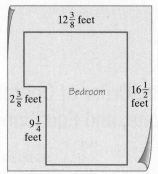

99. In your own words, explain how to add two fractions with different denominators.

100. In your own words, explain how to multiply two fractions.

The following trail chart is given to visitors at the Lakeview Forest Preserve.

Trail Name	*Distance (miles)*
Robin Path	$3\dfrac{1}{2}$
Red Falls	$5\dfrac{1}{2}$
Green Way	$2\dfrac{1}{8}$
Autumn Walk	$1\dfrac{3}{4}$

101. How much longer is Red Falls Trail than Green Way Trail?

102. Find the total distance traveled by someone who hiked along all four trails.

CONCEPT EXTENSIONS

The graph shown is called a circle graph or a pie chart. Use the graph to answer Exercises 103 through 106.

Fraction of U.S. Screens by Type

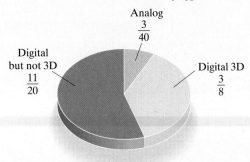

Data from Motion Picture Association of America

103. What fraction of U.S. movie screens are analog?

104. What fraction of U.S. movie screens are digital but not 3D?

105. What fraction of U.S. movie screens are digital?

106. What fraction of U.S. movie screens are analog or digital 3D?

For Exercises 107 through 110, determine whether the work is correct or incorrect. If incorrect, find the error and correct. See the Concept Check in this section.

107. $\dfrac{12}{24} \overset{?}{=} \dfrac{2+4+6}{2+4+6+12} = \dfrac{1}{12}$

108. $\dfrac{30}{60} \overset{?}{=} \dfrac{2\cdot3\cdot5}{2\cdot2\cdot3\cdot5} = \dfrac{1}{2}$

109. $\dfrac{2}{7} + \dfrac{9}{7} \overset{?}{=} \dfrac{11}{14}$

110. $\dfrac{16}{28} \overset{?}{=} \dfrac{2\cdot5+6\cdot1}{2\cdot5+6\cdot3} = \dfrac{1}{3}$

1.4 Exponents, Order of Operations, Variable Expressions, and Equations

OBJECTIVES

1 Define and Use Exponents and the Order of Operations.

2 Evaluate Algebraic Expressions, Given Replacement Values for Variables.

3 Determine Whether a Number Is a Solution of a Given Equation.

4 Translate Phrases into Expressions and Sentences into Statements.

OBJECTIVE

1 Using Exponents and the Order of Operations

Frequently in algebra, products occur that contain repeated multiplication of the same factor. For example, the volume of a cube whose sides each measure 2 centimeters is $(2\cdot2\cdot2)$ cubic centimeters. We may use **exponential notation** to write such products in a more compact form. For example,

$$2\cdot2\cdot2 \quad may\ be\ written\ as \quad 2^3.$$

The 2 in 2^3 is called the **base**; it is the repeated factor. The 3 in 2^3 is called the **exponent** and is the number of times the base is used as a factor. The expression 2^3 is called an **exponential expression.**

$$\underset{\text{base}}{} 2^{\overset{\text{exponent}}{3}} = 2\cdot2\cdot2 = 8$$
2 is a factor 3 times

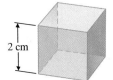

Volume is $(2\cdot2\cdot2)$ cubic centimeters.

EXAMPLE 1 Evaluate the following.

a. 3^2 [read as "3 squared" or as "3 to the second power"]

b. 5^3 [read as "5 cubed" or as "5 to the third power"]

c. 2^4 [read as "2 to the fourth power"]

d. 7^1 e. $\left(\dfrac{3}{7}\right)^2$

Solution

a. $3^2 = 3\cdot3 = 9$ b. $5^3 = 5\cdot5\cdot5 = 125$

c. $2^4 = 2\cdot2\cdot2\cdot2 = 16$ d. $7^1 = 7$

e. $\left(\dfrac{3}{7}\right)^2 = \left(\dfrac{3}{7}\right)\left(\dfrac{3}{7}\right) = \dfrac{9}{49}$

PRACTICE

1   Evaluate.

a. 1^3 **b.** 5^2 **c.** $\left(\dfrac{1}{10}\right)^2$ **d.** 9^1 **e.** $\left(\dfrac{2}{5}\right)^3$ ■

> **Helpful Hint**
>
> $2^3 \neq 2 \cdot 3$ since 2^3 indicates repeated **multiplication** of the same factor.
>
> $$2^3 = 2 \cdot 2 \cdot 2 = 8, \text{ whereas } 2 \cdot 3 = 6.$$

Using symbols for mathematical operations is a great convenience. However, the more operation symbols present in an expression, the more careful we must be when performing the indicated operation. For example, in the expression $2 + 3 \cdot 7$, do we add first or multiply first? To eliminate confusion, **grouping symbols** are used. Examples of grouping symbols are parentheses ( ), brackets [ ], braces { }, and the fraction bar. If we wish $2 + 3 \cdot 7$ to be simplified by adding first, we enclose $2 + 3$ in parentheses.

$$(2 + 3) \cdot 7 = 5 \cdot 7 = 35$$

If we wish to multiply first, $3 \cdot 7$ may be enclosed in parentheses.

$$2 + (3 \cdot 7) = 2 + 21 = 23$$

To eliminate confusion when no grouping symbols are present, use the following agreed-upon order of operations.

> **Order of Operations**
>
> Simplify expressions using the order below. If grouping symbols such as parentheses are present, simplify expressions within those first, starting with the innermost set. If fraction bars are present, simplify the numerator and the denominator separately.
>
> **1.** Evaluate exponential expressions.
> **2.** Perform multiplications or divisions in order from left to right.
> **3.** Perform additions or subtractions in order from left to right.

Now simplify $2 + 3 \cdot 7$. There are no grouping symbols and no exponents, so we multiply and then add.

$$2 + 3 \cdot 7 = 2 + 21 \quad \text{Multiply.}$$
$$= 23 \quad \text{Add.}$$

EXAMPLE 2   Simplify each expression.

a. $6 \div 3 + 5^2$ **b.** $20 \div 5 \cdot 4$ **c.** $\dfrac{2(12 + 3)}{|-15|}$ **d.** $3 \cdot 4^2$ **e.** $\dfrac{3}{2} \cdot \dfrac{1}{2} - \dfrac{1}{2}$

Solution

a. Evaluate 5^2 first.

$$6 \div 3 + 5^2 = 6 \div 3 + 25$$

Next divide, then add.

$$= 2 + 25 \quad \text{Divide.}$$
$$= 27 \quad \text{Add.}$$

b. $20 \div 5 \cdot 4 = 4 \cdot 4$
$$= 16$$

> **Helpful Hint**
>
> Remember to multiply or divide in order from left to right.

c. First, simplify the numerator and the denominator separately.

$$\frac{2(12+3)}{|-15|} = \frac{2(15)}{15} \quad \text{Simplify numerator and denominator separately.}$$

$$= \frac{30}{15}$$

$$= 2 \quad \text{Simplify.}$$

d. In this example, only the 4 is squared. The factor of 3 is not part of the base because no grouping symbol includes it as part of the base.

$$3 \cdot 4^2 = 3 \cdot 16 \quad \text{Evaluate the exponential expression.}$$

$$= 48 \quad \text{Multiply.}$$

e. The order of operations applies to operations with fractions in exactly the same way as it applies to operations with whole numbers.

$$\frac{3}{2} \cdot \frac{1}{2} - \frac{1}{2} = \frac{3}{4} - \frac{1}{2} \quad \text{Multiply.}$$

$$= \frac{3}{4} - \frac{2}{4} \quad \text{The least common denominator is 4.}$$

$$= \frac{1}{4} \quad \text{Subtract.} \qquad \square$$

PRACTICE

2 Simplify each expression.

a. $6 + 3 \cdot 9$ **b.** $4^3 \div 8 + 3$ **c.** $\left(\frac{2}{3}\right)^2 \cdot |-8|$

d. $\dfrac{9(14-6)}{|-2|}$ **e.** $\dfrac{7}{4} \cdot \dfrac{1}{4} - \dfrac{1}{4}$

> **Helpful Hint**
>
> Be careful when evaluating an exponential expression. In $3 \cdot 4^2$, the exponent 2 applies only to the base 4. In $(3 \cdot 4)^2$, the parentheses are a grouping symbol, so the exponent 2 applies to the product $3 \cdot 4$. Thus, we multiply first.
>
> $$3 \cdot 4^2 = 3 \cdot 16 = 48 \qquad (3 \cdot 4)^2 = (12)^2 = 144$$

Expressions that include many grouping symbols can be confusing. When simplifying these expressions, keep in mind that grouping symbols separate the expression into distinct parts. Each is then simplified separately.

EXAMPLE 3   Simplify: $\dfrac{3 + |4 - 3| + 2^2}{6 - 3}$

Solution   The fraction bar serves as a grouping symbol and separates the numerator and denominator. Simplify each separately. Also, the absolute value bars here serve as a grouping symbol. We begin in the numerator by simplifying within the absolute value bars.

$$\frac{3 + |4 - 3| + 2^2}{6 - 3} = \frac{3 + |1| + 2^2}{6 - 3} \quad \begin{array}{l}\text{Simplify the expression inside} \\ \text{the absolute value bars.}\end{array}$$

$$= \frac{3 + 1 + 2^2}{3} \quad \begin{array}{l}\text{Find the absolute value and} \\ \text{simplify the denominator.}\end{array}$$

$$= \frac{3 + 1 + 4}{3} \quad \begin{array}{l}\text{Evaluate the exponential} \\ \text{expression.}\end{array}$$

$$= \frac{8}{3} \quad \text{Simplify the numerator.} \qquad \square$$

PRACTICE

3 Simplify: $\dfrac{6^2 - 5}{3 + |6 - 5| \cdot 8}$

EXAMPLE 4   Simplify: $3[4 + 2(10 - 1)]$

Solution   Notice that both parentheses and brackets are used as grouping symbols. Start with the innermost set of grouping symbols.

$$3[4 + 2(10 - 1)] = 3[4 + 2(9)] \quad \text{Simplify the expression in parentheses.}$$
$$= 3[4 + 18] \quad \text{Multiply.}$$
$$= 3[22] \quad \text{Add.}$$
$$= 66 \quad \text{Multiply.}$$

PRACTICE
4   Simplify: $4[25 - 3(5 + 3)]$

EXAMPLE 5   Simplify: $\dfrac{8 + 2 \cdot 3}{2^2 - 1}$

Solution

$$\frac{8 + 2 \cdot 3}{2^2 - 1} = \frac{8 + 6}{4 - 1} = \frac{14}{3}$$

PRACTICE
5   Simplify: $\dfrac{36 \div 9 + 5}{5^2 - 3}$

OBJECTIVE

2   Evaluating Algebraic Expressions

In algebra, we use symbols, usually letters such as x, y, or z, to represent unknown numbers. A symbol that is used to represent a number is called a **variable**. An **algebraic expression** is a collection of numbers, variables, operation symbols, and grouping symbols. For example,

$$2x, \quad -3, \quad 2x + 10, \quad 5(p^2 + 1), \quad \text{and} \quad \frac{3y^2 - 6y + 1}{5}$$

are algebraic expressions.

Expression	Meaning
$2x$	$2 \cdot x$
$5(p^2 + 1)$	$5 \cdot (p^2 + 1)$
$3y^2$	$3 \cdot y^2$
xy	$x \cdot y$

If we give a specific value to a variable, we can **evaluate an algebraic expression.** To evaluate an algebraic expression means to find its numerical value once we know the values of the variables.

Algebraic expressions are often used in problem solving. For example, the expression

$$16t^2$$

gives the distance in feet (neglecting air resistance) that an object will fall in t seconds.

EXAMPLE 6 Evaluate each expression if $x = 3$ and $y = 2$.

a. $2x - y$ **b.** $\dfrac{3x}{2y}$ **c.** $\dfrac{x}{y} + \dfrac{y}{2}$ **d.** $x^2 - y^2$

Solution

a. Replace x with 3 and y with 2.

$$2x - y = 2(3) - 2 \quad \text{Let } x = 3 \text{ and } y = 2.$$
$$= 6 - 2 \qquad \text{Multiply.}$$
$$= 4 \qquad \text{Subtract.}$$

b. $\dfrac{3x}{2y} = \dfrac{3 \cdot 3}{2 \cdot 2} = \dfrac{9}{4}$ Let $x = 3$ and $y = 2$.

c. Replace x with 3 and y with 2. Then simplify.

$$\dfrac{x}{y} + \dfrac{y}{2} = \dfrac{3}{2} + \dfrac{2}{2} = \dfrac{5}{2}$$

d. Replace x with 3 and y with 2.

$$x^2 - y^2 = 3^2 - 2^2 = 9 - 4 = 5$$

PRACTICE
6 Evaluate each expression if $x = 2$ and $y = 5$.

a. $2x + y$ **b.** $\dfrac{4x}{3y}$ **c.** $\dfrac{3}{x} + \dfrac{x}{y}$ **d.** $x^3 + y^2$

OBJECTIVE

3 Determining Whether a Number Is a Solution of an Equation

Many times, a problem-solving situation is modeled by an equation. An **equation** is a mathematical statement that two expressions have equal value. An equal sign "=" is used to equate the two expressions. For example,

$$3 + 2 = 5, \quad 7x = 35, \quad \dfrac{2(x - 1)}{3} = 0, \text{ and } I = PRT \text{ are all equations.}$$

> **Helpful Hint**
> An equation contains an equal sign "=". An algebraic expression does not.

✔ **CONCEPT CHECK**

Which of the following are equations? Which are expressions?
a. $5x = 8$ **b.** $5x - 8$ **c.** $12y + 3x$ **d.** $12y = 3x$

When an equation contains a variable, deciding which values of the variable make the equation a true statement is called **solving** the equation for the variable. A **solution** of an equation is a value for the variable that makes the equation true. For example, 3 is a solution of the equation $x + 4 = 7$ because if x is replaced with 3, the statement is true.

$$x + 4 = 7$$
$$\downarrow$$
$$3 + 4 = 7 \quad \text{Replace } x \text{ with 3.}$$
$$7 = 7 \quad \text{True}$$

Similarly, 1 is not a solution of the equation $x + 4 = 7$ because $1 + 4 = 7$ is **not** a true statement.

EXAMPLE 7   Decide whether 2 is a solution of $3x + 10 = 8x$.

Solution   Replace x with 2 and see if a true statement results.

$$3x + 10 = 8x \qquad \text{Original equation}$$
$$3(2) + 10 \stackrel{?}{=} 8(2) \qquad \text{Replace } x \text{ with 2.}$$
$$6 + 10 \stackrel{?}{=} 16 \qquad \text{Simplify each side.}$$
$$16 = 16 \qquad \text{True}$$

Since we arrived at a true statement after replacing x with 2 and simplifying both sides of the equation, 2 is a solution of the equation.   □

PRACTICE

7   Decide whether 4 is a solution of $9x - 6 = 7x$.   ■

OBJECTIVE

4   **Translating Phrases to Expressions and Sentences to Statements**

Now that we know how to represent an unknown number by a variable, let's practice translating phrases into algebraic expressions and sentences into statements. Oftentimes, solving problems requires the ability to translate word phrases and sentences into symbols. Below is a list of some key words and phrases to help us translate.

> **Helpful Hint**
> Order matters when subtracting and dividing, so be especially careful with these translations.

Addition (+)	Subtraction (−)	Multiplication (·)	Division (÷)	Equality (=)
Sum	Difference of	Product	Quotient	Equals
Plus	Minus	Times	Divide	Gives
Added to	Subtracted from	Multiply	Into	Is/Was/Should be
More than	Less than	Twice	Ratio	Yields
Increased by	Decreased by	Of	Divided by	Amounts to
Total	Less			Represents/ Is the same as

EXAMPLE 8   Write an algebraic expression that represents each phrase. Let the variable x represent the unknown number.

a. The sum of a number and 3   **b.** The product of 3 and a number
c. Twice a number   **d.** 10 decreased by a number
e. 5 times a number, increased by 7

Solution

a. $x + 3$ since "sum" means to add
b. $3 \cdot x$ and $3x$ are both ways to denote the product of 3 and x
c. $2 \cdot x$ or $2x$
d. $10 - x$ because "decreased by" means to subtract
e. $\underbrace{5x}_{5 \text{ times a number}} + 7$ □

PRACTICE

8   Write an algebraic expression that represents each phrase. Let the variable x represent the unknown number.

a. Six times a number   **b.** A number decreased by 8
c. The product of a number and 9   **d.** Two times a number, plus 3
e. The sum of 7 and a number   ■

Helpful Hint

Make sure you understand the difference when translating phrases containing "decreased by," "subtracted from," and "less than."

Phrase	*Translation*
A number decreased by 10	$x - 10$
A number subtracted from 10	$10 - x$
10 less than a number	$x - 10$
A number less 10	$x - 10$

Notice the order.

Now let's practice translating sentences into equations.

EXAMPLE 9 Write each sentence as an equation or inequality. Let *x* represent the unknown number.

a. The quotient of 15 and a number is 4.

b. Three subtracted from 12 is a number.

c. Four times a number, added to 17, is not equal to 21.

d. Triple a number is less than 48.

Solution

a. In words: the quotient of 15 and a number   is   4

Translate: $$\frac{15}{x} = 4$$

b. In words: three subtracted **from** 12   is   a number

Translate: $$12 - 3 = x$$

Care must be taken when the operation is subtraction. The expression $3 - 12$ would be incorrect. Notice that $3 - 12 \neq 12 - 3$.

c. In words: four times a number   added to   17   is not equal to   21

Translate: $$4x + 17 \neq 21$$

d. In words: triple a number   is less than   48

Translate: $$3x < 48$$

PRACTICE

9 Write each sentence as an equation or inequality. Let *x* represent the unknown number.

a. A number increased by 7 is equal to 13.

b. Two less than a number is 11.

c. Double a number, added to 9, is not equal to 25.

d. Five times 11 is greater than or equal to an unknown number.

Graphing Calculator Explorations

Exponents

To evaluate exponential expressions on a scientific calculator, find the key marked y^x or $\wedge$. To evaluate, for example, 3^5, press the following keys: $\boxed{3}$ $\boxed{y^x}$ $\boxed{5}$ $\boxed{=}$ or $\boxed{3}$ $\boxed{\wedge}$ $\boxed{5}$ $\boxed{=}$.

$\updownarrow$ or

$\boxed{\text{ENTER}}$

The display should read $\boxed{\quad 243}$ or $\boxed{\begin{array}{l}3\wedge 5 \\ \quad\quad 243\end{array}}$

Order of Operations

Some calculators follow the order of operations, and others do not. To see whether your calculator has the order of operations built in, use your calculator to find $2 + 3 \cdot 4$. To do this, press the following sequence of keys:

$\boxed{2}$ $\boxed{+}$ $\boxed{3}$ $\boxed{\times}$ $\boxed{4}$ $\boxed{=}$.

$\updownarrow$ or

$\boxed{\text{ENTER}}$

The correct answer is 14 because the order of operations is to multiply before we add. If the calculator displays $\boxed{\quad 14}$, then it has the order of operations built in.

Even if the order of operations is built in, parentheses must sometimes be inserted. For example, to simplify $\dfrac{5}{12 - 7}$, press the keys

$\boxed{5}$ $\boxed{\div}$ $\boxed{(}$ $\boxed{1}$ $\boxed{2}$ $\boxed{-}$ $\boxed{7}$ $\boxed{)}$ $\boxed{=}$.

$\updownarrow$ or

$\boxed{\text{ENTER}}$

The display should read $\boxed{\quad 1}$ or $\boxed{\begin{array}{l}5/(12 - 7) \\ \quad\quad\quad\quad 1\end{array}}$

Use a calculator to evaluate each expression.

1. 5^4

2. 7^4

3. 9^5

4. 8^6

5. $2(20 - 5)$

6. $3(14 - 7) + 21$

7. $24(862 - 455) + 89$

8. $99 + (401 + 962)$

9. $\dfrac{4623 + 129}{36 - 34}$

10. $\dfrac{956 - 452}{89 - 86}$

✔ **Vocabulary, Readiness & Video Check**

Use the choices below to fill in each blank.

equation	variable	base	grouping
expression	solution	solving	exponent

1. In the expression 5^2, the 5 is called the _____ and the 2 is called the _____ .

2. The symbols ( ), [ ], and { } are examples of _____ symbols.

3. A symbol that is used to represent a number is called a(n) _____ .

4. A collection of numbers, variables, operation symbols, and grouping symbols is called a(n) _____ .

5. A mathematical statement that two expressions are equal is called a(n) _____ .

6. A value for the variable that makes an equation a true statement is called a(n) _____ .

7. Deciding what values of a variable make an equation a true statement is called _____ the equation.

Martin-Gay Interactive Videos

See Video 1.4

Watch the section lecture video and answer the following questions.

OBJECTIVE
1

8. In ▥ Example 3 and the lecture before, what is the main point made about the order of operations?

OBJECTIVE
2

9. What happens with the replacement value for z in ▥ Example 6 and why?

OBJECTIVE
3

10. Is the value 0 a solution of the equation given in ▥ Example 9? How is this determined?

OBJECTIVE
4

11. Earlier in this video the point was made that equations have =, while expressions do not. In the lecture before ▥ Example 10, translating from English to math is discussed and another difference between expressions and equations is explained. What is it?

1.4 Exercise Set   MyMathLab® ▶

Evaluate. See Example 1.

1. 3^5

2. 2^5

3. 3^3

4. 4^4

5. 1^5

6. 1^8

7. 5^1

8. 8^1

9. 7^2

10. 9^2

11. $\left(\dfrac{2}{3}\right)^4$

12. $\left(\dfrac{6}{11}\right)^2$

13. $\left(\dfrac{1}{5}\right)^3$

14. $\left(\dfrac{1}{2}\right)^5$

15. $(1.2)^2$

16. $(1.5)^2$

17. $(0.04)^3$

18. $(0.03)^3$

MIXED PRACTICE

Simplify each expression. See Examples 2 through 5.

19. $5 + 6 \cdot 2$

20. $8 + 5 \cdot 3$

21. $4 \cdot 8 - 6 \cdot 2$

22. $12 \cdot 5 - 3 \cdot 6$

23. $2(8 - 3)$

24. $5(6 - 2)$

25. $2 + (5 - 2) + 4^2$

26. $6 - 2 \cdot 2 + 2^5$

27. $5 \cdot 3^2$

28. $2 \cdot 5^2$

29. $\dfrac{1}{4} \cdot \dfrac{2}{3} - \dfrac{1}{6}$

30. $\dfrac{3}{4} \cdot \dfrac{1}{2} + \dfrac{2}{3}$

31. $2[5 + 2(8 - 3)]$

32. $3[4 + 3(6 - 4)]$

33. $\dfrac{19 - 3 \cdot 5}{6 - 4}$

34. $\dfrac{4 \cdot 3 + 2}{4 + 3 \cdot 2}$

35. $\dfrac{|6 - 2| + 3}{8 + 2 \cdot 5}$

36. $\dfrac{15 - |3 - 1|}{12 - 3 \cdot 2}$

37. $\dfrac{3 + 3(5 + 3)}{3^2 + 1}$

38. $\dfrac{3 + 6(8 - 5)}{4^2 + 2}$

39. $\dfrac{6 + |8 - 2| + 3^2}{18 - 3}$

40. $\dfrac{16 + |13 - 5| + 4^2}{17 - 5}$

41. $2 + 3[10(4 \cdot 5 - 16) - 30]$

42. $3 + 4[8(5 \cdot 5 - 20) - 39]$

43. $\left(\dfrac{2}{3}\right)^3 + \dfrac{1}{9} + \dfrac{1}{3} \cdot \dfrac{4}{3}$

44. $\left(\dfrac{3}{8}\right)^2 + \dfrac{1}{4} + \dfrac{1}{8} \cdot \dfrac{3}{2}$

For Exercises 45 and 46, match each expression in the first column with its value in the second column.

45.
a. $(6 + 2) \cdot (5 + 3)$	19
b. $(6 + 2) \cdot 5 + 3$	22
c. $6 + 2 \cdot 5 + 3$	64
d. $6 + 2 \cdot (5 + 3)$	43

46.
a. $(1 + 4) \cdot 6 - 3$	15
b. $1 + 4 \cdot (6 - 3)$	13
c. $1 + 4 \cdot 6 - 3$	27
d. $(1 + 4) \cdot (6 - 3)$	22

Evaluate each expression when x = 1, y = 3, and z = 5. See Example 6.

47. $3y$

48. $4x$

49. $\dfrac{z}{5x}$

50. $\dfrac{y}{2z}$

51. $3x - 2$

52. $6y - 8$

▶ **53.** $|2x + 3y|$

54. $|5z - 2y|$

55. $xy + z$

56. $yz - x$

57. $5y^2$

58. $2z^2$

Evaluate each expression if x = 12, y = 8, and z = 4. See Example 6.

59. $\dfrac{x}{z} + 3y$

60. $\dfrac{y}{z} + 8x$

61. $x^2 - 3y + x$

62. $y^2 - 3x + y$

▶ **63.** $\dfrac{x^2 + z}{y^2 + 2z}$

64. $\dfrac{y^2 + x}{x^2 + 3y}$

Neglecting air resistance, the expression $16t^2$ gives the distance in feet an object will fall in t seconds.

65. Complete the chart below. To evaluate $16t^2$, remember to first find t^2, then multiply by 16.

Time t (in seconds)	Distance $16t^2$ (in feet)
1	
2	
3	
4	

66. Does an object fall the same distance *during* each second? Why or why not? (See Exercise 65.)

Decide whether the given number is a solution of the given equation. See Example 7.

67. Is 5 a solution of $3x + 30 = 9x$?

68. Is 6 a solution of $2x + 7 = 3x$?

69. Is 0 a solution of $2x + 6 = 5x - 1$?

70. Is 2 a solution of $4x + 2 = x + 8$?

71. Is 8 a solution of $2x - 5 = 5$?

▶ **72.** Is 6 a solution of $3x - 10 = 8$?

73. Is 2 a solution of $x + 6 = x + 6$?

74. Is 10 a solution of $x + 6 = x + 6$?

▶ **75.** Is 0 a solution of $x = 5x + 15$?

76. Is 1 a solution of $4 = 1 - x$?

TRANSLATING

Write each phrase as an algebraic expression. Let x represent the unknown number. See Example 8.

77. Fifteen more than a number

78. A number increased by 9

79. Five subtracted from a number

80. Five decreased by a number

81. The ratio of a number and 4

82. The quotient of a number and 9

▶ **83.** Three times a number, increased by 22

84. Twice a number, decreased by 72

TRANSLATING

Write each sentence as an equation or inequality. Use x to represent any unknown number. See Example 9.

▶ **85.** One increased by two equals the quotient of nine and three.

86. Four subtracted from eight is equal to two squared.

▶ **87.** Three is not equal to four divided by two.

88. The difference of sixteen and four is greater than ten.

89. The sum of 5 and a number is 20.

90. Seven subtracted from a number is 0.

91. The product of 7.6 and a number is 17.

92. 9.1 times a number equals 4.

93. Thirteen minus three times a number is 13.

94. Eight added to twice a number is 42.

CONCEPT EXTENSIONS

Fill in each blank with one of the following:
add   subtract   multiply   divide

95. To simplify the expression $1 + 3 \cdot 6$, first _____.

96. To simplify the expression $(1 + 3) \cdot 6$, first _____.

97. To simplify the expression $(20 - 4) \cdot 2$, first _____.

98. To simplify the expression $20 - 4 \div 2$, first _____.

99. Are parentheses necessary in the expression $2 + (3 \cdot 5)$? Explain your answer.

100. Are parentheses necessary in the expression $(2 + 3) \cdot 5$? Explain your answer.

△ *Recall that perimeter measures the distance around a plane figure and area measures the amount of surface of a plane figure. The expression $2l + 2w$ gives the perimeter of the rectangle below (measured in units), and the expression lw gives its area (measured in square units). Complete the chart below for the given lengths and widths. Be sure to include units.*

	Length: l	Width: w	Perimeter of Rectangle: $2l + 2w$	Area of Rectangle: lw
101.	4 in.	3 in.		
102.	6 in.	1 in.		
103.	5.3 in.	1.7 in.		
104.	4.6 in.	2.4 in.		

105. Study the perimeters and areas found in the chart on the previous page. Do you notice any trends?

106. In your own words, explain the difference between an expression and an equation.

107. Insert one set of parentheses so that the following expression simplifies to 32.

$$20 - 4 \cdot 4 \div 2$$

108. Insert one set of parentheses so that the following expression simplifies to 28.

$$2 \cdot 5 + 3^2$$

Determine whether each is an expression or an equation. See the Concept Check in this section.

109. a. $5x + 6$
　　 b. $2a = 7$
　　 c. $3a + 2 = 9$
　　 d. $4x + 3y - 8z$
　　 e. $5^2 - 2(6 - 2)$

110. a. $3x^2 - 26$
　　 b. $3x^2 - 26 = 1$
　　 c. $2x - 5 = 7x - 5$
　　 d. $9y + x - 8$
　　 e. $3^2 - 4(5 - 3)$

111. Why is 4^3 usually read as "four cubed"? (*Hint:* What is the volume of the **cube** below?)

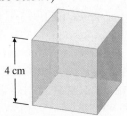

112. Why is 8^2 usually read as "eight squared"? (*Hint:* What is the area of the **square** below?)

113. Write any expression, using 3 or more numbers, that simplifies to 11.

114. Write any expression, using 4 or more numbers, that simplifies to 7.

115. The area of a figure is the total enclosed surface of the figure. Area is measured in square units. The expression lw represents the area of a rectangle when l is its length and w is its width. Find the area of the following rectangular shaped lot.

116. A trapezoid is a four-sided figure with exactly one pair of parallel sides. The expression $\frac{1}{2}h(B + b)$ represents its area, when B and b are the lengths of the two parallel sides and h is the height between these sides. Find the area if $B = 15$ inches, $b = 7$ inches, and $h = 5$ inches.

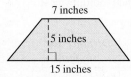

117. The expression $\frac{d}{t}$ represents the average speed in miles per hour if a distance of d miles is traveled in t hours. Find the speed to the nearest whole number if the distance between Dallas, Texas, and Kaw City, Oklahoma, is 432 miles, and it takes Peter Callac 8.5 hours to drive the distance.

118. The expression $\frac{I}{PT}$ represents the rate of interest being charged if a loan of P dollars for T years required I dollars in interest to be paid. Find the interest rate if a $650 loan for 3 years to buy a used IBM personal computer requires $126.75 in interest to be paid.

1.5 Adding Real Numbers

OBJECTIVES

1　Add Real Numbers.

2　Solve Applications That Involve Addition of Real Numbers.

3　Find the Opposite of a Number.

OBJECTIVE

1　Adding Real Numbers

Real numbers can be added, subtracted, multiplied, divided, and raised to powers, just as whole numbers can. We use a number line to help picture the addition of real numbers. We begin by adding numbers with the same sign.

EXAMPLE 1　Add:　$3 + 2$

Solution　Recall that 3 and 2 are called **addends.** We start at 0 on a number line and draw an arrow representing the addend 3. This arrow is three units long and points to the right since 3 is positive. From the tip of this arrow, we draw another arrow, representing the addend 2. The number below the tip of this arrow is the sum, 5.

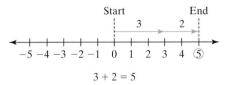

$$3 + 2 = 5$$

PRACTICE
1   Add using a number line: $2 + 4$

EXAMPLE 2   Add: $-1 + (-2)$

Solution Here, -1 and -2 are addends. We start at 0 on a number line and draw an arrow representing -1. This arrow is one unit long and points to the left since -1 is negative. From the tip of this arrow, we draw another arrow, representing -2. The number below the tip of this arrow is the sum, -3.

$$-1 + (-2) = -3$$

PRACTICE
2   Add using a number line: $-2 + (-3)$

Thinking of signed numbers as money earned or lost might help make addition more meaningful. Earnings can be thought of as positive numbers. If \$1 is earned and later another \$3 is earned, the total amount earned is \$4. In other words, $1 + 3 = 4$.

On the other hand, losses can be thought of as negative numbers. If \$1 is lost and later another \$3 is lost, a total of \$4 is lost. In other words,

$$(-1) + (-3) = -4.$$

Using a number line each time we add two numbers can be time consuming. Instead, we can notice patterns in the previous examples and write rules for adding signed numbers. When adding two numbers with the same sign, notice that the sign of the sum is the same as the sign of the addends.

Adding Two Numbers with the Same Sign

Add their absolute values. Use their common sign as the sign of the sum.

EXAMPLE 3   Add.

a. $-3 + (-7)$ **b.** $-1 + (-20)$ **c.** $-2 + (-10)$

Solution Notice that each time, we are adding numbers with the same sign.

a. $-3 + (-7) = -10$ ← Add their absolute values: $3 + 7 = 10$.
　　　　　　　　　　　　　└── Use their common sign.

b. $-1 + (-20) = -21$ ← Add their absolute values: $1 + 20 = 21$.
　　　　　　　　　　　　　└── Common sign.

c. $-2 + (-10) = -12$ ← Add their absolute values.
　　　　　　　　　　　　　└── Common sign.

PRACTICE
3   Add. **a.** $-5 + (-8)$ **b.** $-31 + (-1)$

Adding numbers whose signs are not the same can also be pictured on a number line.

EXAMPLE 4 Add: $-4 + 6$

Solution

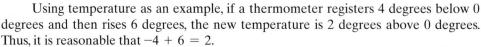

$$-4 + 6 = 2$$

PRACTICE
4 Add using a number line: $-3 + 8$

Using temperature as an example, if a thermometer registers 4 degrees below 0 degrees and then rises 6 degrees, the new temperature is 2 degrees above 0 degrees. Thus, it is reasonable that $-4 + 6 = 2$.

Once again, we can observe a pattern: when adding two numbers with different signs, the sign of the sum is the same as the sign of the addend whose absolute value is larger.

Adding Two Numbers with Different Signs

Subtract the smaller absolute value from the larger absolute value. Use the sign of the number whose absolute value is larger as the sign of the sum.

EXAMPLE 5 Add.

    a. $3 + (-7)$ **b.** $-2 + 10$ **c.** $0.2 + (-0.5)$

Solution Notice that each time, we are adding numbers with different signs.

    a. $3 + (-7) = -4 \leftarrow$ Subtract their absolute values: $7 - 3 = 4$.
                      The negative number, -7, has the larger absolute value so the sum is negative.

    b. $-2 + 10 = 8 \longleftarrow$ Subtract their absolute values: $10 - 2 = 8$.
                      The positive number, 10, has the larger absolute value so the sum is positive.

    c. $0.2 + (-0.5) = -0.3 \leftarrow$ Subtract their absolute values: $0.5 - 0.2 = 0.3$.
                      The negative number, -0.5, has the larger absolute value so the sum is negative.

PRACTICE
5 Add.

    a. $15 + (-18)$ **b.** $-19 + 20$ **c.** $-0.6 + 0.4$

In general, we have the following:

Adding Real Numbers

To add two real numbers

1. with the _same sign_, add their absolute values. Use their common sign as the sign of the answer.

2. with _different signs_, subtract their absolute values. Give the answer the same sign as the number with the larger absolute value.

EXAMPLE 6   Add.

a. $-8 + (-11)$ b. $-5 + 35$ c. $0.6 + (-1.1)$

d. $-\dfrac{7}{10} + \left(-\dfrac{1}{10}\right)$ e. $11.4 + (-4.7)$ f. $-\dfrac{3}{8} + \dfrac{2}{5}$

Solution

a. $-8 + (-11) = -19$ Same sign. Add absolute values and use the common sign.

b. $-5 + 35 = 30$ Different signs. Subtract absolute values and use the sign of the number with the larger absolute value.

c. $0.6 + (-1.1) = -0.5$ Different signs.

d. $-\dfrac{7}{10} + \left(-\dfrac{1}{10}\right) = -\dfrac{8}{10} = -\dfrac{4}{5}$ Same sign.

e. $11.4 + (-4.7) = 6.7$

f. $-\dfrac{3}{8} + \dfrac{2}{5} = -\dfrac{15}{40} + \dfrac{16}{40} = \dfrac{1}{40}$ ☐

> **Helpful Hint**
>
> Don't forget that a common denominator is needed when adding or subtracting fractions. The common denominator here is 40.

PRACTICE
6   Add.

a. $-\dfrac{3}{5} + \left(-\dfrac{2}{5}\right)$ b. $3 + (-9)$

c. $2.2 + (-1.7)$ d. $-\dfrac{2}{7} + \dfrac{3}{10}$ ■

EXAMPLE 7   Add.

a. $3 + (-7) + (-8)$ b. $[7 + (-10)] + [-2 + |-4|]$

Solution

a. Perform the additions from left to right.

$$3 + (-7) + (-8) = -4 + (-8)$$ Adding numbers with different signs.
$$= -12$$ Adding numbers with like signs.

b. Simplify inside brackets first.

$$[7 + (-10)] + [-2 + |-4|] = [-3] + [-2 + 4]$$
$$= [-3] + [2]$$
$$= -1$$ Add.   ☐

> **Helpful Hint**
>
> Don't forget that the brackets are a grouping symbol. We simplify within them first.

PRACTICE
7   Add.

a. $8 + (-5) + (-9)$ b. $[-8 + 5] + [-5 + |-2|]$ ■

 CONCEPT CHECK

What is wrong with the following calculation?

$5 + (-22) = 17$

OBJECTIVE
2   Solving Applications by Adding Real Numbers

Positive and negative numbers are often used in everyday life. Stock market returns show gains and losses as positive and negative numbers. Temperatures in cold climates often dip into the negative range, commonly referred to as "below zero" temperatures. Bank statements report deposits and withdrawals as positive and negative numbers.

EXAMPLE 8 Calculating Temperature

In Philadelphia, Pennsylvania, the record extreme high temperature is 104°F. Decrease this temperature by 115 degrees, and the result is the record extreme low temperature. Find this temperature. (*Source:* National Climatic Data Center)

Solution:

In words:	extreme low temperature	=	extreme high temperature	+	decrease of 115°
Translate:	extreme low temperature	=	104	+	(−115)

$$= -11$$

The record extreme low temperature in Philadelphia, Pennsylvania, is −11°F. ☐

PRACTICE
8   If the temperature was −7° Fahrenheit at 6 a.m., and it rose 4 degrees by 7 a.m. and then rose another 7 degrees in the hour from 7 a.m. to 8 a.m., what was the temperature at 8 a.m.? ■

OBJECTIVE
3   Finding the Opposite of a Number

To help us subtract real numbers in the next section, we first review the concept of opposites. The graphs of 4 and −4 are shown on a number line below.

```
         4 units      4 units
    |←————————→|←————————→|
 ─┼──●──┼──┼──┼──┼──┼──┼──┼──●──┼─
  −5 −4 −3 −2 −1  0  1  2  3  4  5
```

Notice that 4 and −4 lie on opposite sides of 0, and each is 4 units away from 0.

This relationship between −4 and +4 is an important one. Such numbers are known as **opposites** or **additive inverses** of each other.

Opposites or Additive Inverses

Two numbers that are the same distance from 0 but lie on opposite sides of 0 are called **opposites** or **additive inverses** of each other.

EXAMPLE 9   Find the opposite or additive inverse of each number.

   a. 5   **b.** −6   **c.** $\dfrac{1}{2}$ **d.** −4.5

Solution

   a. The opposite of 5 is −5. Notice that 5 and −5 are on opposite sides of 0 when plotted on a number line and are equal distances away.

   b. The opposite of −6 is 6.

   c. The opposite of $\dfrac{1}{2}$ is $-\dfrac{1}{2}$.

   d. The opposite of −4.5 is 4.5. ☐

PRACTICE
9   Find the opposite or additive inverse of each number.

   a. $-\dfrac{5}{9}$ **b.** 8   **c.** 6.2   **d.** −3 ■

We use the symbol "−" to represent the phrase "the opposite of" or "the additive inverse of." In general, if a is a number, we write the opposite or additive inverse of a as $-a$. We know that the opposite of -3 is 3. Notice that this translates as

the opposite of -3 is 3

$$- \quad (-3) \quad = \quad 3$$

This is true in general.

> If a is a number, then $-(-a) = a$.

EXAMPLE 10   Simplify each expression.

 a. $-(-10)$ **b.** $-\left(-\dfrac{1}{2}\right)$ **c.** $-(-2x)$ **d.** $-|-6|$

Solution

 a. $-(-10) = 10$ **b.** $-\left(-\dfrac{1}{2}\right) = \dfrac{1}{2}$ **c.** $-(-2x) = 2x$

 d. Since $|-6| = 6$, then $-|-6| = -6$.

PRACTICE
10 Simplify each expression.

 a. $-|-15|$ **b.** $-\left(-\dfrac{3}{5}\right)$ **c.** $-(-5y)$ **d.** $-(-8)$ ■

Let's discover another characteristic about opposites. Notice that the sum of a number and its opposite is 0.

$$10 + (-10) = 0$$
$$-3 + 3 = 0$$
$$\frac{1}{2} + \left(-\frac{1}{2}\right) = 0$$

In general, we can write the following:

> The sum of a number a and its opposite $-a$ is 0.
>
> $$a + (-a) = 0$$

This is why opposites are also called additive inverses. Notice that this also means that the opposite of 0 is then 0 since $0 + 0 = 0$.

✓ **Vocabulary, Readiness & Video Check**

Use the choices below to fill in each blank. Not all choices will be used.

 a positive number n opposites
 a negative number 0 $-n$

1. Two numbers that are the same distance from 0 but lie on opposite sides of 0 are called _____.

2. If n is a number, then $n + (-n) = $ _____.

3. If n is a number, then $-(-n) = $ _____.

4. The sum of two negative numbers is always _____.

Martin-Gay Interactive Videos

See Video 1.5 🍎

Watch the section lecture video and answer the following questions.

OBJECTIVE 1
5. Complete this statement based on the lecture given before ▦ Example 1. To add two numbers with the same sign, add their_____ and use their common sign as the sign of the sum.

OBJECTIVE 1
6. What is the sign of the sum in ▦ Example 6 and why?

OBJECTIVE 2
7. What is the real life application of negative numbers used in ▦ Example 9? The answer to ▦ Example 9 is −6. What does this number mean in the context of the problem?

OBJECTIVE 3
8. ▦ Example 12 illustrates the idea that if *a* is a real number, the opposite of −*a* is *a*. ▦ Example 13 looks similar to ▦ Example 12, but it's actually quite different. Explain the difference.

1.5   Exercise Set   MyMathLab®

MIXED PRACTICE

Add. See Examples 1 through 7.

1. −6 + 3
2. 9 + (−12)
3. −6 + (−8)
4. −6 + (−14)
5. 8 + (−7)
6. 6 + (−4)
7. −14 + 2
8. −10 + 5
9. −2 + (−3)
10. −7 + (−4)
11. −9 + (−3)
12. 7 + (−5)
13. −7 + 3
14. −5 + 9
15. 10 + (−3)
16. 8 + (−6)
17. 5 + (−7)
18. 3 + (−6)
19. −16 + 16
20. 23 + (−23)
21. 27 + (−46)
22. 53 + (−37)
23. −18 + 49
24. −26 + 14
25. −33 + (−14)
26. −18 + (−26)
27. 6.3 + (−8.4)
28. 9.2 + (−11.4)
29. $|-8| + (-16)$
30. $|-6| + (-61)$
31. 117 + (−79)
32. 144 + (−88)
33. −9.6 + (−3.5)
34. −6.7 + (−7.6)
35. $-\dfrac{3}{8} + \dfrac{5}{8}$
36. $-\dfrac{5}{12} + \dfrac{7}{12}$
37. $-\dfrac{7}{16} + \dfrac{1}{4}$
38. $-\dfrac{5}{9} + \dfrac{1}{3}$
39. $-\dfrac{7}{10} + \left(-\dfrac{3}{5}\right)$
40. $-\dfrac{5}{6} + \left(-\dfrac{2}{3}\right)$
41. −15 + 9 + (−2)
42. −9 + 15 + (−5)
43. −21 + (−16) + (−22)
44. −18 + (−6) + (−40)
45. −23 + 16 + (−2)
46. −14 + (−3) + 11
47. $|5 + (-10)|$
48. $|7 + (-17)|$
49. 6 + (−4) + 9
50. 8 + (−2) + 7
51. [−17 + (−4)] + [−12 + 15]
52. [−2 + (−7)] + [−11 + 22]
53. $|9 + (-12)| + |-16|$

54. $|43 + (-73)| + |-20|$
55. −1.3 + [0.5 + (−0.3) + 0.4]
56. −3.7 + [0.1 + (−0.6) + 8.1]

Solve. See Example 8.

57. The low temperature in Anoka, Minnesota, was −15° last night. During the day, it rose only 9°. Find the high temperature for the day.

58. On January 2, 1943, the temperature was −4° at 7:30 a.m. in Spearfish, South Dakota. Incredibly, it got 49° warmer in the next 2 minutes. To what temperature did it rise by 7:32?

59. The lowest point in Africa is −512 feet at Lake Assal in Djibouti. If you are standing at a point 658 feet above Lake Assal, what is your elevation? (*Source:* Microsoft Encarta)

60. The lowest elevation in Australia is −52 feet at Lake Eyre. If you are standing at a point 439 feet above Lake Eyre, what is your elevation? (*Source:* National Geographic Society)

A negative net income results when a company spends more money than it brings in.

61. Johnson Outdoors Inc. had the following quarterly net incomes during its 2014 fiscal year. (*Source:* Johnsonoutdoors.com)

Quarter of Fiscal 2014	Net Income (in millions)
First	$7.4
Second	$4.7
Third	−$0.8
Fourth	−$2.2

What was the total net income for fiscal year 2014?

62. LeapFrog Enterprises Inc. had the following quarterly net incomes during its 2013 fiscal year. (*Source:* Leapfroginvestors.com)

Quarter of Fiscal 2013	Net Income (in millions)
First	−$3.0
Second	−$3.2
Third	$26.4
Fourth	$63.9

What was the total net income for fiscal year 2013?

In golf, scores that are under par for the entire round are shown as negative scores; positive scores are shown for scores that are over par, and 0 is par.

63. Austin Ernst was the winner of the 2014 Portland Classic in Oregon. Her scores were −3, −3, −3, and −5. What was her overall score? (*Source:* Ladies Professional Golf Association)

64. During the 2015 Hyundai Tournament of champions in Maui, Hawaii, Patrick Reed won with scores of −6, −4, −5, and −6. What was his overall score? (*Source:* Professional Golfers' Association of America)

Find each additive inverse or opposite. See Example 9.

65. 6   **66.** 4   **67.** −2

68. −8   **69.** 0   **70.** $-\dfrac{1}{4}$

71. $|-6|$ **72.** $|-11|$

Simplify each of the following. See Example 10.

73. $-|-2|$ **74.** $-(-3)$ **75.** $-|0|$

76. $\left|-\dfrac{2}{3}\right|$ **77.** $-\left|-\dfrac{2}{3}\right|$ **78.** $-(-7)$

Decide whether the given number is a solution of the given equation.

79. Is −4 a solution of $x + 9 = 5$?

80. Is 10 a solution of $7 = -x + 3$?

81. Is −1 a solution of $y + (-3) = -7$?

82. Is −6 a solution of $1 = y + 7$?

CONCEPT EXTENSIONS

The following bar graph shows each month's average daily low temperature in degrees Fahrenheit for Barrow, Alaska. Use this graph to answer Exercises 83 through 88.

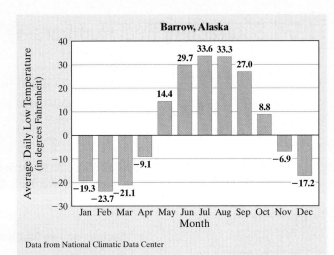

Data from National Climatic Data Center

83. For what month is the graphed temperature the highest?

84. For what month is the graphed temperature the lowest?

85. For what month is the graphed temperature positive *and* closest to 0°?

86. For what month is the graphed temperature negative *and* closest to 0°?

87. Find the average of the temperatures shown for the months of April, May, and October. (To find the average of three temperatures, find their sum and divide by 3.)

88. Find the average of the temperatures shown for the months of January, September, and October.

Each calculation below is incorrect. Find the error and correct it. See the Concept Check in this section.

89. $7 + (-10) \stackrel{?}{=} 17$ **90.** $-4 + 14 \stackrel{?}{=} -18$

91. $-10 + (-12) \stackrel{?}{=} -120$ **92.** $-15 + (-17) \stackrel{?}{=} 32$

If a is a positive number and b is a negative number, fill in the blanks with the words positive or negative.

93. $-a$ is _____.   **94.** $-b$ is _____.

95. $a + a$ is _____.   **96.** $b + b$ is _____.

For Exercises 97 through 100, determine whether each statement is true or false.

97. The sum of two negative numbers is always a negative number.

98. The sum of two positive numbers is always a positive number.

99. The sum of a positive number and a negative number is always a negative number.

100. The sum of zero and a negative number is always a negative number.

101. In your own words, explain how to find the opposite of a number.

102. In your own words, explain why 0 is the only number that is its own opposite.

103. Explain why adding a negative number to another negative number always gives a negative sum.

104. When a positive and a negative number are added, sometimes the sum is positive, sometimes it is zero, and sometimes it is negative. Explain why and when this happens.

1.6 | Subtracting Real Numbers

OBJECTIVES

1 Subtract Real Numbers.
2 Add and Subtract Real Numbers.
3 Evaluate Algebraic Expressions Using Real Numbers.
4 Solve Applications That Involve Subtraction of Real Numbers.
5 Find Complementary and Supplementary Angles.

OBJECTIVE

1 Subtracting Real Numbers

Now that addition of signed numbers has been discussed, we can explore subtraction. We know that $9 - 7 = 2$. Notice that $9 + (-7) = 2$ also. This means that

$$9 - 7 = 9 + (-7)$$

Notice that the difference of 9 and 7 is the same as the sum of 9 and the opposite of 7. In general, we have the following.

> **Subtracting Two Real Numbers**
>
> If a and b are real numbers, then $a - b = a + (-b)$.

In other words, to find the difference of two numbers, add the first number to the opposite of the second number.

EXAMPLE I Subtract.

a. $-13 - 4$ b. $5 - (-6)$ c. $3 - 6$ d. $-1 - (-7)$

Solution

a.
$$-13 - 4 = -13 + (-4)$$ Add -13 to the opposite of $+4$, which is -4.

$$= -17$$

b.
$$5 - (-6) = 5 + (6)$$ Add 5 to the opposite of -6, which is 6.

$$= 11$$

c. $3 - 6 = 3 + (-6)$ Add 3 to the opposite of 6, which is -6.
$$= -3$$

d. $-1 - (-7) = -1 + (7) = 6$ □

PRACTICE

1 Subtract.

a. $-7 - 6$ b. $-8 - (-1)$ c. $9 - (-3)$ d. $5 - 7$ ▪

> **Helpful Hint**
>
> Study the patterns indicated.
>
> No change ——┐ ┌—— Change to addition.
>   └—— Change to opposite.
>
> $$5 - 11 = 5 + (-11) = -6$$
> $$-3 - 4 = -3 + (-4) = -7$$
> $$7 - (-1) = 7 + (1) = 8$$

EXAMPLE 2   Subtract.

   a. $5.3 - (-4.6)$ **b.** $-\dfrac{3}{10} - \dfrac{5}{10}$ **c.** $-\dfrac{2}{3} - \left(-\dfrac{4}{5}\right)$

Solution

   a. $5.3 - (-4.6) = 5.3 + (4.6) = 9.9$

   b. $-\dfrac{3}{10} - \dfrac{5}{10} = -\dfrac{3}{10} + \left(-\dfrac{5}{10}\right) = -\dfrac{8}{10} = -\dfrac{4}{5}$

   c. $-\dfrac{2}{3} - \left(-\dfrac{4}{5}\right) = -\dfrac{2}{3} + \left(\dfrac{4}{5}\right) = -\dfrac{10}{15} + \dfrac{12}{15} = \dfrac{2}{15}$ The common denominator is 15.   ☐

PRACTICE
2   Subtract.

   a. $8.4 - (-2.5)$ **b.** $-\dfrac{5}{8} - \left(-\dfrac{1}{8}\right)$ **c.** $-\dfrac{3}{4} - \dfrac{1}{5}$ ■

EXAMPLE 3   Subtract 8 from -4.

Solution Be careful when interpreting this: The order of numbers in subtraction is important. 8 is to be subtracted **from** -4.

$$-4 - 8 = -4 + (-8) = -12$$ ☐

PRACTICE
3   Subtract 5 from -2.   ■

OBJECTIVE
2   Adding and Subtracting Real Numbers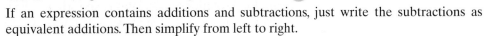

If an expression contains additions and subtractions, just write the subtractions as equivalent additions. Then simplify from left to right.

EXAMPLE 4   Simplify each expression.

   a. $-14 - 8 + 10 - (-6)$ **b.** $1.6 - (-10.3) + (-5.6)$

Solution

   a. $-14 - 8 + 10 - (-6) = -14 + (-8) + 10 + 6$
                       $= -6$

   b. $1.6 - (-10.3) + (-5.6) = 1.6 + 10.3 + (-5.6)$
                         $= 6.3$ ☐

PRACTICE
4   Simplify each expression.

   a. $-15 - 2 - (-4) + 7$ **b.** $3.5 + (-4.1) - (-6.7)$ ■

    When an expression contains parentheses and brackets, remember the order of operations. Start with the innermost set of parentheses or brackets and work your way outward.

EXAMPLE 5   Simplify each expression.

a. $-3 + [(-2 - 5) - 2]$ **b.** $2^3 - |10| + [-6 - (-5)]$

Solution

a. Start with the innermost set of parentheses. Rewrite $-2 - 5$ as a sum.

$$
\begin{aligned}
-3 + [(-2 - 5) - 2] &= -3 + [(-2 + (-5)) - 2] \\
&= -3 + [(-7) - 2] \qquad \text{Add: } -2 + (-5). \\
&= -3 + [-7 + (-2)] \qquad \text{Write } -7 - 2 \text{ as a sum.} \\
&= -3 + [-9] \qquad \text{Add.} \\
&= -12 \qquad \text{Add.}
\end{aligned}
$$

b. Start simplifying the expression inside the brackets by writing $-6 - (-5)$ as a sum.

$$
\begin{aligned}
2^3 - |10| + [-6 - (-5)] &= 2^3 - |10| + [-6 + 5] \\
&= 2^3 - |10| + [-1] \qquad \text{Add.} \\
&= 8 - 10 + (-1) \qquad \text{Evaluate } 2^3 \text{ and } |10|. \\
&= 8 + (-10) + (-1) \qquad \text{Write } 8 - 10 \text{ as a sum.} \\
&= -2 + (-1) \qquad \text{Add.} \\
&= -3 \qquad \text{Add.} \qquad \square
\end{aligned}
$$

PRACTICE

5   Simplify each expression.

a. $-4 + [(-8 - 3) - 5]$ **b.** $|-13| - 3^2 + [2 - (-7)]$ ■

OBJECTIVE

3   Evaluating Algebraic Expressions

Knowing how to evaluate expressions for given replacement values is helpful when checking solutions of equations and when solving problems whose unknowns satisfy given expressions. The next example illustrates this.

EXAMPLE 6   Find the value of each expression when $x = 2$ and $y = -5$.

a. $\dfrac{x - y}{12 + x}$ **b.** $x^2 - 3y$

Solution

a. Replace x with 2 and y with -5. Be sure to put parentheses around -5 to separate signs. Then simplify the resulting expression.

$$
\begin{aligned}
\frac{x - y}{12 + x} &= \frac{2 - (-5)}{12 + 2} \\
&= \frac{2 + 5}{14} \\
&= \frac{7}{14} = \frac{1}{2}
\end{aligned}
$$

b. Replace x with 2 and y with -5 and simplify.

$$
\begin{aligned}
x^2 - 3y &= 2^2 - 3(-5) \\
&= 4 - 3(-5) \\
&= 4 - (-15) \\
&= 4 + 15 \\
&= 19 \qquad \square
\end{aligned}
$$

PRACTICE
6   Find the value of each expression when $x = -3$ and $y = 4$.

   a. $\dfrac{7 - x}{2y + x}$ **b.** $y^2 + x$

Helpful Hint

For additional help when replacing variables with replacement values, first place parentheses around any variables.

For Example 6b on the previous page, we have

$$x^2 - 3y = \underbrace{(x)^2 - 3(y)}_{\substack{\text{Place parentheses} \\ \text{around variables}}} = \underbrace{(2)^2 - 3(-5)}_{\substack{\text{Replace variables} \\ \text{with values}}} = 4 - 3(-5) = 4 - (-15) = 4 + 15 = 19$$

OBJECTIVE
4   **Solving Applications by Subtracting Real Numbers** ▶

One use of positive and negative numbers is in recording altitudes above and below sea level, as shown in the next example.

EXAMPLE 7   Finding a Change in Elevation

The highest point in the United States is the top of Mount McKinley, at a height of 20,320 feet above sea level. The lowest point is Death Valley, California, which is 282 feet below sea level. How much higher is Mount McKinley than Death Valley? (*Source:* U.S. Geological Survey)

Solution: To find "how much higher," we subtract. Don't forget that since Death Valley is 282 feet *below* sea level, we represent its height by -282. Draw a diagram to help visualize the problem.

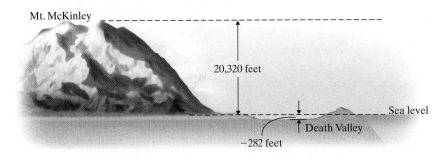

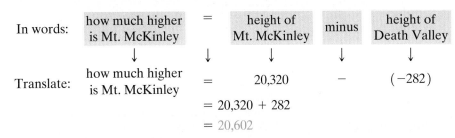

In words:	how much higher is Mt. McKinley	=	height of Mt. McKinley	minus	height of Death Valley
	↓	↓	↓	↓	↓
Translate:	how much higher is Mt. McKinley	=	20,320	−	(-282)

$$= 20{,}320 + 282$$
$$= 20{,}602$$

Thus, Mount McKinley is 20,602 feet higher than Death Valley.   □

PRACTICE
7   On Tuesday morning, a bank account balance was $282. On Thursday, the account balance had dropped to $-\$75$. Find the overall change in this account balance.

OBJECTIVE

5 Finding Complementary and Supplementary Angles

A knowledge of geometric concepts is needed by many professionals, such as doctors, carpenters, electronic technicians, gardeners, machinists, and pilots, just to name a few. With this in mind, we review the geometric concepts of **complementary** and **supplementary angles.**

Complementary and Supplementary Angles

Two angles are **complementary** if their sum is 90°.

$$x + y = 90°$$

Two angles are **supplementary** if their sum is 180°.

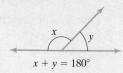

$$x + y = 180°$$

△ **EXAMPLE 8**   Find each unknown complementary or supplementary angle.

a.   b.

Solution

a. These angles are complementary, so their sum is 90°. This means that x is 90° − 38°.

$$x = 90° − 38° = 52°$$

b. These angles are supplementary, so their sum is 180°. This means that y is 180° − 62°.

$$y = 180° − 62° = 118°$$ □

PRACTICE

8   Find each unknown complementary or supplementary angle.

a.   b.

✓ **Vocabulary, Readiness & Video Check**

Translate each phrase. Let x represent "a number." Use the choices below to fill in each blank.

   $7 − x$ $x − 7$

1. 7 minus a number _____

2. 7 subtracted from a number _____

3. A number decreased by 7 _____

4. 7 less a number _____

5. A number less than 7 _____

6. A number subtracted from 7 _____

Multiple choice: Select the correct lettered response following each exercise.

7. To evaluate $x - y$ for $x = -10$ and $y = -14$, we replace x with -10 and y with -14 and evaluate _____.

   a. $10 - 14$ **b.** $-10 - 14$ **c.** $-14 - 10$ **d.** $-10 - (-14)$

8. The expression $-5 - 10$ equals _____.

   a. $5 - 10$ **b.** $5 + 10$ **c.** $-5 + (-10)$ **d.** $10 - 5$

Martin-Gay Interactive Videos

See Video 1.6

Watch the section lecture video and answer the following questions.

OBJECTIVE 1
9. Complete this statement based on the lecture given before 🎞 Example 1. To subtract two real numbers, change the operation to _____ and take the _____ of the second number.

OBJECTIVE 2
10. When simplifying 🎞 Example 5, what is the result of the first step and why is the expression rewritten in this way?

OBJECTIVE 3
11. In 🎞 Example 7, why are you told to be especially careful when working with the replacement value in the numerator?

OBJECTIVE 4
12. For 🎞 Example 8, why is the overall vertical change represented as a negative number?

OBJECTIVE 5
13. The definition of supplementary angles is given just before 🎞 Example 9. Explain how this definition is used to solve 🎞 Example 9.

1.6 Exercise Set   MyMathLab▸

MIXED PRACTICE

Subtract. See Examples 1 and 2.

1. $-6 - 4$ **2.** $-12 - 8$

3. $4 - 9$ **4.** $8 - 11$

▸ **5.** $16 - (-3)$ **6.** $12 - (-5)$

7. $\dfrac{1}{2} - \dfrac{1}{3}$ **8.** $\dfrac{3}{4} - \dfrac{7}{8}$

9. $-16 - (-18)$ **10.** $-20 - (-48)$

▸ **11.** $-6 - 5$ **12.** $-8 - 4$

13. $7 - (-4)$ **14.** $3 - (-6)$

15. $-6 - (-11)$ **16.** $-4 - (-16)$

17. $16 - (-21)$ **18.** $15 - (-33)$

19. $9.7 - 16.1$ **20.** $8.3 - 11.2$

21. $-44 - 27$ **22.** $-36 - 51$

23. $-21 - (-21)$ **24.** $-17 - (-17)$

25. $-2.6 - (-6.7)$ **26.** $-6.1 - (-5.3)$

▸ **27.** $-\dfrac{3}{11} - \left(-\dfrac{5}{11}\right)$ **28.** $-\dfrac{4}{7} - \left(-\dfrac{1}{7}\right)$

29. $-\dfrac{1}{6} - \dfrac{3}{4}$ **30.** $-\dfrac{1}{10} - \dfrac{7}{8}$

31. $8.3 - (-0.62)$ **32.** $4.3 - (-0.87)$

TRANSLATING

Translate each phrase to an expression and simplify. See Example 3.

33. Subtract -5 from 8.   **34.** Subtract 3 from -2.

35. Subtract -1 from -6.   **36.** Subtract 17 from 1.

37. Subtract 8 from 7.   ▸ **38.** Subtract 9 from -4.

39. Decrease -8 by 15.   **40.** Decrease 11 by -14.

Simplify each expression. (Remember the order of operations.) See Examples 4 and 5.

▸ **41.** $-10 - (-8) + (-4) - 20$

42. $-16 - (-3) + (-11) - 14$

43. $5 - 9 + (-4) - 8 - 8$

44. $7 - 12 + (-5) - 2 + (-2)$

45. $-6 - (2 - 11)$ **46.** $-9 - (3 - 8)$

47. $3^3 - 8 \cdot 9$ **48.** $2^3 - 6 \cdot 3$

49. $2 - 3(8 - 6)$ **50.** $4 - 6(7 - 3)$

51. $(3 - 6) + 4^2$ **52.** $(2 - 3) + 5^2$

53. $-2 + [(8 - 11) - (-2 - 9)]$

54. $-5 + [(4 - 15) - (-6) - 8]$

▸ **55.** $|-3| + 2^2 + [-4 - (-6)]$

56. $|-2| + 6^2 + (-3 - 8)$

Evaluate each expression when $x = -5$, $y = 4$, and $t = 10$. See Example 6.

57. $x - y$
58. $y - x$
59. $|x| + 2t - 8y$
60. $|x + t - 7y|$
61. $\dfrac{9 - x}{y + 6}$
62. $\dfrac{15 - x}{y + 2}$
63. $y^2 - x$
64. $t^2 - x$
65. $\dfrac{|x - (-10)|}{2t}$
66. $\dfrac{|5y - x|}{6t}$

Solve. See Example 7.

67. Within 24 hours in 1916, the temperature in Browning, Montana, fell from 44°F to −56°F. How large a drop in temperature was this?

68. Much of New Orleans is below sea level. If George descends 12 feet from an elevation of 5 feet above sea level, what is his new elevation?

69. The coldest temperature ever recorded on Earth was −129°F in Antarctica. The warmest temperature ever recorded was 134°F in Death Valley, California. How many degrees warmer is 134°F than −129°F? (*Source:* World Meteorological Organization)

70. The coldest temperature ever recorded in the United States was −80°F in Alaska. The warmest temperature ever recorded was 134°F in California. How many degrees warmer is 134°F than −80°F? (*Source: The World Almanac*)

71. Mauna Kea in Hawaii has an elevation of 13,796 feet above sea level. The Mid-America Trench in the Pacific Ocean has an elevation of 21,857 feet below sea level. Find the difference in elevation between those two points. (*Source:* National Geographic Society and Defense Mapping Agency)

72. A woman received a statement of her charge account at Old Navy. She spent $93 on purchases last month. She returned an $18 top because she didn't like the color. She also returned a $26 nightshirt because it was damaged. What does she actually owe on her account?

73. A commercial jetliner hits an air pocket and drops 250 feet. After climbing 120 feet, it drops another 178 feet. What is its overall vertical change?

74. In some card games, it is possible to have a negative score. Lavonne Schultz currently has a score of 15 points. She then loses 24 points. What is her new score?

75. The highest point in Africa is Mt. Kilimanjaro, Tanzania, at an elevation of 19,340 feet. The lowest point is Lake Assal, Djibouti, at 512 feet below sea level. How much higher is Mt. Kilimanjaro than Lake Assal? (*Source:* National Geographic Society)

76. The airport in Bishop, California, is at an elevation of 4101 feet above sea level. The nearby Furnace Creek Airport in Death Valley, California, is at an elevation of 226 feet below sea level. How much higher in elevation is the Bishop Airport than the Furnace Creek Airport? (*Source:* National Climatic Data Center)

Find each unknown complementary or supplementary angle. See Example 8.

77.
78.

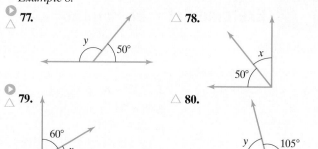

79.
80.

Decide whether the given number is a solution of the given equation.

81. Is −4 a solution of $x - 9 = 5$?
82. Is 3 a solution of $x - 10 = -7$?
83. Is −2 a solution of $-x + 6 = -x - 1$?
84. Is −10 a solution of $-x - 6 = -x - 1$?
85. Is 2 a solution of $-x - 13 = -15$?
86. Is 5 a solution of $4 = 1 - x$?

MIXED PRACTICE—TRANSLATING (*SECTIONS 1.5, 1.6*)

Translate each phrase to an algebraic expression. Use "x" to represent "a number."

87. The sum of −5 and a number.
88. The difference of −3 and a number.
89. Subtract a number from −20.
90. Add a number and −36.

CONCEPT EXTENSIONS

Recall the bar graph from Section 1.5. It shows each month's average daily low temperature in degrees Fahrenheit for Barrow, Alaska. Use this graph to answer Exercises 91 through 94.

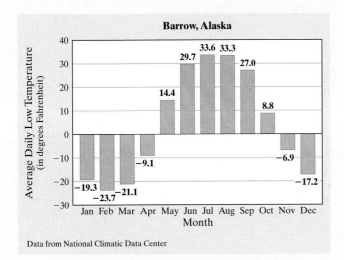

Data from National Climatic Data Center

91. Record the monthly increases and decreases in the low temperature from the previous month.

Month	Monthly Increase or Decrease (from the previous month)
February	
March	
April	
May	
June	

92. Record the monthly increases and decreases in the low temperature from the previous month.

Month	Monthly Increase or Decrease (from the previous month)
July	
August	
September	
October	
November	
December	

93. Which month had the greatest increase in temperature?

94. Which month had the greatest decrease in temperature?

95. Find two numbers whose difference is -5.

96. Find two numbers whose difference is -9.

*Each calculation below is **incorrect**. Find the error and correct it.*

97. $9 - (-7) \overset{?}{=} 2$

98. $-4 > 8 \overset{?}{=} 4$

99. $10 - 30 \overset{?}{=} 20$

100. $-3 - (-10) \overset{?}{=} -13$

If p is a positive number and n is a negative number, determine whether each statement is true or false. Explain your answer.

101. $p - n$ is always a positive number.

102. $n - p$ is always a negative number.

103. $|n| - |p|$ is always a positive number.

104. $|n - p|$ is always a positive number.

Without calculating, determine whether each answer is positive or negative. Then use a calculator to find the exact difference.

105. $56{,}875 - 87{,}262$

106. $4.362 - 7.0086$

Integrated Review   Operations on Real Numbers

Sections 1.1–1.6

Answer the following with positive, negative, or 0.

1. The opposite of a positive number is a _____ number.

2. The sum of two negative numbers is a _____ number.

3. The absolute value of a negative number is a _____ number.

4. The absolute value of zero is _____ .

5. The reciprocal of a positive number is a _____ number.

6. The sum of a number and its opposite is _____ .

7. The absolute value of a positive number is a _____ number.

8. The opposite of a negative number is a _____ number.

Fill in the chart:

	Number	Opposite	Absolute Value
9.	$\frac{1}{7}$		
10.	$-\frac{12}{5}$		
11.		-3	
12.		$\frac{9}{11}$	

Perform each indicated operation and simplify.

13. $-19 + (-23)$

14. $7 - (-3)$

15. $-15 + 17$

16. $-8 - 10$

17. $18 + (-25)$

18. $-2 + (-37)$

19. $-14 - (-12)$

20. $5 - 14$

21. $4.5 - 7.9$

22. $-8.6 - 1.2$

23. $-\dfrac{3}{4} - \dfrac{1}{7}$

24. $\dfrac{2}{3} - \dfrac{7}{8}$

25. $-9 - (-7) + 4 - 6$

26. $11 - 20 + (-3) - 12$

27. $24 - 6(14 - 11)$

28. $30 - 5(10 - 8)$

29. $(7 - 17) + 4^2$

30. $9^2 + (10 - 30)$

31. $|-9| + 3^2 + (-4 - 20)$

32. $|-4 - 5| + 5^2 + (-50)$

33. $-7 + [(1 - 2) + (-2 - 9)]$

34. $-6 + [(-3 + 7) + (4 - 15)]$

35. Subtract 5 from 1.

36. Subtract -2 from -3.

37. Subtract $-\dfrac{2}{5}$ from $\dfrac{1}{4}$.

38. Subtract $\dfrac{1}{10}$ from $-\dfrac{5}{8}$.

39. $2(19 - 17)^3 - 3(-7 + 9)^2$

40. $3(10 - 9)^2 + 6(20 - 19)^3$

Evaluate each expression when $x = -2$, $y = -1$, and $z = 9$.

41. $x - y$

42. $x + y$

43. $y + z$

44. $z - y$

45. $\dfrac{|5z - x|}{y - x}$

46. $\dfrac{|-x - y + z|}{2z}$

1.7 Multiplying and Dividing Real Numbers

OBJECTIVES

1 Multiply Real Numbers.

2 Find the Reciprocal of a Real Number.

3 Divide Real Numbers.

4 Evaluate Expressions Using Real Numbers.

5 Solve Applications That Involve Multiplication or Division of Real Numbers.

OBJECTIVE

1 Multiplying Real Numbers

In this section, we discover patterns for multiplying and dividing real numbers. To discover sign rules for multiplication, recall that multiplication is repeated addition. Thus $3 \cdot 2$ means that 2 is an addend 3 times. That is,

$$2 + 2 + 2 = 3 \cdot 2$$

which equals 6. Similarly, $3 \cdot (-2)$ means -2 is an addend 3 times. That is,

$$(-2) + (-2) + (-2) = 3 \cdot (-2)$$

Since $(-2) + (-2) + (-2) = -6$, $3 \cdot (-2) = -6$. This suggests that the product of a positive number and a negative number is a negative number.

What about the product of two negative numbers? To find out, consider the following pattern.

Factor decreases by 1 each time

$$\left.\begin{array}{l} -3 \cdot 2 = -6 \\ -3 \cdot 1 = -3 \\ -3 \cdot 0 = 0 \end{array}\right\} \text{ Product increases by 3 each time.}$$

This pattern continues as

Factor decreases by 1 each time

$$\left.\begin{array}{l} -3 \cdot -1 = 3 \\ -3 \cdot -2 = 6 \end{array}\right\} \text{ Product increases by 3 each time.}$$

This suggests that the product of two negative numbers is a positive number.

Multiplying Real Numbers

1. The product of two numbers with the *same* sign is a positive number.

2. The product of two numbers with *different* signs is a negative number.

EXAMPLE 1   Multiply.

a. $(-8)(4)$ b. $14(-1)$ c. $-9(-10)$

Solution

a. $-8(4) = -32$ b. $14(-1) = -14$ c. $-9(-10) = 90$ □

PRACTICE
1   Multiply.

a. $8(-5)$ b. $(-3)(-4)$ c. $(-6)(9)$ ■

We know that any whole number multiplied by zero equals zero. This remains true for real numbers.

Zero as a Factor

If b is a real number, then $b \cdot 0 = 0$. Also, $0 \cdot b = 0$.

EXAMPLE 2   Perform the indicated operations.

a. $(7)(0)(-6)$ b. $(-2)(-3)(-4)$
c. $(-1)(5)(-9)$ d. $(-4)(-11) - (5)(-2)$

Solution

a. By the order of operations, we multiply from left to right. Notice that, because one of the factors is 0, the product is 0.

$$(7)(0)(-6) = 0(-6) = 0$$

b. Multiply two factors at a time, from left to right.

$$(-2)(-3)(-4) = (6)(-4) \quad \text{Multiply } (-2)(-3).$$
$$= -24$$

c. Multiply from left to right.

$$(-1)(5)(-9) = (-5)(-9) \quad \text{Multiply } (-1)(5).$$
$$= 45$$

d. Follow the rules for order of operations.

$$(-4)(-11) - (5)(-2) = 44 - (-10) \quad \text{Find each product.}$$
$$= 44 + 10 \qquad \text{Add 44 to the opposite of } -10.$$
$$= 54 \qquad \text{Add.} \quad □$$

PRACTICE
2   Perform the indicated operations.

a. $(-1)(-5)(-6)$ b. $(-3)(-2)(4)$
c. $(-4)(0)(5)$ d. $(-2)(-3) - (-4)(5)$ ■

Helpful Hint

You may have noticed from the example that if we multiply:

- an _even_ number of negative numbers, the product is _positive_.
- an _odd_ number of negative numbers, the product is _negative_.

✔ **CONCEPT CHECK**

What is the sign of the product of five negative numbers? Explain.

Answer to Concept Check:
negative

Multiplying signed decimals or fractions is carried out exactly the same way as multiplying integers.

EXAMPLE 3 Multiply.

a. $(-1.2)(0.05)$ b. $\dfrac{2}{3} \cdot \left(-\dfrac{7}{10}\right)$ c. $\left(-\dfrac{4}{5}\right)(-20)$

Solution

a. The product of two numbers with different signs is negative.

$$(-1.2)(0.05) = -[(1.2)(0.05)]$$
$$= -0.06$$

b. $\dfrac{2}{3} \cdot \left(-\dfrac{7}{10}\right) = -\dfrac{2 \cdot 7}{3 \cdot 10} = -\dfrac{2 \cdot 7}{3 \cdot 2 \cdot 5} = -\dfrac{7}{15}$

c. $\left(-\dfrac{4}{5}\right)(-20) = \dfrac{4 \cdot 20}{5 \cdot 1} = \dfrac{4 \cdot 4 \cdot 5}{5 \cdot 1} = \dfrac{16}{1}$ or 16

PRACTICE
3 Multiply.

a. $(0.23)(-0.2)$ b. $\left(-\dfrac{3}{5}\right) \cdot \left(\dfrac{4}{9}\right)$ c. $\left(-\dfrac{7}{12}\right)(-24)$

Now that we know how to multiply positive and negative numbers, let's see how we find the values of $(-4)^2$ and -4^2, for example. Although these two expressions look similar, the difference between the two is the parentheses. In $(-4)^2$, the parentheses tell us that the base, or repeated factor, is -4. In -4^2, only 4 is the base. Thus,

$$(-4)^2 = (-4)(-4) = 16 \quad \text{The base is } -4.$$
$$-4^2 = -(4 \cdot 4) = -16 \quad \text{The base is } 4.$$

EXAMPLE 4 Evaluate.

a. $(-2)^3$ b. -2^3 c. $(-3)^2$ d. -3^2

Solution

a. $(-2)^3 = (-2)(-2)(-2) = -8$ The base is -2.
b. $-2^3 = -(2 \cdot 2 \cdot 2) = -8$ The base is 2.
c. $(-3)^2 = (-3)(-3) = 9$ The base is -3.
d. $-3^2 = -(3 \cdot 3) = -9$ The base is 3.

PRACTICE
4 Evaluate.

a. $(-6)^2$ b. -6^2 c. $(-4)^3$ d. -4^3

Helpful Hint

Be careful when identifying the base of an exponential expression.

$$(-3)^2 \qquad\qquad -3^2$$
Base is -3 Base is 3
$$(-3)^2 = (-3)(-3) = 9 \qquad -3^2 = -(3 \cdot 3) = -9$$

OBJECTIVE

2   Finding Reciprocals

Just as every difference of two numbers $a - b$ can be written as the sum $a + (-b)$, so too every quotient of two numbers can be written as a product. For example, the quotient $6 \div 3$ can be written as $6 \cdot \dfrac{1}{3}$. Recall that the pair of numbers 3 and $\dfrac{1}{3}$ has a special relationship. Their product is 1 and they are called reciprocals or **multiplicative inverses** of each other.

> **Reciprocals or Multiplicative Inverses**
>
> Two numbers whose product is 1 are called reciprocals or multiplicative inverses of each other.

Notice that **0 has no multiplicative inverse** since 0 multiplied by any number is never 1 but always 0.

EXAMPLE 5   Find the reciprocal of each number.

    a. 22   **b.** $\dfrac{3}{16}$ **c.** -10 **d.** $-\dfrac{9}{13}$

Solution

    a. The reciprocal of 22 is $\dfrac{1}{22}$ since $22 \cdot \dfrac{1}{22} = 1$.

    b. The reciprocal of $\dfrac{3}{16}$ is $\dfrac{16}{3}$ since $\dfrac{3}{16} \cdot \dfrac{16}{3} = 1$.

    c. The reciprocal of -10 is $-\dfrac{1}{10}$.

    d. The reciprocal of $-\dfrac{9}{13}$ is $-\dfrac{13}{9}$.

PRACTICE

5   Find the reciprocal of each number.

    a. $\dfrac{8}{3}$ **b.** 15   **c.** $-\dfrac{2}{7}$ **d.** -5

OBJECTIVE

3   Dividing Real Numbers

We may now write a quotient as an equivalent product.

> **Quotient of Two Real Numbers**
>
> If a and b are real numbers and b is not 0, then
>
> $$a \div b = \frac{a}{b} = a \cdot \frac{1}{b}$$

In other words, the quotient of two real numbers is the product of the first number and the multiplicative inverse or reciprocal of the second number.

EXAMPLE 6   Use the definition of the quotient of two numbers to divide.

    a. $-18 \div 3$ **b.** $\dfrac{-14}{-2}$ **c.** $\dfrac{20}{-4}$

Solution

    a. $-18 \div 3 = -18 \cdot \dfrac{1}{3} = -6$ **b.** $\dfrac{-14}{-2} = -14 \cdot -\dfrac{1}{2} = 7$

    c. $\dfrac{20}{-4} = 20 \cdot -\dfrac{1}{4} = -5$

(Continued on next page)

PRACTICE
6 Use the definition of the quotient of two numbers to divide.

a. $\dfrac{16}{-2}$

b. $24 \div (-6)$

c. $\dfrac{-35}{-7}$

Since the quotient $a \div b$ can be written as the product $a \cdot \dfrac{1}{b}$, it follows that sign patterns for dividing two real numbers are the same as sign patterns for multiplying two real numbers.

> **Multiplying and Dividing Real Numbers**
>
> 1. The product or quotient of two numbers with the *same* sign is a positive number.
> 2. The product or quotient of two numbers with *different* signs is a negative number.

EXAMPLE 7   Divide.

a. $\dfrac{-24}{-4}$

b. $\dfrac{-36}{3}$

c. $\dfrac{2}{3} \div \left(-\dfrac{5}{4}\right)$

d. $-\dfrac{3}{2} \div 9$

Solution

a. $\dfrac{-24}{-4} = 6$

b. $\dfrac{-36}{3} = -12$

c. $\dfrac{2}{3} \div \left(-\dfrac{5}{4}\right) = \dfrac{2}{3} \cdot \left(-\dfrac{4}{5}\right) = -\dfrac{8}{15}$

d. $-\dfrac{3}{2} \div 9 = -\dfrac{3}{2} \cdot \dfrac{1}{9} = -\dfrac{3 \cdot 1}{2 \cdot 9} = -\dfrac{3 \cdot 1}{2 \cdot 3 \cdot 3} = -\dfrac{1}{6}$

PRACTICE
7 Divide.

a. $\dfrac{-18}{-6}$

b. $\dfrac{-48}{3}$

c. $\dfrac{3}{5} \div \left(-\dfrac{1}{2}\right)$

d. $-\dfrac{4}{9} \div 8$

✔ **CONCEPT CHECK**

What is wrong with the following calculation?

$\dfrac{-36}{-9} = -4$

The definition of the quotient of two real numbers does not allow for division by 0 because 0 does not have a multiplicative inverse. There is no number we can multiply 0 by to get 1. How then do we interpret $\dfrac{3}{0}$? We say that division by 0 is not allowed or not defined and that $\dfrac{3}{0}$ does not represent a real number. The denominator of a fraction can never be 0.

Can the numerator of a fraction be 0? Can we divide 0 by a number? Yes. For example,

$$\frac{0}{3} = 0 \cdot \frac{1}{3} = 0$$

In general, the quotient of 0 and any nonzero number is 0.

> **Zero as a Divisor or Dividend**
>
> 1. The quotient of any nonzero real number and 0 is undefined. In symbols, if $a \neq 0$, $\dfrac{a}{0}$ is **undefined**.
> 2. The quotient of 0 and any real number except 0 is 0. In symbols, if $a \neq 0$, $\dfrac{0}{a} = 0$.

EXAMPLE 8   Perform the indicated operations.

a. $\dfrac{1}{0}$

b. $\dfrac{0}{-3}$

c. $\dfrac{0(-8)}{2}$

Solution

a. $\dfrac{1}{0}$ is undefined

b. $\dfrac{0}{-3} = 0$

c. $\dfrac{0(-8)}{2} = \dfrac{0}{2} = 0$ □

PRACTICE
8   Perform the indicated operations.

a. $\dfrac{0}{-2}$

b. $\dfrac{-4}{0}$

c. $\dfrac{-5}{6(0)}$ ■

Notice that $\dfrac{12}{-2} = -6, -\dfrac{12}{2} = -6$, and $\dfrac{-12}{2} = -6$. This means that

$$\frac{12}{-2} = -\frac{12}{2} = \frac{-12}{2}$$

In words, a single negative sign in a fraction can be written in the denominator, in the numerator, or in front of the fraction without changing the value of the fraction. Thus,

$$\frac{1}{-7} = \frac{-1}{7} = -\frac{1}{7}$$

In general, if a and b are real numbers, $b \neq 0$, then $\dfrac{a}{-b} = \dfrac{-a}{b} = -\dfrac{a}{b}$.

OBJECTIVE
4   Evaluating Expressions

Examples combining basic arithmetic operations along with the principles of order of operations help us review these concepts.

EXAMPLE 9   Simplify each expression.

a. $\dfrac{(-12)(-3) + 3}{-7 - (-2)}$

b. $\dfrac{2(-3)^2 - 20}{-5 + 4}$

Solution

a. First, simplify the numerator and denominator separately, then divide.

$$\frac{(-12)(-3) + 3}{-7 - (-2)} = \frac{36 + 3}{-7 + 2}$$

$$= \frac{39}{-5} \text{ or } -\frac{39}{5}$$

b. Simplify the numerator and denominator separately, then divide.

$$\frac{2(-3)^2 - 20}{-5 + 4} = \frac{2 \cdot 9 - 20}{-5 + 4} = \frac{18 - 20}{-5 + 4} = \frac{-2}{-1} = 2$$ □

PRACTICE
9   Simplify each expression.

a. $\dfrac{(-8)(-11) - 4}{-9 - (-4)}$

b. $\dfrac{3(-2)^3 - 9}{-6 + 3}$ ■

Using what we have learned about multiplying and dividing real numbers, we continue to practice evaluating algebraic expressions.

EXAMPLE 10 If $x = -2$ and $y = -4$, evaluate each expression.

a. $5x - y$ **b.** $x^4 - y^2$ **c.** $\dfrac{3x}{2y}$

Solution

a. Replace x with -2 and y with -4 and simplify.

$$5x - y = 5(-2) - (-4) = -10 - (-4) = -10 + 4 = -6$$

b. Replace x with -2 and y with -4.

$$x^4 - y^2 = (-2)^4 - (-4)^2 \quad \text{Substitute the given values for the variables.}$$
$$= 16 - (16) \quad \text{Evaluate exponential expressions.}$$
$$= 0 \quad \text{Subtract.}$$

c. Replace x with -2 and y with -4 and simplify.

$$\frac{3x}{2y} = \frac{3(-2)}{2(-4)} = \frac{-6}{-8} = \frac{3}{4}$$

PRACTICE
10 If $x = -5$ and $y = -2$, evaluate each expression.

a. $7y - x$ **b.** $x^2 - y^3$ **c.** $\dfrac{2x}{3y}$

OBJECTIVE
5 Solving Applications That Involve Multiplying or Dividing Numbers

Many real-life problems involve multiplication and division of numbers.

EXAMPLE 11 **Calculating a Total Golf Score**

A professional golfer finished seven strokes under par (-7) for each of three days of a tournament. What was her total score for the tournament?

Solution Although the key word is "total," since this is repeated addition of the same number, we multiply.

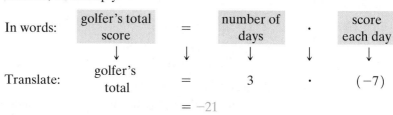

In words: golfer's total score = number of days · score each day

Translate: golfer's total = 3 · (-7)

$$= -21$$

Thus, the golfer's total score was -21, or 21 strokes under par.

PRACTICE
11 A card player had a score of -13 for each of four games. Find the total score.

Graphing Calculator Explorations

Entering Negative Numbers on a Scientific Calculator

To enter a negative number on a scientific calculator, find a key marked $\boxed{+/-}$. (On some calculators, this key is marked $\boxed{\text{CHS}}$ for "change sign.") To enter -8, for example, press the keys $\boxed{8}$ $\boxed{+/-}$. The display will read $\boxed{-8}$.

Entering Negative Numbers on a Graphing Calculator

To enter a negative number on a graphing calculator, find a key marked $\boxed{(-)}$. Do not confuse this key with the key $\boxed{-}$, which is used for subtraction. To enter -8, for example, press the keys $\boxed{(-)}\boxed{8}$. The display will read $\boxed{-8}$.

Operations with Real Numbers

To evaluate $-2(7 - 9) - 20$ on a calculator, press the keys

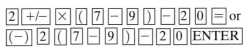

$\boxed{2}\boxed{+/-}\boxed{\times}\boxed{(}\boxed{(}\boxed{7}\boxed{-}\boxed{9}\boxed{)}\boxed{-}\boxed{2}\boxed{0}\boxed{=}$ or
$\boxed{(-)}\boxed{2}\boxed{(}\boxed{(}\boxed{7}\boxed{-}\boxed{9}\boxed{)}\boxed{-}\boxed{2}\boxed{0}\boxed{\text{ENTER}}$

The display will read $\boxed{-16}$ or $\boxed{\begin{array}{r} -2(7 - 9) - 20 \\ -16 \end{array}}$.

Use a calculator to simplify each expression.

1. $-38(26 - 27)$ **2.** $-59(-8) + 1726$

3. $134 + 25(68 - 91)$ **4.** $45(32) - 8(218)$

5. $\dfrac{-50(294)}{175 - 265}$ **6.** $\dfrac{-444 - 444.8}{-181 - 324}$

7. $9^5 - 4550$ **8.** $5^8 - 6259$

9. $(-125)^2$ (Be careful.)   **10.** -125^2 (Be careful.)

✔ Vocabulary, Readiness & Video Check

Use the choices below to fill in each blank. Some choices may be used more than once.

   positive   0   negative   undefined

1. If n is a real number, then $n \cdot 0 = $ _____ and $0 \cdot n = $ _____.

2. If n is a real number, but not 0, then $\dfrac{0}{n} = $ _____ and we say $\dfrac{n}{0}$ is _____.

3. The product of two negative numbers is a _____ number.

4. The quotient of two negative numbers is a _____ number.

5. The quotient of a positive number and a negative number is a _____ number.

6. The product of a positive number and a negative number is a _____ number.

7. The reciprocal of a positive number is a _____ number.

8. The opposite of a positive number is a _____ number.

Martin-Gay Interactive Videos

See Video 1.7 🔵

Watch the section lecture video and answer the following questions.

OBJECTIVE 1

9. Explain the significance of the use of parentheses when comparing 🎬 Examples 6 and 7.

OBJECTIVE 2

10. In 🎬 Example 9, why is the reciprocal equal to $\dfrac{3}{2}$ and not $-\dfrac{3}{2}$?

OBJECTIVE 3

11. Before 🎬 Example 11, the sign rules for division of real numbers are discussed. Are the sign rules for division the same as for multiplication? Why or why not?

OBJECTIVE 4

12. In 🎬 Example 17, the importance of placing the replacement values in parentheses when evaluating is emphasized. Why?

OBJECTIVE 5

13. In 🎬 Example 18, explain why each loss of 4 yards is represented by -4 and not 4.

1.7 Exercise Set   MyMathLab®

Multiply. See Examples 1 through 3.

1. $-6(4)$ **2.** $-8(5)$

3. $2(-1)$ **4.** $7(-4)$

5. $-5(-10)$ **6.** $-6(-11)$

7. $-3 \cdot 4$ **8.** $-2 \cdot 8$

9. $-7 \cdot 0$ **10.** $-6 \cdot 0$

11. $2(-9)$ **12.** $3(-5)$

13. $-\dfrac{1}{2}\left(-\dfrac{3}{5}\right)$ **14.** $-\dfrac{1}{8}\left(-\dfrac{1}{3}\right)$

15. $-\dfrac{3}{4}\left(-\dfrac{8}{9}\right)$ **16.** $-\dfrac{5}{6}\left(-\dfrac{3}{10}\right)$

17. $5(-1.4)$ **18.** $6(-2.5)$

19. $-0.2(-0.7)$ **20.** $-0.5(-0.3)$

21. $-10(80)$ **22.** $-20(60)$

23. $4(-7)$ **24.** $5(-9)$

25. $(-5)(-5)$ **26.** $(-7)(-7)$

27. $\dfrac{2}{3}\left(-\dfrac{4}{9}\right)$ **28.** $\dfrac{2}{7}\left(-\dfrac{2}{11}\right)$

29. $-11(11)$ **30.** $-12(12)$

31. $-\dfrac{20}{25}\left(\dfrac{5}{16}\right)$ **32.** $-\dfrac{25}{36}\left(\dfrac{6}{15}\right)$

33. $(-1)(2)(-3)(-5)$ **34.** $(-2)(-3)(-4)(-2)$

Perform the indicated operations. See Example 2.

35. $(-2)(5) - (-11)(3)$ **36.** $8(-3) - 4(-5)$

37. $(-6)(-1)(-2) - (-5)$ **38.** $20 - (-4)(3)(-2)$

Decide whether each statement is true or false.

39. The product of three negative integers is negative.

40. The product of three positive integers is positive.

41. The product of four negative integers is negative.

42. The product of four positive integers is positive.

Evaluate. See Example 4.

43. $(-2)^4$ **44.** -2^4

45. -1^5 **46.** $(-1)^5$

47. $(-5)^2$ **48.** -5^2

49. -7^2 **50.** $(-7)^2$

Find each reciprocal or multiplicative inverse. See Example 5.

51. 9 **52.** 100 **53.** $\dfrac{2}{3}$

54. $\dfrac{1}{7}$ **55.** -14 **56.** -8

57. $-\dfrac{3}{11}$ **58.** $-\dfrac{6}{13}$ **59.** 0.2

60. 1.5 **61.** $\dfrac{1}{-6.3}$ **62.** $\dfrac{1}{-8.9}$

Divide. See Examples 6 through 8.

63. $\dfrac{18}{-2}$ **64.** $\dfrac{20}{-10}$ **65.** $\dfrac{-16}{-4}$

66. $\dfrac{-18}{-6}$ **67.** $\dfrac{-48}{12}$ **68.** $\dfrac{-60}{5}$

69. $\dfrac{0}{-4}$ **70.** $\dfrac{0}{-9}$ **71.** $-\dfrac{15}{3}$

72. $-\dfrac{24}{8}$ **73.** $\dfrac{5}{0}$ **74.** $\dfrac{3}{0}$

75. $\dfrac{-12}{-4}$ **76.** $\dfrac{-45}{-9}$ **77.** $\dfrac{30}{-2}$

78. $\dfrac{14}{-2}$ **79.** $\dfrac{6}{7} \div \left(-\dfrac{1}{3}\right)$

80. $\dfrac{4}{5} \div \left(-\dfrac{1}{2}\right)$ **81.** $-\dfrac{5}{9} \div \left(-\dfrac{3}{4}\right)$

82. $-\dfrac{1}{10} \div \left(-\dfrac{8}{11}\right)$ **83.** $-\dfrac{4}{9} \div \dfrac{4}{9}$

84. $-\dfrac{5}{12} \div \dfrac{5}{12}$

MIXED PRACTICE

Simplify. See Examples 1 through 9.

85. $\dfrac{-9(-3)}{-6}$ **86.** $\dfrac{-6(-3)}{-4}$

87. $\dfrac{12}{9 - 12}$ **88.** $\dfrac{-15}{1 - 4}$

89. $\dfrac{-6^2 + 4}{-2}$ **90.** $\dfrac{3^2 + 4}{5}$

91. $\dfrac{8 + (-4)^2}{4 - 12}$ **92.** $\dfrac{6 + (-2)^2}{4 - 9}$

93. $\dfrac{22 + (3)(-2)}{-5 - 2}$ **94.** $\dfrac{-20 + (-4)(3)}{1 - 5}$

95. $\dfrac{-3 - 5^2}{2(-7)}$ **96.** $\dfrac{-2 - 4^2}{3(-6)}$

97. $\dfrac{6 - 2(-3)}{4 - 3(-2)}$ **98.** $\dfrac{8 - 3(-2)}{2 - 5(-4)}$

99. $\dfrac{-3 - 2(-9)}{-15 - 3(-4)}$ **100.** $\dfrac{-4 - 8(-2)}{-9 - 2(-3)}$

101. $\dfrac{|5 - 9| + |10 - 15|}{|2(-3)|}$ **102.** $\dfrac{|-3 + 6| + |-2 + 7|}{|-2 \cdot 2|}$

If $x = -5$ and $y = -3$, evaluate each expression. See Example 10.

103. $3x + 2y$ **104.** $4x + 5y$

105. $2x^2 - y^2$ **106.** $x^2 - 2y^2$

107. $x^3 + 3y$ **108.** $y^3 + 3x$

109. $\dfrac{2x - 5}{y - 2}$ **110.** $\dfrac{2y - 12}{x - 4}$

111. $\dfrac{-3 - y}{x - 4}$ **112.** $\dfrac{4 - 2x}{y + 3}$

TRANSLATING

Translate each phrase into an expression. Use x to represent "a number." See Example 11.

113. The product of −71 and a number

114. The quotient of −8 and a number

115. Subtract a number from −16.

116. The sum of a number and −12

117. −29 increased by a number

118. The difference of a number and −10

119. Divide a number by −33.

120. Multiply a number by −17.

Solve. See Example 11.

121. A football team lost four yards on each of three consecutive plays. Represent the total loss as a product of signed numbers and find the total loss.

122. Joe Norstrom lost $400 on each of seven consecutive days in the stock market. Represent his total loss as a product of signed numbers and find his total loss.

123. A deep-sea diver must move up or down in the water in short steps to keep from getting a physical condition called the "bends." Suppose a diver moves down from the surface in five steps of 20 feet each. Represent his total movement as a product of signed numbers and find the total depth.

124. A weather forecaster predicts that the temperature will drop five degrees each hour for the next six hours. Represent this drop as a product of signed numbers and find the total drop in temperature.

Decide whether the given number is a solution of the given equation.

125. Is 7 a solution of $-5x = -35$?

126. Is −4 a solution of $2x = x - 1$?

127. Is −20 a solution of $\dfrac{x}{10} = 2$?

128. Is −3 a solution of $\dfrac{45}{x} = -15$?

129. Is 5 a solution of $-3x - 5 = -20$?

130. Is −4 a solution of $2x + 4 = x + 8$?

CONCEPT EXTENSIONS

Study the bar graph below showing the average surface temperatures of planets. Use Exercises 131 and 132 to complete the planet temperatures on the graph. (Pluto is now classified as a dwarf planet.)

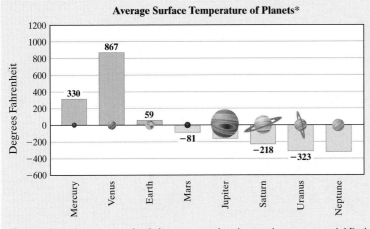

Average Surface Temperature of Planets*

Degrees Fahrenheit

Mercury 330, Venus 867, Earth 59, Mars −81, Saturn −218, Uranus −323

*For some planets, the temperature given is the temperature where the atmosphere pressure equals 1 Earth atmosphere; data from *The World Almanac*

131. The surface temperature of Jupiter is twice the temperature of Mars. Find this temperature.

132. The surface temperature of Neptune is equal to the temperature of Mercury divided by −1. Find this temperature.

133. Explain why the product of an even number of negative numbers is a positive number.

134. If *a* and *b* are any real numbers, is the statement $a \cdot b = b \cdot a$ always true? Why or why not?

135. Find any real numbers that are their own reciprocal.

136. Explain why 0 has no reciprocal.

If q is a negative number, r is a negative number, and t is a positive number, determine whether each expression simplifies to a positive or negative number. If it is not possible to determine, state so.

137. $\dfrac{q}{r \cdot t}$

138. $q^2 \cdot r \cdot t$

139. $q + t$

140. $t + r$

141. $t(q + r)$

142. $r(q - t)$

Write each of the following as an expression and evaluate.

143. The sum of −2 and the quotient of −15 and 3

144. The sum of 1 and the product of −8 and −5

145. Twice the sum of −5 and −3

146. 7 subtracted from the quotient of 0 and 5

1.8 Properties of Real Numbers

OBJECTIVE

1 Using the Commutative and Associative Properties

In this section, we give names to properties of real numbers with which we are already familiar. Throughout this section, the variables a, b, and c represent real numbers.

We know that order does not matter when adding numbers. For example, we know that $7 + 5$ is the same as $5 + 7$. This property is given a special name—the **commutative property of addition.** We also know that order does not matter when multiplying numbers. For example, we know that $-5(6) = 6(-5)$. This property means that multiplication is commutative also and is called the **commutative property of multiplication.**

Commutative Properties

Addition: $a + b = b + a$

Multiplication: $a \cdot b = b \cdot a$

These properties state that the *order* in which any two real numbers are added or multiplied does not change their sum or product. For example, if we let $a = 3$ and $b = 5$, then the commutative properties guarantee that

$$3 + 5 = 5 + 3 \quad \text{and} \quad 3 \cdot 5 = 5 \cdot 3$$

Helpful Hint

Is subtraction also commutative? Try an example. Does $3 - 2 = 2 - 3$? **No!** The left side of this statement equals 1; the right side equals -1. There is no commutative property of subtraction. Similarly, there is no commutative property for division. For example, $10 \div 2$ does not equal $2 \div 10$.

EXAMPLE 1 Use a commutative property to complete each statement.

a. $x + 5 = $ _____ **b.** $3 \cdot x = $ _____

Solution

a. $x + 5 = 5 + x$ By the commutative property of addition

b. $3 \cdot x = x \cdot 3$ By the commutative property of multiplication ☐

PRACTICE

1 Use a commutative property to complete each statement.

a. $x \cdot 8 = $ ___ **b.** $x + 17 = $ _____ ■

✔ CONCEPT CHECK

Which of the following pairs of actions are commutative?

a. "raking the leaves" and "bagging the leaves"

b. "putting on your left glove" and "putting on your right glove"

c. "putting on your coat" and "putting on your shirt"

d. "reading a novel" and "reading a newspaper"

Let's now discuss grouping numbers. We know that when we add three numbers, the way in which they are grouped or associated does not change their sum. For example, we know that $2 + (3 + 4) = 2 + 7 = 9$. This result is the same if we group the numbers differently. In other words, $(2 + 3) + 4 = 5 + 4 = 9$ also. Thus, $2 + (3 + 4) = (2 + 3) + 4$. This property is called the **associative property of addition.**

We also know that changing the grouping of numbers when multiplying does not change their product. For example, $2 \cdot (3 \cdot 4) = (2 \cdot 3) \cdot 4$ (check it). This is the **associative property of multiplication.**

Associative Properties

Addition: $(a + b) + c = a + (b + c)$

Multiplication: $(a \cdot b) \cdot c = a \cdot (b \cdot c)$

These properties state that the way in which three numbers are *grouped* does not change their sum or their product.

EXAMPLE 2   Use an associative property to complete each statement.

a. $5 + (4 + 6) = $ _____

b. $(-1 \cdot 2) \cdot 5 = $ _____

Solution

a. $5 + (4 + 6) = (5 + 4) + 6$ By the associative property of addition

b. $(-1 \cdot 2) \cdot 5 = -1 \cdot (2 \cdot 5)$ By the associative property of multiplication   □

PRACTICE
2   Use an associative property to complete each statement.

a. $(2 + 9) + 7 = $ _____

b. $-4 \cdot (2 \cdot 7) = $ _____   ■

Helpful Hint

Remember the difference between the commutative properties and the associative properties. The commutative properties have to do with the *order* of numbers, and the associative properties have to do with the *grouping* of numbers.

Let's now illustrate how these properties can help us simplify expressions.

EXAMPLE 3   Simplify each expression.

a. $10 + (x + 12)$ **b.** $-3(7x)$

Solution

a. $10 + (x + 12) = 10 + (12 + x)$ By the commutative property of addition

$= (10 + 12) + x$ By the associative property of addition

$= 22 + x$ Add.

b. $-3(7x) = (-3 \cdot 7)x$ By the associative property of multiplication

$= -21x$ Multiply.   □

PRACTICE
3   Simplify each expression.

a. $(5 + x) + 9$ **b.** $5(-6x)$ ■

OBJECTIVE
2   Using the Distributive Property

The **distributive property of multiplication over addition** is used repeatedly throughout algebra. It is useful because it allows us to write a product as a sum or a sum as a product.
We know that $7(2 + 4) = 7(6) = 42$. Compare that with $7(2) + 7(4) = 14 + 28 = 42$. Since both original expressions equal 42, they must equal each other, or

$$7(2 + 4) = 7(2) + 7(4)$$

This is an example of the distributive property. The product on the left side of the equal sign is equal to the sum on the right side. We can think of the 7 as being distributed to each number inside the parentheses.

Distributive Property of Multiplication Over Addition

$$a(b + c) = ab + ac$$

Since multiplication is commutative, this property can also be written as

$$(b + c)a = ba + ca$$

The distributive property can also be extended to more than two numbers inside the parentheses. For example,

$$3(x + y + z) = 3(x) + 3(y) + 3(z)$$
$$= 3x + 3y + 3z$$

Since we define subtraction in terms of addition, the distributive property is also true for subtraction. For example,

$$2(x - y) = 2(x) - 2(y)$$
$$= 2x - 2y$$

EXAMPLE 4 Use the distributive property to write each expression without parentheses. Then simplify if possible.

a. $2(x + y)$ **b.** $-5(-3 + 2z)$ **c.** $5(x + 3y - z)$

d. $-1(2 - y)$ **e.** $-(3 + x - w)$ **f.** $\dfrac{1}{2}(6x + 14) + 10$

Solution

a. $2(x + y) = 2 \cdot x + 2 \cdot y$
$$= 2x + 2y$$

b. $-5(-3 + 2z) = -5(-3) + (-5)(2z)$
$$= 15 - 10z$$

c. $5(x + 3y - z) = 5(x) + 5(3y) - 5(z)$
$$= 5x + 15y - 5z$$

d. $-1(2 - y) = (-1)(2) - (-1)(y)$
$$= -2 + y$$

> **Helpful Hint**
> Notice in part **(e)** that $-(3 + x - w)$ is first rewritten as $-1(3 + x - w)$.

e. $-(3 + x - w) = -1(3 + x - w)$
$$= (-1)(3) + (-1)(x) - (-1)(w)$$
$$= -3 - x + w$$

f. $\dfrac{1}{2}(6x + 14) + 10 = \dfrac{1}{2}(6x) + \dfrac{1}{2}(14) + 10$ Apply the distributive property.
$$= 3x + 7 + 10 \qquad \text{Multiply.}$$
$$= 3x + 17 \qquad \text{Add.} \qquad \square$$

PRACTICE
4 Use the distributive property to write each expression without parentheses. Then simplify if possible.

a. $5(x - y)$

b. $-6(4 + 2t)$

c. $2(3x - 4y - z)$

d. $(3 - y) \cdot (-1)$

e. $-(x - 7 + 2s)$

f. $\frac{1}{2}(2x + 4) + 9$

We can use the distributive property in reverse to write a sum as a product.

EXAMPLE 5 Use the distributive property to write each sum as a product.

a. $8 \cdot 2 + 8 \cdot x$

b. $7s + 7t$

Solution

a. $8 \cdot 2 + 8 \cdot x = 8(2 + x)$

b. $7s + 7t = 7(s + t)$

PRACTICE
5 Use the distributive property to write each sum as a product.

a. $5 \cdot w + 5 \cdot 3$

b. $9w + 9z$

OBJECTIVE
3 Using the Identity and Inverse Properties

Next, we look at the **identity properties.**

The number 0 is called the identity for addition because when 0 is added to any real number, the result is the same real number. In other words, the _identity_ of the real number is not changed.

The number 1 is called the identity for multiplication because when a real number is multiplied by 1, the result is the same real number. In other words, the _identity_ of the real number is not changed.

Identities for Addition and Multiplication

0 is the identity element for addition.

$$a + 0 = a \quad \text{and} \quad 0 + a = a$$

1 is the identity element for multiplication.

$$a \cdot 1 = a \quad \text{and} \quad 1 \cdot a = a$$

Notice that 0 is the _only_ number that can be added to any real number with the result that the sum is the same real number. Also, 1 is the _only_ number that can be multiplied by any real number with the result that the product is the same real number.

Additive inverses or **opposites** were introduced in Section 1.5. Two numbers are called additive inverses or opposites if their sum is 0. The additive inverse or opposite of 6 is -6 because $6 + (-6) = 0$. The additive inverse or opposite of -5 is 5 because $-5 + 5 = 0$.

Reciprocals or **multiplicative inverses** were introduced in Section 1.3. Two nonzero numbers are called reciprocals or multiplicative inverses if their product is 1. The reciprocal or multiplicative inverse of $\frac{2}{3}$ is $\frac{3}{2}$ because $\frac{2}{3} \cdot \frac{3}{2} = 1$. Likewise, the reciprocal of -5 is $-\frac{1}{5}$ because $-5\left(-\frac{1}{5}\right) = 1$.

✔ **CONCEPT CHECK**

Which of the following, $1, -\frac{10}{3}, \frac{3}{10}, 0, \frac{10}{3}, -\frac{3}{10}$, is the

a. opposite of $-\frac{3}{10}$?   **b.** reciprocal of $-\frac{3}{10}$?

Additive or Multiplicative Inverses

The numbers a and $-a$ are additive inverses or opposites of each other because their sum is 0; that is,

$$a + (-a) = 0$$

The numbers b and $\frac{1}{b}$ (for $b \neq 0$) are reciprocals or multiplicative inverses of each other because their product is 1; that is,

$$b \cdot \frac{1}{b} = 1$$

EXAMPLE 6   Name the property or properties illustrated by each true statement.

Solution

a. $3 \cdot y = y \cdot 3$	Commutative property of multiplication (order changed)
b. $(x + 7) + 9 = x + (7 + 9)$	Associative property of addition (grouping changed)
c. $(b + 0) + 3 = b + 3$	Identity element for addition
d. $0.2 \cdot (z \cdot 5) = 0.2 \cdot (5 \cdot z)$	Commutative property of multiplication (order changed)
e. $-2 \cdot \left(-\frac{1}{2}\right) = 1$	Multiplicative inverse property
f. $-2 + 2 = 0$	Additive inverse property
g. $-6 \cdot (y \cdot 2) = (-6 \cdot 2) \cdot y$	Commutative and associative properties of multiplication (order and grouping changed)

PRACTICE

6   Name the property or properties illustrated by each true statement.

a. $(7 \cdot 3x) \cdot 4 = (3x \cdot 7) \cdot 4$	Commutative property of multiplication
b. $6 + (3 + y) = (6 + 3) + y$	Associative property of addition
c. $8 + (t + 0) = 8 + t$	Identity element for addition
d. $-\frac{3}{4} \cdot \left(-\frac{4}{3}\right) = 1$	Multiplicative inverse property
e. $(2 + x) + 5 = 5 + (2 + x)$	Commutative property of addition
f. $3 + (-3) = 0$	Additive inverse property
g. $(-3b) \cdot 7 = (-3 \cdot 7) \cdot b$	Commutative and associative properties of multiplication

Answers to Concept Check:
a. $\frac{3}{10}$ **b.** $-\frac{10}{3}$

✓ Vocabulary, Readiness & Video Check

Use the choices below to fill in each blank.

distributive property   associative property of multiplication   commutative property of addition
opposites or additive inverses   associative property of addition
reciprocals or multiplicative inverses   commutative property of multiplication

1. $x + 5 = 5 + x$ is a true statement by the _____ .

2. $x \cdot 5 = 5 \cdot x$ is a true statement by the _____ .

3. $3(y + 6) = 3 \cdot y + 3 \cdot 6$ is true by the _____ .

4. $2 \cdot (x \cdot y) = (2 \cdot x) \cdot y$ is a true statement by the _____ .

5. $x + (7 + y) = (x + 7) + y$ is a true statement by the _____ .

6. The numbers $-\dfrac{2}{3}$ and $-\dfrac{3}{2}$ are called _____ .

7. The numbers $-\dfrac{2}{3}$ and $\dfrac{2}{3}$ are called _____ .

Martin-Gay Interactive Videos

See Video 1.8 🎥

Watch the section lecture video and answer the following questions.

OBJECTIVE
1

8. The commutative properties are discussed in 🎞 Examples 1 and 2 and the associative properties are discussed in 🎞 Examples 3–7. What's the one word used again and again to describe the commutative property? The associative property?

OBJECTIVE
2

9. In 🎞 Example 10, what point is made about the term 2?

OBJECTIVE
3

10. Complete these statements based on the lecture given before 🎞 Example 12.

- The identity element for addition is _____ because if we add _____ to any real number, the result is that real number.

- The identity element for multiplication is _____ because any real number times _____ gives a result of that original real number.

1.8 Exercise Set   MyMathLab®

Use a commutative property to complete each statement. See Example 1.

1. $x + 16 =$ _____   **2.** $4 + y =$ _____

3. $-4 \cdot y =$ _____   **4.** $-2 \cdot x =$ _____

5. $xy =$ _____   **6.** $ab =$ _____

7. $2x + 13 =$ _____   **8.** $19 + 3y =$ _____

Use an associative property to complete each statement. See Example 2.

9. $(xy) \cdot z =$ _____   **10.** $3 \cdot (xy) =$ _____

11. $2 + (a + b) =$ _____   **12.** $(y + 4) + z =$ _____

13. $4 \cdot (ab) =$ _____   **14.** $(-3y) \cdot z =$ _____

15. $(a + b) + c =$ _____

16. $6 + (r + s) =$ _____

Use the commutative and associative properties to simplify each expression. See Example 3.

17. $8 + (9 + b)$ **18.** $(r + 3) + 11$

19. $4(6y)$ **20.** $2(42x)$

21. $\dfrac{1}{5}(5y)$ **22.** $\dfrac{1}{8}(8z)$

23. $(13 + a) + 13$ **24.** $7 + (x + 4)$

25. $-9(8x)$ **26.** $-3(12y)$

27. $\dfrac{3}{4}\left(\dfrac{4}{3}s\right)$ **28.** $\dfrac{2}{7}\left(\dfrac{7}{2}r\right)$

29. $\dfrac{2}{3} + \left(\dfrac{4}{3} + x\right)$ **30.** $\dfrac{7}{9} + \left(\dfrac{2}{9} + y\right)$

Use the distributive property to write each expression without parentheses. Then simplify the result. See Example 4.

31. $4(x + y)$ **32.** $7(a + b)$

33. $9(x - 6)$ **34.** $11(y - 4)$

35. $2(3x + 5)$ **36.** $5(7 + 8y)$

37. $7(4x - 3)$ **38.** $3(8x - 1)$

39. $3(6 + x)$ **40.** $2(x + 5)$

41. $-2(y - z)$ **42.** $-3(z - y)$

43. $-7(3y + 5)$

44. $-5(2r + 11)$

45. $5(x + 4m + 2)$

46. $8(3y + z - 6)$

47. $-4(1 - 2m + n)$

48. $-4(4 + 2p + 5q)$

49. $-(5x + 2)$

50. $-(9r + 5)$

51. $-(r - 3 - 7p)$

52. $-(q - 2 + 6r)$

53. $\frac{1}{2}(6x + 8)$

54. $\frac{1}{4}(4x - 2)$

55. $-\frac{1}{3}(3x - 9y)$

56. $-\frac{1}{5}(10a - 25b)$

57. $3(2r + 5) - 7$

58. $10(4s + 6) - 40$

59. $-9(4x + 8) + 2$

60. $-11(5x + 3) + 10$

61. $-4(4x + 5) - 5$

62. $-6(2x + 1) - 1$

Use the distributive property to write each sum as a product. See Example 5.

63. $4 \cdot 1 + 4 \cdot y$ **64.** $14 \cdot z + 14 \cdot 5$

65. $11x + 11y$ **66.** $9a + 9b$

67. $(-1) \cdot 5 + (-1) \cdot x$ **68.** $(-3)a + (-3)b$

69. $30a + 30b$ **70.** $25x + 25y$

Name the properties illustrated by each true statement. See Example 6.

71. $3 \cdot 5 = 5 \cdot 3$

72. $4(3 + 8) = 4 \cdot 3 + 4 \cdot 8$

73. $2 + (x + 5) = (2 + x) + 5$

74. $(x + 9) + 3 = (9 + x) + 3$

75. $9(3 + 7) = 9 \cdot 3 + 9 \cdot 7$

76. $1 \cdot 9 = 9$

77. $(4 \cdot y) \cdot 9 = 4 \cdot (y \cdot 9)$

78. $6 \cdot \frac{1}{6} = 1$

79. $0 + 6 = 6$

80. $(a + 9) + 6 = a + (9 + 6)$

81. $-4(y + 7) = -4 \cdot y + (-4) \cdot 7$

82. $(11 + r) + 8 = (r + 11) + 8$

83. $-4 \cdot (8 \cdot 3) = (8 \cdot -4) \cdot 3$

84. $r + 0 = r$

CONCEPT EXTENSIONS

Fill in the table with the opposite (additive inverse) and the reciprocal (multiplicative inverse). Assume that the value of each expression is not 0.

	Expression	Opposite	Reciprocal
85.	8		
86.	$-\frac{2}{3}$		
87.	x		
88.	$4y$		
89.			$\frac{1}{2x}$
90.		$7x$	

Decide whether each statement is true or false. See the second Concept Check in this section.

91. The opposite of $-\frac{a}{2}$ is $-\frac{2}{a}$.

92. The reciprocal of $-\frac{a}{2}$ is $\frac{a}{2}$.

Determine which pairs of actions are commutative. See the first Concept Check in this section.

93. "taking a test" and "studying for the test"

94. "putting on your shoes" and "putting on your socks"

95. "putting on your left shoe" and "putting on your right shoe"

96. "reading the sports section" and "reading the comics section"

97. "mowing the lawn" and "trimming the hedges"

98. "baking a cake" and "eating the cake"

99. "dialing a number" and "turning on the cell phone"

100. "feeding the dog" and "feeding the cat"

Name the property illustrated by each step.

101. a. $\triangle + (\square + \bigcirc) = (\square + \bigcirc) + \triangle$

     b. $ = (\bigcirc + \square) + \triangle$

     c. $ = \bigcirc + (\square + \triangle)$

102. a. $(x + y) + z = x + (y + z)$
   b. $= (y + z) + x$
   c. $= (z + y) + x$

↘ **103.** Explain why 0 is called the identity element for addition.

↘ **104.** Explain why 1 is called the identity element for multiplication.

↘ **105.** Write an example that shows that division is not commutative.

↘ **106.** Write an example that shows that subtraction is not commutative.

Chapter 1 Vocabulary Check

Fill in each blank with one of the words or phrases listed below.

set	inequality symbols	opposites	absolute value	numerator
denominator	grouping symbols	exponent	base	reciprocals
variable	equation	solution		

1. The symbols $\neq$, $<$, and $>$ are called _____ .

2. A mathematical statement that two expressions are equal is called a(n) _____ .

3. The _____ of a number is the distance between that number and 0 on a number line.

4. A symbol used to represent a number is called a(n) _____ .

5. Two numbers that are the same distance from 0 but lie on opposite sides of 0 are called _____ .

6. The number in a fraction above the fraction bar is called the _____ .

7. A(n) _____ of an equation is a value for the variable that makes the equation a true statement.

8. Two numbers whose product is 1 are called _____ .

9. In 2^3, the 2 is called the _____ and the 3 is called the _____ .

10. The number in a fraction below the fraction bar is called the _____ .

11. Parentheses and brackets are examples of _____ .

12. A(n) _____ is a collection of objects.

Chapter 1 Highlights

DEFINITIONS AND CONCEPTS	EXAMPLES
Section 1.2 Symbols and Sets of Numbers	
A **set** is a collection of objects, called **elements,** enclosed in braces.	$\{a, c, e\}$
Natural Numbers: $\{1, 2, 3, 4, \dots\}$	Given the set $\left\{-3.4, \sqrt{3}, 0, \frac{2}{3}, 5, -4\right\}$, list the numbers that belong to the set of
Whole Numbers: $\{0, 1, 2, 3, 4, \dots\}$	
Integers: $\{\dots, -3, -2, -1, 0, 1, 2, 3, \dots\}$	Natural numbers: 5
Rational Numbers: {real numbers that can be expressed as a quotient of integers}	Whole numbers: 0, 5
	Integers: $-4, 0, 5$
Irrational Numbers: {real numbers that cannot be expressed as a quotient of integers}	Rational numbers: $-4, -3.4, 0, \frac{2}{3}, 5$
	Irrational Numbers: $\sqrt{3}$
Real Numbers: {all numbers that correspond to a point on the number line}	Real numbers: $-4, -3.4, 0, \frac{2}{3}, \sqrt{3}, 5$
	(continued)

DEFINITIONS AND CONCEPTS	EXAMPLES

Section 1.2 Symbols and Sets of Numbers (continued)

A line used to picture numbers is called a **number line.**

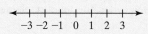

The **absolute value** of a real number a, denoted by $|a|$, is the distance between a and 0 on a number line.

$$|5| = 5 \qquad |0| = 0 \qquad |-2| = 2$$

Symbols: $=$ is equal to

$-7 = -7$

$\neq$ is not equal to

$3 \neq -3$

$>$ is greater than

$4 > 1$

$<$ is less than

$1 < 4$

$\leq$ is less than or equal to

$6 \leq 6$

$\geq$ is greater than or equal to

$18 \geq -\dfrac{1}{3}$

Order Property for Real Numbers

For any two real numbers a and b, a is less than b if a is to the left of b on a number line.

$$-3 < 0 \qquad 0 > -3 \qquad 0 < 2.5 \qquad 2.5 > 0$$

Section 1.3 Fractions and Mixed Numbers

A quotient of two integers is called a **fraction.**
The **numerator** of a fraction is the top number.
The **denominator** of a fraction is the bottom number.

$\dfrac{13}{17}$ ← numerator
   ← denominator

If $a \cdot b = c$, then a and b are **factors** and c is the **product.**

$$7 \quad \cdot \quad 9 \quad = \quad 63$$
$$\downarrow \qquad\quad \downarrow \qquad\qquad \downarrow$$
$$\text{factor} \qquad \text{factor} \qquad\quad \text{product}$$

A fraction is in **lowest terms** or **simplest form** when the numerator and the denominator have no factors in common other than 1.

$\dfrac{13}{17}$ is in simplest form.

To write a fraction in simplest form, factor the numerator and the denominator; then apply the fundamental principle.

Write in simplest form.

$$\frac{6}{14} = \frac{2 \cdot 3}{2 \cdot 7} = \frac{3}{7}$$

Two fractions are **reciprocals** if their product is 1.
The reciprocal of $\dfrac{a}{b}$ is $\dfrac{b}{a}$.

The reciprocal of $\dfrac{6}{25}$ is $\dfrac{25}{6}$.

To multiply fractions, numerator times numerator is the numerator of the product and denominator times denominator is the denominator of the product.

Perform the indicated operations.

$$\frac{2}{5} \cdot \frac{3}{7} = \frac{6}{35}$$

To divide fractions, multiply the first fraction by the reciprocal of the second fraction.

$$\frac{5}{9} \div \frac{2}{7} = \frac{5}{9} \cdot \frac{7}{2} = \frac{35}{18}$$

To add fractions with the same denominator, add the numerators and place the sum over the common denominator.

$$\frac{5}{11} + \frac{3}{11} = \frac{8}{11}$$

To subtract fractions with the same denominator, subtract the numerators and place the difference over the common denominator.

$$\frac{13}{15} - \frac{3}{15} = \frac{10}{15} = \frac{2}{3}$$

Fractions that represent the same quantity are called **equivalent fractions.**

$$\frac{1}{5} = \frac{1 \cdot 4}{5 \cdot 4} = \frac{4}{20}$$

$\dfrac{1}{5}$ and $\dfrac{4}{20}$ are equivalent fractions.

DEFINITIONS AND CONCEPTS	EXAMPLES

Section 1.4   Exponents, Order of Operations, Variable Expressions, and Equations

The expression a^n is an **exponential expression.** The number a is called the **base;** it is the repeated factor.
The number n is called the **exponent;** it is the number of times that the base is a factor.

$$4^3 = 4 \cdot 4 \cdot 4 = 64$$

$$7^2 = 7 \cdot 7 = 49$$

Order of Operations

Simplify expressions in the following order. If grouping symbols are present, simplify expressions within those first, starting with the innermost set. Also, simplify the numerator and the denominator of a fraction separately.

1. Simplify exponential expressions.
2. Multiply or divide in order from left to right.
3. Add or subtract in order from left to right.

$$\frac{8^2 + 5(7-3)}{3 \cdot 7} = \frac{8^2 + 5(4)}{21}$$

$$= \frac{64 + 5(4)}{21}$$

$$= \frac{64 + 20}{21}$$

$$= \frac{84}{21}$$

$$= 4$$

A symbol used to represent a number is called a **variable.**

Examples of variables are:

$$q, x, z$$

An **algebraic expression** is a collection of numbers, variables, operation symbols, and grouping symbols.

Examples of algebraic expressions are:

$$5x, 2(y-6), \frac{q^2 - 3q + 1}{6}$$

To evaluate an algebraic expression containing a variable, substitute a given number for the variable and simplify.

Evaluate $x^2 - y^2$ if $x = 5$ and $y = 3$.

$$x^2 - y^2 = (5)^2 - (3)^2$$

$$= 25 - 9$$

$$= 16$$

A mathematical statement that two expressions are equal is called an **equation.**

Examples of equations are:

$$3x - 9 = 20$$

$$A = \pi r^2$$

A **solution** of an equation is a value for the variable that makes the equation a true statement.

Determine whether 4 is a solution of $5x + 7 = 27$.

$$5x + 7 = 27$$

$$5(4) + 7 \stackrel{?}{=} 27$$

$$20 + 7 \stackrel{?}{=} 27$$

$$27 = 27 \quad \text{True}$$

4 is a solution.

Section 1.5   Adding Real Numbers

To Add Two Numbers with the Same Sign
1. Add their absolute values.
2. Use their common sign as the sign of the sum.

To Add Two Numbers with Different Signs
1. Subtract their absolute values.
2. Use the sign of the number whose absolute value is larger as the sign of the sum.

Add.

$$10 + 7 = 17$$

$$-3 + (-8) = -11$$

$$-25 + 5 = -20$$

$$14 + (-9) = 5$$

(continued)

DEFINITIONS AND CONCEPTS	EXAMPLES

Section 1.5   Adding Real Numbers (continued)

Two numbers that are the same distance from 0 but lie on opposite sides of 0 are called **opposites** or **additive inverses**. The opposite of a number a is denoted by $-a$.

The sum of a number a and its opposite, $-a$, is 0.

$$a + (-a) = 0$$

If a is a number, then $-(-a) = a$.

The opposite of -7 is 7.
The opposite of 123 is -123.

$$-4 + 4 = 0$$
$$12 + (-12) = 0$$
$$-(-8) = 8$$
$$-(-14) = 14$$

Section 1.6   Subtracting Real Numbers

To subtract two numbers a and b, add the first number a to the opposite of the second number b.

$$a - b = a + (-b)$$

Subtract.

$$3 - (-44) = 3 + 44 = 47$$
$$-5 - 22 = -5 + (-22) = -27$$
$$-30 - (-30) = -30 + 30 = 0$$

Section 1.7   Multiplying and Dividing Real Numbers

Quotient of two real numbers

$$\frac{a}{b} = a \cdot \frac{1}{b}$$

Multiplying and Dividing Real Numbers

The product or quotient of two numbers with the same sign is a positive number. The product or quotient of two numbers with different signs is a negative number.

Products and Quotients Involving Zero

The product of 0 and any number is 0.

$$b \cdot 0 = 0 \quad \text{and} \quad 0 \cdot b = 0$$

The quotient of a nonzero number and 0 is undefined.

$$\frac{b}{0} \text{ is undefined.}$$

The quotient of 0 and any nonzero number is 0.

$$\frac{0}{b} = 0$$

Multiply or divide.

$$\frac{42}{2} = 42 \cdot \frac{1}{2} = 21$$

$$7 \cdot 8 = 56 \quad -7 \cdot (-8) = 56$$
$$-2 \cdot 4 = -8 \quad 2 \cdot (-4) = -8$$
$$\frac{90}{10} = 9 \quad \frac{-90}{-10} = 9$$
$$\frac{42}{-6} = -7 \quad \frac{-42}{6} = -7$$

$$-4 \cdot 0 = 0 \quad 0 \cdot \left(-\frac{3}{4}\right) = 0$$

$$\frac{-85}{0} \text{ is undefined.}$$

$$\frac{0}{18} = 0 \quad \frac{0}{-47} = 0$$

Section 1.8   Properties of Real Numbers

Commutative Properties
Addition: $a + b = b + a$
Multiplication: $a \cdot b = b \cdot a$

Associative Properties
Addition: $(a + b) + c = a + (b + c)$
Multiplication: $(a \cdot b) \cdot c = a \cdot (b \cdot c)$

$$3 + (-7) = -7 + 3$$
$$-8 \cdot 5 = 5 \cdot (-8)$$

$$(5 + 10) + 20 = 5 + (10 + 20)$$
$$(-3 \cdot 2) \cdot 11 = -3 \cdot (2 \cdot 11)$$

DEFINITIONS AND CONCEPTS	EXAMPLES
Section 1.8 Properties of Real Numbers (continued)	

Two numbers whose product is 1 are called **multiplicative inverses** or **reciprocals**. The reciprocal of a nonzero number a is $\frac{1}{a}$ because $a \cdot \frac{1}{a} = 1$.

The reciprocal of 3 is $\frac{1}{3}$.

The reciprocal of $-\frac{2}{5}$ is $-\frac{5}{2}$.

Distributive Property
$$a(b + c) = a \cdot b + a \cdot c$$

$$5(6 + 10) = 5 \cdot 6 + 5 \cdot 10$$
$$-2(3 + x) = -2 \cdot 3 + (-2)(x)$$

Identities
$$a + 0 = a \quad 0 + a = a$$
$$a \cdot 1 = a \quad 1 \cdot a = a$$

$$5 + 0 = 5 \quad 0 + (-2) = -2$$
$$-14 \cdot 1 = -14 \quad 1 \cdot 27 = 27$$

Inverses

Additive or opposite: $a + (-a) = 0$

Multiplicative or reciprocal: $b \cdot \frac{1}{b} = 1$

$$7 + (-7) = 0$$
$$3 \cdot \frac{1}{3} = 1$$

Chapter 1 Review

(1.2) Insert $<$, $>$, or $=$ in the appropriate space to make the following statements true.

1. 8   10

2. 7   2

3. -4 -5

4. $\frac{12}{2}$ -8

5. $|-7|$ $|-8|$

6. $|-9|$ -9

7. $-|-1|$ -1

8. $|-14|$ $-(-14)$

9. 1.2   1.02

10. $-\frac{3}{2}$ $-\frac{3}{4}$

TRANSLATING

Translate each statement into symbols.

11. Four is greater than or equal to negative three.

12. Six is not equal to five.

13. 0.03 is less than 0.3.

14. New York City has 155 museums and 400 art galleries. Write an inequality comparing the numbers 155 and 400. (*Source:* Absolute Trivia.com)

Given the following sets of numbers, list the numbers in each set that also belong to the set of:

a. Natural numbers

b. Whole numbers

c. Integers

d. Rational numbers

e. Irrational numbers

f. Real numbers

15. $\left\{-6, 0, 1, 1\frac{1}{2}, 3, \pi, 9.62\right\}$

16. $\left\{-3, -1.6, 2, 5, \frac{11}{2}, 15.1, \sqrt{5}, 2\pi\right\}$

The following chart shows the gains and losses in dollars of Density Oil and Gas stock for a particular week.

Day	Gain or Loss in Dollars
Monday	+1
Tuesday	−2
Wednesday	+5
Thursday	+1
Friday	−4

17. Which day showed the greatest loss?

18. Which day showed the greatest gain?

(1.3) Write the number as a product of prime factors.

19. 36

20. 120

Perform the indicated operations. Write results in lowest terms.

21. $\frac{8}{15} \cdot \frac{27}{30}$

22. $\frac{7}{8} \div \frac{21}{32}$

23. $\frac{7}{15} + \frac{5}{6}$

24. $\frac{3}{4} - \frac{3}{20}$

25. $2\frac{3}{4} + 6\frac{5}{8}$

26. $7\frac{1}{6} - 2\frac{2}{3}$

27. $5 \div \frac{1}{3}$

28. $2 \cdot 8\frac{3}{4}$

Each circle represents a whole, or 1. Determine the unknown part of the circle.

29.

30.

Find the area and the perimeter of each figure.

△ **31.**

△ **32.**

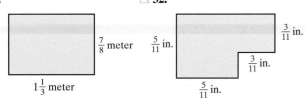

Octuplets were born in the U.S. in 2009. The following chart gives the octuplets' birthweights. The babies are listed in order of birth.

Baby	Gender	Birthweight (pounds)
Baby A	boy	$2\frac{1}{2}$
Baby B	girl	$2\frac{1}{8}$
Baby C	boy	$3\frac{1}{16}$
Baby D	girl	$2\frac{3}{16}$
Baby E	boy	$1\frac{3}{4}$
Baby F	boy	$2\frac{9}{16}$
Baby G	boy	$1\frac{13}{16}$
Baby H	boy	$2\frac{7}{16}$

33. What was the total weight of the boy octuplets?

34. What was the total weight of the girl octuplets?

35. Find the combined weight of all eight octuplets.

36. Which baby weighed the most?

37. Which baby weighed the least?

38. How much more did the heaviest baby weigh than the lightest baby?

(1.4) *Choose the correct answer for each statement.*

39. The expression $6 \cdot 3^2 + 2 \cdot 8$ simplifies to
a. −52   **b.** 448   **c.** 70   **d.** 64

40. The expression $68 - 5 \cdot 2^3$ simplifies to
a. −232   **b.** 28   **c.** 38   **d.** 504

Simplify each expression.

41. $\left(\dfrac{2}{7}\right)^2$

42. $\left(\dfrac{3}{4}\right)^3$

43. $3(1 + 2 \cdot 5) + 4$

44. $8 + 3(2 \cdot 6 - 1)$

45. $\dfrac{4 + |6 - 2| + 8^2}{4 + 6 \cdot 4}$

46. $5[3(2 + 5) - 5]$

TRANSLATING

Translate each word statement into symbols.

47. The difference of twenty and twelve is equal to the product of two and four.

48. The quotient of nine and two is greater than negative five.

Evaluate each expression if $x = 6, y = 2,$ and $z = 8$.

49. $2x + 3y$

50. $x(y + 2z)$

51. $\dfrac{x}{y} + \dfrac{z}{2y}$

52. $x^2 - 3y^2$

△ **53.** The expression $180 - a - b$ represents the measure of the unknown angle of the given triangle. Replace a with 37 and b with 80 to find the measure of the unknown angle.

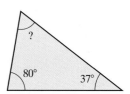

△ **54.** The expression $360 - a - b - c$ represents the measure of the unknown angle of the given quadrilateral. Replace a with 93, b with 80, and c with 82 to find the measure of the unknown angle.

Decide whether the given number is a solution of the given equation.

55. Is $x = 3$ a solution of $7x - 3 = 18$?

56. Is $x = 1$ a solution of $3x^2 + 4 = x - 1$?

(1.5) *Find the additive inverse or the opposite.*

57. −9

58. $\dfrac{2}{3}$

59. $|-2|$

60. $-|-7|$

Find the following sums.

61. $-15 + 4$

62. $-6 + (-11)$

63. $\dfrac{1}{16} + \left(-\dfrac{1}{4}\right)$

64. $-8 + |-3|$

65. $-4.6 + (-9.3)$

66. $-2.8 + 6.7$

(1.6) Perform the indicated operations.

67. $6 - 20$

68. $-3.1 - 8.4$

69. $-6 - (-11)$

70. $4 - 15$

71. $-21 - 16 + 3(8 - 2)$

72. $\dfrac{11 - (-9) + 6(8 - 2)}{2 + 3 \cdot 4}$

Evaluate each expression for $x = 3$, $y = -6$, and $z = -9$. Then choose the correct evaluation.

73. $2x^2 - y + z$

    a. 15   **b.** 3   **c.** 27   **d.** -3

74. $\dfrac{|y - 4x|}{2x}$

    a. 3   **b.** 1   **c.** -1 **d.** -3

75. At the beginning of the week, the price of Density Oil and Gas stock from Exercises 17 and 18 is $50 per share. Find the price of a share of stock at the end of the week.

76. Find the price of a share of stock by the end of the day on Wednesday.

(1.7) Find the multiplicative inverse or reciprocal.

77. -6

78. $\dfrac{3}{5}$

Simplify each expression.

79. $6(-8)$

80. $(-2)(-14)$

81. $\dfrac{-18}{-6}$

82. $\dfrac{42}{-3}$

83. $\dfrac{4(-3) + (-8)}{2 + (-2)}$

84. $\dfrac{3(-2)^2 - 5}{-14}$

85. $\dfrac{-6}{0}$

86. $\dfrac{0}{-2}$

87. $-4^2 - (-3 + 5) \div (-1) \cdot 2$

88. $-5^2 - (2 - 20) \div (-3) \cdot 3$

If $x = -5$ and $y = -2$, evaluate each expression.

89. $x^2 - y^4$

90. $x^2 - y^3$

TRANSLATING

Translate each phrase into an expression. Use x to represent a number.

91. The product of -7 and a number

92. The quotient of a number and -13

93. Subtract a number from -20

94. The sum of -1 and a number

(1.8) Name the property illustrated.

95. $-6 + 5 = 5 + (-6)$

96. $6 \cdot 1 = 6$

97. $3(8 - 5) = 3 \cdot 8 - 3 \cdot (5)$

98. $4 + (-4) = 0$

99. $2 + (3 + 9) = (2 + 3) + 9$

100. $2 \cdot 8 = 8 \cdot 2$

101. $6(8 + 5) = 6 \cdot 8 + 6 \cdot 5$

102. $(3 \cdot 8) \cdot 4 = 3 \cdot (8 \cdot 4)$

103. $4 \cdot \dfrac{1}{4} = 1$

104. $8 + 0 = 8$

Use the distributive property to write each expression without parentheses.

105. $5(y - 2)$

106. $-3(z + y)$

107. $-(7 - x + 4z)$

108. $\dfrac{1}{2}(6z - 10)$

109. $-4(3x + 5) - 7$

110. $-8(2y + 9) - 1$

MIXED REVIEW

Insert $<$, $>$, or $=$ in the space between each pair of numbers.

111. $-|-11|$ $|11.4|$

112. $-1\dfrac{1}{2}$ $-2\dfrac{1}{2}$

Perform the indicated operations.

113. $-7.2 + (-8.1)$

114. $14 - 20$

115. $4(-20)$

116. $\dfrac{-20}{4}$

117. $-\dfrac{4}{5}\left(\dfrac{5}{16}\right)$

118. $-0.5(-0.3)$

119. $8 \div 2 \cdot 4$

120. $(-2)^4$

121. $\dfrac{-3 - 2(-9)}{-15 - 3(-4)}$

122. $5 + 2[(7 - 5)^2 + (1 - 3)]$

123. $-\dfrac{5}{8} \div \dfrac{3}{4}$

124. $\dfrac{-15 + (-4)^2 + |-9|}{10 - 2 \cdot 5}$

△ **125.** A trim carpenter needs a piece of quarter round molding $6\dfrac{1}{8}$ feet long for a bathroom. She finds a piece $7\dfrac{1}{2}$ feet long. How long a piece does she need to cut from the $7\dfrac{1}{2}$-foot-long molding in order to use it in the bathroom?

1c

Chapter 1 Getting Ready for the Test

*All the exercises below are **Multiple Choice.** Choose the correct letter(s). Also, letters may be used more than once.*
Select the given operation between the two numbers.

1. For $-5 + (-3)$, the operation is

    A. addition   **B.** subtraction   **C.** multiplication   **D.** division

2. For $-5(-3)$, the operation is

    A. addition   **B.** subtraction   **C.** multiplication   **D.** division

Identify each as an

    A. equation   or an   **B.** expression

3. $6x + 2 + 4x - 10$ **4.** $6x + 2 = 4x - 10$

5. $-2(x - 1) = 12$ **6.** $-7\left(x + \dfrac{1}{2}\right) - 22$

For the exercises below, a and b are negative numbers. State whether each expression simplifies to

    A. positive number   **B.** negative number   **C.** 0   **D.** not possible to determine

7. $a + b$ **8.** $a \cdot b$

9. $\dfrac{a}{b}$ **10.** $a - 0$

11. $0 \cdot b$ **12.** $a - b$

13. $0 + b$ **14.** $\dfrac{0}{a}$

The exercise statement and the correct answer are given. Select the correct directions.

    A. Find the opposite.   **B.** Find the reciprocal.   **C.** Evaluate or simplify.

15. 5   Answer: $\dfrac{1}{5}$ **16.** $3 + 2(-8)$ Answer: -13

17. 2^3 Answer: 8   **18.** -7 Answer: 7

Chapter 1 Test   MyMathLab®   You Tube™

Translate the statement into symbols.

1. The absolute value of negative seven is greater than five.

2. The sum of nine and five is greater than or equal to four.

Simplify the expression.

3. $-13 + 8$ **4.** $-13 - (-2)$

5. $12 \div 4 \cdot 3 - 6 \cdot 2$ **6.** $(13)(-3)$

7. $(-6)(-2)$ **8.** $\dfrac{|-16|}{-8}$

9. $\dfrac{-8}{0}$ **10.** $\dfrac{|-6| + 2}{5 - 6}$

11. $\dfrac{1}{2} - \dfrac{5}{6}$ **12.** $5\dfrac{3}{4} - 1\dfrac{1}{8}$

13. $-0.6 + 1.875$ **14.** $3(-4)^2 - 80$

15. $6[5 + 2(3 - 8) - 3]$ **16.** $\dfrac{-12 + 3 \cdot 8}{4}$

17. $\dfrac{(-2)(0)(-3)}{-6}$

Insert $<$, $>$, or $=$ in the appropriate space to make each of the following statements true.

18. -3 -7 **19.** 4 -8

20. 2 $|-3|$ **21.** $|-2|$ $-1 - (-3)$

22. In the state of Massachusetts, there are 2221 licensed child care centers and 10,993 licensed home-based child care providers. Write an inequality statement comparing the numbers 2221 and 10,993. (*Source:* Children's Foundation)

23. Given $\left\{-5, -1, 0, \dfrac{1}{4}, 1, 7, 11.6, \sqrt{7}, 3\pi\right\}$, list the numbers in this set that also belong to the set of:

    a. Natural numbers

    b. Whole numbers

    c. Integers

    d. Rational numbers

    e. Irrational numbers

    f. Real numbers

If $x = 6$, $y = -2$, and $z = -3$, evaluate each expression.

24. $x^2 + y^2$ **25.** $x + yz$

26. $2 + 3x - y$ **27.** $\dfrac{y + z - 1}{x}$

Identify the property illustrated by each expression.

28. $8 + (9 + 3) = (8 + 9) + 3$

29. $6 \cdot 8 = 8 \cdot 6$

30. $-6(2 + 4) = -6 \cdot 2 + (-6) \cdot 4$

31. $\dfrac{1}{6}(6) = 1$

32. Find the opposite of -9.

33. Find the reciprocal of $-\dfrac{1}{3}$.

The New Orleans Saints were 22 yards from the goal when the following series of gains and losses occurred.

	Gains and Losses in Yards
First Down	5
Second Down	−10
Third Down	−2
Fourth Down	29

34. During which down did the greatest loss of yardage occur?

35. Was a touchdown scored?

36. The temperature at the Winter Olympics was a frigid 14 degrees below zero in the morning, but by noon it had risen 31 degrees. What was the temperature at noon?

37. A health insurance provider had net incomes of $356 million, $460 million, and −$166 million in 3 consecutive years. What was the health insurance provider's total net income for these three years?

38. A stockbroker decided to sell 280 shares of stock, which decreased in value by $1.50 per share yesterday. How much money did she lose?

Equations, Inequalities, and Problem Solving

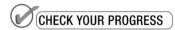

Much of mathematics relates to deciding which statements are true and which are false. For example, the statement $x + 7 = 15$ is an equation stating that the sum $x + 7$ has the same value as 15. Is this statement true or false? It is false for some values of x and true for just one value of x, namely 8. Our purpose in this chapter is to learn ways of deciding which values make an equation or an inequality true.

What Are iOS and Android Systems?

Smartphones, tablets, and iPads are everywhere. What are the operating systems behind these devices? Two such systems are iOS and Android. iOS is a mobile operating system developed by Apple, Inc., for Apple hardware, and Android is a mobile operating system developed by Google, primarily for touchscreen devices such as smartphones and tablet computers. The average American now spends 162 minutes, that is, 2 hours and 42 minutes, daily on one (or more) of these devices. This is an increase of 4 minutes a day from last year, and it seems that this amount of time will only continue to grow.

In Section 2.7, Exercises 33 through 36, we will explore how this time is spent.

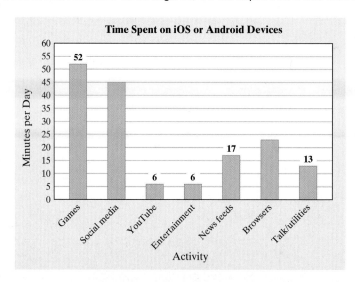

2.1 Simplifying Algebraic Expressions

OBJECTIVES

1 Identify Terms, Like Terms, and Unlike Terms.

2 Combine Like Terms.

3 Use the Distributive Property to Remove Parentheses.

4 Write Word Phrases as Algebraic Expressions.

As we explore in this section, an expression such as $3x + 2x$ is not as simple as possible because—even without replacing x by a value—we can perform the indicated addition.

OBJECTIVE

1 Identifying Terms, Like Terms, and Unlike Terms

Before we practice simplifying expressions, some new language of algebra is presented. A **term** is a number or the product of a number and variables raised to powers.

Terms

$$-y, \quad 2x^3, \quad -5, \quad 3xz^2, \quad \frac{2}{y}, \quad 0.8z$$

The **numerical coefficient** (sometimes also simply called the **coefficient**) of a term is the numerical factor. The numerical coefficient of $3x$ is 3. Recall that $3x$ means $3 \cdot x$.

Term	Numerical Coefficient
$3x$	3
$\dfrac{y^3}{5}$	$\dfrac{1}{5}$ since $\dfrac{y^3}{5}$ means $\dfrac{1}{5} \cdot y^3$
$0.7ab^3c^5$	0.7
z	1
$-y$	-1
-5	-5

> **Helpful Hint**
>
> The term $-y$ means $-1y$ and thus has a numerical coefficient of -1.
> The term z means $1z$ and thus has a numerical coefficient of 1.

EXAMPLE 1   Identify the numerical coefficient of each term.

  a. $-3y$ **b.** $22z^4$ **c.** y **d.** $-x$ **e.** $\dfrac{x}{7}$

Solution

  a. The numerical coefficient of $-3y$ is -3.

  b. The numerical coefficient of $22z^4$ is 22.

  c. The numerical coefficient of y is 1, since y is $1y$.

  d. The numerical coefficient of $-x$ is -1, since $-x$ is $-1x$.

  e. The numerical coefficient of $\dfrac{x}{7}$ is $\dfrac{1}{7}$, since $\dfrac{x}{7}$ means $\dfrac{1}{7} \cdot x$.

PRACTICE

1 Identify the numerical coefficient of each term.

  a. t **b.** $-7x$ **c.** $-\dfrac{w}{5}$ **d.** $43x^4$ **e.** $-b$

Terms with the same variables raised to exactly the same powers are called **like terms**. Terms that aren't like terms are called **unlike terms**.

Like Terms	Unlike Terms	Reason
$3x, 2x$	$5x, 5x^2$	Why? Same variable x but different powers x and x^2
$-6x^2y, 2x^2y, 4x^2y$	$7y, 3z, 8x^2$	Why? Different variables
$2ab^2c^3, ac^3b^2$	$6abc^3, 6ab^2$	Why? Different variables and different powers

> **Helpful Hint**
>
> In like terms, each variable and its exponent must match exactly, but these factors don't need to be in the same order.
>
> $$2x^2y \text{ and } 3yx^2 \text{ are like terms.}$$

EXAMPLE 2 Determine whether the terms are like or unlike.

a. $2x, 3x^2$ b. $4x^2y, x^2y, -2x^2y$ c. $-2yz, -3zy$ d. $-x^4, x^4$

Solution

a. Unlike terms, since the exponents on x are not the same.

b. Like terms, since each variable and its exponent match.

c. Like terms, since $zy = yz$ by the commutative property.

d. Like terms.

PRACTICE
2 Determine whether the terms are like or unlike.

a. $-4xy, 5yx$ b. $5q, -3q^2$

c. $3ab^2, -2ab^2, 43ab^2$ d. $y^5, \dfrac{y^5}{2}$

OBJECTIVE
2 Combining Like Terms

An algebraic expression containing the sum or difference of like terms can be simplified by applying the distributive property. For example, by the distributive property, we rewrite the sum of the like terms $3x + 2x$ as

$$3x + 2x = (3 + 2)x = 5x$$

Also,

$$-y^2 + 5y^2 = -1y^2 + 5y^2 = (-1 + 5)y^2 = 4y^2$$

Simplifying the sum or difference of like terms is called **combining like terms.**

EXAMPLE 3 Simplify each expression by combining like terms.

a. $7x - 3x$ b. $10y^2 + y^2$
c. $8x^2 + 2x - 3x$ d. $9n^2 - 5n^2 + n^2$

Solution

a. $7x - 3x = (7 - 3)x = 4x$
b. $10y^2 + y^2 = 10y^2 + 1y^2 = (10 + 1)y^2 = 11y^2$
c. $8x^2 + 2x - 3x = 8x^2 + (2 - 3)x = 8x^2 - x$
d. $9n^2 - 5n^2 + n^2 = (9 - 5 + 1)n^2 = 5n^2$

PRACTICE
3 Simplify each expression by combining like terms.

a. $-3y + 11y$ b. $4x^2 + x^2$
c. $5x - 3x^2 + 8x^2$ d. $20y^2 + 2y^2 - y^2$

To write →

The previous example suggests the following:

> **Combining Like Terms**
>
> To **combine like terms,** add the numerical coefficients and multiply the result by the common variable factors.

EXAMPLE 4   Simplify each expression by combining like terms.

a. $2x + 3x + 5 + 2$ b. $-5a - 3 + a + 2$ c. $4y - 3y^2$

d. $2.3x + 5x - 6$ e. $-\dfrac{1}{2}b + b$

Solution Use the distributive property to combine like terms.

a. $2x + 3x + 5 + 2 = (2 + 3)x + (5 + 2)$
$= 5x + 7$

b. $-5a - 3 + a + 2 = -5a + 1a + (-3 + 2)$
$= (-5 + 1)a + (-3 + 2)$
$= -4a - 1$

c. $4y - 3y^2$ These two terms cannot be combined because they are unlike terms.

d. $2.3x + 5x - 6 = (2.3 + 5)x - 6$
$= 7.3x - 6$

e. $-\dfrac{1}{2}b + b = -\dfrac{1}{2}b + 1b = \left(-\dfrac{1}{2} + 1\right)b = \dfrac{1}{2}b$ □

PRACTICE
4   Use the distributive property to combine like terms.

a. $3y + 8y - 7 + 2$ b. $6x - 3 - x - 3$ c. $\dfrac{3}{4}t - t$

d. $9y + 3.2y + 10 + 3$ e. $5z - 3z^4$

OBJECTIVE
3 Using the Distributive Property ▷

Simplifying expressions makes frequent use of the distributive property to also remove parentheses.

It may be helpful to study the examples below.

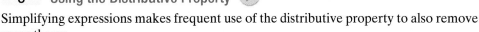

$$+(3a + 2) = +1(3a + 2) = +1(3a) + (+1)(2) = 3a + 2$$
means

$$-(3a + 2) = -1(3a + 2) = -1(3a) + (-1)(2) = -3a - 2$$
means

EXAMPLE 5   Find each product by using the distributive property to remove parentheses.

a. $5(3x + 2)$ b. $-2(y + 0.3z - 1)$ c. $-(9x + y - 2z + 6)$

Solution

a. $5(3x + 2) = 5 \cdot 3x + 5 \cdot 2$ Apply the distributive property.
$= 15x + 10$ Multiply.

(Continued on next page)

b. $-2(y + 0.3z - 1) = -2(y) + (-2)(0.3z) + (-2)(-1)$ Apply the distributive property.

$\qquad\qquad\qquad\quad = -2y - 0.6z + 2$ Multiply.

c. $-(9x + y - 2z + 6) = -1(9x + y - 2z + 6)$ Distribute -1

$\qquad\qquad\qquad\quad = -1(9x) - 1(y) - 1(-2z) - 1(6)$ over each term.

$\qquad\qquad\qquad\quad = -9x - y + 2z - 6$ ☐

PRACTICE

5   Find each product by using the distributive property to remove parentheses.

   a. $3(2x - 7)$ **b.** $-5(x - 0.5z - 5)$

   c. $-(2x - y + z - 2)$ ■

Helpful Hint

If a "$-$" sign precedes parentheses, the sign of each term inside the parentheses is changed when the distributive property is applied to remove parentheses.

Examples:

$$-(2x + 1) = -2x - 1 \qquad -(-5x + y - z) = 5x - y + z$$
$$-(x - 2y) = -x + 2y \qquad -(-3x - 4y - 1) = 3x + 4y + 1$$

When simplifying an expression containing parentheses, we often use the distributive property in both directions—first to remove parentheses and then again to combine any like terms.

EXAMPLE 6   Simplify each expression.

   a. $3(2x - 5) + 1$ **b.** $-2(4x + 7) - (3x - 1)$ **c.** $9 + 3(4x - 10)$

Solution

   a. $3(2x - 5) + 1 = 6x - 15 + 1$ Apply the distributive property.

$\qquad\qquad\qquad\quad = 6x - 14$ Combine like terms.

   b. $-2(4x + 7) - (3x - 1) = -8x - 14 - 3x + 1$ Apply the distributive property.

$\qquad\qquad\qquad\qquad\qquad = -11x - 13$ Combine like terms.

   c. $9 + 3(4x - 10) = 9 + 12x - 30$ Apply the distributive property.

$\qquad\qquad\qquad\quad = -21 + 12x$ Combine like terms.

$\qquad\qquad\qquad\quad$ or $12x - 21$ ☐

Helpful Hint

Don't forget to use the distributive property and multiply before adding or subtracting like terms.

PRACTICE

6   Simplify each expression.

   a. $4(9x + 1) + 6$ **b.** $-7(2x - 1) - (6 - 3x)$ **c.** $8 - 5(6x + 5)$ ■

EXAMPLE 7   Write the phrase below as an algebraic expression. Then simplify if possible.

     "Subtract $4x - 2$ from $2x - 3$."

Solution "Subtract $4x - 2$ **from** $2x - 3$" translates to $(2x - 3) - (4x - 2)$. Next, simplify the algebraic expression.

$$(2x - 3) - (4x - 2) = 2x - 3 - 4x + 2 \quad \text{Apply the distributive property.}$$
$$= -2x - 1 \quad \text{Combine like terms.} \quad ☐$$

PRACTICE
7 Write the phrase below as an algebraic expression. Then simplify if possible.

"Subtract $7x - 1$ from $2x + 3$." ■

OBJECTIVE

4 Writing Word Phrases as Algebraic Expressions ▶

Next, we practice writing word phrases as algebraic expressions.

EXAMPLE 8 Write the following phrases as algebraic expressions and simplify if possible. Let x represent the unknown number.

a. Twice a number, plus 6

b. The difference of a number and 4, divided by 7

c. Five added to triple the sum of a number and 1

d. The sum of twice a number, 3 times the number, and 5 times the number

Solution

a. In words: twice a number   plus   6

Translate: $2x$ $+$ 6

b. In words: the difference of a number and 4   divided by   7

Translate: $(x - 4)$ $\div$ 7 or $\dfrac{x - 4}{7}$

c. In words: five   added to   triple   the sum of a number and 1

Translate: 5 $+$ $3 \cdot$ $(x + 1)$

Next, we simplify this expression.

$$5 + 3(x + 1) = 5 + 3x + 3 \quad \text{Use the distributive property.}$$
$$= 8 + 3x \quad \text{Combine like terms.}$$

d. The phrase "the sum of" means that we add.

In words: twice a number   added to   3 times the number   added to   5 times the number

Translate: $2x$ $+$ $3x$ $+$ $5x$

Now let's simplify.

$$2x + 3x + 5x = 10x \quad \text{Combine like terms.} \qquad \square$$

PRACTICE
8 Write the following phrases as algebraic expressions and simplify if possible. Let x represent the unknown number.

a. Three added to double a number

b. Six subtracted from the sum of 5 and a number

c. Two times the sum of 3 and a number, increased by 4

d. The sum of a number, half the number, and 5 times the number ■

✓ Vocabulary, Readiness & Video Check

Use the choices below to fill in each blank. Some choices may be used more than once.

like	numerical coefficient	term	distributive
unlike	combine like terms	expression	

1. $23y^2 + 10y - 6$ is called a(n) _____ while $23y^2$, $10y$, and -6 are each called a(n) _____.

2. To simplify $x + 4x$, we _____.

3. The term y has an understood _____ of 1.

4. The terms $7z$ and $7y$ are _____ terms and the terms $7z$ and $-z$ are _____ terms.

5. For the term $-\frac{1}{2}xy^2$, the number $-\frac{1}{2}$ is the _____.

6. $5(3x - y)$ equals $15x - 5y$ by the _____ property.

Martin-Gay Interactive Videos

See Video 2.1 ⊙

Watch the section lecture video and answer the following questions.

OBJECTIVE 1
7. Example 7 shows two terms with exactly the same variables. Why are these terms not considered like terms?

OBJECTIVE 2
8. Example 8 shows us that when combining like terms, we are actually applying what property?

OBJECTIVE 3
9. The expression in Example 11 shows a minus sign before parentheses. When using the distributive property to multiply and remove parentheses, what number are we actually distributing to each term within the parentheses?

OBJECTIVE 4
10. Write the phrase given in Example 14, translate it into an algebraic expression, then simplify it. Why are we able to simplify it?

2.1 Exercise Set MyMathLab® ⊙

Identify the numerical coefficient of each term. See Example 1.

1. $-7y$
2. $3x$
3. x
4. $-y$
5. $17x^2y$
6. $1.2xyz$

Indicate whether the terms in each list are like or unlike. See Example 2.

7. $5y, -y$
8. $-2x^2y, 6xy$
9. $2z, 3z^2$
10. $ab^2, -7ab^2$
11. $8wz, \frac{1}{7}zw$
12. $7.4p^3q^2, 6.2p^3q^2r$

Simplify each expression by combining any like terms. See Examples 3 and 4.

13. $7y + 8y$
14. $3x + 2x$
15. $8w - w + 6w$
16. $c - 7c + 2c$
17. $3b - 5 - 10b - 4$
18. $6g + 5 - 3g - 7$
19. $m - 4m + 2m - 6$

20. $a + 3a - 2 - 7a$
21. $5g - 3 - 5 - 5g$
22. $8p + 4 - 8p - 15$
23. $6.2x - 4 + x - 1.2$
24. $7.9y - 0.7 - y + 0.2$
25. $6x - 5x + x - 3 + 2x$
26. $8h + 13h - 6 + 7h - h$
27. $7x^2 + 8x^2 - 10x^2$
28. $8x^3 + x^3 - 11x^3$
29. $6x + 0.5 - 4.3x - 0.4x + 3$
30. $0.4y - 6.7 + y - 0.3 - 2.6y$

Simplify each expression. First use the distributive property to remove any parentheses. See Examples 5 and 6.

31. $5(y - 4)$
32. $7(r - 3)$
33. $-2(x + 2)$
34. $-4(y + 6)$
35. $7(d - 3) + 10$
36. $9(z + 7) - 15$
37. $-5(2x - 3y + 6)$
38. $-2(4x - 3z - 1)$

39. $-(3x - 2y + 1)$

40. $-(y + 5z - 7)$

41. $5(x + 2) - (3x - 4)$

42. $4(2x - 3) - 2(x + 1)$

Write each of the following as an algebraic expression. Simplify if possible. See Example 7.

43. Add $6x + 7$ to $4x - 10$.

44. Add $3y - 5$ to $y + 16$.

45. Subtract $7x + 1$ from $3x - 8$.

46. Subtract $4x - 7$ from $12 + x$.

47. Subtract $5m - 6$ from $m - 9$.

48. Subtract $m - 3$ from $2m - 6$.

MIXED PRACTICE

Simplify each expression. See Examples 3 through 7.

49. $2k - k - 6$

50. $7c - 8 - c$

51. $-9x + 4x + 18 - 10x$

52. $5y - 14 + 7y - 20y$

53. $-4(3y - 4) + 12y$

54. $-3(2x + 5) - 6x$

55. $3(2x - 5) - 5(x - 4)$

56. $2(6x - 1) - (x - 7)$

57. $-2(3x - 4) + 7x - 6$

58. $8y - 2 - 3(y + 4)$

59. $5k - (3k - 10)$

60. $-11c - (4 - 2c)$

61. Subtract $6x - 1$ from $3x + 4$

62. Subtract $4 + 3y$ from $8 - 5y$

63. $3.4m - 4 - 3.4m - 7$

64. $2.8w - 0.9 - 0.5 - 2.8w$

65. $\frac{1}{3}(7y - 1) + \frac{1}{6}(4y + 7)$

66. $\frac{1}{5}(9y + 2) + \frac{1}{10}(2y - 1)$

67. $2 + 4(6x - 6)$

68. $8 + 4(3x - 4)$

69. $0.5(m + 2) + 0.4m$

70. $0.2(k + 8) - 0.1k$

71. $10 - 3(2x + 3y)$

72. $14 - 11(5m + 3n)$

73. $6(3x - 6) - 2(x + 1) - 17x$

74. $7(2x + 5) - 4(x + 2) - 20x$

75. $\frac{1}{2}(12x - 4) - (x + 5)$

76. $\frac{1}{3}(9x - 6) - (x - 2)$

TRANSLATING

Write each phrase as an algebraic expression and simplify if possible. Let x represent the unknown number. See Examples 7 and 8.

77. Twice a number, decreased by four

78. The difference of a number and two, divided by five

79. Seven added to double a number

80. Eight more than triple a number

81. Three-fourths of a number, increased by twelve

82. Eleven, increased by two-thirds of a number

83. The sum of 5 times a number and -2, added to 7 times the number

84. The sum of 3 times a number and 10, subtracted from 9 times the number

85. Eight times the sum of a number and six

86. Six times the difference of a number and five

87. Double a number, minus the sum of the number and ten

88. Half a number, minus the product of the number and eight

89. The sum of 2, three times a number, -9, and four times the number

90. The sum of twice a number, -1, five times the number, and -12

REVIEW AND PREVIEW

Evaluate the following expressions for the given values. See Section 1.7.

91. If $x = -1$ and $y = 3$, find $y - x^2$.

92. If $g = 0$ and $h = -4$, find $gh - h^2$.

93. If $a = 2$ and $b = -5$, find $a - b^2$.

94. If $x = -3$, find $x^3 - x^2 + 4$.

95. If $y = -5$ and $z = 0$, find $yz - y^2$.

96. If $x = -2$, find $x^3 - x^2 - x$.

CONCEPT EXTENSIONS

97. Recall that the perimeter of a figure is the total distance around the figure. Given the following rectangle, express the perimeter as an algebraic expression containing the variable x.

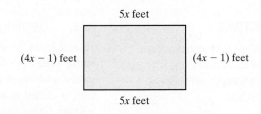

5x feet

(4x − 1) feet   (4x − 1) feet

5x feet

△ **98.** Given the following triangle, express its perimeter as an algebraic expression containing the variable x.

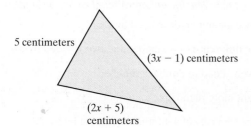

5 centimeters

$(3x - 1)$ centimeters

$(2x + 5)$ centimeters

Given the following two rules, determine whether each scale in Exercises 99 through 102 is balanced.

Rule 1:

1 cone balances 1 cube

Rule 2:

1 cylinder balances 2 cubes

99.

100.

101.

102.

Write each algebraic expression described.

103. Write an expression with 4 terms that simplifies to $3x - 4$.

104. Write an expression of the form _____ (_____ + _____) whose product is $6x + 24$.

105. To convert from feet to inches, we multiply by 12. For example, the number of inches in 2 feet is $12 \cdot 2$ inches. If one board has a length of $(x + 2)$ *feet* and a second board has a length of $(3x - 1)$ *inches*, express their total length in inches as an algebraic expression.

106. The value of 7 nickels is $5 \cdot 7$ cents. Likewise, the value of x nickels is $5x$ cents. If the money box in a drink machine contains x *nickels*, $3x$ *dimes*, and $(30x - 1)$ *quarters*, express their total value in cents as an algebraic expression.

107. In your own words, explain how to combine like terms.

108. Do like terms always contain the same numerical coefficients? Explain your answer.

For Exercises 109 through 114, see the example below.

Example

Simplify: $-3xy + 2x^2y - (2xy - 1)$

Solution

$$-3xy + 2x^2y - (2xy - 1)$$
$$= -3xy + 2x^2y - 2xy + 1 = -5xy + 2x^2y + 1$$

Simplify each expression.

109. $5b^2c^3 + 8b^3c^2 - 7b^3c^2$

110. $4m^4p^2 + m^4p^2 - 5m^2p^4$

111. $3x - (2x^2 - 6x) + 7x^2$

112. $9y^2 - (6xy^2 - 5y^2) - 8xy^2$

113. $-(2x^2y + 3z) + 3z - 5x^2y$

114. $-(7c^3d - 8c) - 5c - 4c^3d$

2.2   **The Addition Property of Equality**

OBJECTIVES

1 Define Linear Equations and Use the Addition Property of Equality to Solve Linear Equations.

2 Write Word Phrases as Algebraic Expressions.

OBJECTIVE

1   Defining Linear Equations and Using the Addition Property

Recall from Section 1.4 that an equation is a statement that two expressions have the same value. Also, a value of the variable that makes an equation a true statement is called a solution or root of the equation. The process of finding the solution of an equation is called **solving** the equation for the variable. In this section, we concentrate on solving **linear equations** in one variable.

> **Linear Equation in One Variable**
>
> **A linear equation in one variable** can be written in the form
>
> $$ax + b = c$$
>
> where a, b, and c are real numbers and $a \neq 0$.

Evaluating both sides of a linear equation for a given value of the variable, as we did in Section 1.4, can tell us whether that value is a solution, but we can't rely on evaluating both sides of an equation as our method of solving it.

Instead, to solve a linear equation in x, we write a series of simpler equations, all *equivalent* to the original equation, so that the final equation has the form

$$x = \textbf{number} \quad \textbf{or} \quad \textbf{number} = x$$

Equivalent equations are equations that have the same solution. This means that the "number" above is the solution of the original equation.

The first property of equality that helps us write simpler equivalent equations is the **addition property of equality.**

> **Addition Property of Equality**
>
> If a, b, and c are real numbers, then
>
> $$a = b \quad \text{and} \quad a + c = b + c$$
>
> are equivalent equations.

This property guarantees that adding the same number to both sides of an equation does not change the solution of the equation. Since subtraction is defined in terms of addition, we may also **subtract the same number from both sides** without changing the solution.

A good way to picture a true equation is as a balanced scale. Since it is balanced, each side of the scale weighs the same.

If the same weight is added to or subtracted from each side, the scale remains balanced.

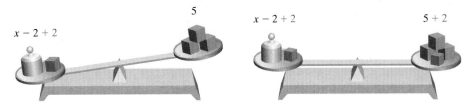

We use the addition property of equality to write equivalent equations until the variable is by itself on one side of the equation, and the equation looks like "$x = $ number" or "number $= x$."

EXAMPLE 1   Solve: $x - 7 = 10$ for x

Solution To solve for x, we want x alone on one side of the equation. To do this, we add 7 to both sides of the equation.

$$x - 7 = 10$$
$$x - 7 + 7 = 10 + 7 \quad \text{Add 7 to both sides.}$$
$$x = 17 \quad \text{Simplify.}$$

(Continued on next page)

The solution of the equation $x = 17$ is obviously 17. Since we are writing equivalent equations, the solution of the equation $x - 7 = 10$ is also 17.

Check: To check, replace x with 17 in the original equation.

$$x - 7 = 10$$
$$17 - 7 \stackrel{?}{=} 10 \quad \text{Replace } x \text{ with 17 in the original equation.}$$
$$10 = 10 \quad \text{True}$$

Since the statement is true, 17 is the solution, or we can say that the solution set is $\{17\}$. ☐

PRACTICE

1 Solve: $x + 3 = -5$ for x ■

✔ **CONCEPT CHECK**

Use the addition property to fill in the blanks so that the middle equation simplifies to the last equation.

$$x - 5 = 3$$
$$x - 5 + \underline{} = 3 + \underline{}$$
$$x = 8$$

EXAMPLE 2 Solve: $y + 0.6 = -1.0$ for y

Solution To get y alone on one side of the equation, subtract 0.6 from both sides of the equation.

$$y + 0.6 = -1.0$$
$$y + 0.6 - 0.6 = -1.0 - 0.6 \quad \text{Subtract 0.6 from both sides.}$$
$$y = -1.6 \quad \text{Combine like terms.}$$

Check: To check the proposed solution, -1.6, replace y with -1.6 in the original equation.

$$y + 0.6 = -1.0$$
$$-1.6 + 0.6 \stackrel{?}{=} -1.0 \quad \text{Replace } y \text{ with } -1.6 \text{ in the original equation.}$$
$$-1.0 = -1.0 \quad \text{True}$$

The solution is -1.6, or we can say that the solution set is $\{-1.6\}$. ☐

PRACTICE

2 Solve: $y - 0.3 = -2.1$ for y ■

EXAMPLE 3 Solve: $\dfrac{1}{2} = x - \dfrac{3}{4}$

Solution To get x alone, we add $\dfrac{3}{4}$ to both sides.

$$\frac{1}{2} = x - \frac{3}{4}$$
$$\frac{1}{2} + \frac{3}{4} = x - \frac{3}{4} + \frac{3}{4} \quad \text{Add } \frac{3}{4} \text{ to both sides.}$$
$$\frac{1}{2} \cdot \frac{2}{2} + \frac{3}{4} = x \quad \text{The LCD is 4.}$$
$$\frac{2}{4} + \frac{3}{4} = x \quad \text{Add the fractions.}$$
$$\frac{5}{4} = x$$

Check:

$$\frac{1}{2} = x - \frac{3}{4} \quad \text{Original equation}$$

$$\frac{1}{2} \stackrel{?}{=} \frac{5}{4} - \frac{3}{4} \quad \text{Replace } x \text{ with } \frac{5}{4}.$$

$$\frac{1}{2} \stackrel{?}{=} \frac{2}{4} \quad \text{Subtract.}$$

$$\frac{1}{2} = \frac{1}{2} \quad \text{True}$$

The solution is $\frac{5}{4}$.

PRACTICE
3   Solve: $\frac{2}{5} = x + \frac{3}{10}$

Helpful Hint

We may solve an equation so that the variable is alone on *either* side of the equation. For example, $\frac{5}{4} = x$ is equivalent to $x = \frac{5}{4}$.

EXAMPLE 4   Solve: $5t - 5 = 6t + 2$ for t

Solution To solve for t, we first want all terms containing t on one side of the equation and all other terms on the other side of the equation. To do this, first subtract $5t$ from both sides of the equation.

$$5t - 5 = 6t + 2$$

$$5t - 5 - 5t = 6t + 2 - 5t \quad \text{Subtract } 5t \text{ from both sides.}$$

$$-5 = t + 2 \quad \text{Combine like terms.}$$

Next, subtract 2 from both sides, and the variable t will be isolated.

$$-5 = t + 2$$

$$-5 - 2 = t + 2 - 2 \quad \text{Subtract 2 from both sides.}$$

$$-7 = t$$

Check: Check the solution, -7, in the original equation. The solution is -7.

PRACTICE
4   Solve: $4t + 7 = 5t - 3$ for t

Many times, it is best to simplify one or both sides of an equation before applying the addition property of equality.

EXAMPLE 5   Solve: $2x + 3x - 5 + 7 = 10x + 3 - 6x - 4$

Solution First we simplify both sides of the equation.

$$2x + 3x - 5 + 7 = 10x + 3 - 6x - 4$$
$$5x + 2 = 4x - 1 \quad \begin{array}{l}\text{Combine like terms on}\\ \text{each side of the equation.}\end{array}$$

Next, we want all terms with a variable on one side of the equation and all numbers on the other side.

$$5x + 2 - 4x = 4x - 1 - 4x \quad \text{Subtract } 4x \text{ from both sides.}$$

$$x + 2 = -1 \quad \text{Combine like terms.}$$

$$x + 2 - 2 = -1 - 2 \quad \text{Subtract 2 from both sides to get } x \text{ alone.}$$

$$x = -3 \quad \text{Combine like terms.}$$

(Continued on next page)

Check:

$$2x + 3x - 5 + 7 = 10x + 3 - 6x - 4$$ Original equation

$$2(-3) + 3(-3) - 5 + 7 \overset{?}{=} 10(-3) + 3 - 6(-3) - 4$$ Replace x with -3.

$$-6 - 9 - 5 + 7 \overset{?}{=} -30 + 3 + 18 - 4$$ Multiply.

$$-13 = -13$$ True

The solution is -3. ☐

PRACTICE
5   Solve: $8x - 5x - 3 + 9 = x + x + 3 - 7$ ■

If an equation contains parentheses, we use the distributive property to remove them, as before. Then we combine any like terms.

EXAMPLE 6   Solve: $6(2a - 1) - (11a + 6) = 7$

Solution $6(2a - 1) - 1(11a + 6) = 7$

$$6(2a) + 6(-1) - 1(11a) - 1(6) = 7$$ Apply the distributive property.

$$12a - 6 - 11a - 6 = 7$$ Multiply.

$$a - 12 = 7$$ Combine like terms.

$$a - 12 + 12 = 7 + 12$$ Add 12 to both sides.

$$a = 19$$ Simplify.

Check: Check by replacing a with 19 in the original equation. ☐

PRACTICE
6   Solve: $4(2a - 3) - (7a + 4) = 2$ ■

EXAMPLE 7   Solve: $3 - x = 7$

Solution First we subtract 3 from both sides.

$$3 - x = 7$$

$$3 - x - 3 = 7 - 3$$ Subtract 3 from both sides.

$$-x = 4$$ Simplify.

We have not yet solved for x since x is not alone. However, this equation does say that the opposite of x is 4. If the opposite of x is 4, then x is the opposite of 4, or $x = -4$. If $-x = 4$, then $x = -4$.

Check: $3 - x = 7$ Original equation

$$3 - (-4) \overset{?}{=} 7$$ Replace x with -4.

$$3 + 4 \overset{?}{=} 7$$ Add.

$$7 = 7$$ True

The solution is -4. ☐

PRACTICE
7   Solve: $12 - x = 20$ ■

OBJECTIVE
2   Writing Word Phrases as Algebraic Expressions ▶

Next, we practice writing word phrases as algebraic expressions.

EXAMPLE 8

a. The sum of two numbers is 8. If one number is 3, find the other number.

b. The sum of two numbers is 8. If one number is x, write an expression representing the other number.

c. An 8-foot board is cut into two pieces. If one piece is x feet, express the length of the other piece in terms of x.

Solution

a. If the sum of two numbers is 8 and one number is 3, we find the other number by subtracting 3 from 8. The other number is $8 - 3$ or 5.

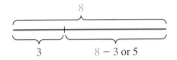

b. If the sum of two numbers is 8 and one number is x, we find the other number by subtracting x from 8. The other number is represented by $8 - x$.

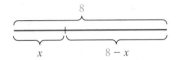

c. If an 8-foot board is cut into two pieces and one piece is x feet, we find the other length by subtracting x from 8. The other piece is $(8 - x)$ feet.

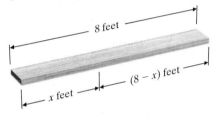

PRACTICE
8

a. The sum of two numbers is 9. If one number is 2, find the other number.

b. The sum of two numbers is 9. If one number is x, write an expression representing the other number.

c. A 9-foot rope is cut into two pieces. If one piece is x feet, express the length of the other piece in terms of x.

EXAMPLE 9   The Verrazano-Narrows Bridge in New York City is the longest suspension bridge in North America. The Golden Gate Bridge in San Francisco is 60 feet shorter than the Verrazano-Narrows Bridge. If the length of the Verrazano-Narrows Bridge is m feet, express the length of the Golden Gate Bridge as an algebraic expression in m. (*Source:* Survey of State Highway Engineers)

Solution Since the Golden Gate is 60 feet shorter than the Verrazano-Narrows Bridge, we have that its length is

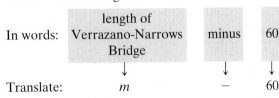

In words:	length of Verrazano-Narrows Bridge	minus	60
Translate:	m	$-$	60

The Golden Gate Bridge is $(m - 60)$ feet long.

PRACTICE
9

Currently, the fastest train in the world is the Shanghai Maglev. The French TGV is 67.2 mph slower than the Maglev. If the speed of the Maglev is s miles per hour, express the speed of the French TGV as an algebraic expression in s.

Vocabulary, Readiness & Video Check

Use the choices below to fill in each blank. Not all choices will be used.

addition	solving	expression	true
equivalent	equation	solution	false

1. The difference between an equation and an expression is that a(n) _____ contains an equal sign, whereas a(n) _____ does not.

2. _____ equations are equations that have the same solution.

3. A value of the variable that makes an equation a true statement is called a(n) _____ of the equation.

4. The process of finding the solution of an equation is called _____ the equation for the variable.

5. By the _____ property of equality, $x = -2$ and $x + 10 = -2 + 10$ are equivalent equations.

6. True or false: The equations $x = \dfrac{1}{2}$ and $\dfrac{1}{2} = x$ are equivalent equations. _____

Martin-Gay Interactive Videos

See Video 2.2 ◉

Watch the section lecture video and answer the following questions.

OBJECTIVE 1

7. Complete this statement based on the lecture given before ▤ Example 1. The addition property of equality means that if we have an equation, we can add the same real number to _____ of the equation and have an equivalent equation.

OBJECTIVE 1

8. What explanation is given during the solving of ▤ Example 1 to explain how and why we check the possible solution?

OBJECTIVE 2

9. Suppose we were to solve ▤ Example 8 again, this time letting the area of the Sahara Desert be x square miles. Use this to express the area of the Gobi Desert as an algebraic expression in x.

2.2 **Exercise Set** MyMathLab® ◉

Solve each equation. Check each solution. See Examples 1 through 3.

1. $x + 7 = 10$

2. $x + 14 = 25$

3. $x - 2 = -4$

4. $y - 9 = 1$

5. $-2 = t - 5$

6. $-17 = x + 3$

7. $r - 8.6 = -8.1$

8. $t - 9.2 = -6.8$

9. $\dfrac{3}{4} = \dfrac{1}{3} + f$

10. $\dfrac{3}{8} = c + \dfrac{1}{6}$

11. $5b - 0.7 = 6b$

12. $9x + 5.5 = 10x$

13. $7x - 3 = 6x$

14. $18x - 9 = 19x$

15. $y + \dfrac{11}{25} = -\dfrac{3}{25}$

16. $z + \dfrac{9}{19} = -\dfrac{2}{19}$

Solve each equation. Don't forget to first simplify each side of the equation if possible. Check each solution. See Examples 4 through 7.

17. $7x + 2x = 8x - 3$

18. $3n + 2n = 7 + 4n$

19. $\dfrac{5}{6}x + \dfrac{1}{6}x = -9$

20. $\dfrac{13}{11}y - \dfrac{2}{11}y = -3$

21. $2y + 10 = 5y - 4y$

22. $4x - 4 = 10x - 7x$

23. $-5(n - 2) = 8 - 4n$

24. $-4(z - 3) = 2 - 3z$

25. $\dfrac{3}{7}x + 2 = -\dfrac{4}{7}x - 5$

26. $\dfrac{1}{5}x - 1 = -\dfrac{4}{5}x - 13$

27. $5x - 6 = 6x - 5$

28. $2x + 7 = x - 10$

29. $8y + 2 - 6y = 3 + y - 10$

30. $4p - 11 - p = 2 + 2p - 20$

31. $-3(x - 4) = -4x$

32. $-2(x - 1) = -3x$

33. $\dfrac{3}{8}x - \dfrac{1}{6} = -\dfrac{5}{8}x - \dfrac{2}{3}$

34. $\dfrac{2}{5}x - \dfrac{1}{12} = -\dfrac{3}{5}x - \dfrac{3}{4}$

35. $2(x - 4) = x + 3$

36. $3(y + 7) = 2y - 5$

37. $3(n - 5) - (6 - 2n) = 4n$

38. $5(3 + z) - (8z + 9) = -4z$

39. $-2(x + 6) + 3(2x - 5) = 3(x - 4) + 10$

40. $-5(x + 1) + 4(2x - 3) = 2(x + 2) - 8$

MIXED PRACTICE

Solve. See Examples 1 through 7.

41. $-11 = 3 + x$

42. $-8 = 8 + z$

43. $x - \dfrac{2}{5} = -\dfrac{3}{20}$

44. $y - \dfrac{4}{7} = -\dfrac{3}{14}$

45. $3x - 6 = 2x + 5$

46. $7y + 2 = 6y + 2$

47. $13x - 9 + 2x - 5 = 12x - 1 + 2x$

48. $15x + 20 - 10x - 9 = 25x + 8 - 21x - 7$

49. $7(6 + w) = 6(2 + w)$

50. $6(5 + c) = 5(c - 4)$

51. $n + 4 = 3.6$

52. $m + 2 = 7.1$

53. $10 - (2x - 4) = 7 - 3x$

54. $15 - (6 - 7k) = 2 + 6k$

55. $\frac{1}{3} = x + \frac{2}{3}$

56. $\frac{1}{11} = y + \frac{10}{11}$

57. $-6.5 - 4x - 1.6 - 3x = -6x + 9.8$

58. $-1.4 - 7x - 3.6 - 2x = -8x + 4.4$

59. $-3\left(x - \frac{1}{4}\right) = -4x$

60. $-2\left(x - \frac{1}{7}\right) = -3x$

61. $7(m - 2) - 6(m + 1) = -20$

62. $-4(x - 1) - 5(2 - x) = -6$

63. $0.8t + 0.2(t - 0.4) = 1.75$

64. $0.6v + 0.4(0.3 + v) = 2.34$

TRANSLATING

See Examples 8 and 9.

65. Two numbers have a sum of 20. If one number is p, express the other number in terms of p.

66. Two numbers have a sum of 13. If one number is y, express the other number in terms of y.

67. A 10-foot board is cut into two pieces. If one piece is x feet long, express the other length in terms of x.

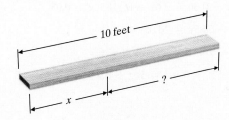

68. A 5-foot piece of string is cut into two pieces. If one piece is x feet long, express the other length in terms of x.

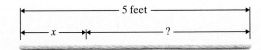

69. Two angles are *supplementary* if their sum is 180°. If one angle measures $x°$, express the measure of its supplement in terms of x.

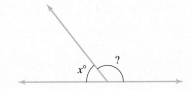

70. Two angles are *complementary* if their sum is 90°. If one angle measures $x°$, express the measure of its complement in terms of x.

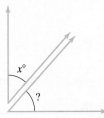

71. In a recent year, the number of graduate students at the University of Texas at Austin was approximately 28,000 fewer than the number of undergraduate students. If the number of undergraduate students was n, how many graduate students attend UT Austin? (*Source:* University of Texas at Austin)

72. The longest interstate highway in the U.S. is I-90, which connects Seattle, Washington, and Boston, Massachusetts. The second longest interstate highway, I-80 (connecting San Francisco, California, and Teaneck, New Jersey), is 178.5 miles shorter than I-90. If the length of I-80 is m miles, express the length of I-90 as an algebraic expression in m. (*Source:* U.S. Department of Transportation—Federal Highway Administration)

73. The area of the Sahara Desert in Africa is 7 times the area of the Gobi Desert in Asia. If the area of the Gobi Desert is x square miles, express the area of the Sahara Desert as an algebraic expression in x.

74. The largest meteorite in the world is the Hoba West located in Namibia. Its weight is 3 times the weight of the Armanty meteorite located in Outer Mongolia. If the weight of the Armanty meteorite is y kilograms, express the weight of the Hoba West meteorite as an algebraic expression in y.

REVIEW AND PREVIEW

Find the reciprocal or multiplicative inverse of each. See Section 1.7.

75. $\dfrac{5}{8}$ **76.** $\dfrac{7}{6}$ **77.** 2

78. 5 **79.** $-\dfrac{1}{9}$ **80.** $-\dfrac{3}{5}$

Perform each indicated operation and simplify. See Section 1.7

81. $\dfrac{3x}{3}$ **82.** $\dfrac{-2y}{-2}$ **83.** $-5\left(-\dfrac{1}{5}y\right)$

84. $7\left(\dfrac{1}{7}r\right)$ **85.** $\dfrac{3}{5}\left(\dfrac{5}{3}x\right)$ **86.** $\dfrac{9}{2}\left(\dfrac{2}{9}x\right)$

CONCEPT EXTENSIONS

△ **87.** The sum of the angles of a triangle is 180°. If one angle of a triangle measures $x°$ and a second angle measures $(2x + 7)°$, express the measure of the third angle in terms of x. Simplify the expression.

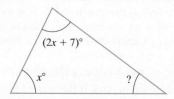

△ **88.** A quadrilateral is a four-sided figure like the one shown below. The sum of the angles of a quadrilateral is 360°. If one angle measures $x°$, a second angle measures $3x°$, and a third angle measures $5x°$, express the measure of the fourth angle in terms of x. Simplify the expression.

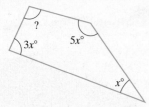

89. Write two terms whose sum is $-3x$.

90. Write four terms whose sum is $2y - 6$.

91. In your own words, explain what is meant by the solution of an equation.

92. In your own words, explain how to check a solution of an equation.

A nurse's aide has two patients that are each to consume 1000 ml of fluid for the night. Use this information for Exercises 93 and 94.

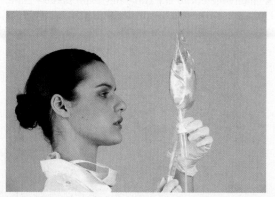

93. Patient intake thus far:

200 ml, 150 ml, and 400 ml.

To determine the remaining fluid needed for this patient, solve for x: $200 + 150 + 400 + x = 1000$

94. Patient intake thus far:

100 ml, 250 ml, and 500 ml.

To determine the remaining fluid needed for this patient, solve for x: $100 + 250 + 500 + x = 1000$

95. Let $x = 1$ and then $x = 2$ in the equation $x + 5 = x + 6$. Is either number a solution? How many solutions do you think this equation has? Explain your answer.

96. Let $x = 1$ and then $x = 2$ in the equation $x + 3 = x + 3$. Is either number a solution? How many solutions do you think this equation has? Explain your answer.

Use the addition property to fill in numbers between the parentheses so that the middle equation simplifies to the last equation. See the Concept Check in this section.

97.
$$x - 4 = -9$$
$$x - 4 + (\ \ ) = -9 + (\ \ )$$
$$x = -5$$

98.
$$a + 9 = 15$$
$$a + 9 + (\ \ ) = 15 + (\ \ )$$
$$a = 6$$

Fill in the blanks with numbers of your choice so that each equation has the given solution. Note: Each blank may be replaced with a different number.

99. ____ $+ x =$ ____; Solution: -3

100. $x -$ ____ $=$ ____; Solution: -10

Use a calculator to determine whether the given value is a solution of the given equation.

101. $1.23x - 0.06 = 2.6x - 0.1285$; $x = 0.05$

102. $8.13 + 5.85y = 20.05y - 8.91$; $y = 1.2$

103. $3(a + 4.6) = 5a + 2.5$; $a = 6.3$

104. $7(z - 1.7) + 9.5 = 5(z + 3.2) - 9.2$; $z = 4.8$

2.3 | The Multiplication Property of Equality

OBJECTIVE

1 Using the Multiplication Property

As useful as the addition property of equality is, it cannot help us solve every type of linear equation in one variable. For example, adding or subtracting a value on both sides of the equation does not help solve

$$\frac{5}{2}x = 15.$$

Instead, we apply another important property of equality, the **multiplication property of equality.**

Multiplication Property of Equality

If a, b, and c are real numbers and $c \neq 0$, then

$$a = b \qquad \text{and} \qquad ac = bc$$

are equivalent equations.

This property guarantees that multiplying both sides of an equation by the same nonzero number does not change the solution of the equation. Since division is defined in terms of multiplication, we may also **divide both sides of the equation by the same nonzero number** without changing the solution.

Picturing again our balanced scale, if we multiply or divide the weight on each side by the same nonzero number, the scale (or equation) remains balanced.

$2x$ $\qquad\qquad$ 6 $\qquad\qquad$ $\frac{2x}{2}$ or x $\qquad\qquad$ $\frac{6}{2}$ or 3

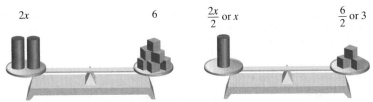

EXAMPLE I   Solve: $\frac{5}{2}x = 15$ for x

Solution To get x alone, multiply both sides of the equation by the reciprocal of $\frac{5}{2}$, which is $\frac{2}{5}$.

$$\frac{5}{2}x = 15$$

$$\frac{2}{5} \cdot \frac{5}{2}x = \frac{2}{5} \cdot 15 \qquad \text{Multiply both sides by } \frac{2}{5}.$$

$$\left(\frac{2}{5} \cdot \frac{5}{2}\right)x = \frac{2}{5} \cdot 15 \qquad \text{Apply the associative property.}$$

$$1x = 6 \qquad \text{Simplify.}$$

or

$$x = 6$$

Check: Replace x with 6 in the original equation.

$$\frac{5}{2}x = 15 \qquad \text{Original equation}$$

$$\frac{5}{2}(6) \stackrel{?}{=} 15 \qquad \text{Replace } x \text{ with 6.}$$

$$15 = 15 \qquad \text{True}$$

(Continued on next page)

The solution is 6, or we say that the solution set is $\{6\}$.

PRACTICE

1   Solve: $\dfrac{4}{5}x = 16$ for x

In the equation $\dfrac{5}{2}x = 15$, $\dfrac{5}{2}$ is the coefficient of x. When the coefficient of x is a *fraction,* we will get x alone by multiplying by the reciprocal. When the coefficient of x is an integer or a decimal, it is usually more convenient to divide both sides by the coefficient. (Dividing by a number is, of course, the same as multiplying by the reciprocal of the number.)

EXAMPLE 2   Solve: $-3x = 33$

Solution Recall that $-3x$ means $-3 \cdot x$. To get x alone, we divide both sides by the coefficient of x, that is, -3.

$$-3x = 33$$

$$\frac{-3x}{-3} = \frac{33}{-3} \quad \text{Divide both sides by } -3.$$

$$1x = -11 \quad \text{Simplify.}$$

$$x = -11$$

Check:

$$-3x = 33 \quad \text{Original equation}$$

$$-3(-11) \overset{?}{=} 33 \quad \text{Replace } x \text{ with } -11.$$

$$33 = 33 \quad \text{True}$$

The solution is -11, or the solution set is $\{-11\}$.

PRACTICE

2   Solve: $8x = -96$

EXAMPLE 3   Solve: $\dfrac{y}{7} = 20$

Solution Recall that $\dfrac{y}{7} = \dfrac{1}{7}y$. To get y alone, we multiply both sides of the equation by 7, the reciprocal of $\dfrac{1}{7}$.

$$\frac{y}{7} = 20$$

$$\frac{1}{7}y = 20$$

$$7 \cdot \frac{1}{7}y = 7 \cdot 20 \quad \text{Multiply both sides by 7.}$$

$$1y = 140 \quad \text{Simplify.}$$

$$y = 140$$

Check:

$$\frac{y}{7} = 20 \quad \text{Original equation}$$

$$\frac{140}{7} \overset{?}{=} 20 \quad \text{Replace } y \text{ with 140.}$$

$$20 = 20 \quad \text{True}$$

The solution is 140.

PRACTICE

3   Solve: $\dfrac{x}{5} = 13$

EXAMPLE 4   Solve: $3.1x = 4.96$

Solution

$$3.1x = 4.96$$

$$\frac{3.1x}{3.1} = \frac{4.96}{3.1} \quad \text{Divide both sides by 3.1.}$$

$$1x = 1.6 \quad \text{Simplify.}$$

$$x = 1.6$$

Check: Check by replacing x with 1.6 in the original equation. The solution is 1.6.   □

PRACTICE
4   Solve: $2.7x = 4.05$ ■

EXAMPLE 5   Solve: $-\frac{2}{3}x = -\frac{5}{2}$

Solution   To get x alone, we multiply both sides of the equation by $-\frac{3}{2}$, the reciprocal of the coefficient of x.

$$-\frac{2}{3}x = -\frac{5}{2}$$

$$-\frac{3}{2} \cdot -\frac{2}{3}x = -\frac{3}{2} \cdot -\frac{5}{2} \quad \text{Multiply both sides by } -\frac{3}{2}, \text{ the reciprocal of } -\frac{2}{3}.$$

$$x = \frac{15}{4} \quad \text{Simplify.}$$

> **Helpful Hint**
> Don't forget to multiply _both_ sides by $-\frac{3}{2}$.

Check: Check by replacing x with $\frac{15}{4}$ in the original equation. The solution is $\frac{15}{4}$.   □

PRACTICE
5   Solve: $-\frac{5}{3}x = \frac{4}{7}$ ■

OBJECTIVE
2   Using Both the Addition and Multiplication Properties

We are now ready to combine the skills learned in the last section with the skills learned from this section to solve equations by applying more than one property.

EXAMPLE 6   Solve: $-z - 4 = 6$

Solution   First, get $-z$, the term containing the variable, alone on one side of the equation. To do so, add 4 to both sides of the equation.

$$-z - 4 + 4 = 6 + 4 \quad \text{Add 4 to both sides.}$$

$$-z = 10 \quad \text{Simplify.}$$

Next, recall that $-z$ means $-1 \cdot z$. To get z alone, either multiply or divide both sides of the equation by -1. In this example, we divide.

$$-z = 10$$

$$\frac{-z}{-1} = \frac{10}{-1} \quad \text{Divide both sides by the coefficient } -1.$$

$$z = -10 \quad \text{Simplify.}$$

(Continued on next page)

Check: To check, replace z with -10 in the original equation. The solution is -10. ☐

PRACTICE
6 Solve: $-y + 3 = -8$ ■

Don't forget to simplify one or both sides of an equation if possible.

EXAMPLE 7 Solve: $12a - 8a = 10 + 2a - 13 - 7$

Solution First, simplify both sides of the equation by combining like terms.

$$12a - 8a = 10 + 2a - 13 - 7$$
$$4a = 2a - 10 \qquad \text{Combine like terms.}$$

To get all terms containing a variable on one side, subtract $2a$ from both sides.

$$4a - 2a = 2a - 10 - 2a \qquad \text{Subtract } 2a \text{ from both sides.}$$
$$2a = -10 \qquad \text{Simplify.}$$
$$\frac{2a}{2} = \frac{-10}{2} \qquad \text{Divide both sides by 2.}$$
$$a = -5 \qquad \text{Simplify.}$$

Check: Check by replacing a with -5 in the original equation. The solution is -5. ☐

PRACTICE
7 Solve: $6b - 11b = 18 + 2b - 6 + 9$ ■

EXAMPLE 8 Solve: $7x - 3 = 5x + 9$

Solution To get x alone on one side, let's first use the addition property to get variable terms on one side of the equation and numbers on the other side. One way to get variable terms on one side of this equation is to subtract $5x$ from both sides.

$$7x - 3 = 5x + 9$$
$$7x - 3 - 5x = 5x + 9 - 5x \qquad \text{Subtract } 5x \text{ from both sides.}$$
$$2x - 3 = 9 \qquad \text{Simplify.}$$

Now, to get numbers on the other side, let's add 3 to both sides.

$$2x - 3 + 3 = 9 + 3 \qquad \text{Add 3 to both sides.}$$
$$2x = 12 \qquad \text{Simplify.}$$

Use the multiplication property to get x alone.

$$\frac{2x}{2} = \frac{12}{2} \qquad \text{Divide both sides by 2.}$$
$$x = 6 \qquad \text{Simplify.}$$

Check: To check, replace x with 6 in the original equation to see that a true statement results. The solution is 6. ☐

PRACTICE
8 Solve: $10x - 4 = 7x + 14$ ■

If an equation has parentheses, don't forget to use the distributive property to remove them. Then combine any like terms.

EXAMPLE 9   Solve: $5(2x + 3) = -1 + 7$

Solution

$$5(2x + 3) = -1 + 7$$
$$5(2x) + 5(3) = -1 + 7 \quad \text{Apply the distributive property.}$$
$$10x + 15 = 6 \quad \text{Multiply and write } -1 + 7 \text{ as } 6.$$
$$10x + 15 - 15 = 6 - 15 \quad \text{Subtract 15 from both sides.}$$
$$10x = -9 \quad \text{Simplify.}$$
$$\frac{10x}{10} = -\frac{9}{10} \quad \text{Divide both sides by 10.}$$
$$x = -\frac{9}{10} \quad \text{Simplify.}$$

Check: To check, replace x with $-\frac{9}{10}$ in the original equation to see that a true statement results. The solution is $-\frac{9}{10}$. ☐

PRACTICE
9   Solve: $4(3x - 2) = -1 + 4$ ◼

OBJECTIVE
3   Writing Word Phrases as Algebraic Expressions

Next, we continue to sharpen our problem-solving skills by writing word phrases as algebraic expressions.

EXAMPLE 10   If x is the first of three consecutive integers, express the sum of the three integers in terms of x. Simplify if possible.

Solution   An example of three consecutive integers is

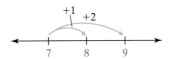

The second consecutive integer is always 1 more than the first, and the third consecutive integer is 2 more than the first. If x is the first of three consecutive integers, the three consecutive integers are

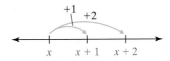

Their sum is

In words:	first integer	+	second integer	+	third integer
	↓		↓		↓
Translate:	x	+	$(x + 1)$	+	$(x + 2)$

which simplifies to $3x + 3$. ☐

PRACTICE
10   If x is the first of three consecutive *even* integers, express their sum in terms of x. ◼

Below are examples of consecutive even and odd integers.

Consecutive Even Integers:

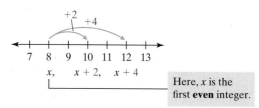

Here, x is the
first **even** integer.

Consecutive Odd Integers:

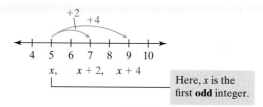

Here, x is the
first **odd** integer.

> **Helpful Hint**
> If x is an odd integer, then $x + 2$ is the next odd integer. This 2 simply means that odd integers are always 2 units from each other. (The same is true for even integers. They are always 2 units from each other.)
>
>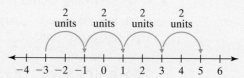

✓ Vocabulary, Readiness & Video Check

Use the choices below to fill in each blank. Not all choices will be used.

true	addition	false	multiplication

1. By the _____ property of equality, $y = \dfrac{1}{2}$ and $5 \cdot y = 5 \cdot \dfrac{1}{2}$ are equivalent equations.

2. True or false: The equations $\dfrac{z}{4} = 10$ and $4 \cdot \dfrac{z}{4} = 10$ are equivalent equations. _____

3. True or false: The equations $-7x = 30$ and $\dfrac{-7x}{-7} = \dfrac{30}{7}$ are equivalent equations. _____

4. By the _____ property of equality, $9x = -63$ and $\dfrac{9x}{9} = \dfrac{-63}{9}$ are equivalent equations.

Martin-Gay Interactive Videos

See Video 2.3 ▸

Watch the section lecture video and answer the following questions.

OBJECTIVE 1

5. Complete this statement based on the lecture given before ▦ Example 1. We can multiply both sides of an equation by the ____ nonzero number and have an equivalent equation.

OBJECTIVE 2

6. Both the addition and multiplication properties of equality are used to solve ▦ Examples 4–6. In each of these exercises, what property is applied first? What property is applied last? What conclusion, if any, can you make?

OBJECTIVE 3

7. Let x be the first of four consecutive integers, as in ▦ Example 8. Now express the sum of the second integer and the fourth integer as an algebraic expression containing x.

2.3   Exercise Set   MyMathLab®

Solve each equation. Check each solution. See Examples 1 through 5.

1. $-5x = -20$ **2.** $-7x = -49$

3. $3x = 0$ **4.** $2x = 0$

5. $-x = -12$ **6.** $-y = 8$

7. $\frac{2}{3}x = -8$ **8.** $\frac{3}{4}n = -15$

9. $\frac{1}{2} = \frac{1}{6}d$ **10.** $\frac{1}{4} = \frac{1}{8}v$

11. $\frac{a}{2} = 1$ **12.** $\frac{d}{15} = 2$

13. $\frac{k}{-7} = 0$ **14.** $\frac{f}{-5} = 0$

15. $10.71 = 1.7x$ **16.** $19.55 = 8.5y$

Solve each equation. Check each solution. See Examples 6 and 7.

17. $2x - 4 = 16$ **18.** $3x - 1 = 26$

19. $-x + 2 = 22$ **20.** $-x + 4 = -24$

21. $6a + 3 = 3$ **22.** $8t + 5 = 5$

23. $\frac{x}{3} - 2 = -5$ **24.** $\frac{b}{4} - 1 = -7$

25. $6z - z = -2 + 2z - 1 - 6$

26. $4a + a = -1 + 3a - 1 - 2$

27. $1 = 0.4x - 0.6x - 5$ **28.** $19 = 0.4x - 0.9x - 6$

29. $\frac{2}{3}y - 11 = -9$ **30.** $\frac{3}{5}x - 14 = -8$

31. $\frac{3}{4}t - \frac{1}{2} = \frac{1}{3}$ **32.** $\frac{2}{7}z - \frac{1}{5} = \frac{1}{2}$

Solve each equation. See Examples 8 and 9.

33. $8x + 20 = 6x + 18$ **34.** $11x + 13 = 9x + 9$

35. $3(2x + 5) = -18 + 9$ **36.** $2(4x + 1) = -12 + 6$

37. $2x - 5 = 20x + 4$ **38.** $6x - 4 = -2x - 10$

39. $2 + 14 = -4(3x - 4)$ **40.** $8 + 4 = -6(5x - 2)$

41. $-6y - 3 = -5y - 7$ **42.** $-17z - 4 = -16z - 20$

43. $\frac{1}{2}(2x - 1) = -\frac{1}{7} - \frac{3}{7}$ **44.** $\frac{1}{3}(3x - 1) = -\frac{1}{10} - \frac{2}{10}$

45. $-10z - 0.5 = -20z + 1.6$ **46.** $-14y - 1.8 = -24y + 3.9$

47. $-4x + 20 = 4x - 20$ **48.** $-3x + 15 = 3x - 15$

MIXED PRACTICE

See Examples 1 through 9.

49. $42 = 7x$ **50.** $81 = 3x$

51. $4.4 = -0.8x$ **52.** $6.3 = -0.6x$

53. $6x + 10 = -20$ **54.** $10y + 15 = -5$

55. $5 - 0.3k = 5$ **56.** $2 - 0.4p = 2$

57. $13x - 5 = 11x - 11$ **58.** $20x - 20 = 16x - 40$

59. $9(3x + 1) = 4x - 5x$ **60.** $7(2x + 1) = 18x - 19x$

61. $-\frac{3}{7}p = -2$ **62.** $-\frac{4}{5}r = -5$

63. $-\frac{4}{3}x = 12$ **64.** $-\frac{10}{3}x = 30$

65. $-2x - \frac{1}{2} = \frac{7}{2}$ **66.** $-3n - \frac{1}{3} = \frac{8}{3}$

67. $10 = 2x - 1$ **68.** $12 = 3j - 4$

69. $10 - 3x - 6 - 9x = 7$ **70.** $12x + 30 + 8x - 6 = 10$

71. $z - 5z = 7z - 9 - z$ **72.** $t - 6t = -13 + t - 3t$

73. $-x - \frac{4}{5} = x + \frac{1}{2} + \frac{2}{5}$ **74.** $x + \frac{3}{7} = -x + \frac{1}{3} + \frac{4}{7}$

75. $-15 + 37 = -2(x + 5)$ **76.** $-19 + 74 = -5(x + 3)$

TRANSLATING

Write each algebraic expression described. Simplify if possible. See Example 10.

77. If x represents the first of two consecutive odd integers, express the sum of the two integers in terms of x.

78. If x is the first of four consecutive even integers, write their sum as an algebraic expression in x.

79. If x is the first of four consecutive integers, express the sum of the first integer and the third integer as an algebraic expression containing the variable x.

80. If x is the first of two consecutive integers, express the sum of 20 and the second consecutive integer as an algebraic expression containing the variable x.

81. Classrooms on one side of the science building are all numbered with consecutive even integers. If the first room on this side of the building is numbered x, write an expression in x for the sum of five classroom numbers in a row. Then simplify this expression.

82. Two sides of a quadrilateral have the same length, x, an odd integer. The other two sides have the same length, both being the next consecutive odd integer. Write the sum of these lengths. Then simplify this expression.

REVIEW AND PREVIEW

Simplify each expression. See Section 2.1.

83. $5x + 2(x - 6)$

84. $-7y + 2y - 3(y + 1)$

85. $6(2z + 4) + 20$

86. $8(z - 6) + 7z - 1$

87. $-(3a - 3) + 2a - 6$

88. $-(x - 1) + x$

Insert $<$, $>$, or $=$ in the appropriate space to make each statement true. See Sections 1.2 and 1.7.

89. $(-3)^2 \quad -3^2$

90. $(-2)^4 \quad -2^4$

91. $(-2)^3 \quad -2^3$

92. $(-4)^3 \quad -4^3$

CONCEPT EXTENSIONS

For Exercises 93 and 94, fill in the blank with a number so that each equation has the given solution.

93. $6x = $ ____; solution: -8

94. ____ $x = 10$; solution: $\dfrac{1}{2}$

95. The equation $3x + 6 = 2x + 10 + x - 4$ is true for all real numbers. Substitute a few real numbers for x to see that this is so and then try solving the equation. Describe what happens.

96. The equation $6x + 2 - 2x = 4x + 1$ has no solution. Try solving this equation for x and describe what happens.

97. From the results of Exercises 95 and 96, when do you think an equation has all real numbers as its solutions?

98. From the results of Exercises 95 and 96, when do you think an equation has no solution?

99. A licensed nurse practitioner is instructed to give a patient 2100 milligrams of an antibiotic over a period of 36 hours. If the antibiotic is to be given every 4 hours starting immediately, how much antibiotic should be given in each dose? To answer this question, solve the equation $9x = 2100$.

100. Suppose you are a pharmacist and a customer asks you the following question. His child is to receive 13.5 milliliters of a nausea medicine over a period of 54 hours. If the nausea medicine is to be administered every 6 hours starting immediately, how much medicine should be given in each dose? (*Hint:* See the last sentence for Exercise 99.)

Solve each equation.

101. $-3.6x = 10.62$

102. $4.95y = -31.185$

103. $7x - 5.06 = -4.92$

104. $0.06y + 2.63 = 2.5562$

2.4 | Solving Linear Equations

OBJECTIVES

1 Apply a General Strategy for Solving a Linear Equation.

2 Solve Equations Containing Fractions.

3 Solve Equations Containing Decimals.

4 Recognize Identities and Equations with No Solution.

OBJECTIVE

1 Applying a General Strategy for Solving a Linear Equation

We now present a general strategy for solving linear equations. One new piece of strategy is a suggestion to "clear an equation of fractions" as a first step. Doing so makes the equation less tedious, since operating on integers is usually more convenient than operating on fractions.

Solving Linear Equations in One Variable

Step 1. Multiply on both sides by the least common denominator (LCD) to clear the equation of fractions if they occur.

Step 2. Use the distributive property to remove parentheses if they occur.

Step 3. Simplify each side of the equation by combining like terms.

Step 4. Get all variable terms on one side and all numbers on the other side by using the addition property of equality.

Step 5. Get the variable alone by using the multiplication property of equality.

Step 6. Check the solution by substituting it into the original equation.

EXAMPLE 1   Solve: $4(2x - 3) + 7 = 3x + 5$

Solution   There are no fractions, so we begin with Step 2.

$$4(2x - 3) + 7 = 3x + 5$$

Step 2. $8x - 12 + 7 = 3x + 5$ Apply the distributive property.

Step 3. $8x - 5 = 3x + 5$ Combine like terms.

Step 4.   Get all variable terms on the same side of the equation by subtracting $3x$ from both sides, then adding 5 to both sides.

$$8x - 5 - 3x = 3x + 5 - 3x$$ Subtract $3x$ from both sides.

$$5x - 5 = 5$$ Simplify.

$$5x - 5 + 5 = 5 + 5$$ Add 5 to both sides.

$$5x = 10$$ Simplify.

Step 5.   Use the multiplication property of equality to get x alone.

$$\frac{5x}{5} = \frac{10}{5}$$ Divide both sides by 5.

$$x = 2$$ Simplify.

Step 6.   Check.

Helpful Hint
When checking solutions, remember to use the original written equation.

$$4(2x - 3) + 7 = 3x + 5$$ Original equation

$$4[2(2) - 3] + 7 \stackrel{?}{=} 3(2) + 5$$ Replace x with 2.

$$4(4 - 3) + 7 \stackrel{?}{=} 6 + 5$$

$$4(1) + 7 \stackrel{?}{=} 11$$

$$4 + 7 \stackrel{?}{=} 11$$

$$11 = 11$$ True

The solution is 2 or the solution set is $\{2\}$.

PRACTICE
1   Solve: $2(4a - 9) + 3 = 5a - 6$

EXAMPLE 2   Solve: $8(2 - t) = -5t$

Solution   First, we apply the distributive property.

$$8(2 - t) = -5t$$

Step 2. $16 - 8t = -5t$ Use the distributive property.

Step 4. $16 - 8t + 8t = -5t + 8t$ To get variable terms on one side, add $8t$ to both sides.

$$16 = 3t$$ Combine like terms.

Step 5. $\dfrac{16}{3} = \dfrac{3t}{3}$ Divide both sides by 3.

$$\frac{16}{3} = t$$ Simplify.

Step 6.   Check.

$$8(2 - t) = -5t$$ Original equation

$$8\left(2 - \frac{16}{3}\right) \stackrel{?}{=} -5\left(\frac{16}{3}\right)$$ Replace t with $\frac{16}{3}$.

$$8\left(\frac{6}{3} - \frac{16}{3}\right) \stackrel{?}{=} -\frac{80}{3}$$ The LCD is 3.

(Continued on next page)

$$8\left(-\frac{10}{3}\right) \overset{?}{=} -\frac{80}{3} \quad \text{Subtract fractions.}$$

$$-\frac{80}{3} = -\frac{80}{3} \quad \text{True}$$

The solution is $\frac{16}{3}$.

PRACTICE

2 Solve: $7(x - 3) = -6x$

OBJECTIVE

2 Solving Equations Containing Fractions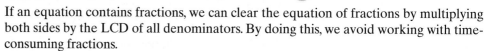

If an equation contains fractions, we can clear the equation of fractions by multiplying both sides by the LCD of all denominators. By doing this, we avoid working with time-consuming fractions.

EXAMPLE 3 Solve: $\frac{x}{2} - 1 = \frac{2}{3}x - 3$

Solution We begin by clearing fractions. To do this, we multiply both sides of the equation by the LCD of 2 and 3, which is 6.

$$\frac{x}{2} - 1 = \frac{2}{3}x - 3$$

Step 1.
$$6\left(\frac{x}{2} - 1\right) = 6\left(\frac{2}{3}x - 3\right) \quad \text{Multiply both sides by the LCD, 6.}$$

Step 2.
$$6\left(\frac{x}{2}\right) - 6(1) = 6\left(\frac{2}{3}x\right) - 6(3) \quad \text{Apply the distributive property.}$$

$$3x - 6 = 4x - 18 \quad \text{Simplify.}$$

Helpful Hint

Don't forget to multiply _each_ term by the LCD.

There are no longer grouping symbols and no like terms on either side of the equation, so we continue with Step 4.

Step 4.
$$3x - 6 = 4x - 18$$
$$3x - 6 - 3x = 4x - 18 - 3x \quad \text{To get variable terms on one side, subtract } 3x \text{ from both sides.}$$
$$-6 = x - 18 \quad \text{Simplify.}$$
$$-6 + 18 = x - 18 + 18 \quad \text{Add 18 to both sides.}$$
$$12 = x \quad \text{Simplify.}$$

Step 5. The variable is now alone, so there is no need to apply the multiplication property of equality.

Step 6. Check.

$$\frac{x}{2} - 1 = \frac{2}{3}x - 3 \quad \text{Original equation}$$

$$\frac{12}{2} - 1 \overset{?}{=} \frac{2}{3} \cdot 12 - 3 \quad \text{Replace } x \text{ with 12.}$$

$$6 - 1 \overset{?}{=} 8 - 3 \quad \text{Simplify.}$$

$$5 = 5 \quad \text{True}$$

The solution is 12.

PRACTICE

3 Solve: $\frac{3}{5}x - 2 = \frac{2}{3}x - 1$

EXAMPLE 4   Solve: $\dfrac{2(a+3)}{3} = 6a + 2$

Solution We clear the equation of fractions first.

$$\frac{2(a+3)}{3} = 6a + 2$$

Step 1. $3 \cdot \dfrac{2(a+3)}{3} = 3(6a+2)$ Clear the fraction by multiplying both sides by the LCD, 3.

$$2(a+3) = 3(6a+2)$$

Step 2. Next, we use the distributive property and remove parentheses.

$$2a + 6 = 18a + 6 \qquad \text{Apply the distributive property.}$$

Step 4. $2a + 6 - 6 = 18a + 6 - 6$ Subtract 6 from both sides.

$$2a = 18a$$

$$2a - 18a = 18a - 18a \qquad \text{Subtract } 18a \text{ from both sides.}$$

$$-16a = 0$$

Step 5. $\dfrac{-16a}{-16} = \dfrac{0}{-16}$ Divide both sides by -16.

$$a = 0 \qquad \text{Write the fraction in simplest form.}$$

Step 6. To check, replace a with 0 in the original equation. The solution is 0.

PRACTICE 4   Solve: $\dfrac{4(y+3)}{3} = 5y - 7$

> **Helpful Hint**
> Remember: When solving an equation, it makes no difference on which side of the equation variable terms lie. Just make sure that constant terms (number terms) lie on the other side.

OBJECTIVE
3   Solving Equations Containing Decimals

When solving a problem about money, you may need to solve an equation containing decimals. If you choose, you may multiply to clear the equation of decimals.

EXAMPLE 5   Solve: $0.25x + 0.10(x - 3) = 0.05(22)$

Solution First we clear this equation of decimals by multiplying both sides of the equation by 100. Recall that multiplying a decimal number by 100 has the effect of moving the decimal point 2 places to the right.

$$0.25x + 0.10(x - 3) = 0.05(22)$$

> **Helpful Hint**
> By the distributive property, 0.10 is multiplied by x and -3. Thus to multiply each term here by 100, we only need to multiply 0.10 by 100.

Step 1. $0.25x + 0.10(x - 3) = 0.05(22)$ Multiply both sides by 100.

$$25x + 10(x - 3) = 5(22)$$

Step 2. $25x + 10x - 30 = 110$ Apply the distributive property.

Step 3. $35x - 30 = 110$ Combine like terms.

Step 4. $35x - 30 + 30 = 110 + 30$ Add 30 to both sides.

$$35x = 140 \qquad \text{Combine like terms.}$$

(Continued on next page)

Step 5.
$$\frac{35x}{35} = \frac{140}{35} \quad \text{Divide both sides by 35.}$$
$$x = 4$$

Step 6. To check, replace x with 4 in the original equation. The solution is 4. ☐

PRACTICE
5 Solve: $0.35x + 0.09(x + 4) = 0.03(12)$ ■

OBJECTIVE

4 Recognizing Identities and Equations with No Solution

So far, each equation that we have solved has had a single solution. However, not every equation in one variable has a single solution. Some equations have no solution, while others have an infinite number of solutions. For example,

$$x + 5 = x + 7$$

has no solution since no matter which **real number** we replace x with, the equation is false.

real number $+ 5 =$ same **real number** $+ 7$ **FALSE**

On the other hand,

$$x + 6 = x + 6$$

has infinitely many solutions since x can be replaced by any real number and the equation is always true.

real number $+ 6 =$ same **real number** $+ 6$ **TRUE**

The equation $x + 6 = x + 6$ is called an **identity.** The next two examples illustrate special equations like these.

EXAMPLE 6   Solve: $-2(x - 5) + 10 = -3(x + 2) + x$

Solution

$$-2(x - 5) + 10 = -3(x + 2) + x$$
$$-2x + 10 + 10 = -3x - 6 + x \quad \text{Apply the distributive property on both sides.}$$
$$-2x + 20 = -2x - 6 \quad \text{Combine like terms.}$$
$$-2x + 20 + 2x = -2x - 6 + 2x \quad \text{Add } 2x \text{ to both sides.}$$
$$20 = -6 \quad \text{Combine like terms.}$$

The final equation contains no variable terms, and there is no value for x that makes $20 = -6$ a true equation. We conclude that there is **no solution** to this equation. In set notation, we can indicate that there is no solution with the empty set, { }, or use the empty set or null set symbol, $\varnothing$. In this chapter, we will simply write *no solution*. ☐

PRACTICE
6 Solve: $4(x + 4) - x = 2(x + 11) + x$ ■

EXAMPLE 7   Solve: $3(x - 4) = 3x - 12$

Solution

$$3(x - 4) = 3x - 12$$
$$3x - 12 = 3x - 12 \quad \text{Apply the distributive property.}$$

The left side of the equation is now identical to the right side. Every real number may be substituted for x and a true statement will result. We arrive at the same conclusion if we continue.

$$3x - 12 = 3x - 12$$
$$3x - 12 + 12 = 3x - 12 + 12 \quad \text{Add 12 to both sides.}$$
$$3x = 3x \quad\quad\quad\quad\quad \text{Combine like terms.}$$
$$3x - 3x = 3x - 3x \quad\quad \text{Subtract } 3x \text{ from both sides.}$$
$$0 = 0$$

Again, one side of the equation is identical to the other side. Thus, $3(x - 4) = 3x - 12$ is an **identity** and **all real numbers** are solutions. In set notation, this is $\{$ all real numbers $\}$. □

PRACTICE

7   Solve: $12x - 18 = 9(x - 2) + 3x$ ■

✔ **CONCEPT CHECK**

Suppose you have simplified several equations and obtain the following results. What can you conclude about the solutions to the original equation?

a. $7 = 7$ b. $x = 0$ c. $7 = -4$

 Graphing Calculator Explorations

Checking Equations

We can use a calculator to check possible solutions of equations. To do this, replace the variable by the possible solution and evaluate both sides of the equation separately.

Equation: $3x - 4 = 2(x + 6)$ *Solution: $x = 16$*
$$3x - 4 = 2(x + 6) \quad \text{Original equation}$$
$$3(16) - 4 \stackrel{?}{=} 2(16 + 6) \quad \text{Replace } x \text{ with 16.}$$

Now evaluate each side with your calculator.

Evaluate left side:

$\boxed{3}\;\boxed{\times}\;\boxed{16}\;\boxed{-}\;\boxed{4}$ then $\boxed{=}$ or $\boxed{\text{ENTER}}$ Display: $\boxed{44}$ or $\begin{array}{r} 3*16 - 4 \\ 44 \end{array}$

Evaluate right side:

$\boxed{2}\;\boxed{(}\;\boxed{16}\;\boxed{+}\;\boxed{6}\;\boxed{)}$ then $\boxed{=}$ or $\boxed{\text{ENTER}}$ Display: $\boxed{44}$ or $\begin{array}{r} 2(16 + 6) \\ 44 \end{array}$

Since the left side equals the right side, the solution checks.

Use a calculator to check the possible solutions to each equation.

1. $2x = 48 + 6x$; $x = -12$ **2.** $-3x - 7 = 3x - 1$; $x = -1$
3. $5x - 2.6 = 2(x + 0.8)$; $x = 4.4$ **4.** $-1.6x - 3.9 = -6.9x - 25.6$; $x = 5$
5. $\dfrac{564x}{4} = 200x - 11(649)$; $x = 121$ **6.** $20(x - 39) = 5x - 432$; $x = 23.2$

Answers to Concept Check:
a. Every real number is a solution.
b. The solution is 0.
c. There is no solution.

Vocabulary, Readiness & Video Check

Throughout algebra, it is important to be able to identify equations and expressions.

Remember,
- an equation contains an equal sign and
- an expression does not.

Also,
- we solve equations and
- we simplify or perform operations on expressions.

Identify each as an equation or an expression.

1. $x = -7$ _____

2. $x - 7$ _____

3. $4y - 6 + 9y + 1$ _____

4. $4y - 6 = 9y + 1$ _____

5. $\dfrac{1}{x} - \dfrac{x-1}{8}$ _____

6. $\dfrac{1}{x} - \dfrac{x-1}{8} = 6$ _____

7. $0.1x + 9 = 0.2x$ _____

8. $0.1x^2 + 9y - 0.2x^2$ _____

Martin-Gay Interactive Videos

See Video 2.4

Watch the section lecture video and answer the following questions.

OBJECTIVE 1

9. The general strategy for solving linear equations in one variable is discussed after Example 1. How many properties are mentioned in this strategy and what are they?

OBJECTIVE 2

10. In the first step for solving Example 2, both sides of the equation are being multiplied by the LCD. Why is the distributive property mentioned?

OBJECTIVE 3

11. In Example 3, why is the number of decimal places in each term of the equation important?

OBJECTIVE 4

12. Complete each statement based on Examples 4 and 5.

When solving an equation and all variable terms subtract out:

(a) If you have a true statement, then the equation has ____ solution(s).

(b) If you have a false statement, then the equation has ____ solution(s).

2.4 **Exercise Set** MyMathLab®

Solve each equation. See Examples 1 and 2.

1. $-4y + 10 = -2(3y + 1)$

2. $-3x + 1 = -2(4x + 2)$

3. $15x - 8 = 10 + 9x$

4. $15x - 5 = 7 + 12x$

5. $-2(3x - 4) = 2x$

6. $-(5x - 10) = 5x$

7. $5(2x - 1) - 2(3x) = 1$

8. $3(2 - 5x) + 4(6x) = 12$

9. $-6(x - 3) - 26 = -8$

10. $-4(n - 4) - 23 = -7$

11. $8 - 2(a + 1) = 9 + a$

12. $5 - 6(2 + b) = b - 14$

13. $4x + 3 = -3 + 2x + 14$

14. $6y - 8 = -6 + 3y + 13$

15. $-2y - 10 = 5y + 18$

16. $-7n + 5 = 8n - 10$

Solve each equation. See Examples 3 through 5.

17. $\dfrac{2}{3}x + \dfrac{4}{3} = -\dfrac{2}{3}$

18. $\dfrac{4}{5}x - \dfrac{8}{5} = -\dfrac{16}{5}$

19. $\dfrac{3}{4}x - \dfrac{1}{2} = 1$

20. $\dfrac{2}{9}x - \dfrac{1}{3} = 1$

21. $0.50x + 0.15(70) = 35.5$

22. $0.40x + 0.06(30) = 9.8$

23. $\dfrac{2(x + 1)}{4} = 3x - 2$

24. $\dfrac{3(y + 3)}{5} = 2y + 6$

25. $x + \dfrac{7}{6} = 2x - \dfrac{7}{6}$

26. $\dfrac{5}{2}x - 1 = x + \dfrac{1}{4}$

27. $0.12(y - 6) + 0.06y = 0.08y - 0.70$

28. $0.60(z - 300) + 0.05z = 0.70z - 205$

Solve each equation. See Examples 6 and 7.

29. $4(3x + 2) = 12x + 8$

30. $14x + 7 = 7(2x + 1)$

31. $\dfrac{x}{4} + 1 = \dfrac{x}{4}$

32. $\dfrac{x}{3} - 2 = \dfrac{x}{3}$

33. $3x - 7 = 3(x + 1)$

34. $2(x - 5) = 2x + 10$

35. $-2(6x - 5) + 4 = -12x + 14$

36. $-5(4y - 3) + 2 = -20y + 17$

MIXED PRACTICE

Solve. See Examples 1 through 7.

37. $\dfrac{6(3 - z)}{5} = -z$

38. $\dfrac{4(5 - w)}{3} = -w$

39. $-3(2t - 5) + 2t = 5t - 4$

40. $-(4a - 7) - 5a = 10 + a$

41. $5y + 2(y - 6) = 4(y + 1) - 2$

42. $9x + 3(x - 4) = 10(x - 5) + 7$

43. $\dfrac{3(x - 5)}{2} = \dfrac{2(x + 5)}{3}$

44. $\dfrac{5(x - 1)}{4} = \dfrac{3(x + 1)}{2}$

45. $0.7x - 2.3 = 0.5$

46. $0.9x - 4.1 = 0.4$

▶ **47.** $5x - 5 = 2(x + 1) + 3x - 7$

48. $3(2x - 1) + 5 = 6x + 2$

49. $4(2n + 1) = 3(6n + 3) + 1$

50. $4(4y + 2) = 2(1 + 6y) + 8$

51. $x + \dfrac{5}{4} = \dfrac{3}{4}x$

52. $\dfrac{7}{8}x + \dfrac{1}{4} = \dfrac{3}{4}x$

▶ **53.** $\dfrac{x}{2} - 1 = \dfrac{x}{5} + 2$

54. $\dfrac{x}{5} - 7 = \dfrac{x}{3} - 5$

▶ **55.** $2(x + 3) - 5 = 5x - 3(1 + x)$

56. $4(2 + x) + 1 = 7x - 3(x - 2)$

57. $0.06 - 0.01(x + 1) = -0.02(2 - x)$

58. $-0.01(5x + 4) = 0.04 - 0.01(x + 4)$

59. $\dfrac{9}{2} + \dfrac{5}{2}y = 2y - 4$

60. $3 - \dfrac{1}{2}x = 5x - 8$

61. $-2y - 10 = 5y + 18$

62. $7n + 5 = 10n - 10$

63. $0.6x - 0.1 = 0.5x + 0.2$

64. $0.2x - 0.1 = 0.6x - 2.1$

65. $0.02(6t - 3) = 0.12(t - 2) + 0.18$

66. $0.03(2m + 7) = 0.06(5 + m) - 0.09$

TRANSLATING

Write each phrase as an algebraic expression. Use x for the unknown number. See Section 2.1.

67. A number subtracted from -8

68. Three times a number

69. The sum of -3 and twice a number

70. The difference of 8 and twice a number

71. The product of 9 and the sum of a number and 20

72. The quotient of -12 and the difference of a number and 3

See Section 2.1.

73. A plot of land is in the shape of a triangle. If one side is x meters, a second side is $(2x - 3)$ meters, and a third side is $(3x - 5)$ meters, express the perimeter of the lot as a simplified expression in x.

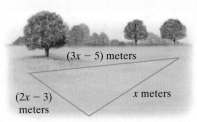

$(3x - 5)$ meters

$(2x - 3)$ meters

x meters

74. A portion of a board has length x feet. The other part has length $(7x - 9)$ feet. Express the total length of the board as a simplified expression in x.

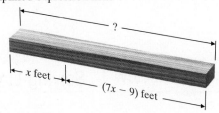

?

x feet

$(7x - 9)$ feet

CONCEPT EXTENSIONS

See the Concept Check in this section.

75. a. Solve: $x + 3 = x + 3$ for x

 b. If you simplify an equation and get $0 = 0$, what can you conclude about the solution(s) of the original equation?

 c. On your own, construct an equation for which every real number is a solution.

76. a. Solve: $x + 3 = x + 5$ for x

 b. If you simplify an equation and get $3 = 5$, what can you conclude about the solution(s) of the original equation?

 c. On your own, construct an equation that has no solution.

For Exercises 77 through 82, match each equation in the first column with its solution in the second column. Items in the second column may be used more than once.

77. $5x + 1 = 5x + 1$

78. $3x + 1 = 3x + 2$

79. $2x - 6x - 10 = -4x + 3 - 10$

80. $x - 11x - 3 = -10x - 1 - 2$

81. $9x - 20 = 8x - 20$

82. $-x + 15 = x + 15$

A. all real numbers

B. no solution

C. 0

83. Explain the difference between simplifying an expression and solving an equation.

84. On your own, write an expression and then an equation. Label each.

For Exercises 85 and 86, **a.** *Write an equation for perimeter.* **b.** *Solve the equation in part (a).* **c.** *Find the length of each side.*

85. The perimeter of a geometric figure is the sum of the lengths of its sides. The perimeter of the following pentagon (five-sided figure) is 28 centimeters.

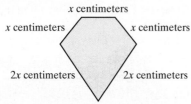

x centimeters

x centimeters   x centimeters

2x centimeters   2x centimeters

86. The perimeter of the following triangle is 35 meters.

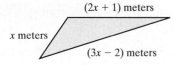

(2x + 1) meters

x meters

(3x − 2) meters

Fill in the blanks with numbers of your choice so that each equation has the given solution. Note: Each blank may be replaced by a different number.

87. $x +$ _____ $= 2x -$ _____ ; solution: 9

88. $-5x -$ _____ $=$ _____ ; solution: 2

Solve.

89. $1000(7x - 10) = 50(412 + 100x)$

90. $1000(x + 40) = 100(16 + 7x)$

91. $0.035x + 5.112 = 0.010x + 5.107$

92. $0.127x - 2.685 = 0.027x - 2.38$

For Exercises 93 through 96, see the example below.

Example

Solve: $t(t + 4) = t^2 - 2t + 6$

Solution
$$t(t + 4) = t^2 - 2t + 6$$
$$t^2 + 4t = t^2 - 2t + 6$$
$$t^2 + 4t - t^2 = t^2 - 2t + 6 - t^2$$
$$4t = -2t + 6$$
$$4t + 2t = -2t + 6 + 2t$$
$$6t = 6$$
$$t = 1$$

Solve each equation.

93. $x(x - 3) = x^2 + 5x + 7$

94. $t^2 - 6t = t(8 + t)$

95. $2z(z + 6) = 2z^2 + 12z - 8$

96. $y^2 - 4y + 10 = y(y - 5)$

Integrated Review   Solving Linear Equations

Sections 2.1–2.4

Solve. Feel free to use the steps given in Section 2.4.

1. $x - 10 = -4$

2. $y + 14 = -3$

3. $9y = 108$

4. $-3x = 78$

5. $-6x + 7 = 25$

6. $5y - 42 = -47$

7. $\frac{2}{3}x = 9$

8. $\frac{4}{5}z = 10$

9. $\frac{r}{-4} = -2$

10. $\frac{y}{-8} = 8$

11. $6 - 2x + 8 = 10$

12. $-5 - 6y + 6 = 19$

13. $2x - 7 = 2x - 27$

14. $3 + 8y = 8y - 2$

15. $-3a + 6 + 5a = 7a - 8a$

16. $4b - 8 - b = 10b - 3b$

17. $-\frac{2}{3}x = \frac{5}{9}$

18. $-\frac{3}{8}y = -\frac{1}{16}$

19. $10 = -6n + 16$

20. $-5 = -2m + 7$

21. $3(5c - 1) - 2 = 13c + 3$

22. $4(3t + 4) - 20 = 3 + 5t$

23. $\frac{2(z + 3)}{3} = 5 - z$

24. $\frac{3(w + 2)}{4} = 2w + 3$

25. $-2(2x - 5) = -3x + 7 - x + 3$

26. $-4(5x - 2) = -12x + 4 - 8x + 4$

27. $0.02(6t - 3) = 0.04(t - 2) + 0.02$

28. $0.03(m + 7) = 0.02(5 - m) + 0.03$

29. $-3y = \dfrac{4(y - 1)}{5}$ **30.** $-4x = \dfrac{5(1 - x)}{6}$

31. $\dfrac{5}{3}x - \dfrac{7}{3} = x$ **32.** $\dfrac{7}{5}n + \dfrac{3}{5} = -n$

33. $9(3x - 1) = -4 + 49$

34. $12(2x + 1) = -6 + 66$

35. $\dfrac{1}{10}(3x - 7) = \dfrac{3}{10}x + 5$

36. $\dfrac{1}{7}(2x - 5) = \dfrac{2}{7}x + 1$

37. $5 + 2(3x - 6) = -4(6x - 7)$

38. $3 + 5(2x - 4) = -7(5x + 2)$

2.5   An Introduction to Problem Solving

OBJECTIVES

1 Solve Problems Involving Direct Translations.

2 Solve Problems Involving Relationships Among Unknown Quantities.

3 Solve Problems Involving Consecutive Integers.

OBJECTIVE

1   Solving Direct Translation Problems

In previous sections, we practiced writing word phrases and sentences as algebraic expressions and equations to help prepare for problem solving. We now use these translations to help write equations that model a problem. The problem-solving steps given next may be helpful.

General Strategy for Problem Solving

1. UNDERSTAND the problem. During this step, become comfortable with the problem. Some ways of doing this are to:

   Read and reread the problem.

   Choose a variable to represent the unknown.

   Construct a drawing whenever possible.

   Propose a solution and check. Pay careful attention to how you check your proposed solution. This will help when writing an equation to model the problem.

2. TRANSLATE the problem into an equation.

3. SOLVE the equation.

4. INTERPRET the results: *Check* the proposed solution in the stated problem and state your conclusion.

Much of problem solving involves a direct translation from a sentence to an equation.

EXAMPLE 1   Finding an Unknown Number

Twice a number, added to seven, is the same as three subtracted from the number. Find the number.

Solution   Translate the sentence into an equation and solve.

	twice a number	added to	seven	is the same as	three subtracted from the number
In words:	↓	↓	↓	↓	↓
Translate:	$2x$	$+$	7	$=$	$x - 3$

> **Helpful Hint**
> Order matters when subtracting (and dividing), so be especially careful with these translations.

To solve, begin by subtracting x from both sides to get all variable terms on one side.

$$2x + 7 = x - 3$$
$$2x + 7 - x = x - 3 - x \qquad \text{Subtract } x \text{ from both sides.}$$
$$x + 7 = -3 \qquad \text{Combine like terms.}$$
$$x + 7 - 7 = -3 - 7 \qquad \text{Subtract 7 from both sides.}$$
$$x = -10 \qquad \text{Combine like terms.}$$

Check the solution in the problem as it was originally stated. To do so, replace "number" in the sentence with -10. Twice "-10" added to 7 is the same as 3 subtracted from "-10."

$$2(-10) + 7 = -10 - 3$$
$$-13 = -13$$

The unknown number is -10. □

PRACTICE

1 Three times a number, minus 6, is the same as two times a number, plus 3. Find the number. ■

Helpful Hint

When checking solutions, go back to the original stated problem, rather than to your equation, in case errors have been made in translating into an equation.

EXAMPLE 2 Finding an Unknown Number

Twice the sum of a number and 4 is the same as four times the number, decreased by 12. Find the number.

Solution

1. UNDERSTAND. Read and reread the problem. If we let

$$x = \text{the unknown number, then}$$

"the sum of a number and 4" translates to "$x + 4$" and "four times the number" translates to "$4x$."

2. TRANSLATE.

twice	the sum of a number and 4	is the same as	four times the number	decreased by	12
↓	↓	↓	↓	↓	↓
2	$(x + 4)$	$=$	$4x$	$-$	12

3. SOLVE.

$$2(x + 4) = 4x - 12$$
$$2x + 8 = 4x - 12 \qquad \text{Apply the distributive property.}$$
$$2x + 8 - 4x = 4x - 12 - 4x \qquad \text{Subtract } 4x \text{ from both sides.}$$
$$-2x + 8 = -12$$
$$-2x + 8 - 8 = -12 - 8 \qquad \text{Subtract 8 from both sides.}$$
$$-2x = -20$$
$$\frac{-2x}{-2} = \frac{-20}{-2} \qquad \text{Divide both sides by } -2.$$
$$x = 10$$

4. INTERPRET.

Check: Check this solution in the problem as it was originally stated. To do so, replace "number" with 10. Twice the sum of "10" and 4 is 28, which is the same as 4 times "10" decreased by 12.

State: The number is 10. □

PRACTICE

2 Three times a number, decreased by 4, is the same as double the difference of the number and 1. ■

OBJECTIVE

2 Solving Problems Involving Relationships Among Unknown Quantities ▷

The next three examples have to do with relationships among unknown quantities.

EXAMPLE 3   **Finding the Length of a Board**

Balsa wood sticks are commonly used for building models (for example, bridge models). A 48-inch balsa wood stick is to be cut into two pieces so that the longer piece is 3 times the shorter. Find the length of each piece.

Solution

1. UNDERSTAND the problem. To do so, read and reread the problem. You may also want to propose a solution. For example, if 10 inches represents the length of the shorter piece, then $3(10) = 30$ inches is the length of the longer piece, since it is 3 times the length of the shorter piece. This guess gives a total stick length of 10 inches + 30 inches = 40 inches, too short. However, the purpose of proposing a solution is not to guess correctly but to help understand the problem better and how to model it.

   Since the length of the longer piece is given in terms of the length of the shorter piece, let's let

$$x = \text{length of shorter piece; then}$$
$$3x = \text{length of longer piece}$$

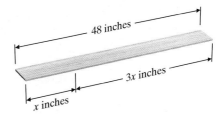

2. TRANSLATE the problem. First, we write the equation in words.

length of shorter piece	added to	length of longer piece	equals	total length of stick
↓	↓	↓	↓	↓
x	$+$	$3x$	$=$	48

3. SOLVE.

$$x + 3x = 48$$
$$4x = 48 \qquad \text{Combine like terms.}$$
$$\frac{4x}{4} = \frac{48}{4} \qquad \text{Divide both sides by 4.}$$
$$x = 12$$

4. INTERPRET.

Check: Check the solution in the stated problem. If the shorter piece of stick is 12 inches, the longer piece is $3 \cdot (12 \text{ inches}) = 36$ inches, and the sum of the two pieces is 12 inches + 36 inches = 48 inches.

State: The shorter piece of balsa wood is 12 inches, and the longer piece of balsa wood is 36 inches.   □

Helpful Hint

Make sure that units are included in your answer, if appropriate.

PRACTICE

3   A 45-inch board is to be cut into two pieces so that the longer piece is 4 times the shorter. Find the length of each piece.   ■

EXAMPLE 4   **Finding the Number of Republican and Democratic Representatives**

The 114th Congress began on January 3, 2015, and had a total of 435 Democrat and Republican representatives. There were 59 fewer Democratic representatives than Republican. Find the number of representatives from each party. (*Source:* Congress.gov)

Solution

1. UNDERSTAND the problem. Read and reread the problem. Let's suppose that there were 200 Republican representatives. Since there were 59 fewer Democrats than Republicans, there must have been $200 - 59 = 141$ Democrats. The total number of Republicans and Democrats was then $200 + 141 = 341$. This is incorrect since the total should be 435, but we now have a better understanding of the problem.

In general, if we let

$$x = \text{number of Republicans, then}$$
$$x - 59 = \text{number of Democrats}$$

2. TRANSLATE the problem. First, we write the equation in words.

number of Republicans	added to	number of Democrats	equals	435
↓	↓	↓	↓	↓
x	$+$	$(x - 59)$	$=$	435

3. SOLVE.

$$x + (x - 59) = 435$$
$$2x - 59 = 435 \qquad \text{Combine like terms.}$$
$$2x - 59 + 59 = 435 + 59 \qquad \text{Add 59 to both sides.}$$
$$2x = 494$$
$$\frac{2x}{2} = \frac{494}{2} \qquad \text{Divide both sides by 2.}$$
$$x = 247$$

4. INTERPRET.

Check: If there were 247 Republican representatives, then there were $247 - 59 = 188$ Democratic representatives. The total number of representatives was then $247 + 188 = 435$. The results check.

State: There were 247 Republican and 188 Democratic representatives at the beginning of the 114th Congress.   □

PRACTICE

   In 2015, there were 7 fewer Democratic State Governors than Republican State Governors. Find the number of State Governors from each party. Alaska had an independent governor, so use a total of 49, representing the other 49 states. (*Source:* National Conference of State Legislatures).   ■

EXAMPLE 5   **Finding Angle Measures**

If the two walls of the Vietnam Veterans Memorial in Washington, D.C., were connected, an isosceles triangle would be formed. The measure of the third angle is 97.5° more than the measure of either of the other two equal angles. Find the measure of the third angle. (*Source:* National Park Service)

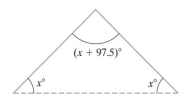

Solution

1. **UNDERSTAND.** Read and reread the problem. We then draw a diagram (recall that an isosceles triangle has two angles with the same measure) and let

$$x = \text{degree measure of one angle}$$
$$x = \text{degree measure of the second equal angle}$$
$$x + 97.5 = \text{degree measure of the third angle}$$

2. **TRANSLATE.** Recall that the sum of the measures of the angles of a triangle equals 180.

measure of first angle	measure of second angle	measure of third angle	equals	180
↓	↓	↓	↓	↓
x +	x	+ $(x + 97.5)$	=	180

3. **SOLVE.**

$$x + x + (x + 97.5) = 180$$

$$3x + 97.5 = 180 \qquad \text{Combine like terms.}$$

$$3x + 97.5 - 97.5 = 180 - 97.5 \quad \text{Subtract 97.5 from both sides.}$$

$$3x = 82.5$$

$$\frac{3x}{3} = \frac{82.5}{3} \qquad \text{Divide both sides by 3.}$$

$$x = 27.5$$

4. **INTERPRET.**

Check: If $x = 27.5$, then the measure of the third angle is $x + 97.5 = 125$. The sum of the angles is then $27.5 + 27.5 + 125 = 180$, the correct sum.

State: The third angle measures 125°.*

PRACTICE

5 The second angle of a triangle measures three times as large as the first. If the third angle measures 55° more than the first, find the measures of all three angles.

OBJECTIVE

3 Solving Consecutive Integer Problems

The next example has to do with consecutive integers. Recall what we have learned thus far about these integers.

	Example	_General Representation_
Consecutive Integers	11, 12, 13 ↳+1 ↗ +1 ↗	Let x be an integer. x, $x + 1$, $x + 2$ ↳+1 ↗↳+1 ↗
Consecutive Even Integers	38, 40, 42 ↳+2 ↗ +2 ↗	Let x be an **even** integer. x, $x + 2, x + 4$ ↳+2 ↗↳+2 ↗
Consecutive Odd Integers	57, 59, 61 ↳+2 ↗ +2 ↗	Let x be an **odd** integer. x, $x + 2, x + 4$ ↳+2 ↗↳+2 ↗

* The two walls actually meet at an angle of 125 degrees 12 minutes. The measurement of 97.5° given in the problem is an approximation.

EXAMPLE 6 Some states have a single area code for the entire state. Two such states have area codes that are consecutive odd integers. If the sum of these integers is 1208, find the two area codes. (*Source:* North American Numbering Plan Administration)

Solution

1. UNDERSTAND. Read and reread the problem. If we let

$$x = \text{the first odd integer, then}$$
$$x + 2 = \text{the next odd integer}$$

> **Helpful Hint**
>
> Remember, the 2 here means that odd integers are 2 units apart, for example, the odd integers 13 and 13 + 2 = 15.

2. TRANSLATE.

first odd integer	the sum of	next odd integer	is	1208
↓	↓	↓	↓	↓
x	$+$	$(x + 2)$	$=$	1208

3. SOLVE.

$$x + x + 2 = 1208$$
$$2x + 2 = 1208$$
$$2x + 2 - 2 = 1208 - 2$$
$$2x = 1206$$
$$\frac{2x}{2} = \frac{1206}{2}$$
$$x = 603$$

4. INTERPRET.

Check: If $x = 603$, then the next odd integer $x + 2 = 603 + 2 = 605$. Notice their sum, $603 + 605 = 1208$, as needed.

State: The area codes are 603 and 605.

Note: New Hampshire's area code is 603 and South Dakota's area code is 605. □

PRACTICE
6 The sum of three consecutive even integers is 144. Find the integers. ■

✓ Vocabulary, Readiness & Video Check

Fill in the table.

	A number:	→	Double the number:	→	Double the number, decreased by 31:
1.	x				
2.	A number: x	→	Three times the number:	→	Three times the number, increased by 17:
3.	A number: x	→	The sum of the number and 5:	→	Twice the sum of the number and 5:
4.	A number: x	→	The difference of the number and 11:	→	Seven times the difference of the number and 11:
5.	A number: y	→	The difference of 20 and the number:	→	The difference of 20 and the number, divided by 3:
6.	A number: y	→	The sum of −10 and the number:	→	The sum of −10 and the number, divided by 9:

Martin-Gay Interactive Videos

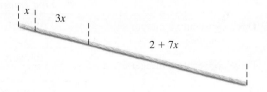

See Video 2.5

Watch the section lecture video and answer the following questions.

OBJECTIVE 1

7. At the end of ▤ Example 1, where are you told is the best place to check the solution of an application problem?

OBJECTIVE 2

8. The solution of the equation for ▤ Example 3 is $x = 43$. Why is this not the solution to the application?

OBJECTIVE 3

9. What are two things that should be checked to make sure the solution of ▤ Example 4 is correct?

2.5   Exercise Set   MyMathLab®

TRANSLATING

Write each of the following as an equation. Then solve. See Examples 1 and 2.

1. The sum of six times a number, and 1, is equal to five times the number. Find the number.

2. The difference of three times a number, and 1, is the same as twice the number. Find the number.

3. Three times a number, minus 6, is equal to two times the number, plus 8. Find the number.

4. The sum of 4 times a number, and −2, is equal to the sum of 5 times the number, and −2. Find the number.

5. Twice the difference of a number and 8 is equal to three times the sum of the number and 3. Find the number.

6. Five times the sum of a number and −1 is the same as 6 times the difference of the number and 5. Find the number.

7. Twice the sum of −2 and a number is the same as the number decreased by $\frac{1}{2}$. Find the number.

8. If the difference of a number and four is doubled, the result is $\frac{1}{4}$ less than the number. Find the number.

Solve. For Exercises 9 and 10, the solutions have been started for you. See Examples 3 through 5.

9. A 25-inch piece of steel is cut into three pieces so that the second piece is twice as long as the first piece, and the third piece is one inch more than five times the length of the first piece. Find the lengths of the pieces.

Start the solution:

1. UNDERSTAND the problem. Reread it as many times as needed.

2. TRANSLATE into an equation. (Fill in the blanks below.)

total length of steel	equals	length of first piece	plus	length of second piece	plus	length of third piece
↓	↓	↓	↓	↓	↓	↓
25	=	____	+	____	+	____

Finish with:

3. SOLVE and   **4.** INTERPRET

10. A 46-foot piece of rope is cut into three pieces so that the second piece is three times as long as the first piece, and the third piece is two feet more than seven times the length of the first piece. Find the lengths of the pieces.

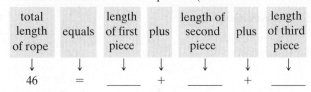

Start the solution:

1. UNDERSTAND the problem. Reread it as many times as needed.

2. TRANSLATE into an equation. (Fill in the blanks below.)

total length of rope	equals	length of first piece	plus	length of second piece	plus	length of third piece
↓	↓	↓	↓	↓	↓	↓
46	=	____	+	____	+	____

Finish with:

3. SOLVE and   **4.** INTERPRET

11. A 40-inch board is to be cut into three pieces so that the second piece is twice as long as the first piece, and the third piece is 5 times as long as the first piece. If x represents the length of the first piece, find the lengths of all three pieces.

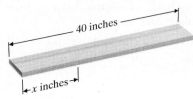

12. A 21-foot beam is to be cut into three pieces so that the second and the third piece are each 3 times the length of the first piece. If x represents the length of the shorter piece, find the lengths of all three pieces.

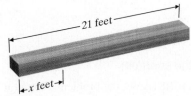

For Exercises 13 and 14, use each table to find the value of x. Then write a sentence to explain, in words, the meaning and the value of x. (Source: IHS Screen Digest)

13. The fastest growing type of movie screen in 2014 was 3D.

Type of Screen	*Number of Screens*
3D	x
Non-3D	10,973 more than x
Total screens	43,265

14. The vast majority of movie screens in the United States in 2014 were digital.

Type of Screen	*Number of Screens*
Analog	x
Digital	39,771 more than x
Total screens	43,265

△ **15.** The flag of Equatorial Guinea contains an isosceles triangle. (Recall that an isosceles triangle contains two angles with the same measure.) If the measure of the third angle of the triangle is 30° more than twice the measure of either of the other two angles, find the measure of each angle of the triangle. (*Hint:* Recall that the sum of the measures of the angles of a triangle is 180°.)

△ **16.** The flag of Brazil contains a parallelogram. One angle of the parallelogram is 15° less than twice the measure of the angle next to it. Find the measure of each angle. (*Hint:* Recall that opposite angles of a parallelogram have the same measure and that the sum of the measures of the angles is 360°.)

Solve. See Example 6. For Exercises 17 through 24, fill in the table. Most of the first row has been completed for you.

	First Integer →	*Next Integers*	→	*Indicated Sum*
17. Three consecutive integers:	Integer: x	$x + 1$ $\quad$ $x + 2$		Sum of the three consecutive integers, simplified:
18. Three consecutive integers:	Integer: x			Sum of the second and third consecutive integers, simplified:
19. Three consecutive even integers:	Even integer: x			Sum of the first and third even consecutive integers, simplified:
20. Three consecutive odd integers:	Odd integer: x			Sum of the three consecutive odd integers, simplified:
21. Four consecutive integers:	Integer: x			Sum of the four consecutive integers, simplified:
22. Four consecutive integers:	Integer: x			Sum of the first and fourth consecutive integers, simplified:
23. Three consecutive odd integers:	Odd integer: x			Sum of the second and third consecutive odd integers, simplified:
24. Three consecutive even integers:	Even integer: x			Sum of the three consecutive even integers, simplified:

25. The left and right page numbers of an open book are two consecutive integers whose sum is 469. Find these page numbers.

26. The room numbers of two adjacent classrooms are two consecutive even numbers. If their sum is 654, find the classroom numbers.

27. To make an international telephone call, you need the code for the country you are calling. The codes for Belgium, France, and Spain are three consecutive integers whose sum is 99. Find the code for each country. (*Source: The World Almanac and Book of Facts*, 2007)

28. To make an international telephone call, you need the code for the country you are calling. The codes for Mali Republic, Côte d'Ivoire, and Niger are three consecutive odd integers whose sum is 675. Find the code for each country.

MIXED PRACTICE

Solve. See Examples 1 through 6.

29. The area of the Sahara Desert is 7 times the area of the Gobi Desert. If the sum of their areas is 4,000,000 square miles, find the area of each desert.

30. The largest meteorite in the world is the Hoba West, located in Namibia. Its weight is 3 times the weight of the Armanty meteorite, located in Outer Mongolia. If the sum of their weights is 88 tons, find the weight of each.

31. A 17-foot piece of string is cut into two pieces so that the longer piece is 2 feet longer than twice the length of the shorter piece. Find the lengths of both pieces.

32. A 25-foot wire is to be cut so that the longer piece is one foot longer than 5 times the length of the shorter piece. Find the length of each piece.

33. Five times a number, subtracted from ten, is triple the number. Find the number.

34. Nine is equal to ten subtracted from double a number. Find the number.

35. The greatest producer of diamonds in carats is Botswana. This country produces about four times the amount produced in Angola. If the total produced in both countries is 40,000,000 carats, find the amount produced in each country. (*Source: Diamond Facts.*)

36. Beetles have the greatest number of different species. There are twenty times the number of beetle species as grasshopper species, and the total number of species for both is 420,000. Find the number of species for each type of insect.

37. The measures of the angles of a triangle are 3 consecutive even integers. Find the measure of each angle.

38. A quadrilateral is a polygon with 4 sides. The sum of the measures of the 4 angles in a quadrilateral is 360°. If the measures of the angles of a quadrilateral are consecutive odd integers, find the measures.

39. For the 2014 Winter Olympics, the total number of medals won by athletes from each of the countries of Netherlands, Canada, and Norway are three consecutive integers whose sum is 75. Find the number of medals for each country.

40. The code to unlock a student's combination lock happens to be three consecutive odd integers whose sum is 51. Find the integers.

41. If the sum of a number and five is tripled, the result is one less than twice the number. Find the number.

42. Twice the sum of a number and six equals three times the sum of the number and four. Find the number.

43. Two angles are supplementary if their sum is 180°. A larger angle measures eight degrees more than three times the measure of a smaller angle. If x represents the measure of the smaller angle and these two angles are supplementary, find the measure of each angle.

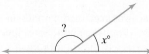

44. Two angles are complementary if their sum is 90°. A larger angle measures three degrees less than twice the measure of a smaller angle. If x represents the measure of the smaller angle and these two angles are complementary, find the measure of each angle.

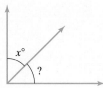

45. If the quotient of a number and 4 is added to $\frac{1}{2}$, the result is $\frac{3}{4}$. Find the number.

46. The sum of $\frac{1}{5}$ and twice a number is equal to $\frac{4}{5}$ subtracted from three times the number. Find the number.

47. The sum of $\frac{2}{3}$ and four times a number is equal to $\frac{5}{6}$ subtracted from five times the number. Find the number.

48. If $\frac{3}{4}$ is added to three times a number, the result is $\frac{1}{2}$ subtracted from twice the number. Find the number.

49. Currently, the two fastest trains in the world are both Chinese, the Shanghai Maglev and the Harmony CRH. The sum of their fastest speeds is 503 miles per hour. If the maximum speed of the Maglev is 31 miles per hour faster than the speed of the Harmony, find the speeds of each. (*Source:* Railway-technology.com)

50. The Pentagon is the world's largest office building in terms of floor space. It has three times the amount of floor space as the Empire State Building. If the total floor space for these two buildings is approximately 8700 thousand square feet, find the floor space of each building.

51. One-third of a number is five-sixths. Find the number.

52. Seven-eighths of a number is one-half. Find the number.

53. The number of counties in California and the number of counties in Montana are consecutive even integers whose sum is 114. If California has more counties than Montana, how many counties does each state have? (*Source: The World Almanac and Book of Facts*)

54. A student is building a bookcase with stepped shelves for her dorm room. She buys a 48-inch board and wants to cut the board into three pieces with lengths equal to three consecutive even integers. Find the three board lengths.

55. A geodesic dome, based on the design by Buckminster Fuller, is composed of two types of triangular panels. One of these is an isosceles triangle. In one geodesic dome, the measure of the third angle is 76.5° more than the measure of either of the two equal angles. Find the measure of the third angle. (*Source:* Buckminster Fuller Institute)

56. The measures of the angles of a particular triangle are such that the second and third angles are each four times larger than the smallest angle. Find the measures of the angles of this triangle.

57. A 30-foot piece of siding is cut into three pieces so that the second piece is four times as long as the first piece and the third piece is five times as long as the first piece. If x represents the length of the first piece, find the lengths of all three pieces.

58. A 48-foot-long piece of cable wire is to be cut into three pieces so that the second piece is five times as long as the first piece and the third piece is six times as long as the first piece. If x represents the length of the first piece, find the lengths of all three pieces.

The graph below shows the best-selling video for 2014. Use this graph for Exercises 59 through 64.

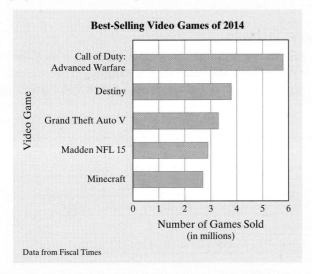

Best-Selling Video Games of 2014

Data from Fiscal Times

59. Which video game is the best-selling game of 2014?

60. Which video games sold between 3 and 5 million copies in 2014?

61. Madden NFL 15 and Destiny together sold 6.7 million copies in 2014. Destiny sold 0.9 million copies more than Madden NFL 15. Find the number of sales of each video game.

62. Grand Theft Auto V and Minecraft together sold 6 million copies in 2014. Grand Theft Auto V sold 0.6 million more copies than Minecraft. Find the number of sales of each video game.

Compare the lengths of the bars in the graph with your results for the exercises below. Are your answers reasonable?

63. Exercise 61   **64.** Exercise 62

REVIEW AND PREVIEW

Evaluate each expression for the given values. See Section 1.4.

65. $2W + 2L$; $W = 7$ and $L = 10$

66. $\frac{1}{2} Bh$; $B = 14$ and $h = 22$

67. πr^2; $r = 15$ **68.** $r \cdot t$; $r = 15$ and $t = 2$

CONCEPT EXTENSIONS

69. A golden rectangle is a rectangle whose length is approximately 1.6 times its width. The early Greeks thought that a rectangle with these dimensions was the most pleasing to the eye, and examples of the golden rectangle are found in many early works of art. For example, the Parthenon in Athens contains many examples of golden rectangles.

Mike Hallahan would like to plant a rectangular garden in the shape of a golden rectangle. If he has 78 feet of fencing available, find the dimensions of the garden.

70. Dr. Dorothy Smith gave the students in her geometry class at the University of New Orleans the following question. Is it possible to construct a triangle such that the second angle of the triangle has a measure that is twice the measure of the first angle and the measure of the third angle is 5 times the measure of the first? If so, find the measure of each angle. (*Hint:* Recall that the sum of the measures of the angles of a triangle is 180°.)

71. Only male crickets chirp. They chirp at different rates depending on their species and the temperature of their environment. Suppose a certain species is currently chirping at a rate of 90 chirps per minute. At this rate, how many chirps occur in one hour? In one 24-hour day? In one year?

72. The human eye blinks once every 5 seconds on average. How many times does the average eye blink in one hour? In one 16-hour day while awake? In one year while awake?

73. In your own words, explain why a solution of a word problem should be checked using the original wording of the problem and not the equation written from the wording.

74. Give an example of how you recently solved a problem using mathematics.

Recall from Exercise 69 that a golden rectangle is a rectangle whose length is approximately 1.6 times its width.

75. It is thought that for about 75% of adults, a rectangle in the shape of the golden rectangle is the most pleasing to the eye. Draw three rectangles, one in the shape of the golden rectangle, and poll your class. Do the results agree with the percentage given above?

76. Examples of golden rectangles can be found today in architecture and manufacturing packaging. Find an example of a golden rectangle in your home. A few suggestions: the front face of a book, the floor of a room, the front of a box of food.

For Exercises 77 and 78, measure the dimensions of each rectangle and decide which one best approximates the shape of a golden rectangle.

77.

78.

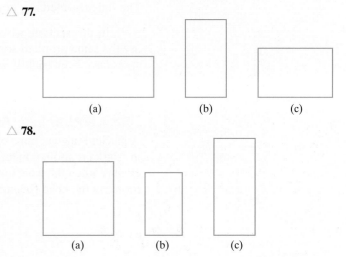

(a)   (b)   (c)

2.6   Formulas and Problem Solving

OBJECTIVE

1   Using Formulas to Solve Problems

An equation that describes a known relationship among quantities, such as distance, time, volume, weight, and money, is called a **formula.** These quantities are represented by letters and are thus variables of the formula. Here are some common formulas and their meanings.

Formulas	*Their Meanings*
$A = lw$	Area of a rectangle = length · width
$I = PRT$	Simple interest = principal · rate · time
$P = a + b + c$	Perimeter of a triangle = side a + side b + side c
$d = rt$	distance = rate · time
$V = lwh$	Volume of a rectangular solid = length · width · height
$F = \left(\dfrac{9}{5}\right)C + 32$ or $F = 1.8C + 32$	degrees Fahrenheit = $\left(\dfrac{9}{5}\right)$ · degrees Celsius + 32

Formulas are valuable tools because they allow us to calculate measurements as long as we know certain other measurements. For example, if we know we traveled a distance of 100 miles at a rate of 40 miles per hour, we can replace the variables d and r in the formula $d = rt$ and find our time, t.

$$d = rt \quad \text{Formula.}$$
$$100 = 40t \quad \text{Replace } d \text{ with 100 and } r \text{ with 40.}$$

This is a linear equation in one variable, t. To solve for t, divide both sides of the equation by 40.

$$\frac{100}{40} = \frac{40t}{40} \quad \text{Divide both sides by 40.}$$

$$\frac{5}{2} = t \quad \text{Simplify.}$$

The time traveled is $\dfrac{5}{2}$ hours, or $2\dfrac{1}{2}$ hours, or 2.5 hours.

In this section, we solve problems that can be modeled by known formulas. We use the same problem-solving steps that were introduced in the previous section. These steps have been slightly revised to include formulas.

EXAMPLE I   Finding Time Given Rate and Distance

A glacier is a giant mass of rocks and ice that flows downhill like a river. Portage Glacier in Alaska is about 6 miles, or 31,680 *feet,* long and moves 400 *feet* per year. Icebergs are created when the front end of the glacier flows into Portage Lake. How long does it take for ice at the head (beginning) of the glacier to reach the lake?

Solution

1. UNDERSTAND. Read and reread the problem. The appropriate formula needed to solve this problem is the distance formula, $d = rt$. To become familiar with this formula, let's find the distance that ice traveling at a rate of 400 feet per year travels in 100 years. To do so, we let time t be 100 years and rate r be the given 400 feet per year and substitute these values into the formula $d = rt$. We then have that distance $d = 400(100) = 40{,}000$ feet. Since we are interested in finding how long it takes ice to travel 31,680 feet, we now know that it is less than 100 years.

   Since we are using the formula $d = rt$, we let

   t = the time in years for ice to reach the lake

   r = rate or speed of ice

   d = distance from beginning of glacier to lake.

2. TRANSLATE. To translate into an equation, we use the formula $d = rt$ and let distance $d = 31{,}680$ feet and rate $r = 400$ feet per year.

$$d = r \cdot t$$
$$31{,}680 = 400 \cdot t \quad \text{Let } d = 31{,}680 \text{ and } r = 400.$$

3. SOLVE. Solve the equation for t. To solve for t, divide both sides by 400.

$$\frac{31{,}680}{400} = \frac{400 \cdot t}{400} \quad \text{Divide both sides by 400.}$$
$$79.2 = t \quad \text{Simplify.}$$

4. INTERPRET.

Check: To check, substitute 79.2 for t and 400 for r in the distance formula and check to see that the distance is 31,680 feet.

State: It takes 79.2 years for the ice at the head of Portage Glacier to reach the lake.

Helpful Hint
Don't forget to include units if appropriate.

PRACTICE

1   The Stromboli Volcano, in Italy, began erupting in 2002 and continues to be active after a dormant period of over 17 years. In 2007, a volcanologist measured the lava flow to be moving at 5 meters/second. If the path the lava follows to the sea is 580 meters long, how long does it take the lava to reach the sea? (_Source:_ Thorsten Boeckel and CNN)

△ **EXAMPLE 2** Calculating the Length of a Garden

Charles Pecot can afford enough fencing to enclose a rectangular garden with a perimeter of 140 feet. If the width of his garden must be 30 feet, find the length.

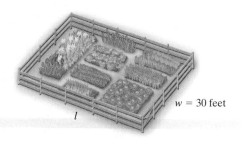

$w = 30$ feet

l

Solution

1. UNDERSTAND. Read and reread the problem. The formula needed to solve this problem is the formula for the perimeter of a rectangle, $P = 2l + 2w$. Before continuing, let's become familiar with this formula.

l = the length of the rectangular garden

w = the width of the rectangular garden

P = perimeter of the garden

2. TRANSLATE. To translate into an equation, we use the formula $P = 2l + 2w$ and let perimeter $P = 140$ feet and width $w = 30$ feet.

$$P = 2l + 2w$$
$$\downarrow \qquad \downarrow$$
$$140 = 2l + 2(30) \quad \text{Let } P = 140 \text{ and } w = 30.$$

3. SOLVE.

$$140 = 2l + 2(30)$$
$$140 = 2l + 60 \qquad\qquad \text{Multiply } 2(30).$$
$$140 - 60 = 2l + 60 - 60 \quad \text{Subtract 60 from both sides.}$$
$$80 = 2l \qquad\qquad\qquad \text{Combine like terms.}$$
$$40 = l \qquad\qquad\qquad \text{Divide both sides by 2.}$$

4. INTERPRET.

Check: Substitute 40 for l and 30 for w in the perimeter formula and check to see that the perimeter is 140 feet.

State: The length of the rectangular garden is 40 feet. ☐

PRACTICE

2 Evelyn Gryk fenced in part of her backyard for a dog run. The dog run was 40 feet in length and used 98 feet of fencing. Find the width of the dog run. ■

EXAMPLE 3 Finding an Equivalent Temperature

The average minimum temperature for July in Shanghai, China, is 77° Fahrenheit. Find the equivalent temperature in degrees Celsius.

Solution

1. UNDERSTAND. Read and reread the problem. A formula that can be used to solve this problem is the formula for converting degrees Celsius to degrees Fahrenheit, $F = \frac{9}{5}C + 32$. Before continuing, become familiar with this formula. Using this formula, we let

C = temperature in degrees Celsius, and

F = temperature in degrees Fahrenheit.

2. TRANSLATE. To translate into an equation, we use the formula $F = \frac{9}{5}C + 32$ and let degrees Fahrenheit $F = 77$.

Formula: $F = \frac{9}{5}C + 32$

Substitute: $77 = \frac{9}{5}C + 32$ Let $F = 77$.

3. SOLVE.

$$77 = \frac{9}{5}C + 32$$

$$77 - 32 = \frac{9}{5}C + 32 - 32 \quad \text{Subtract 32 from both sides.}$$

$$45 = \frac{9}{5}C \qquad\qquad\qquad \text{Combine like terms.}$$

$$\frac{5}{9} \cdot 45 = \frac{5}{9} \cdot \frac{9}{5}C \qquad\qquad \text{Multiply both sides by } \frac{5}{9}.$$

$$25 = C \qquad\qquad\qquad\quad \text{Simplify.}$$

4. INTERPRET.

Check: To check, replace C with 25 and F with 77 in the formula and see that a true statement results.

State: Thus, 77° Fahrenheit is equivalent to 25° Celsius.

Note: There is a formula for directly converting degrees Fahrenheit to degrees Celsius. It is $C = \frac{5}{9}(F - 32)$, as we shall see in Example 8.   □

PRACTICE

3   The average minimum temperature for July in Sydney, Australia, is 8° Celsius. Find the equivalent temperature in degrees Fahrenheit.   ■

In the next example, we again use the formula for perimeter of a rectangle as in Example 2. In Example 2, we knew the width of the rectangle. In this example, both the length and width are unknown.

△ **EXAMPLE 4**   **Finding Road Sign Dimensions**

The length of a rectangular road sign is 2 feet less than three times its width. Find the dimensions if the perimeter is 28 feet.

Solution

1. UNDERSTAND. Read and reread the problem. Recall that the formula for the perimeter of a rectangle is $P = 2l + 2w$. Draw a rectangle and guess the solution. If the width of the rectangular sign is 5 feet, its length is 2 feet less than 3 times the width or $3(5 \text{ feet}) - 2 \text{ feet} = 13 \text{ feet}$. The perimeter P of the rectangle is then $2(13 \text{ feet}) + 2(5 \text{ feet}) = 36 \text{ feet}$, too much. We now know that the width is less than 5 feet.

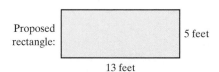

Proposed rectangle: 5 feet

13 feet

Let

w = the width of the rectangular sign; then

$3w - 2$ = the length of the sign.

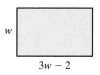

Draw a rectangle and label it with the assigned variables.

2. TRANSLATE.

Formula: $P = 2l + 2w$ or

Substitute: $28 = 2(3w - 2) + 2w.$

3. SOLVE.

$$28 = 2(3w - 2) + 2w$$
$$28 = 6w - 4 + 2w \qquad \text{Apply the distributive property.}$$
$$28 = 8w - 4$$
$$28 + 4 = 8w - 4 + 4 \qquad \text{Add 4 to both sides.}$$
$$32 = 8w$$
$$\frac{32}{8} = \frac{8w}{8} \qquad \text{Divide both sides by 8.}$$
$$4 = w$$

4. INTERPRET.

Check: If the width of the sign is 4 feet, the length of the sign is $3(4 \text{ feet}) - 2 \text{ feet} = 10 \text{ feet}.$ This gives a perimeter of $P = 2(4 \text{ feet}) + 2(10 \text{ feet}) = 28 \text{ feet}$, the correct perimeter.

State: The width of the sign is 4 feet, and the length of the sign is 10 feet.   □

PRACTICE

4   The new street signs along Route 114 have a length that is 3 inches more than 5 times the width. Find the dimensions of the signs if the perimeter of the signs is 66 inches.   ■

OBJECTIVE

2   **Solving a Formula for One of Its Variables**

We say that the formula

$$F = \frac{9}{5}C + 32$$

is solved for F because F is alone on one side of the equation, and the other side of the equation contains no F's. Suppose that we need to convert many Fahrenheit temperatures to equivalent degrees Celsius. In this case, it is easier to perform this task by solving the formula $F = \frac{9}{5}C + 32$ for C. (See Example 8.) For this reason, it is important to be able to solve an equation for any one of its specified variables. For example, the formula $d = rt$ is solved for d in terms of r and t. We can also solve $d = rt$ for t in terms of d and r. To solve for t, divide both sides of the equation by r.

$$d = rt$$
$$\frac{d}{r} = \frac{rt}{r} \qquad \text{Divide both sides by } r.$$
$$\frac{d}{r} = t \qquad \text{Simplify.}$$

To solve a formula or an equation for a specified variable, we use the same steps as for solving a linear equation. These steps are listed next.

> **Solving Equations for a Specified Variable**
>
> **Step 1.** Multiply on both sides to clear the equation of fractions if they occur.
>
> **Step 2.** Use the distributive property to remove parentheses if they occur.
>
> **Step 3.** Simplify each side of the equation by combining like terms.
>
> **Step 4.** Get all terms containing the specified variable on one side and all other terms on the other side by using the addition property of equality.
>
> **Step 5.** Get the specified variable alone by using the multiplication property of equality.

 EXAMPLE 5   Solve: $V = lwh$ for l

Solution This formula is used to find the volume of a box. To solve for l, divide both sides by wh.

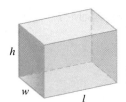

$$V = lwh$$

$$\frac{V}{wh} = \frac{lwh}{wh} \quad \text{Divide both sides by } wh.$$

$$\frac{V}{wh} = l \quad \text{Simplify.}$$

Since we have l alone on one side of the equation, we have solved for l in terms of V, w, and h. Remember that it does not matter on which side of the equation we isolate the variable. □

PRACTICE

5   Solve: $I = PRT$ for R

EXAMPLE 6   Solve: $y = mx + b$ for x

Solution The term containing the variable we are solving for, mx, is on the right side of the equation. Get mx alone by subtracting b from both sides.

$$y = mx + b$$

$$y - b = mx + b - b \quad \text{Subtract } b \text{ from both sides.}$$

$$y - b = mx \quad \text{Combine like terms.}$$

Next, solve for x by dividing both sides by m.

$$\frac{y - b}{m} = \frac{mx}{m}$$

$$\frac{y - b}{m} = x \quad \text{Simplify.} \quad \square$$

PRACTICE

6   Solve: $H = 5as + 10a$ for s

> ✔ **CONCEPT CHECK**
> Solve:
> **a.** ⬤ = ▮ − ▮ for ▮   **b.** ⬤ = ▮ · ▲ − ▮ for ▮

 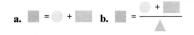

 EXAMPLE 7   Solve: $P = 2l + 2w$ for w

Solution This formula relates the perimeter of a rectangle to its length and width. Find the term containing the variable w. Get this term, $2w$, alone by subtracting $2l$ from both sides.

The 2's may *not* be divided out here. Although 2 is a factor of the denominator, 2 is *not* a factor of the numerator since it is not a factor of both terms in the numerator.

$$P = 2l + 2w$$
$$P - 2l = 2l + 2w - 2l \quad \text{Subtract } 2l \text{ from both sides.}$$
$$P - 2l = 2w \quad \text{Combine like terms.}$$
$$\frac{P - 2l}{2} = \frac{2w}{2} \quad \text{Divide both sides by 2.}$$
$$\frac{P - 2l}{2} = w \quad \text{Simplify.}$$

PRACTICE

7 Solve: $N = F + d(n - 1)$ for d

The next example has an equation containing a fraction. We will first clear the equation of fractions and then solve for the specified variable.

EXAMPLE 8 Solve: $F = \frac{9}{5}C + 32$ for C

Solution

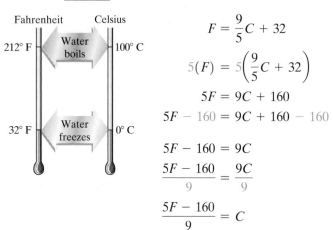

$$F = \frac{9}{5}C + 32$$
$$5(F) = 5\left(\frac{9}{5}C + 32\right) \quad \text{Clear the fraction by multiplying both sides by the LCD.}$$
$$5F = 9C + 160 \quad \text{Distribute the 5.}$$
$$5F - 160 = 9C + 160 - 160 \quad \text{To get the term containing the variable } C \text{ alone, subtract 160 from both sides.}$$
$$5F - 160 = 9C \quad \text{Combine like terms.}$$
$$\frac{5F - 160}{9} = \frac{9C}{9} \quad \text{Divide both sides by 9.}$$
$$\frac{5F - 160}{9} = C \quad \text{Simplify.}$$

Note: An equivalent way to write this formula is $C = \frac{5}{9}(F - 32)$.

PRACTICE

8 Solve: $A = \frac{1}{2}a(b + B)$ for B

Vocabulary, Readiness & Video Check

Martin-Gay Interactive Videos

See Video 2.6

Watch the section lecture video and answer the following questions.

OBJECTIVE 1
1. Complete this statement based on the lecture given before ▥ Example 1. A formula is an equation that describes known_____ among quantities.

OBJECTIVE 1
2. In ▥ Example 2, how are the units for the solution determined?

OBJECTIVE 2
3. During ▥ Example 4, why is the equation $5x = 30$ shown?

EXAMPLE 2 Solve $x + 4 \leq -6$ for x. Graph the solution set and write it in interval notation.

Solution To solve for x, subtract 4 from both sides of the inequality.

$$-12\ -11\ -10\ -9\ -8\ -7\ -6$$

$$
\begin{array}{ll}
x + 4 \leq -6 & \text{Original inequality} \\
x + 4 - 4 \leq -6 - 4 & \text{Subtract 4 from both sides.} \\
x \leq -10 & \text{Simplify.}
\end{array}
$$

The solution set is $(-\infty, -10\,]$.

PRACTICE
2 Solve $x + 11 \geq 6$. Graph the solution set and write it in interval notation.

Helpful Hint

Notice that any number less than or equal to -10 is a solution to $x \leq -10$. For example, solutions include

$$-10, \ -200, \ -11\frac{1}{2}, \ -7\pi, \ -\sqrt{130}, \ -50.3$$

An important difference between linear equations and linear inequalities is shown when we multiply or divide both sides of an inequality by a nonzero real number. For example, start with the true statement $6 < 8$ and multiply both sides by 2. As we see below, the resulting inequality is also true.

$$
\begin{array}{ll}
6 < 8 & \text{True} \\
2(6) < 2(8) & \text{Multiply both sides by 2.} \\
12 < 16 & \text{True}
\end{array}
$$

But if we start with the same true statement $6 < 8$ and multiply both sides by -2, the resulting inequality is not a true statement.

$$
\begin{array}{ll}
6 < 8 & \text{True} \\
-2(6) < -2(8) & \text{Multiply both sides by } -2. \\
-12 < -16 & \text{False}
\end{array}
$$

Notice, however, that if we reverse the direction of the inequality symbol, the resulting inequality is true.

$$
\begin{array}{ll}
-12 < -16 & \text{False} \\
-12 > -16 & \text{True}
\end{array}
$$

This demonstrates the multiplication property of inequality.

Multiplication Property of Inequality

1. If a, b, and c are real numbers, and c is **positive,** then

$$a < b \qquad \text{and} \qquad ac < bc$$

are equivalent inequalities.

2. If a, b, and c are real numbers, and c is **negative,** then

$$a < b \qquad \text{and} \qquad ac > bc$$

are equivalent inequalities.

Because division is defined in terms of multiplication, this property also holds true when dividing both sides of an inequality by a nonzero number. If we multiply or divide both sides of an inequality by a negative number, **the direction of the inequality symbol must be reversed for the inequalities to remain equivalent.**

We can also picture the solutions on a number line. If we use open/closed-circle notation, the graph of $\{x|x < 3\}$ looks like the following.

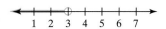

In this text, a convenient notation, called **interval notation,** will be used to write solution sets of inequalities. To help us understand this notation, a different graphing notation will be used. Instead of an open circle, we use a parenthesis; instead of a closed circle, we use a bracket. With this new notation, the graph of $\{x|x < 3\}$ now looks like

and can be represented in interval notation as $(-\infty, 3)$. The symbol $-\infty$, read as "negative infinity," does not indicate a number but does indicate that the shaded arrow to the left never ends. In other words, the interval $(-\infty, 3)$ includes *all* numbers less than 3.

Picturing the solutions of an inequality on a number line is called **graphing** the solutions or graphing the inequality, and the picture is called the **graph** of the inequality.

To graph $\{x|x \leq 3\}$ or simply $x \leq 3$, shade the numbers to the left of 3 and place a bracket at 3 on the number line as shown in the margin. The bracket indicates that 3 **is** a solution: 3 **is** less than or equal to 3. In interval notation, we write $(-\infty, 3]$.

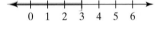

Helpful Hint

When writing an inequality in interval notation, it may be easier to graph the inequality first, then write it in interval notation. To help, think of the number line as approaching $-\infty$ to the left and $+\infty$ or ∞ to the right. Then simply write the interval notation by following your shading from left to right.

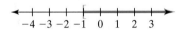

EXAMPLE 1   Graph $x \geq -1$. Then write the solutions in interval notation.

Solution   We place a bracket at -1 since the inequality symbol is $\geq$ and -1 is greater than or equal to -1. Then we shade to the right of -1.

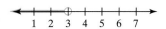

In interval notation, this is $[-1, \infty)$.

PRACTICE

1   Graph $x < 5$. Then write the solutions in interval notation.

OBJECTIVE

2   Solving Linear Inequalities ▶

When solutions of a linear inequality are not immediately obvious, they are found through a process similar to the one used to solve a linear equation. Our goal is to get the variable alone, and we use properties of inequality similar to properties of equality.

Addition Property of Inequality

If a, b, and c are real numbers, then

$$a < b \quad \text{and} \quad a + c < b + c$$

are equivalent inequalities.

This property also holds true for subtracting values, since subtraction is defined in terms of addition. In other words, adding or subtracting the same quantity from both sides of an inequality does not change the solution of the inequality.

2.9 | Solving Linear Inequalities

OBJECTIVES

1 Define Linear Inequality in One Variable, Graph Solution Sets on a Number Line, and Use Interval Notation.

2 Solve Linear Inequalities.

3 Solve Compound Inequalities.

4 Solve Inequality Applications.

OBJECTIVE

1 Graphing Solution Sets to Linear Inequalities and Using Interval Notation

In Chapter 1, we reviewed these inequality symbols and their meanings:

$<$ means "is less than" $\leq$ means "is less than or equal to"

$>$ means "is greater than" $\geq$ means "is greater than or equal to"

Equations	Inequalities
$x = 3$	$x \leq 3$
$5n - 6 = 14$	$5n - 6 < 14$
$12 = 7 - 3y$	$12 \geq 7 - 3y$
$\dfrac{x}{4} - 6 = 1$	$\dfrac{x}{4} - 6 > 1$

A linear inequality is similar to a linear equation except that the equality symbol is replaced with an inequality symbol.

Linear Inequality in One Variable

A **linear inequality in one variable** is an inequality that can be written in the form

$$ax + b < c$$

where a, b, and c are real numbers and a is not 0.

This definition and all other definitions, properties, and steps in this section also hold true for the inequality symbols $>$, $\geq$, and $\leq$.

A **solution of an inequality** is a value of the variable that makes the inequality a true statement. The solution set is the set of all solutions. For the inequality $x < 3$, replacing x with any number less than 3, that is, to the left of 3 on a number line, makes the resulting inequality true. This means that any number less than 3 is a solution of the inequality $x < 3$.

Since there are infinitely many such numbers, we cannot list all the solutions of the inequality. We *can* use set notation and write

$$\{x \quad | \quad x < 3\}.$$

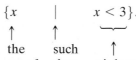

Recall that this is read   the set of   such x is less than 3.
all x that

per second, how long does it take light from the Sun to reach us?

88. Light travels at a rate of 186,000 miles per second. If our moon is 238,860 miles from Earth, how long does it take light from the moon to reach us? (Round to the nearest tenth of a second.)

238,860 miles

89. A glacier is a giant mass of rocks and ice that flows downhill like a river. Exit Glacier, near Seward, Alaska, moves at a rate of 20 inches a day. Find the distance in feet the glacier moves in a year. (Assume 365 days a year. Round to 2 decimal places.)

90. Flying fish do not *actually* fly, but glide. They have been known to travel a distance of 1300 feet at a rate of 20 miles per hour. How many seconds does it take to travel this distance? (*Hint:* First convert miles per hour to feet per second. Recall that 1 mile = 5280 feet. Round to the nearest tenth of a second.)

91. A Japanese "bullet" train set a new world record for train speed at 581 kilometers per hour during a manned test run on the Yamanashi Maglev Test Line in 2003. The Yamanashi Maglev Test Line is 42.8 kilometers long. How many *minutes* would a test run on the Yamanashi Line last at this record-setting speed? Round to the nearest hundredth of a minute. (*Source:* Japan Railways Central Co.)

92. The Boeing X-51 is an unmanned demonstration aircraft for hypersonic flight testing. In May 2010, it successfully completed a free flight at about 3800 mph. Neglecting altitude, if the circumference of Earth is approximately 25,000 miles, how long would it take for the X-51 to travel around Earth? Give your answer in hours and minutes rounded to the nearest whole minute.

93. In the United States, a notable hang glider flight was a 303-mile, $8\frac{1}{2}$-hour flight from New Mexico to Kansas. What was the average rate during this flight?

94. Stalactites join stalagmites to form columns. A column found at Natural Bridge Caverns near San Antonio, Texas, rises 15 feet and has a *diameter* of only 2 inches. Find the volume of this column in cubic inches. Round to the nearest tenth of a cubic inch. (*Hint:* Use the formula for volume of a cylinder and use a calculator approximation for π.)

△ **56.** The perimeter of the following triangle is 82 feet. Find the length of each side.

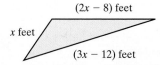

x feet
$(2x - 8)$ feet
$(3x - 12)$ feet

57. The Hawaiian volcano Kilauea is one of the world's most active volcanoes and has had continuous eruptive activity since 1983. Erupting lava flows through a tube system about 11 kilometers to the sea. Assume a lava flow speed of 0.5 kilometer per hour and calculate how long it takes to reach the sea.

58. The world's largest pink ribbon, the sign of the fight against breast cancer, was erected out of pink Post-it® notes on a billboard in New York City in October 2004. If the area of the rectangular billboard covered by the ribbon was approximately 3990 square feet, and the width of the billboard was approximately 57 feet, what was the height of this billboard?

△ **59.** The perimeter of an equilateral triangle is 7 inches more than the perimeter of a square, and the side of the triangle is 5 inches longer than the side of the square. Find the side of the triangle. (*Hint:* An equilateral triangle has three sides the same length.)

△ **60.** A square animal pen and a pen shaped like an equilateral triangle have equal perimeters. Find the length of the sides of each pen if the sides of the triangular pen are fifteen less than twice the sides of the square pen.

61. Find how long it takes a person to drive 135 miles on I-10 if she merges onto I-10 at 10 a.m. and drives nonstop with her cruise control set on 60 mph.

62. Beaumont, Texas, is about 150 miles from Toledo Bend. If Leo Miller leaves Beaumont at 4 a.m. and averages 45 mph, when should he arrive at Toledo Bend?

△ **63.** The longest runway at Los Angeles International Airport has the shape of a rectangle and an area of 1,813,500 square feet. This runway is 150 feet wide. How long is the runway? (*Source:* Los Angeles World Airports)

64. Normal room temperature is about 78°F. Convert this temperature to Celsius.

65. The highest temperature ever recorded in Europe was 122°F in Seville, Spain, in August 1881. Convert this record high temperature to Celsius. (*Source:* National Climatic Data Center)

66. The lowest temperature ever recorded in Oceania was −10°C at the Haleakala Summit in Maui, Hawaii, in January 1961. Convert this record low temperature to Fahrenheit. (*Source:* National Climatic Data Center)

67. The average temperature on the planet Mercury is 167°C. Convert this temperature to degrees Fahrenheit. (*Source:* National Space Science Data Center)

68. The average temperature on the planet Jupiter is −227°F. Convert this temperature to degrees Celsius. Round to the nearest degree. (*Source:* National Space Science Data Center)

69. The Hoberman Sphere is a toy ball that expands and contracts. When it is completely closed, it has a diameter of 9.5 inches. Find the volume of the Hoberman Sphere when

it is completely closed. Use 3.14 for π. Round to the nearest whole cubic inch. (*Hint:* Volume of a sphere $= \frac{4}{3}\pi r^3$. *Source:* Hoberman Designs, Inc.)

70. When the Hoberman Sphere (see Exercise 69) is completely expanded, its diameter is 30 inches. Find the volume of the Hoberman Sphere when it is completely expanded. Use 3.14 for π. (*Source:* Hoberman Designs, Inc.)

REVIEW AND PREVIEW

Write each percent as a decimal.

71. 32%

72. 8%

73. 200%

74. 0.5%

Write each decimal as a percent.

75. 0.17

76. 0.03

77. 7.2

78. 5

CONCEPT EXTENSIONS

△ **79.** The formula $V = lwh$ is used to find the volume of a box. If the length of a box is doubled, the width is doubled, and the height is doubled, how does this affect the volume? Explain your answer.

△ **80.** The formula $A = bh$ is used to find the area of a parallelogram. If the base of a parallelogram is doubled and its height is doubled, how does this affect the area? Explain your answer.

81. Use the Dolbear's Law formula for Exercises 45–48 and calculate when the number of cricket chirps per minute is the same as the temperature in degrees Fahrenheit. (*Hint:* Replace T with N and solve for N or replace N with T and solve for T.)

82. Find the temperature at which the Celsius measurement and the Fahrenheit measurement are the same number.

Solve.

83. $N = R + \dfrac{V}{G}$ for V (Urban forestry: tree plantings per year)

84. $B = \dfrac{F}{P - V}$ for V (Business: break-even point)

Solve. See the Concept Check in this section.

85. ■ − ● · ■ = ▲ for ●

86. ◆ · ■ + ▲ = ● for ■

87. The distance from the Sun to Earth is approximately 93,000,000 miles. If light travels at a rate of 186,000 miles

△ **43.** Piranha fish require 1.5 cubic feet of water per fish to maintain a healthy environment. Find the maximum number of piranhas you could put in a tank measuring 8 feet by 3 feet by 6 feet.

6 feet

3 feet   8 feet

△ **44.** Find the maximum number of goldfish you can put in a cylindrical tank whose diameter is 8 meters and whose height is 3 meters if each goldfish needs 2 cubic meters of water.

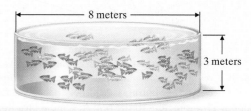

8 meters

3 meters

Dolbear's Law states the relationship between the rate at which Snowy Tree crickets chirp and the air temperature of their environment. The formula is

$$T = 50 + \frac{N - 40}{4}, \text{ where}$$

T = temperature in degrees Fahrenheit and
N = number of chirps per minute

45. If $N = 86$, find the temperature in degrees Fahrenheit, T.

46. If $N = 94$, find the temperature in degrees Fahrenheit, T.

47. If $T = 55°F$, find the number of chirps per minute.

48. If $T = 65°F$, find the number of chirps per minute.

Use the results of Exercises 45–48 to complete each sentence with "increases" or "decreases."

49. As the number of cricket chirps per minute increases, the air temperature of their environment _____.

50. As the air temperature of their environment decreases, the number of cricket chirps per minute _____.

△ **51.** A lawn is in the shape of a trapezoid with a height of 60 feet and bases of 70 feet and 130 feet. How many whole bags of fertilizer must be purchased to cover the lawn if each bag covers 4000 square feet?

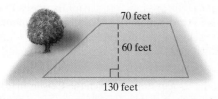

70 feet

60 feet

130 feet

△ **52.** If the area of a right-triangularly shaped sail is 20 square feet and its base is 5 feet, find the height of the sail.

?

5 feet

△ **53.** Maria's Pizza sells one 16-inch cheese pizza or two 10-inch cheese pizzas for $9.99. Determine which size gives more pizza.

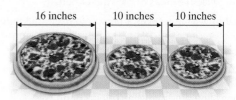

16 inches   10 inches   10 inches

△ **54.** Find how much rope is needed to wrap around Earth at the equator if the radius of Earth is 4000 miles. (*Hint:* Use 3.14 for π and the formula for circumference.)

△ **55.** The perimeter of a geometric figure is the sum of the lengths of its sides. If the perimeter of the following pentagon (five-sided figure) is 48 meters, find the length of each side.

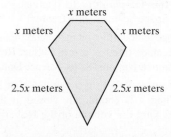

x meters

x meters x meters

2.5x meters   2.5x meters

32. For the purpose of purchasing lumber for a new fence and seed to plant grass,

   a. Find the area and perimeter of the yard below.

   b. Identify whether a fence has to do with area or perimeter and the same with grass seed.

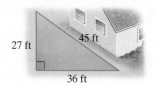

27 ft   45 ft

36 ft

33. A frame shop charges according to both the amount of framing needed to surround the picture and the amount of glass needed to cover the picture.

   a. Find the area and perimeter of the trapezoid-shaped framed picture below.

   b. Identify whether the amount of framing has to do with perimeter or area and the same with the amount of glass.

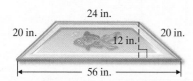

24 in.

20 in.   12 in.   20 in.

56 in.

34. A decorator is painting and placing a border completely around the parallelogram-shaped wall.

   a. Find the area and perimeter of the wall below.

   b. Identify whether the border has to do with perimeter or area and the same with paint.

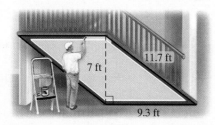

7 ft   11.7 ft

9.3 ft

35. Convert Nome, Alaska's 14°F high temperature to Celsius.

36. Convert Paris, France's low temperature of −5°C to Fahrenheit.

37. An architect designs a rectangular flower garden such that the width is exactly two-thirds of the length. If 260 feet of antique picket fencing are to be used to enclose the garden, find the dimensions of the garden.

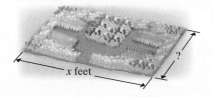

x feet

38. If the length of a rectangular parking lot is 10 meters less than twice its width, and the perimeter is 400 meters, find the length of the parking lot.

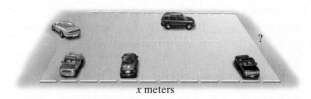

x meters

39. A flower bed is in the shape of a triangle with one side twice the length of the shortest side, and the third side is 30 feet more than the length of the shortest side. Find the dimensions if the perimeter is 102 feet.

?

x   ?

40. The perimeter of a yield sign in the shape of an isosceles triangle is 22 feet. If the shortest side is 2 feet less than the other two sides, find the length of the shortest side. (*Hint:* An isosceles triangle has two sides the same length.)

?

x feet   YIELD   x feet

41. The Cat is a high-speed catamaran auto ferry that operates between Bar Harbor, Maine, and Yarmouth, Nova Scotia. The Cat can make the 138-mile trip in about $2\frac{1}{2}$ hours. Find the catamaran speed for this trip. (*Source:* Bay Ferries)

42. A family is planning their vacation to Disney World. They will drive from a small town outside New Orleans, Louisiana, to Orlando, Florida, a distance of 700 miles. They plan to average a rate of 55 mph. How long will this trip take?

2.6   Exercise Set   MyMathLab®

Substitute the given values into each given formula and solve for the unknown variable. If necessary, round to one decimal place. See Examples 1 through 4.

△ **1.** $A = bh$; $A = 45, b = 15$ (Area of a parallelogram)

2. $d = rt$; $d = 195, t = 3$ (Distance formula)

△ **3.** $S = 4lw + 2wh$; $S = 102, l = 7, w = 3$ (Surface area of a special rectangular box)

△ **4.** $V = lwh$; $l = 14, w = 8, h = 3$ (Volume of a rectangular box)

△ **5.** $A = \frac{1}{2}h(B + b)$; $A = 180, B = 11, b = 7$ (Area of a trapezoid)

△ **6.** $A = \frac{1}{2}h(B + b)$; $A = 60, B = 7, b = 3$ (Area of a trapezoid)

△ **7.** $P = a + b + c$; $P = 30, a = 8, b = 10$ (Perimeter of a triangle)

△ **8.** $V = \frac{1}{3}Ah$; $V = 45, h = 5$ (Volume of a pyramid)

9. $C = 2\pi r$; $C = 15.7$ (use the approximation 3.14 or a calculator approximation for π) (Circumference of a circle)

10. $A = \pi r^2$; $r = 4.5$ (use the approximation 3.14 or a calculator approximation for π) (Area of a circle)

11. $I = PRT$; $I = 3750, P = 25,000, R = 0.05$ (Simple interest formula)

12. $I = PRT$; $I = 1,056,000, R = 0.055, T = 6$ (Simple interest formula)

13. $V = \frac{1}{3}\pi r^2 h$; $V = 565.2, r = 6$ (use a calculator approximation for π) (Volume of a cone)

14. $V = \frac{4}{3}\pi r^3$; $r = 3$ (use a calculator approximation for π) (Volume of a sphere)

Solve each formula for the specified variable. See Examples 5 through 8.

15. $f = 5gh$ for h

△ **16.** $A = \pi ab$ for b

17. $V = lwh$ for w

18. $T = mnr$ for n

19. $3x + y = 7$ for y

20. $-x + y = 13$ for y

21. $A = P + PRT$ for R

22. $A = P + PRT$ for T

23. $V = \frac{1}{3}Ah$ for A

24. $D = \frac{1}{4}fk$ for k

25. $P = a + b + c$ for a

26. $PR = x + y + z + w$ for z

27. $S = 2\pi rh + 2\pi r^2$ for h

△ **28.** $S = 4lw + 2wh$ for h

Solve. For Exercises 29 and 30, the solutions have been started for you. See Examples 1 through 4.

△ **29.** The iconic NASDAQ sign in New York's Times Square has a width of 84 feet and an area of 10,080 square feet. Find the height (or length) of the sign. (*Source:* livedesignonline.com)

Start the solution:

1. UNDERSTAND the problem. Reread it as many times as needed.

2. TRANSLATE into an equation. (Fill in the blanks below.)

Area	=	length	times	width
↓	↓	↓	↓	↓
___	=	x	·	___

Finish with:

3. SOLVE and   4. INTERPRET

△ **30.** The world's largest sign for Coca-Cola is located in Arica, Chile. The rectangular sign has a length of 400 feet and an area of 52,400 square feet. Find the width of the sign. (*Source:* Fabulous Facts about Coca-Cola, Atlanta, GA)

Start the solution:

1. UNDERSTAND the problem. Reread it as many times as needed.

2. TRANSLATE into an equation. (Fill in the blanks below.)

Area	=	length	times	width
↓	↓	↓	↓	↓
___	=	___	·	x

Finish with:

3. SOLVE and   4. INTERPRET

31. For the purpose of purchasing new baseboard and carpet,

a. Find the area and perimeter of the room below (neglecting doors).

b. Identify whether baseboard has to do with area or perimeter and the same with carpet.

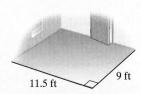

11.5 ft   9 ft

> **Helpful Hint**
>
> Whenever both sides of an inequality are multiplied or divided by a negative number, the direction of the inequality symbol **must be** reversed to form an equivalent inequality.

EXAMPLE 3   Solve $-2x \leq -4$. Graph the solution set and write it in interval notation.

Solution   Remember to reverse the direction of the inequality symbol when dividing by a negative number.

> **Helpful Hint**
>
> Don't forget to reverse the direction of the inequality symbol.

$$-2x \leq -4$$

$$\frac{-2x}{-2} \geq \frac{-4}{-2} \qquad \text{Divide both sides by } -2 \text{ and reverse the direction of the inequality symbol.}$$

$$x \geq 2 \qquad \text{Simplify.}$$

The solution set $[2, \infty)$ is graphed as shown.

PRACTICE

3   Solve $-5x \geq -15$. Graph the solution set and write it in interval notation.

EXAMPLE 4   Solve $2x < -4$. Graph the solution set and write it in interval notation.

Solution

> **Helpful Hint**
>
> Do not reverse the inequality symbol.

$$2x < -4$$

$$\frac{2x}{2} < \frac{-4}{2} \qquad \text{Divide both sides by 2.}$$

$$\qquad \text{Do not reverse the direction of the inequality symbol.}$$

$$x < -2 \qquad \text{Simplify.}$$

The solution set $(-\infty, -2)$ is graphed as shown.

PRACTICE

4   Solve $3x > -9$. Graph the solution set and write it in interval notation.

✔ **CONCEPT CHECK**

Fill in the blank with $<$, $>$, $\leq$, or $\geq$.

a. Since $-8 < -4$, then $3(-8)$_____$3(-4)$.

b. Since $5 \geq -2$, then $\dfrac{5}{-7}$ _____ $\dfrac{-2}{-7}$.

c. If $a < b$, then $2a$_____$2b$.

d. If $a \geq b$, then $\dfrac{a}{-3}$ _____ $\dfrac{b}{-3}$.

Answers to Concept Check:
a. $<$ **b.** $\leq$ **c.** $<$ **d.** $\leq$

The following steps may be helpful when solving inequalities. Notice that these steps are similar to the ones given in Section 2.4 for solving equations.

Solving Linear Inequalities in One Variable

Step 1. Clear the inequality of fractions by multiplying both sides of the inequality by the least common denominator (LCD) of all fractions in the inequality.

Step 2. Remove grouping symbols such as parentheses by using the distributive property.

Step 3. Simplify each side of the inequality by combining like terms.

Step 4. Write the inequality with variable terms on one side and numbers on the other side by using the addition property of inequality.

Step 5. Get the variable alone by using the multiplication property of inequality.

Helpful Hint

Don't forget that if both sides of an inequality are multiplied or divided by a negative number, the direction of the inequality symbol must be reversed.

EXAMPLE 5 Solve $-4x + 7 \geq -9$. Graph the solution set and write it in interval notation.

Solution

$$-4x + 7 \geq -9$$

$$-4x + 7 - 7 \geq -9 - 7 \qquad \text{Subtract 7 from both sides.}$$

$$-4x \geq -16 \qquad \text{Simplify.}$$

$$\frac{-4x}{-4} \leq \frac{-16}{-4} \qquad \begin{array}{l}\text{Divide both sides by } -4 \text{ and reverse} \\ \text{the direction of the inequality symbol.}\end{array}$$

$$x \leq 4 \qquad \text{Simplify.}$$

The solution set $(-\infty, 4]$ is graphed as shown.

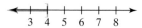

PRACTICE

5 Solve $45 - 7x \leq -4$. Graph the solution set and write it in interval notation.

EXAMPLE 6 Solve $2x + 7 \leq x - 11$. Graph the solution set and write it in interval notation.

Solution

$$2x + 7 \leq x - 11$$

$$2x + 7 - x \leq x - 11 - x \qquad \text{Subtract } x \text{ from both sides.}$$

$$x + 7 \leq -11 \qquad \text{Combine like terms.}$$

$$x + 7 - 7 \leq -11 - 7 \qquad \text{Subtract 7 from both sides.}$$

$$x \leq -18 \qquad \text{Combine like terms.}$$

The graph of the solution set $(-\infty, -18]$ is shown.

PRACTICE

6 Solve $3x + 20 \leq 2x + 13$. Graph the solution set and write it in interval notation.

EXAMPLE 7 Solve $-5x + 7 < 2(x - 3)$. Graph the solution set and write it in interval notation.

Solution

$$-5x + 7 < 2(x - 3)$$

$$-5x + 7 < 2x - 6 \qquad \text{Apply the distributive property.}$$

$$-5x + 7 - 2x < 2x - 6 - 2x \qquad \text{Subtract } 2x \text{ from both sides.}$$

$$-7x + 7 < -6 \qquad \text{Combine like terms.}$$

$$-7x + 7 - 7 < -6 - 7 \qquad \text{Subtract 7 from both sides.}$$

$$-7x < -13 \qquad \text{Combine like terms.}$$

$$\frac{-7x}{-7} > \frac{-13}{-7} \qquad \begin{array}{l}\text{Divide both sides by } -7 \text{ and reverse} \\ \text{the direction of the inequality symbol.}\end{array}$$

$$x > \frac{13}{7} \qquad \text{Simplify.}$$

The graph of the solution set $\left(\dfrac{13}{7}, \infty\right)$ is shown.

PRACTICE

7 Solve $6 - 5x > 3(x - 4)$. Graph the solution set and write it in interval notation.

EXAMPLE 8 Solve $2(x - 3) - 5 \le 3(x + 2) - 18$. Graph the solution set and write it in interval notation.

Solution

$$2(x - 3) - 5 \le 3(x + 2) - 18$$

$$2x - 6 - 5 \le 3x + 6 - 18 \qquad \text{Apply the distributive property.}$$

$$2x - 11 \le 3x - 12 \qquad \text{Combine like terms.}$$

$$-x - 11 \le -12 \qquad \text{Subtract } 3x \text{ from both sides.}$$

$$-x \le -1 \qquad \text{Add 11 to both sides.}$$

$$\frac{-x}{-1} \ge \frac{-1}{-1} \qquad \begin{array}{l}\text{Divide both sides by } -1 \text{ and reverse} \\ \text{the direction of the inequality symbol.}\end{array}$$

$$x \ge 1 \qquad \text{Simplify.}$$

The graph of the solution set $[1, \infty)$ is shown.

PRACTICE

8 Solve $3(x - 4) - 5 \le 5(x - 1) - 12$. Graph the solution set and write it in interval notation.

OBJECTIVE

3 Solving Compound Inequalities ▶

Inequalities containing one inequality symbol are called **simple inequalities,** while inequalities containing two inequality symbols are called **compound inequalities.** A compound inequality is really two simple inequalities in one. The compound inequality

$$3 < x < 5 \quad \text{means} \quad 3 < x \text{ and } x < 5$$

This can be read "x is greater than 3 and less than 5."

A solution of a compound inequality is a value that is a solution of both of the simple inequalities that make up the compound inequality. For example,

$$4\frac{1}{2} \text{ is a solution of } 3 < x < 5 \text{ since } 3 < 4\frac{1}{2} \text{ and } 4\frac{1}{2} < 5.$$

To graph $3 < x < 5$, place parentheses at both 3 and 5 and shade between.

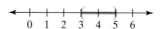

EXAMPLE 9 Graph $2 < x \leq 4$. Write the solutions in interval notation.

Solution Graph all numbers greater than 2 and less than or equal to 4. Place a parenthesis at 2, a bracket at 4, and shade between.

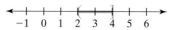

In interval notation, this is $(2, 4]$.

PRACTICE

9 Graph $-3 \leq x < 1$. Write the solutions in interval notation.

When we solve a simple inequality, we isolate the variable on one side of the inequality. When we solve a compound inequality, we isolate the variable in the middle part of the inequality. Also, when solving a compound inequality, we must perform the same operation to all **three** parts of the inequality: left, middle, and right.

EXAMPLE 10 Solve $-1 \leq 2x - 3 < 5$. Graph the solution set and write it in interval notation.

Solution

$$-1 \leq 2x - 3 < 5$$
$$-1 + 3 \leq 2x - 3 + 3 < 5 + 3 \quad \text{Add 3 to all three parts.}$$
$$2 \leq 2x < 8 \quad \text{Combine like terms.}$$
$$\frac{2}{2} \leq \frac{2x}{2} < \frac{8}{2} \quad \text{Divide all three parts by 2.}$$
$$1 \leq x < 4 \quad \text{Simplify.}$$

The graph of the solution set $[1, 4)$ is shown.

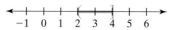

PRACTICE

10 Solve $-4 < 3x + 2 \leq 8$. Graph the solution set and write it in interval notation.

EXAMPLE 11 Solve $3 \leq \dfrac{3x}{2} + 4 \leq 5$. Graph the solution set and write it in interval notation.

Solution

$$3 \leq \frac{3x}{2} + 4 \leq 5$$

$$2(3) \leq 2\left(\frac{3x}{2} + 4\right) \leq 2(5) \quad \begin{array}{l}\text{Multiply all three parts by 2 to clear}\\\text{the fraction.}\end{array}$$

$$6 \leq 3x + 8 \leq 10 \quad \text{Distribute.}$$
$$-2 \leq 3x \leq 2 \quad \text{Subtract 8 from all three parts.}$$
$$\frac{-2}{3} \leq \frac{3x}{3} \leq \frac{2}{3} \quad \text{Divide all three parts by 3.}$$
$$-\frac{2}{3} \leq x \leq \frac{2}{3} \quad \text{Simplify.}$$

The graph of the solution set $\left[-\dfrac{2}{3}, \dfrac{2}{3}\right]$ is shown.

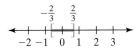

PRACTICE
11 Solve $1 < \dfrac{3}{4}x + 5 < 6$. Graph the solution set and write it in interval notation.

OBJECTIVE
4 Solving Inequality Applications

Problems containing words such as "at least," "at most," "between," "no more than," and "no less than" usually indicate that an inequality should be solved instead of an equation. In solving applications involving linear inequalities, use the same procedure you use to solve applications involving linear equations.

Some Inequality Translations			
≥	≤	<	>
at least	at most	is less than	is greater than
no less than	no more than		

EXAMPLE 12 12 subtracted from 3 times a number is less than 21. Find all numbers that make this statement true.

Solution

1. UNDERSTAND. Read and reread the problem. This is a direct translation problem, and let's let

$$x = \text{the unknown number.}$$

2. TRANSLATE.

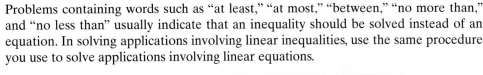

3. SOLVE. $3x - 12 < 21$

$\qquad 3x < 33$ Add 12 to both sides.

$\qquad \dfrac{3x}{3} < \dfrac{33}{3}$ Divide both sides by 3 and do not reverse the direction of the inequality symbol.

$\qquad x < 11$ Simplify.

4. INTERPRET.

Check: Check the translation; then let's choose a number less than 11 to see if it checks. For example, let's check 10. 12 subtracted from 3 times 10 is 12 subtracted from 30, or 18. Since 18 is less than 21, the number 10 checks.

State: All numbers less than 11 make the original statement true.

PRACTICE
12 Twice a number, subtracted from 35, is greater than 15. Find all numbers that make this true.

EXAMPLE 13 Staying within Budget

Marie Chase and Jonathan Edwards are having their wedding reception at the Gallery Reception Hall. They may spend at most $2000 for the reception. If the reception hall charges a $100 cleanup fee plus $36 per person, find the greatest number of people that they can invite and still stay within their budget.

Solution

1. UNDERSTAND. Read and reread the problem. Next, guess a solution. If 40 people attend the reception, the cost is $100 + $36(40) = $100 + $1440 = $1540. Let

$$x = \text{the number of people who attend the reception.}$$

2. TRANSLATE.

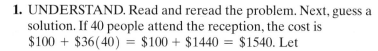

In words:	cleanup fee	+	cost per person	must be less than or equal to	2000
Tlanslate:	100	+	36x	≤	2000

3. SOLVE.

$$100 + 36x \leq 2000$$
$$36x \leq 1900 \quad \text{Subtract 100 from both sides.}$$
$$x \leq 52\frac{7}{9} \quad \text{Divide both sides by 36.}$$

4. INTERPRET.

Check: Since x represents the number of people, we round down to the nearest whole, or 52. Notice that if 52 people attend, the cost is

$$\$100 + \$36(52) = \$1972. \text{ If 53 people attend, the cost is}$$
$$\$100 + \$36(53) = \$2008, \text{ which is more than the given 2000.}$$

State: Marie Chase and Jonathan Edwards can invite at most 52 people to the reception. □

PRACTICE
13 Kasonga is eager to begin his education at his local community college. He has budgeted $1500 for college this semester. His local college charges a $300 matriculation fee and costs an average of $375 for tuition, fees, and books for each three-credit course. Find the greatest number of classes Kasonga can afford to take this semester. ■

✔ **Vocabulary, Readiness & Video Check**

Use the choices below to fill in each blank. Choices may be used more than once.

expression   inequality   equation

1. $6x - 7(x + 9)$ _____   **2.** $6x = 7(x + 9)$ _____
3. $6x < 7(x + 9)$ _____   **4.** $5y - 2 \geq -38$ _____

Decide which number listed is not a solution to each given inequality.

5. $x \geq -3$; $-3, 0, -5, \pi$ _____   **6.** $x < 6$; $-6, |-6|, 0, -3.2$ _____

Martin-Gay Interactive Videos

See Video 2.9

Watch the section lecture video and answer the following questions.

OBJECTIVE 1

7. Using Example 1 from the video as a reference, explain the connection between the graph of an inequality and interval notation.

OBJECTIVE 2

8. The steps for solving a linear inequality in one variable are discussed in the lecture before Example 6. Why are you told to be very careful when you use Step 5?

OBJECTIVE 3

9. For Example 8, explain how the solving would change if the compound inequality simplified to $0 < -3x < 14$ instead of $0 < 3x < 14$.

OBJECTIVE 4

10. What is the phrase in Example 9 that tells you to translate to an *inequality*? What does this phrase translate to?

2.9 Exercise Set MyMathLab®

Graph each set of numbers given in interval notation. Then write an inequality statement in x describing the numbers graphed.

1. $[2, \infty)$

2. $(-3, \infty)$

3. $(-\infty, -5)$

4. $(-\infty, 4]$

Graph each inequality on a number line. Then write the solutions in interval notation. See Example 1.

5. $x \le -1$

6. $y < 0$

7. $x < \dfrac{1}{2}$

8. $z < -\dfrac{2}{3}$

9. $y \ge 5$

10. $x > 3$

Solve each inequality. Graph the solution set and write it in interval notation. See Examples 2 through 4.

11. $2x < -6$

12. $3x > -9$

13. $x - 2 \ge -7$

14. $x + 4 \le 1$

15. $-8x \le 16$

16. $-5x < 20$

Solve each inequality. Graph the solution set and write it in interval notation. See Examples 5 and 6.

17. $3x - 5 > 2x - 8$

18. $3 - 7x \ge 10 - 8x$

19. $4x - 1 \le 5x - 2x$

20. $7x + 3 < 9x - 3x$

Solve each inequality. Graph the solution set and write it in interval notation. See Examples 7 and 8.

21. $x - 7 < 3(x + 1)$

22. $3x + 9 \le 5(x - 1)$

23. $-6x + 2 \ge 2(5 - x)$

24. $-7x + 4 > 3(4 - x)$

25. $4(3x - 1) \le 5(2x - 4)$

26. $3(5x - 4) \le 4(3x - 2)$

27. $3(x + 2) - 6 > -2(x - 3) + 14$

28. $7(x - 2) + x \le -4(5 - x) - 12$

MIXED PRACTICE

Solve the following inequalities. Graph each solution set and write it in interval notation.

29. $-2x \le -40$

30. $-7x > 21$

31. $-9 + x > 7$

32. $y - 4 \le 1$

33. $3x - 7 < 6x + 2$

34. $2x - 1 \ge 4x - 5$

35. $5x - 7x \ge x + 2$

36. $4 - x < 8x + 2x$

37. $\dfrac{3}{4}x > 2$

38. $\dfrac{5}{6}x \ge -8$

39. $3(x - 5) < 2(2x - 1)$

40. $5(x + 4) < 4(2x + 3)$

41. $4(2x + 1) < 4$

42. $6(2 - x) \ge 12$

43. $-5x + 4 \ge -4(x - 1)$

44. $-6x + 2 < -3(x + 4)$

45. $-2(x - 4) - 3x < -(4x + 1) + 2x$

46. $-5(1 - x) + x \le -(6 - 2x) + 6$

47. $\dfrac{1}{4}(x + 4) < \dfrac{1}{5}(2x + 3)$

48. $\dfrac{1}{3}(3x - 1) < \dfrac{1}{2}(x + 4)$

Graph each inequality. Then write the solutions in interval notation. See Example 9.

49. $-1 < x < 3$

50. $2 \le y \le 3$

51. $0 \le y < 2$

52. $-1 \le x \le 4$

Solve each inequality. Graph the solution set and write it in interval notation. See Examples 10 and 11.

53. $-3 < 3x < 6$

54. $-5 < 2x < -2$

55. $2 \le 3x - 10 \le 5$

56. $4 \le 5x - 6 \le 19$

57. $-4 < 2(x - 3) \le 4$

58. $0 < 4(x + 5) \le 8$

59. $-2 < 3x - 5 < 7$

60. $1 < 4 + 2x \le 7$

61. $-6 < 3(x - 2) \le 8$

62. $-5 \le 2(x + 4) < 8$

Solve the following. For Exercises 65 and 66, the solutions have been started for you. See Examples 12 and 13.

63. Six more than twice a number is greater than negative fourteen. Find all numbers that make this statement true.

64. One more than five times a number is less than or equal to ten. Find all such numbers.

65. The perimeter of a rectangle is to be no greater than 100 centimeters and the width must be 15 centimeters. Find the maximum length of the rectangle.

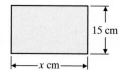

15 cm

x cm

Start the solution:

1. UNDERSTAND the problem. Reread it as many times as needed.

2. TRANSLATE into an equation. (Fill in the blanks below.)

the perimeter of the rectangle	is no greater than	100
↓	↓	↓
$x + 15 + x + 15$	_____	100

Finish with:

3. SOLVE and **4.** INTERPRET

66. One side of a triangle is three times as long as another side, and the third side is 12 inches long. If the perimeter can be no longer than 32 inches, find the maximum lengths of the other two sides.

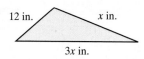

12 in. x in.

$3x$ in.

Start the solution:

1. UNDERSTAND the problem. Reread it as many times as needed.

2. TRANSLATE into an equation. (Fill in the blanks below.)

the perimeter of the rectangle	is no greater than	32
↓	↓	↓
$12 + 3x + x$	_____	32

Finish with:

3. SOLVE and **4.** INTERPRET

67. Ben Holladay bowled 146 and 201 in his first two games. What must he bowl in his third game to have an average of at least 180? (*Hint:* The average of a list of numbers is their sum divided by the number of numbers in the list.)

68. On an NBA team, the two forwards measure 6′8″ and 6′6″ tall and the two guards measure 6′0″ and 5′9″ tall. How tall should the center be if they wish to have a starting team average height of at least 6′5″?

69. Dennis and Nancy Wood are celebrating their 30th wedding anniversary by having a reception at Tiffany Oaks reception hall. They have budgeted $3000 for their reception. If the reception hall charges a $50.00 cleanup fee plus $34 per person, find the greatest number of people that they may invite and still stay within their budget.

70. A surprise retirement party is being planned for Pratap Puri. A total of $860 has been collected for the event, which is to be held at a local reception hall. This reception hall charges a cleanup fee of $40 and $15 per person for drinks and light snacks. Find the greatest number of people that may be invited and still stay within the $860 budget.

71. A 150-pound person uses 5.8 calories per minute when walking at a speed of 4 mph. How long must a person walk at this speed to use at least 200 calories? Round up to the next minute. (*Source:* Home & Garden Bulletin No. 72)

72. A 170-pound person uses 5.3 calories per minute when bicycling at a speed of 5.5 mph. How long must a person ride a bike at this speed to use at least 200 calories? Round up to the next minute. (*Source:* Same as Exercise 71)

73. Twice a number, increased by one, is between negative five and seven. Find all such numbers.

74. Half a number, decreased by four, is between two and three. Find all such numbers.

REVIEW AND PREVIEW

Evaluate the following. See Section 1.4.

75. 2^3

76. 3^3

77. 1^{12} **78.** 0^5

79. $\left(\dfrac{4}{7}\right)^2$ **80.** $\left(\dfrac{2}{3}\right)^3$

CONCEPT EXTENSIONS

Fill in the box with $<, >, \leq,$ *or* $\geq$. *See the Concept Check in this section.*

81. Since $3 < 5$, then $3(-4) \,\square\, 5(-4)$.

82. If $m \leq n$, then $2m \,\square\, 2n$.

83. If $m \leq n$, then $-2m \,\square\, -2n$.

84. If $-x < y$, then $x \,\square\, -y$.

85. When solving an inequality, when must you reverse the direction of the inequality symbol?

86. If both sides of the inequality $-3x < 30$ are divided by -3, do you reverse the direction of the inequality symbol? Why or why not?

Solve.

87. Eric Daly has scores of 75, 83, and 85 on his history tests. Use an inequality to find the scores he can make on his final exam to receive a B in the class. The final exam counts as **two** tests, and a B is received if the final course average is greater than or equal to 80.

88. Maria Lipco has scores of 85, 95, and 92 on her algebra tests. Use an inequality to find the scores she can make on her final exam to receive an A in the course. The final exam counts as **three** tests, and an A is received if the final course average is greater than or equal to 90. Round to one decimal place.

89. Explain how solving a linear inequality is similar to solving a linear equation.

90. Explain how solving a linear inequality is different from solving a linear equation.

91. Explain how solving a linear inequality is different from solving a compound inequality.

92. Explain how solving a linear inequality is similar to solving a compound inequality.

93. The formula $C = 3.14d$ can be used to approximate the circumference of a circle given its diameter. Waldo Manufacturing manufactures and sells a certain washer with an outside circumference of 3 centimeters. The company has decided that a washer whose actual circumference is in the interval $2.9 \leq C \leq 3.1$ centimeters is acceptable. Use a compound inequality and find the corresponding interval for diameters of these washers. (Round to three decimal places.)

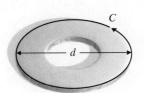

94. A company manufactures plastic Easter eggs that open. The company has determined that if the circumference of the opening of each part of the egg is in the interval $118 \leq C \leq 122$ millimeters, the eggs will open and close comfortably. Use a compound inequality and find the corresponding interval for diameters of these openings. (Round to two decimal places.)

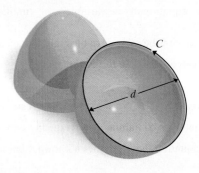

For Exercises 95 through 98, see the example below.

Solve $x(x - 6) > x^2 - 5x + 6$. Graph the solution set and write it in interval notation.

Solution

$$x(x - 6) > x^2 - 5x + 6$$
$$x^2 - 6x > x^2 - 5x + 6$$
$$x^2 - 6x - x^2 > x^2 - 5x + 6 - x^2$$
$$-6x > -5x + 6$$
$$-x > 6$$
$$\dfrac{-x}{-1} < \dfrac{6}{-1}$$
$$x < -6$$

The solution set $(-\infty, -6)$ is graphed as shown.

$$\xleftarrow{\quad}\!\!\!\underset{-7\;\,-6\;\,-5\;\,-4\;\,-3\;\,-2\;\,-1}{\overset{\displaystyle)}{\rule{6cm}{0.4pt}}}\!\!\!\xrightarrow{\quad}$$

Solve each inequality. Graph the solution set and write it in interval notation.

95. $x(x + 4) > x^2 - 2x + 6$

96. $x(x - 3) \geq x^2 - 5x - 8$

97. $x^2 + 6x - 10 < x(x - 10)$

98. $x^2 - 4x + 8 < x(x + 8)$

Chapter 2 Vocabulary Check

Fill in each blank with one of the words or phrases listed below.

like terms	numerical coefficient	linear inequality in one variable	no solution
equivalent equations	formula	compound inequalities	reversed
linear equation in one variable	unlike terms	all real numbers	the same

1. Terms with the same variables raised to exactly the same powers are called _____.

2. If terms are not like terms, they are _____.

3. A(n) _____ can be written in the form $ax + b = c$.

4. A(n) _____ can be written in the form $ax + b < c$ (or $>, \leq, \geq$).

5. Inequalities containing two inequality symbols are called _____.

6. An equation that describes a known relationship among quantities is called a(n) _____.

7. The _____ of a term is its numerical factor.

8. Equations that have the same solution are called _____.

9. The solution(s) to the equation $x + 5 = x + 5$ is/are _____.

10. The solution(s) to the equation $x + 5 = x + 4$ is/are _____.

11. If both sides of an inequality are multiplied or divided by the same positive number, the direction of the inequality symbol is _____.

12. If both sides of an inequality are multiplied or divided by the same negative number, the direction of the inequality symbol is _____.

Chapter 2 Highlights

DEFINITIONS AND CONCEPTS	EXAMPLES

Section 2.1 Simplifying Algebraic Expressions

DEFINITIONS AND CONCEPTS	EXAMPLES
The **numerical coefficient** of a **term** is its numerical factor.	**Term** **Numerical Coefficient** $-7y$ -7 x 1 $\frac{1}{5}a^2b$ $\frac{1}{5}$
Terms with the same variables raised to exactly the same powers are **like terms.**	**Like Terms** **Terms** **Unlike Terms** $12x, -x$ $3y, 3y^2$ $-2xy, 5yx$ $7a^2b, -2ab^2$
To combine like terms, add the numerical coefficients and multiply the result by the common variable factor.	$9y + 3y = 12y$ $-4z^2 + 5z^2 - 6z^2 = -5z^2$
To remove parentheses, apply the distributive property.	$-4(x + 7) + 10(3x - 1)$ $= -4x - 28 + 30x - 10$ $= 26x - 38$

DEFINITIONS AND CONCEPTS	EXAMPLES

Section 2.2   The Addition Property of Equality

A **linear equation in one variable** can be written in the form $ax + b = c$ where $a, b,$ and c are real numbers and $a \neq 0$.

Linear Equations

$$-3x + 7 = 2$$

$$3(x - 1) = -8(x + 5) + 4$$

Equivalent equations are equations that have the same solution.

$x - 7 = 10$ and $x = 17$
are equivalent equations.

Addition Property of Equality

Adding the same number to or subtracting the same number from both sides of an equation does not change its solution.

$$y + 9 = 3$$
$$y + 9 - 9 = 3 - 9$$
$$y = -6$$

Section 2.3   The Multiplication Property of Equality

Multiplication Property of Equality

Multiplying both sides or dividing both sides of an equation by the same nonzero number does not change its solution.

$$\frac{2}{3}a = 18$$

$$\frac{3}{2}\left(\frac{2}{3}a\right) = \frac{3}{2}(18)$$

$$a = 27$$

Section 2.4   Solving Linear Equations

To Solve Linear Equations

Solve: $\dfrac{5(-2x + 9)}{6} + 3 = \dfrac{1}{2}$

1. Clear the equation of fractions.

1. $6 \cdot \dfrac{5(-2x + 9)}{6} + 6 \cdot 3 = 6 \cdot \dfrac{1}{2}$

$$5(-2x + 9) + 18 = 3$$

2. Remove any grouping symbols such as parentheses.

2. $\quad -10x + 45 + 18 = 3 \qquad$ Distributive property

3. Simplify each side by combining like terms.

3. $\quad -10x + 63 = 3 \qquad$ Combine like terms.

4. Write variable terms on one side and numbers on the other side using the addition property of equality.

4. $\quad -10x + 63 - 63 = 3 - 63 \qquad$ Subtract 63.

$$-10x = -60$$

5. Get the variable alone using the multiplication property of equality.

5. $\quad \dfrac{-10x}{-10} = \dfrac{-60}{-10} \qquad$ Divide by -10.

$$x = 6$$

6. Check by substituting in the original equation.

6. $\dfrac{5(-2x + 9)}{6} + 3 = \dfrac{1}{2}$

$$\frac{5(-2 \cdot 6 + 9)}{6} + 3 \stackrel{?}{=} \frac{1}{2}$$

$$\frac{5(-3)}{6} + 3 \stackrel{?}{=} \frac{1}{2}$$

$$-\frac{5}{2} + \frac{6}{2} \stackrel{?}{=} \frac{1}{2}$$

$$\frac{1}{2} = \frac{1}{2} \qquad \text{True}$$

DEFINITIONS AND CONCEPTS	EXAMPLES

Section 2.5 An Introduction to Problem Solving

Problem-Solving Steps	The height of the Hudson volcano in Chile is twice the height of the Kiska volcano in the Aleutian Islands. If the sum of their heights is 12,870 feet, find the height of each.
1. UNDERSTAND the problem.	**1.** Read and reread the problem. Guess a solution and check your guess. Let x be the height of the Kiska volcano. Then $2x$ is the height of the Hudson volcano. x⌶ $2x$⌶ Kiska Hudson
2. TRANSLATE the problem.	**2.** In words:

2. In words:

height of Kiska	added to	height of Hudson	is	12,870
↓	↓	↓	↓	↓
Translate: x	$+$	$2x$	$=$	$12{,}870$

3. SOLVE.	**3.** $$x + 2x = 12{,}870$$ $$3x = 12{,}870$$ $$x = 4290$$
4. INTERPRET the results.	**4.** *Check:* If x is 4290, then $2x$ is 2(4290) or 8580. Their sum is $4290 + 8580$ or 12,870, the required amount. *State:* The Kiska volcano is 4290 feet high and the Hudson volcano is 8580 feet high.

Section 2.6 Formulas and Problem Solving

	Formulas $A = lw$ (area of a rectangle) $I = PRT$ (simple interest)
An equation that describes a known relationship among quantities is called a **formula.**	
If all values for the variables in a formula are known except for one, this unknown value may be found by substituting in the known values and solving.	If $d = 182$ miles and $r = 52$ miles per hour in the formula $d = r \cdot t$, find t. $$d = r \cdot t$$ $$182 = 52 \cdot t \quad \text{Let } d = 182 \text{ and } r = 52.$$ $$3.5 = t$$ The time is 3.5 hours.
To solve a formula for a specified variable, use the same steps as for solving a linear equation. Treat the specified variable as the only variable of the equation.	Solve: $P = 2l + 2w$ for l. $$P = 2l + 2w$$ $$P - 2w = 2l + 2w - 2w \quad \text{Subtract } 2w.$$ $$P - 2w = 2l$$ $$\frac{P - 2w}{2} = \frac{2l}{2} \quad \text{Divide by 2.}$$ $$\frac{P - 2w}{2} = l \quad \text{Simplify.}$$

DEFINITIONS AND CONCEPTS	EXAMPLES

Section 2.9   Solving Linear Inequalities

A **linear inequality in one variable** is an inequality that can be written in one of the forms:

$$ax + b < c \qquad ax + b \leq c$$
$$ax + b > c \qquad ax + b \geq c$$

where a, b, and c are real numbers and a is not 0.

Linear Inequalities

$$2x + 3 < 6 \qquad\qquad 5(x - 6) \geq 10$$

$$\frac{x - 2}{5} > \frac{5x + 7}{2} \qquad \frac{-(x + 8)}{9} \leq \frac{-2x}{11}$$

Addition Property of Inequality

Adding the same number to or subtracting the same number from both sides of an inequality does not change the solutions.

$$y + 4 \leq -1$$
$$y + 4 - 4 \leq -1 - 4 \quad \text{Subtract 4.}$$
$$y \leq -5$$

$(-\infty, -5]$

number line from -6 to 2 showing interval to -5

Multiplication Property of Inequality

Multiplying or dividing both sides of an inequality by the same positive number does not change its solutions.

$$\frac{1}{3}x > -2$$
$$3\left(\frac{1}{3}x\right) > 3 \cdot -2 \quad \text{Multiply by 3.}$$
$$x > -6 \quad (-6, \infty)$$

number line from -6 to 2

Multiplying or dividing both sides of an inequality by the same **negative number and reversing the direction of the inequality symbol** does not change its solutions.

$$-2x \leq 4$$
$$\frac{-2x}{-2} \geq \frac{4}{-2} \quad \text{Divide by } -2, \text{ reverse inequality symbol.}$$
$$x \geq -2 \quad [-2, \infty)$$

number line from -3 to 2

DEFINITIONS AND CONCEPTS	EXAMPLES

Section 2.9   Solving Linear Inequalities (continued)

To Solve Linear Inequalities

1. Clear the equation of fractions.

2. Remove grouping symbols.

3. Simplify each side by combining like terms.

4. Write variable terms on one side and numbers on the other side, using the addition property of inequality.

5. Get the variable alone, using the multiplication property of inequality.

Inequalities containing two inequality symbols are called **compound inequalities.**

To solve a compound inequality, isolate the variable in the middle part of the inequality. Perform the same operation to all three parts of the inequality: left, middle, right.

Solve: $3(x + 2) \leq -2 + 8$

1. No fractions to clear. $3(x + 2) \leq -2 + 8$

2. $\qquad 3x + 6 \leq -2 + 8$ Distributive property

3. $\qquad 3x + 6 \leq 6$ Combine like terms.

4. $\qquad 3x + 6 - 6 \leq 6 - 6$ Subtract 6.

$$3x \leq 0$$

5. $\qquad \dfrac{3x}{3} \leq \dfrac{0}{3}$ Divide by 3.

$$x \leq 0 \quad (-\infty, 0]$$

Compound Inequalities

$$-2 < x < 6$$

$$5 \leq 3(x - 6) < \dfrac{20}{3}$$

Solve: $\qquad -2 < 3x + 1 < 7$

$$-2 - 1 < 3x + 1 - 1 < 7 - 1 \quad \text{Subtract 1.}$$

$$-3 < 3x < 6$$

$$\dfrac{-3}{3} < \dfrac{3x}{3} < \dfrac{6}{3} \qquad \text{Divide by 3.}$$

$$-1 < x < 2 \quad (-1, 2)$$

Chapter 2 Review

(2.1) Simplify the following expressions.

1. $5x - x + 2x$

2. $0.2z - 4.6x - 7.4z$

3. $\dfrac{1}{2}x + 3 + \dfrac{7}{2}x - 5$

4. $\dfrac{4}{5}y + 1 + \dfrac{6}{5}y + 2$

5. $2(n - 4) + n - 10$

6. $3(w + 2) - (12 - w)$

7. Subtract $7x - 2$ from $x + 5$.

8. Subtract $1.4y - 3$ from $y - 0.7$.

Write each of the following as algebraic expressions.

9. Three times a number decreased by 7

10. Twice the sum of a number and 2.8 added to 3 times the number

(2.2) Solve each equation.

11. $8x + 4 = 9x$

12. $5y - 3 = 6y$

13. $\dfrac{2}{7}x + \dfrac{5}{7}x = 6$

14. $3x - 5 = 4x + 1$

15. $2x - 6 = x - 6$

16. $4(x + 3) = 3(1 + x)$

17. $6(3 + n) = 5(n - 1)$

18. $5(2 + x) - 3(3x + 2) = -5(x - 6) + 2$

Use the addition property to fill in the blanks so that the middle equation simplifies to the last equation.

19. $\qquad x - 5 = 3$

$\qquad x - 5 + \underline{\quad} = 3 + \underline{\quad}$

$\qquad\qquad x = 8$

20. $\qquad x + 9 = -2$

$\qquad x + 9 - \underline{\quad} = -2 - \underline{\quad}$

$\qquad\qquad x = -11$

Choose the correct algebraic expression.

21. The sum of two numbers is 10. If one number is x, express the other number in terms of x.

    a. $x - 10$ **b.** $10 - x$

    c. $10 + x$ **d.** $10x$

22. Mandy is 5 inches taller than Melissa. If x inches represents the height of Mandy, express Melissa's height in terms of x.

    a. $x - 5$ **b.** $5 - x$

    c. $5 + x$ **d.** $5x$

△ 23. If one angle measures $x°$, express the measure of its complement in terms of x.

    a. $(180 - x)°$ **b.** $(90 - x)°$

    c. $(x - 180)°$ **d.** $(x - 90)°$

△ **24.** If one angle measures $(x + 5)°$, express the measure of its supplement in terms of x.

a. $(185 + x)°$
b. $(95 + x)°$
c. $(175 - x)°$
d. $(x - 170)°$

(2.3) *Solve each equation.*

25. $\frac{3}{4}x = -9$

26. $\frac{x}{6} = \frac{2}{3}$

27. $-5x = 0$

28. $-y = 7$

29. $0.2x = 0.15$

30. $\frac{-x}{3} = 1$

31. $-3x + 1 = 19$

32. $5x + 25 = 20$

33. $7(x - 1) + 9 = 5x$

34. $7x - 6 = 5x - 3$

35. $-5x + \frac{3}{7} = \frac{10}{7}$

36. $5x + x = 9 + 4x - 1 + 6$

37. Write the sum of three consecutive integers as an expression in x. Let x be the first integer.

38. Write the sum of the first and fourth of four consecutive even integers. Let x be the first even integer.

(2.4) *Solve each equation.*

39. $\frac{5}{3}x + 4 = \frac{2}{3}x$

40. $\frac{7}{8}x + 1 = \frac{5}{8}x$

41. $-(5x + 1) = -7x + 3$

42. $-4(2x + 1) = -5x + 5$

43. $-6(2x - 5) = -3(9 + 4x)$

44. $3(8y - 1) = 6(5 + 4y)$

45. $\frac{3(2 - z)}{5} = z$

46. $\frac{4(n + 2)}{5} = -n$

47. $0.5(2n - 3) - 0.1 = 0.4(6 + 2n)$

48. $-9 - 5a = 3(6a - 1)$

49. $\frac{5(c + 1)}{6} = 2c - 3$

50. $\frac{2(8 - a)}{3} = 4 - 4a$

51. $200(70x - 3560) = -179(150x - 19{,}300)$

52. $1.72y - 0.04y = 0.42$

(2.5) *Solve each of the following.*

53. The height of the Washington Monument is 50.5 inches more than 10 times the length of a side of its square base. If the sum of these two dimensions is 7327 inches, find the height of the Washington Monument. (*Source:* National Park Service)

54. A 12-foot board is to be divided into two pieces so that one piece is twice as long as the other. If x represents the length of the shorter piece, find the length of each piece.

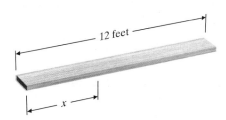

55. In 2015, Target made the decision to close all their Canadian retail stores. Before this decision, Target operated 1926 stores. The number of Target US stores was 69 less than 14 times the number of Target Canada stores. How many Target stores were located in each country?

56. Find three consecutive integers whose sum is -114.

57. The quotient of a number and 3 is the same as the difference of the number and two. Find the number.

58. Double the sum of a number and 6 is the opposite of the number. Find the number.

(2.6) *Substitute the given values into the given formulas and solve for the unknown variable.*

59. $P = 2l + 2w;\quad P = 46, l = 14$

60. $V = lwh;\quad V = 192, l = 8, w = 6$

Solve each equation as indicated.

61. $y = mx + b$ for m

62. $r = vst - 5$ for s

63. $2y - 5x = 7$ for x

64. $3x - 6y = -2$ for y

△ **65.** $C = \pi D$ for π

△ **66.** $C = 2\pi r$ for π

△ **67.** A swimming pool holds 900 cubic meters of water. If its length is 20 meters and its height is 3 meters, find its width.

68. The perimeter of a rectangular billboard is 60 feet and has a length 6 feet longer than its width. Find the dimensions of the billboard.

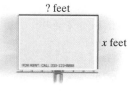

69. A charity 10K race is given annually to benefit a local hospice organization. How long will it take to run/walk a 10K race (10 kilometers or 10,000 meters) if your average pace is 125 **meters** per minute? Give your time in hours and minutes.

70. On April 28, 2001, the highest temperature recorded in the United States was 104°F, which occurred in Death Valley, California. Convert this temperature to degrees Celsius. (*Source:* National Weather Service)

(2.9) *Solve and graph the solutions of each of the following inequalities.*

89. $x > 0$

90. $x \leq -2$

91. $0.5 \leq y < 1.5$

92. $-1 < x < 1$

93. $-3x > 12$

94. $-2x \geq -20$

95. $x + 4 \geq 6x - 16$

96. $5x - 7 > 8x + 5$

97. $-3 < 4x - 1 < 2$

98. $2 \leq 3x - 4 < 6$

99. $4(2x - 5) \leq 5x - 1$

100. $-2(x - 5) > 2(3x - 2)$

101. Tina earns $175 per week plus a 5% commission on all her sales. Find the minimum amount of sales to ensure that she earns at least $300 per week.

102. Ellen Catarella shot rounds of 76, 82, and 79 golfing. What must she shoot on her next round so that her average will be below 80?

MIXED REVIEW

Solve each equation.

103. $6x + 2x - 1 = 5x + 11$

104. $2(3y - 4) = 6 + 7y$

105. $4(3 - a) - (6a + 9) = -12a$

106. $\dfrac{x}{3} - 2 = 5$

107. $2(y + 5) = 2y + 10$

108. $7x - 3x + 2 = 2(2x - 1)$

Solve.

109. The sum of six and twice a number is equal to seven less than the number. Find the number.

110. A 23-inch piece of string is to be cut into two pieces so that the length of the longer piece is three more than four times the shorter piece. If x represents the length of the shorter piece, find the lengths of both pieces.

Solve for the specified variable.

111. $V = \dfrac{1}{3} Ah$ for h

112. What number is 26% of 85?

113. The number 72 is 45% of what number?

114. A company recently increased its number of employees from 235 to 282. Find the percent of increase.

Solve each inequality. Graph the solution set.

115. $4x - 7 > 3x + 2$

116. $-5x < 20$

117. $-3(1 + 2x) + x \geq -(3 - x)$

Chapter 2 Getting Ready for the Test

1c

MULTIPLE CHOICE *Exercises 1–4 below are given. Choose the best directions (choice A, B, C, or D) below for each exercise.*

   A. Solve for x.   **B.** Simplify.   **C.** Identify the numerical coefficient.   **D.** Are these like or unlike terms?

  1. Given: $-3x^2$

  3. Given: $5x^2$ and $4x$

  2. Given: $4x - 5 = 2x + 3$

  4. Given: $4x - 5 + 2x + 3$

MULTIPLE CHOICE

  5. Subtracting $100z$ from $8m$ translates to

    A. $100z - 8m$ **B.** $8m - 100z$ **C.** $-800zm$ **D.** $92zm$

  6. Subtracting $7x - 1$ from $9y$ translates to:

    A. $7x - 1 - 9y$ **B.** $9y - 7x - 1$ **C.** $9y - (7x - 1)$ **D.** $7x - 1 - (9y)$

MATCHING *Match each equation in the first column with its solution in the second column. Items in the second column may be used more than once.*

  7. $7x + 6 = 7x + 9$

  8. $2y - 5 = 2y - 5$

  9. $11x - 13 = 10x - 13$

  10. $x + 15 = -x + 15$

    A. all real numbers

    B. no solution

    C. the solution is 0

MULTIPLE CHOICE

  11. To solve $5(3x - 2) = -(x + 20)$, we first use the distributive property and remove parentheses by multiplying. Once this is done, the equation is

    A. $15x - 2 = -x + 20$ **B.** $15x - 10 = -x - 20$ **C.** $15x - 10 = -x + 20$ **D.** $15x - 7 = -x - 20$

  12. To solve $\dfrac{8x}{3} + 1 = \dfrac{x - 2}{10}$ we multiply through by the LCD, 30. Once this is done, the simplified equation is

    A. $80x + 1 = 3x - 6$ **B.** $80x + 6 = 3x - 6$ **C.** $8x + 1 = x - 2$ **D.** $80x + 30 = 3x - 6$

Chapter 2 Test   MyMathLab® YouTube

Simplify each of the following expressions.

1. $2y - 6 - y - 4$

2. $2.7x + 6.1 + 3.2x - 4.9$

3. $4(x - 2) - 3(2x - 6)$

4. $7 + 2(5y - 3)$

Solve each of the following equations.

5. $-\dfrac{4}{5}x = 4$

6. $4(n - 5) = -(4 - 2n)$

7. $5y - 7 + y = -(y + 3y)$

8. $4z + 1 - z = 1 + z$

9. $\dfrac{2(x + 6)}{3} = x - 5$

10. $\dfrac{1}{2} - x + \dfrac{3}{2} = x - 4$

11. $-0.3(x - 4) + x = 0.5(3 - x)$

12. $-4(a + 1) - 3a = -7(2a - 3)$

13. $-2(x - 3) = x + 5 - 3x$

14. Find the value of x if $y = -14$, $m = -2$, and $b = -2$ in the formula $y = mx + b$.

Solve each of the following equations for the indicated variable.

15. $V = \pi r^2 h$ for h

16. $3x - 4y = 10$ for y

Solve each of the following inequalities. Graph each solution set and write it in interval notation.

17. $3x - 5 \geq 7x + 3$

18. $x + 6 > 4x - 6$

19. $-2 < 3x + 1 < 8$

20. $\dfrac{2(5x + 1)}{3} > 2$

Solve each of the following applications.

21. A number increased by two-thirds of the number is 35. Find the number.

22. A rectangular deck is to be built so that the width and length are two consecutive even integers and the perimeter is 252 feet. Find the dimensions of the deck.

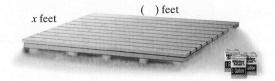

( ) feet

x feet

23. Some states have a single area code for the entire state. Two such states have area codes where one is double the other. If the sum of these integers is 1203, find the two area codes. *(Source:* North American Numbering Plan Administration*)*

24. Sedric Angell invested an amount of money in Amoxil stock that earned an annual 10% return, and then he invested twice that amount in IBM stock that earned an annual 12% return. If his total return from both investments was $2890, find how much he invested in each stock.

25. Two trains leave Los Angeles simultaneously traveling on the same track in opposite directions at speeds of 50 and 64 mph. How long will it take before they are 285 miles apart?

The following graph shows the breakdown of tornadoes occurring in the United States by strength. The corresponding Fujita Tornado Scale categories are shown in parentheses. Use this graph to answer Exercise 26.

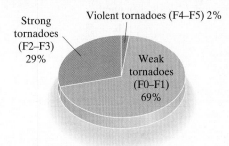

Strong tornadoes (F2–F3) 29%

Violent tornadoes (F4–F5) 2%

Weak tornadoes (F0–F1) 69%

Data from National Climatic Data Center

26. According to the National Climatic Data Center, in an average year, about 800 tornadoes are reported in the United States. How many of these would you expect to be classified as "weak" tornadoes?

27. The number 72 is what percent of 180?

28. The number of employees of a company decreased from 225 to 189. Find this percent of decrease.

Chapter 2 Cumulative Review

1. Given the set $\left\{-2, 0, \frac{1}{4}, -1.5, 112, -3, 11, \sqrt{2}\right\}$, list the numbers in this set that belong to the set of:
   a. Natural numbers
   b. Whole numbers
   c. Integers
   d. Rational numbers
   e. Irrational numbers
   f. Real numbers

2. Given the set $\left\{7, 2, -\frac{1}{5}, 0, \sqrt{3}, -185, 8\right\}$, list the numbers in this set that belong to the set of:
   a. Natural numbers
   b. Whole numbers
   c. Integers
   d. Rational numbers
   e. Irrational numbers
   f. Real numbers

3. Find the absolute value of each number.
   a. $|4|$
   b. $|-5|$
   c. $|0|$
   d. $\left|-\frac{1}{2}\right|$
   e. $|5.6|$

4. Find the absolute value of each number.
   a. $|5|$
   b. $|-8|$
   c. $\left|-\frac{2}{3}\right|$

5. Write each of the following numbers as a product of primes.
   a. 40
   b. 63

6. Write each number as a product of primes.
   a. 44
   b. 90

7. Write $\frac{2}{5}$ as an equivalent fraction with a denominator of 20.

8. Write $\frac{2}{3}$ as an equivalent fraction with a denominator of 24.

9. Simplify: $3[4 + 2(10 - 1)]$
10. Simplify: $5[16 - 4(2 + 1)]$
11. Decide whether 2 is a solution of $3x + 10 = 8x$.
12. Decide whether 3 is a solution of $5x - 2 = 4x$.

Add.
13. $-1 + (-2)$
14. $(-2) + (-8)$
15. $-4 + 6$
16. $-3 + 10$
17. Simplify each expression.
   a. $-(-10)$
   b. $-\left(-\frac{1}{2}\right)$
   c. $-(-2x)$
   d. $-|-6|$

18. Simplify each expression.
   a. $-(-5)$
   b. $-\left(-\frac{2}{3}\right)$
   c. $-(-a)$
   d. $-|-3|$

19. Subtract.
   a. $5.3 - (-4.6)$
   b. $-\frac{3}{10} - \frac{5}{10}$
   c. $-\frac{2}{3} - \left(-\frac{4}{5}\right)$

20. Subtract
   a. $-2.7 - 8.4$
   b. $-\frac{4}{5} - \left(-\frac{3}{5}\right)$
   c. $\frac{1}{4} - \left(-\frac{1}{2}\right)$

21. Find each unknown complementary or supplementary angle.
   a.
   b.
   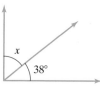
   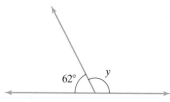

22. Find each unknown complementary or supplementary angle.
   a.
   b.

   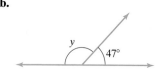

23. Find each product.
   a. $(-1.2)(0.05)$
   b. $\frac{2}{3} \cdot \left(-\frac{7}{10}\right)$
   c. $\left(-\frac{4}{5}\right)(-20)$

24. Find each product.
   a. $(4.5)(-0.08)$
   b. $-\frac{3}{4} \cdot \left(-\frac{8}{17}\right)$

25. Divide.
   a. $\frac{-24}{-4}$
   b. $\frac{-36}{3}$
   c. $\frac{2}{3} \div \left(-\frac{5}{4}\right)$
   d. $-\frac{3}{2} \div 9$

26. Divide.
   a. $\frac{-32}{8}$
   b. $\frac{-108}{-12}$
   c. $\frac{-5}{7} \div \left(\frac{-9}{2}\right)$

27. Use a commutative property to complete each statement.
   a. $x + 5 = $ _____
   b. $3 \cdot x = $ _____

28. Use a commutative property to complete each statement.
   a. $y + 1 = $ _____
   b. $y \cdot 4 = $ _____

29. Use the distributive property to write each sum as a product.

    a. $8 \cdot 2 + 8 \cdot x$

    b. $7s + 7t$

30. Use the distributive property to write each sum as a product.

    a. $4 \cdot y + 4 \cdot \dfrac{1}{3}$

    b. $0.10x + 0.10y$

31. Subtract $4x - 2$ from $2x - 3$.

32. Subtract $10x + 3$ from $-5x + 1$.

Solve.

33. $\dfrac{1}{2} = x - \dfrac{3}{4}$

34. $\dfrac{5}{6} + x = \dfrac{2}{3}$

35. $6(2a - 1) - (11a + 6) = 7$

36. $-3x + 1 - (-4x - 6) = 10$

37. $\dfrac{y}{7} = 20$

38. $\dfrac{x}{4} = 18$

39. $4(2x - 3) + 7 = 3x + 5$

40. $6x + 5 = 4(x + 4) - 1$

41. Twice the sum of a number and 4 is the same as four times the number, decreased by 12. Find the number.

42. A number increased by 4 is the same as 3 times the number decreased by 8. Find the number.

43. Solve: $V = lwh$ for l.

44. Solve: $C = 2\pi r$ for r.

45. Solve $x + 4 \leq -6$ for x. Graph the solution set and write it in interval notation.

46. Solve $x - 3 > 2$ for x. Graph the solution set and write it in interval notation.

CHAPTER 3

Graphing

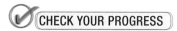

CHECK YOUR PROGRESS

In the previous chapter, we learned to solve and graph the solutions of linear equations and inequalities in one variable. Now we define and present techniques for solving and graphing linear equations and inequalities in two variables.

International Tourist Arrivals Forecast for 2020–2030 (numbers shown in millions)

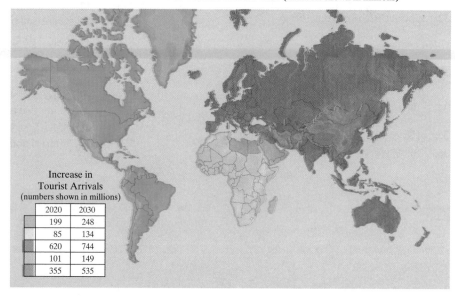

Increase in Tourist Arrivals
(numbers shown in millions)

2020	2030
199	248
85	134
620	744
101	149
355	535

What Is Tourism Toward 2030?

Tourism 2020 Vision is the World Tourism Organization's long-term forecast of world tourism through 2020. *Tourism Towards 2030* is its new program title for longer-term forecasts to 2030. The broken-line graph below shows the forecast for number of tourists, which is extremely important as these numbers greatly affect a country's economy. In Section 3.1, Exercises 1 through 6, we read a bar graph showing the top tourist destinations by country.

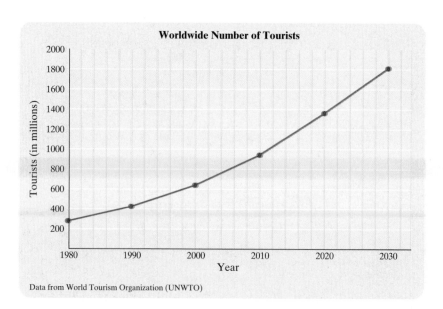

Data from World Tourism Organization (UNWTO)

3.1 | Reading Graphs and the Rectangular Coordinate System

OBJECTIVES

1 Read Bar and Line Graphs.

2 Define the Rectangular Coordinate System and Plot Ordered Pairs of Numbers.

3 Graph Paired Data to Create a Scatter Diagram.

4 Determine Whether an Ordered Pair Is a Solution of an Equation in Two Variables.

5 Find the Missing Coordinate of an Ordered Pair Solution, Given One Coordinate of the Pair.

In today's world, where the exchange of information must be fast and entertaining, graphs are becoming increasingly popular. They provide a quick way of making comparisons, drawing conclusions, and approximating quantities.

OBJECTIVE

1 Reading Bar and Line Graphs

A **bar graph** consists of a series of bars arranged vertically or horizontally. The bar graph in Example 1 shows a comparison of worldwide Internet users by region. The names of the regions are listed vertically and a bar is shown for each region. Corresponding to the length of the bar for each region is a number along a horizontal axis. These horizontal numbers are numbers of Internet users in millions.

EXAMPLE I   The bar graph shows the estimated number of Internet users worldwide by region as of a recent year.

a. Find the region that has the most Internet users and approximate the number of users.

b. How many more users are in the Europe region than the Latin America/Caribbean region?

Solution

a. Since these bars are arranged horizontally, we look for the longest bar, which is the bar representing Asia. To approximate the number associated with this region, we move from the right edge of this bar vertically downward to the Internet Users axis. This region has approximately 1390 million Internet users.

b. The Europe region has approximately 580 million Internet users. The Latin America/Caribbean region has approximately 320 million Internet users. To find how many more users are in the Europe region, we subtract $580 - 320 = 260$ million more Internet users.

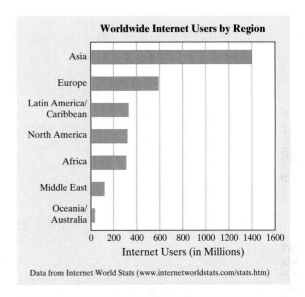

Worldwide Internet Users by Region

Data from Internet World Stats (www.internetworldstats.com/stats.htm)

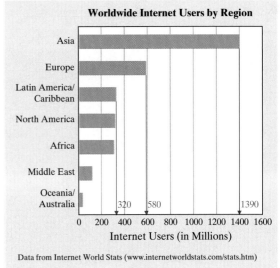

Worldwide Internet Users by Region

Data from Internet World Stats (www.internetworldstats.com/stats.htm)

PRACTICE

1   Use the graph from Example 1 to answer the following.

a. Find the region with the fewest Internet users and approximate the number of users.

b. How many more users are in the Middle East region than in the Oceania/Australia region?

A **line graph** consists of a series of points connected by a line. The next graph is an example of a line graph. It is also sometimes called a **broken-line graph.**

EXAMPLE 2 The line graph shows the relationship between time spent smoking a cigarette and pulse rate. Time is recorded along the horizontal axis in minutes, with 0 minutes being the moment a smoker lights a cigarette. Pulse is recorded along the vertical axis in heartbeats per minute.

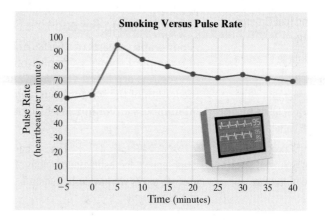

a. What is the pulse rate 15 minutes after a cigarette is lit?

b. When is the pulse rate the lowest?

c. When does the pulse rate show the greatest change?

Solution

a. We locate the number 15 along the time axis and move vertically upward until the line is reached. From this point on the line, we move horizontally to the left until the pulse rate axis is reached. Reading the number of beats per minute, we find that the pulse rate is 80 beats per minute 15 minutes after a cigarette is lit.

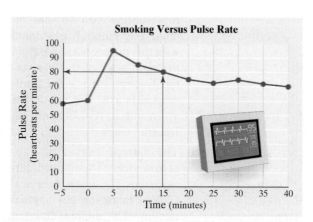

b. We find the lowest point of the line graph, which represents the lowest pulse rate. From this point, we move vertically downward to the time axis. We find that the pulse rate is the lowest at −5 minutes, which means 5 minutes *before* lighting a cigarette.

c. The pulse rate shows the greatest change during the 5 minutes between 0 and 5. Notice that the line graph is *steepest* between 0 and 5 minutes. ☐

PRACTICE

2 Use the graph from Example 2 to answer the following.

a. What is the pulse rate 40 minutes after lighting a cigarette?

b. What is the pulse rate when the cigarette is being lit?

c. When is the pulse rate the highest?

OBJECTIVE

2 Defining the Rectangular Coordinate System and Plotting Ordered Pairs of Numbers ▶

Notice in the previous graph that two numbers are associated with each point of the graph. For example, we discussed earlier that 15 minutes after lighting a cigarette, the pulse rate is 80 beats per minute. If we agree to write the time first and the pulse rate second, we can say there is a point on the graph corresponding to the **ordered pair** of numbers (15, 80). A few more ordered pairs are listed alongside their corresponding points.

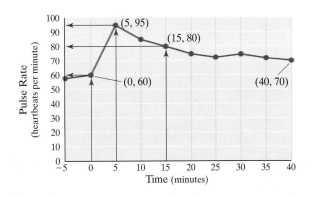

In general, we use this same ordered pair idea to describe the location of a point in a plane (such as a piece of paper). We start with a horizontal and a vertical axis. Each axis is a number line and, for the sake of consistency, we construct our axes to intersect at the 0 coordinate of both. This point of intersection is called the **origin.** Notice that these two number lines or axes divide the plane into four regions called **quadrants.** The quadrants are usually numbered with Roman numerals as shown. The axes are not considered to be in any quadrant.

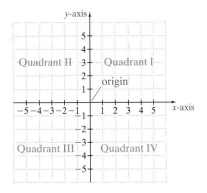

It is helpful to label axes, so we label the horizontal axis the *x*-axis and the vertical axis the *y*-axis. We call the system described above the **rectangular coordinate system.**

Just as with the pulse rate graph, we can then describe the locations of points by ordered pairs of numbers. We list the horizontal *x*-axis measurement first and the vertical *y*-axis measurement second.

To plot or graph the point corresponding to the ordered pair

$$(a, b)$$

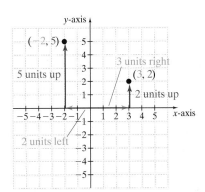

we start at the origin. We then move a units left or right (right if a is positive, left if a is negative). From there, we move b units up or down (up if b is positive, down if b is negative). For example, to plot the point corresponding to the ordered pair (3, 2), we start at the origin, move 3 units right and from there move 2 units up. (See the figure to the left.) The *x*-value, 3, is called the *x*-**coordinate** and the *y*-value, 2, is called the *y*-**coordinate.** From now on, we will call the point with coordinates (3, 2) simply the point (3, 2). The point (−2, 5) is graphed to the left also.

Does the order in which the coordinates are listed matter? Yes! Notice below that the point corresponding to the ordered pair $(2, 3)$ is in a different location than the point corresponding to $(3, 2)$. These two ordered pairs of numbers describe two different points of the plane.

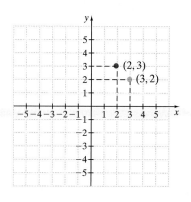

✔ **CONCEPT CHECK**

Is the graph of the point $(-5, 1)$ in the same location as the graph of the point $(1, -5)$? Explain.

Helpful Hint

Don't forget that **each ordered pair corresponds to exactly one point in the plane and that each point in the plane corresponds to exactly one ordered pair.**

EXAMPLE 3 On a single coordinate system, plot each ordered pair. State in which quadrant, if any, each point lies.

a. $(5, 3)$ **b.** $(-5, 3)$ **c.** $(-2, -4)$ **d.** $(1, -2)$ **e.** $(0, 0)$

f. $(0, 2)$ **g.** $(-5, 0)$ **h.** $\left(0, -5\frac{1}{2}\right)$ **i.** $\left(4\frac{2}{3}, -3\right)$

Solution

a. Point $(5, 3)$ lies in quadrant I.

b. Point $(-5, 3)$ lies in quadrant II.

c. Point $(-2, -4)$ lies in quadrant III.

d. Point $(1, -2)$ lies in quadrant IV.

e.–h. Points $(0, 0)$, $(0, 2)$, $(-5, 0)$, and $\left(0, -5\frac{1}{2}\right)$ lie on axes, so they are not in any quadrant.

i. Point $\left(4\frac{2}{3}, -3\right)$ lies in quadrant IV.

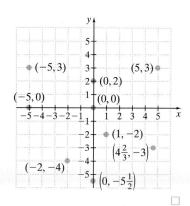

PRACTICE

3 On a single coordinate system, plot each ordered pair. State in which quadrant, if any, each point lies.

a. $(4, -3)$ **b.** $(-3, 5)$ **c.** $(0, 4)$ **d.** $(-6, 1)$

e. $(-2, 0)$ **f.** $(5, 5)$ **g.** $\left(3\frac{1}{2}, 1\frac{1}{2}\right)$ **h.** $(-4, -5)$

From Example 3, notice that the y-coordinate of any point on the x-axis is 0. For example, the point $(-5, 0)$ lies on the x-axis. Also, the x-coordinate of any point on the y-axis is 0. For example, the point $(0, 2)$ lies on the y-axis.

OBJECTIVE

3   Graphing Paired Data

Data that can be represented as an ordered pair is called **paired data.** Many types of data collected from the real world are paired data. For instance, the annual measurement of a child's height can be written as an ordered pair of the form (year, height in inches) and is paired data. The graph of paired data as points in the rectangular coordinate system is called a **scatter diagram.** Scatter diagrams can be used to look for patterns and trends in paired data.

EXAMPLE 4   The table gives the annual net sales (in billions of dollars) for Target stores for the years shown. (*Source:* Corporate.target.com)

Year	Target Net Sales (in billions of dollars)
2009	65
2010	67
2011	70
2012	73
2013	73
2014	73

a. Write this paired data as a set of ordered pairs of the form (year, sales in billions of dollars).

b. Create a scatter diagram of the paired data.

c. What trend in the paired data does the scatter diagram show?

Solution

a. The ordered pairs are (2009, 65), (2010, 67), (2011, 70), (2012, 73), (2013, 73), (2014, 73).

b. We begin by plotting the ordered pairs. Because the x-coordinate in each ordered pair is a year, we label the x-axis "Year" and mark the horizontal axis with the years given. Then we label the y-axis or vertical axis "Net Sales (in billions of dollars)." In this case we can mark the vertical axis in multiples of 2. Since no net sale is less than 64, we use the notation ⤒ to skip to 64, then proceed by multiples of 2.

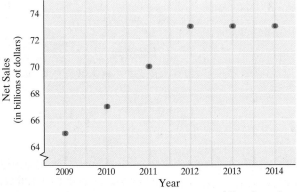

(Continued on next page)

c. The scatter diagram shows that Target net sales were constant or increasing over the years 2009–2014.

☐

PRACTICE

4 The table gives the approximate annual number of wildfires (in thousands) that have occurred in the United States for the years shown. (*Source:* National Interagency Fire Center)

Year	Wildfires (in thousands)
2008	79
2009	79
2010	72
2011	73
2012	56
2013	48
2014	46

a. Write this paired data as a set of ordered pairs of the form (year, number of wildfires in thousands).

b. Create a scatter diagram of the paired data.

■

OBJECTIVE

4 Determining Whether an Ordered Pair Is a Solution

Let's see how we can use ordered pairs to record solutions of equations containing two variables. An equation in one variable such as $x + 1 = 5$ has one solution, which is 4: The number 4 is the value of the variable x that makes the equation true.

An equation in two variables, such as $2x + y = 8$, has solutions consisting of two values, one for x and one for y. For example, $x = 3$ and $y = 2$ is a solution of $2x + y = 8$ because, if x is replaced with 3 and y with 2, we get a true statement.

$$2x + y = 8$$
$$2(3) + 2 = 8$$
$$8 = 8 \quad \text{True}$$

The solution $x = 3$ and $y = 2$ can be written as $(3, 2)$, an **ordered pair** of numbers. The first number, 3, is the x-value and the second number, 2, is the y-value.

In general, an ordered pair is a **solution** of an equation in two variables if replacing the variables by the values of the ordered pair results in a true statement.

EXAMPLE 5 Determine whether each ordered pair is a solution of the equation $x - 2y = 6$.

a. $(6, 0)$ **b.** $(0, 3)$ **c.** $\left(1, -\dfrac{5}{2}\right)$

Solution

a. Let $x = 6$ and $y = 0$ in the equation $x - 2y = 6$.

$$x - 2y = 6$$
$$6 - 2(0) = 6 \quad \text{Replace } x \text{ with 6 and } y \text{ with 0.}$$
$$6 - 0 = 6 \quad \text{Simplify.}$$
$$6 = 6 \quad \text{True}$$

$(6, 0)$ is a solution, since $6 = 6$ is a true statement.

b. Let $x = 0$ and $y = 3$.

$$x - 2y = 6$$
$$0 - 2(3) = 6 \quad \text{Replace } x \text{ with 0 and } y \text{ with 3.}$$
$$0 - 6 = 6$$
$$-6 = 6 \quad \text{False}$$

$(0, 3)$ is *not* a solution, since $-6 = 6$ is a false statement.

c. Let $x = 1$ and $y = -\dfrac{5}{2}$ in the equation.

$$x - 2y = 6$$
$$1 - 2\left(-\dfrac{5}{2}\right) = 6 \quad \text{Replace } x \text{ with 1 and } y \text{ with } -\dfrac{5}{2}.$$
$$1 + 5 = 6$$
$$6 = 6 \quad \text{True}$$

$\left(1, -\dfrac{5}{2}\right)$ is a solution, since $6 = 6$ is a true statement.   □

PRACTICE

5   Determine whether each ordered pair is a solution of the equation $x + 3y = 6$.

   a. $(3, 1)$ **b.** $(6, 0)$ **c.** $\left(-2, \dfrac{2}{3}\right)$ ■

OBJECTIVE

5   Completing Ordered Pair Solutions

If one value of an ordered pair solution of an equation is known, the other value can be determined. To find the unknown value, replace one variable in the equation by its known value. Doing so results in an equation with just one variable that can be solved for the variable using the methods of Chapter 2.

EXAMPLE 6   Complete the following ordered pair solutions for the equation $3x + y = 12$.

   a. $(0, \quad)$ **b.** $(\quad , 6)$ **c.** $(-1, \quad)$

Solution

a. In the ordered pair $(0, \quad)$, the x-value is 0. Let $x = 0$ in the equation and solve for y.

$$3x + y = 12$$
$$3(0) + y = 12 \quad \text{Replace } x \text{ with 0.}$$
$$0 + y = 12$$
$$y = 12$$

The completed ordered pair is $(0, 12)$.

b. In the ordered pair $(\quad , 6)$, the y-value is 6. Let $y = 6$ in the equation and solve for x.

$$3x + y = 12$$
$$3x + 6 = 12 \quad \text{Replace } y \text{ with 6.}$$
$$3x = 6 \quad \text{Subtract 6 from both sides.}$$
$$x = 2 \quad \text{Divide both sides by 3.}$$

The ordered pair is $(2, 6)$.

(Continued on next page)

c. In the ordered pair $(-1, \ \ )$, the x-value is -1. Let $x = -1$ in the equation and solve for y.

$$3x + y = 12$$
$$3(-1) + y = 12 \quad \text{Replace } x \text{ with } -1.$$
$$-3 + y = 12$$
$$y = 15 \quad \text{Add 3 to both sides.}$$

The ordered pair is $(-1, 15)$. □

PRACTICE
6 Complete the following ordered pair solutions for the equation $2x - y = 8$.
a. $(0, \ \ )$ **b.** $(\ \ , 4)$ **c.** $(-3, \ \ )$ ▪

Solutions of equations in two variables can also be recorded in a **table of values,** as shown in the next example.

EXAMPLE 7 Complete the table for the equation $y = 3x$.

	x	y
a.	-1	
b.		0
c.		-9

Solution

a. Replace x with -1 in the equation and solve for y.

$$y = 3x$$
$$y = 3(-1) \quad \text{Let } x = -1.$$
$$y = -3$$

The ordered pair is $(-1, -3)$.

b. Replace y with 0 in the equation and solve for x.

$$y = 3x$$
$$0 = 3x \quad \text{Let } y = 0.$$
$$0 = x \quad \text{Divide both sides by 3.}$$

The ordered pair is $(0, 0)$.

c. Replace y with -9 in the equation and solve for x.

$$y = 3x$$
$$-9 = 3x \quad \text{Let } y = -9.$$
$$-3 = x \quad \text{Divide both sides by 3.}$$

The ordered pair is $(-3, -9)$. The completed table is shown to the left. □

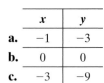

	x	y
a.	-1	-3
b.	0	0
c.	-3	-9

PRACTICE
7 Complete the table for the equation $y = -4x$.

	x	y
a.	-2	
b.		-12
c.	0	

▪

EXAMPLE 8   Complete the table for the equation

$$y = \frac{1}{2}x - 5.$$

	x	y
a.	-2	
b.	0	
c.		0

Solution

a. Let $x = -2$.

$$y = \frac{1}{2}x - 5$$

$$y = \frac{1}{2}(-2) - 5$$

$$y = -1 - 5$$

$$y = -6$$

b. Let $x = 0$.

$$y = \frac{1}{2}x - 5$$

$$y = \frac{1}{2}(0) - 5$$

$$y = 0 - 5$$

$$y = -5$$

c. Let $y = 0$.

$$y = \frac{1}{2}x - 5$$

$$0 = \frac{1}{2}x - 5 \quad \text{Now, solve for } x.$$

$$5 = \frac{1}{2}x \quad \text{Add 5.}$$

$$10 = x \quad \text{Multiply by 2.}$$

Ordered pairs: **a.** $(-2, -6)$,   **b.** $(0, -5)$,   **c.** $(10, 0)$

The completed table is

	x	y
a.	-2	-6
b.	0	-5
c.	10	0

☐

PRACTICE

8   Complete the table for the equation $y = \frac{1}{5}x - 2$.

	x	y
a.	-10	
b.	0	
c.		0

■

EXAMPLE 9   **Finding the Value of a Computer**

A computer was recently purchased for a small business for $2000. The business manager predicts that the computer will be used for 5 years and the value in dollars y of the computer in x years is $y = -300x + 2000$. Complete the table.

x	0	1	2	3	4	5
y						

Solution To find the value of y when x is 0, replace x with 0 in the equation. We use this same procedure to find y when x is 1 and when x is 2.

When x = 0,

$$y = -300x + 2000$$
$$y = -300 \cdot 0 + 2000$$
$$y = 0 + 2000$$
$$y = 2000$$

When x = 1,

$$y = -300x + 2000$$
$$y = -300 \cdot 1 + 2000$$
$$y = -300 + 2000$$
$$y = 1700$$

When x = 2,

$$y = -300x + 2000$$
$$y = -300 \cdot 2 + 2000$$
$$y = -600 + 2000$$
$$y = 1400$$

We have the ordered pairs $(0, 2000)$, $(1, 1700)$, and $(2, 1400)$. This means that in 0 years, the value of the computer is $2000, in 1 year the value of the computer is $1700, and in

(Continued on next page)

2 years the value is $1400. To complete the table of values, we continue the procedure for $x = 3$, $x = 4$, and $x = 5$.

When $x = 3$,	**When $x = 4$,**	**When $x = 5$,**
$y = -300x + 2000$	$y = -300x + 2000$	$y = -300x + 2000$
$y = -300 \cdot 3 + 2000$	$y = -300 \cdot 4 + 2000$	$y = -300 \cdot 5 + 2000$
$y = -900 + 2000$	$y = -1200 + 2000$	$y = -1500 + 2000$
$y = 1100$	$y = 800$	$y = 500$

The completed table is

x	0	1	2	3	4	5
y	2000	1700	1400	1100	800	500

PRACTICE

9 A college student purchased a used car for $12,000. The student predicted that she would need to use the car for four years and the value in dollars y of the car in x years is $y = -1800x + 12,000$. Complete this table.

x	0	1	2	3	4
y					

The ordered pair solutions recorded in the completed table for the example above are graphed below. Notice that the graph gives a visual picture of the decrease in value of the computer.

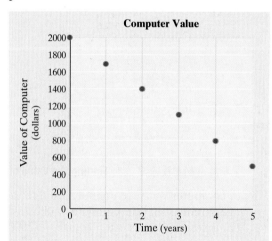

x	y
0	2000
1	1700
2	1400
3	1100
4	800
5	500

Vocabulary, Readiness & Video Check

Use the choices below to fill in each blank. The exercises below all have to do with the rectangular coordinate system.

origin   x-coordinate   x-axis   one   four
quadrants   y-coordinate   y-axis   solution

1. The horizontal axis is called the _____ and the vertical axis is called the _____.

2. The intersection of the horizontal axis and the vertical axis is a point called the _____.

3. The axes divide the plane into regions called _____. There are _____ of these regions.

4. In the ordered pair of numbers $(-2, 5)$, the number -2 is called the _____ and the number 5 is called the _____.

5. Each ordered pair of numbers corresponds to _____ point in the plane.

6. An ordered pair is a(n) _____ of an equation in two variables if replacing the variables by the coordinates of the ordered pair results in a true statement.

Martin-Gay Interactive Videos

See Video 3.1 🔘

Watch the section lecture video and answer the following questions.

OBJECTIVE 1

7. 🎞 Examples 1–3 ask you to answer questions about a bar graph. What information is provided on the horizontal axis of this bar graph? On the vertical axis?

OBJECTIVE 2

8. Several points are plotted in 🎞 Examples 4–11. Where do you always start when plotting a point? How does the 1st coordinate tell you to move? How does the 2nd coordinate tell you to move?

OBJECTIVE 3

9. In the lecture before 🎞 Example 12, what connection is made between data and graphing?

OBJECTIVE 4

10. An ordered pair is a solution of an equation if, when the variables are replaced with their values, a true statement results. In 🎞 Example 13, three ordered pairs are tested. What are the last two points to be tested? What lesson can be learned by the results of testing these two points and why?

OBJECTIVE 5

11. In 🎞 Example 14, when one variable of a linear equation in two variables is replaced by a replacement value, what type of equation results?

3.1 Exercise Set   MyMathLab® ▶

The following bar graph shows the top 10 tourist destinations and the number of tourists that visit each destination per year forecasted for 2020. Use this graph to answer Exercises 1 through 6. See Example 1.

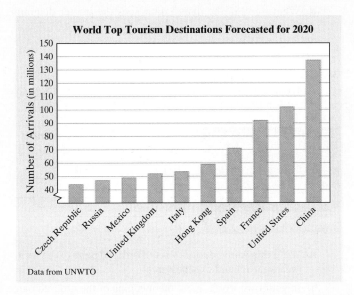

World Top Tourism Destinations Forecasted for 2020

Data from UNWTO

▶ **1.** Which location shown is predicted to be the most popular tourist destination?

2. Which location shown is predicted to be the least popular tourist destination?

▶ **3.** Which locations shown are predicted to have more than 70 million tourists per year?

4. Which locations shown are predicted to have more than 100 million tourists per year?

▶ **5.** Estimate the predicted number of tourists per year whose destination is Italy.

6. Estimate the predicted number of tourists per year whose destination is Mexico.

The following line graph shows the paid attendance at each Super Bowl game from 2008 through 2014. Use this graph to answer Exercises 7 through 10. See Example 2.

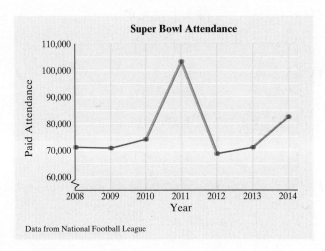

Super Bowl Attendance

Data from National Football League

7. Estimate the Super Bowl attendance in 2014.

8. Estimate the Super Bowl attendance in 2010.

9. Find the year on the graph with the greatest Super Bowl attendance and approximate that attendance.

10. Find the year on the graph with the least Super Bowl attendance and approximate that attendance.

The line graph below shows the number of students per teacher in U.S. public elementary and secondary schools. Use this graph for Exercises 11 through 16. See Example 2.

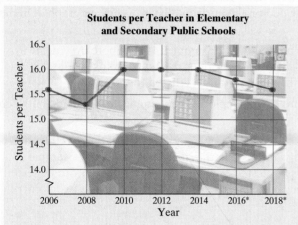

Students per Teacher in Elementary and Secondary Public Schools

Year

Data from National Center for Education Statistics * Some years are projected.

11. Approximate the number of students per teacher predicted in 2016.

12. Approximate the number of students per teacher predicted in 2018.

13. Between what years shown did the greatest increase in number of students per teacher occur?

14. What was the first year shown that the number of students per teacher fell below 15.5?

15. During what period was the student per teacher number at 16?

16. Discuss any trends shown by this line graph.

Plot each ordered pair. State in which quadrant or on which axis each point lies. See Example 3.

17. a. $(1, 5)$ **b.** $(-5, -2)$
    c. $(-3, 0)$ **d.** $(0, -1)$

    e. $(2, -4)$ **f.** $\left(-1, 4\frac{1}{2}\right)$

    g. $(3.7, 2.2)$ **h.** $\left(\frac{1}{2}, -3\right)$

18. a. $(2, 4)$ **b.** $(0, 2)$
    c. $(-2, 1)$ **d.** $(-3, -3)$

    e. $\left(3\frac{3}{4}, 0\right)$ **f.** $(5, -4)$

    g. $(-3.4, 4.8)$ **h.** $\left(\frac{1}{3}, -5\right)$

Find the x- and y-coordinates of each labeled point. See Example 3.

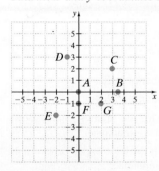

19. *A*
20. *B*
21. *C*
22. *D*
23. *E*
24. *F*
25. *G*

26. *A*
27. *B*
28. *C*
29. *D*
30. *E*
31. *F*
32. *G*

Solve. See Example 4.

33. The table shows the worldwide box office (in billions of dollars) for the movie industry during the years shown. (*Source:* Motion Picture Association of America)

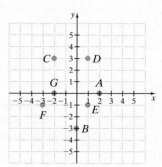

Year	Box Office (in billions of dollars)
2010	21.0
2011	22.4
2012	23.9
2013	25.0
2014	28.0

a. Write this paired data as a set of ordered pairs of the form (year, box office).

b. In your own words, write the meaning of the ordered pair (2014, 28.0).

c. Create a scatter diagram of the paired data. Be sure to label the axes appropriately.

d. What trend in the paired data does the scatter diagram show?

34. The table shows the amount of money (in billions of dollars) Americans spent on their pets for the years shown. (*Source:* American Pet Products Manufacturers Association)

Year	Pet-Related Expenditures (in billions of dollars)
2011	51.0
2012	53.3
2013	55.7
2014	58.5

a. Write this paired data as a set of ordered pairs of the form (year, pet-related expenditures).

b. In your own words, write the meaning of the ordered pair (2014, 58.5).

c. Create a scatter diagram of the paired data. Be sure to label the axes appropriately.

d. What trend in the paired data does the scatter diagram show?

35. Minh, a psychology student, kept a record of how much time she spent studying for each of her 20-point psychology quizzes and her score on each quiz.

Hours Spent Studying	0.50	0.75	1.00	1.25	1.50	1.50	1.75	2.00
Quiz Score	10	12	15	16	18	19	19	20

   a. Write the data as ordered pairs of the form (hours spent studying, quiz score).

   b. In your own words, write the meaning of the ordered pair (1.25, 16).

   c. Create a scatter diagram of the paired data. Be sure to label the axes appropriately.

   d. What might Minh conclude from the scatter diagram?

36. A local lumberyard uses quantity pricing. The table shows the price per board for different amounts of lumber purchased.

Price per Board (in dollars)	Number of Boards Purchased
8.00	1
7.50	10
6.50	25
5.00	50
2.00	100

   a. Write the data as ordered pairs of the form (price per board, number of boards purchased).

   b. In your own words, write the meaning of the ordered pair (2.00, 100).

   c. Create a scatter diagram of the paired data. Be sure to label the axes appropriately.

   d. What trend in the paired data does the scatter diagram show?

37. The table shows the distance from the equator (in miles) and the average annual snowfall (in inches) for each of eight selected U.S. cities. (*Source:* National Climatic Data Center, Wake Forest University Albatross Project)

City	Distance from Equator (in miles)	Average Annual Snowfall (in inches)
1. Atlanta, GA	2313	2
2. Austin, TX	2085	1
3. Baltimore, MD	2711	21
4. Chicago, IL	2869	39
5. Detroit, MI	2920	42
6. Juneau, AK	4038	99
7. Miami, FL	1783	0
8. Winston-Salem, NC	2493	9

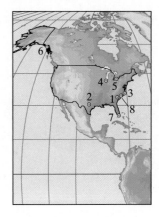

   a. Write this paired data as a set of ordered pairs of the form (distance from equator, average annual snowfall).

   b. Create a scatter diagram of the paired data. Be sure to label the axes appropriately.

   c. What trend in the paired data does the scatter diagram show?

38. The table shows the average farm size (in acres) in the United States during the years shown. (*Source:* National Agricultural Statistics Service)

Year	Average Farm Size (in acres)
2009	418
2010	418
2011	429
2012	433
2013	435
2014	437

   a. Write this paired data as a set of ordered pairs of the form (year, average farm size).

   b. Create a scatter diagram of the paired data. Be sure to label the axes appropriately.

Determine whether each ordered pair is a solution of the given linear equation. See Example 5.

39. $2x + y = 7$; $(3, 1), (7, 0), (0, 7)$

40. $3x + y = 8$; $(2, 3), (0, 8), (8, 0)$

41. $x = -\frac{1}{3}y$; $(0, 0), (3, -9)$

42. $y = -\frac{1}{2}x$; $(0, 0), (4, 2)$

43. $x = 5$; $(4, 5), (5, 4), (5, 0)$

44. $y = -2$; $(-2, 2), (2, -2), (0, -2)$

Complete each ordered pair so that it is a solution of the given linear equation. See Examples 6 through 8.

45. $x - 4y = 4$; $(\quad, -2), (4, \quad)$

46. $x - 5y = -1$; $(\quad, -2), (4, \quad)$

47. $y = \dfrac{1}{4}x - 3$; $(-8, \quad)$, $(\quad, 1)$

48. $y = \dfrac{1}{5}x - 2$; $(-10, \quad)$, $(\quad, 1)$

Complete the table of ordered pairs for each linear equation. See Examples 6 through 8.

49. $y = -7x$

x	y
0	
-1	
	2

50. $y = -9x$

x	y
	0
-3	
	2

51. $y = -x + 2$

x	y
0	
	0
-3	

52. $x = -y + 4$

x	y
	0
0	
	-3

53. $y = \dfrac{1}{2}x$

x	y
0	
-6	
	1

54. $y = \dfrac{1}{3}x$

x	y
0	
-6	
	1

55. $x + 3y = 6$

x	y
0	
	0
	1

56. $2x + y = 4$

x	y
	4
2	
	2

57. $y = 2x - 12$

x	y
0	
	-2
3	

58. $y = 5x + 10$

x	y
	0
	5
0	

59. $2x + 7y = 5$

x	y
0	
	0
	1

60. $x - 6y = 3$

x	y
0	
	1
	-1

MIXED PRACTICE

Complete the table of ordered pairs for each equation. Then plot the ordered pair solutions. See Examples 1 through 7.

61. $x = -5y$

x	y
	0
	1
10	

62. $y = -3x$

x	y
	0
	-2
	9

63. $y = \dfrac{1}{3}x + 2$

x	y
0	
-3	
	0

64. $y = \dfrac{1}{2}x + 3$

x	y
0	
-4	
	0

Solve. See Example 9.

65. The cost in dollars y of producing x computer desks is given by $y = 80x + 5000$.

   a. Complete the table.

x	100	200	300
y			

   b. Find the number of computer desks that can be produced for $8600. (*Hint:* Find x when $y = 8600$.)

66. The hourly wage y of an employee at a certain production company is given by $y = 0.25x + 9$ where x is the number of units produced by the employee in an hour.

   a. Complete the table.

x	0	1	5	10
y				

   b. Find the number of units that an employee must produce each hour to earn an hourly wage of $12.25. (*Hint:* Find x when $y = 12.25$.)

67. The average annual cinema admission price y (in dollars) from 2010 through 2014 is given by $y = 0.09x + 7.85$. In this equation, x represents the number of years after 2010. (*Source:* Motion Picture Association of America)

   a. Complete the table.

x	0	2	4
y			

   b. Find the year in which the average cinema admission price was approximately $8.10.

     (*Hint:* Find x when $y = 8.10$ and round to the nearest whole number.)

   c. Use the given equation to predict when the cinema admission price might be $10.00. (Use the hint for part (b).)

   d. In your own words, write the meaning of the ordered pair $(1, 7.94)$.

68. The average amount of money y spent per person per year on music from iTunes from 2008 to 2013 can be approximated by $y = -5.74x + 38.05$. In this equation, x represents the number of years since 2008. (*Source:* billboard.com)

   a. Complete the table.

x	1	3	5
y			

   b. Find the year in which the yearly average amount spent on music in iTunes was approximately $26.00. (*Hint:* Find x when $y = 26$ and round to the nearest whole number.)

The graph below shows the number of U.S. Walmart stores for each year. Use this graph to answer Exercises 69 through 72.

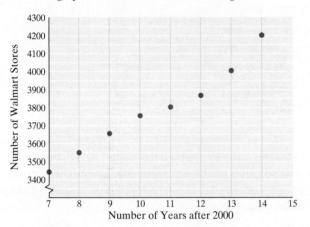

Data from Walmart

69. The ordered pair (14, 4203) is a point of the graph. Write a sentence describing the meaning of this ordered pair.

70. The ordered pair (12, 3868) is a point of the graph. Write a sentence describing the meaning of this ordered pair.

71. Estimate the increase in Walmart stores for years 8, 9, and 10.

72. Use a straightedge or ruler and this graph to predict the number of Walmart stores in the year 2018.

73. Describe what is similar about the coordinates of points whose graph lies on the x-axis.

74. Describe what is similar about the coordinates of points whose graph lies on the y-axis.

REVIEW AND PREVIEW

Solve each equation for y. See Section 2.6.

75. $x + y = 5$

76. $x - y = 3$

77. $2x + 4y = 5$

78. $5x + 2y = 7$

79. $10x = -5y$

80. $4y = -8x$

81. $x - 3y = 6$

82. $2x - 9y = -20$

CONCEPT EXTENSIONS

Answer each exercise with true or false.

83. Point $(-1, 5)$ lies in quadrant IV.

84. Point $(3, 0)$ lies on the y-axis.

85. For the point $\left(-\dfrac{1}{2}, 1.5\right)$, the first value, $-\dfrac{1}{2}$, is the x-coordinate and the second value, 1.5, is the y-coordinate.

86. The ordered pair $\left(2, \dfrac{2}{3}\right)$ is a solution of $2x - 3y = 6$.

For Exercises 87 through 91, fill in each blank with "0," "positive," or "negative." For Exercises 92 and 93, fill in each blank with "x" or "y."

	Point	Location
87.	(_____ , _____)	quadrant III
88.	(_____ , _____)	quadrant I
89.	(_____ , _____)	quadrant IV
90.	(_____ , _____)	quadrant II
91.	(_____ , _____)	origin
92.	(number, 0)	___-axis
93.	(0, number)	___-axis

94. Give an example of an ordered pair whose location is in (or on)

   a. quadrant I   **b.** quadrant II

   c. quadrant III   **d.** quadrant IV

   e. x-axis   **f.** y-axis

Solve. See the first Concept Check in this section.

95. Is the graph of $(3, 0)$ in the same location as the graph of $(0, 3)$? Explain why or why not.

96. Give the coordinates of a point such that if the coordinates are reversed, their location is the same.

97. In general, what points can have coordinates reversed and still have the same location?

98. In your own words, describe how to plot or graph an ordered pair of numbers.

Write an ordered pair for each point described. See the second Concept Check in this section.

99. Point C is four units to the right of the y-axis and seven units below the x-axis.

100. Point D is three units to the left of the origin.

Solve.

101. Find the perimeter of the rectangle whose vertices are the points with coordinates $(-1, 5)$, $(3, 5)$, $(3, -4)$, and $(-1, -4)$.

102. Find the area of the rectangle whose vertices are the points with coordinates $(5, 2)$, $(5, -6)$, $(0, -6)$, and $(0, 2)$.

103. Three vertices of a rectangle are $(-2, -3)$, $(-7, -3)$, and $(-7, 6)$.

   a. Find the coordinates of the fourth vertex of the rectangle.

   b. Find the perimeter of the rectangle.

   c. Find the area of the rectangle.

104. Three vertices of a square are $(-4, -1)$, $(-4, 8)$, and $(5, 8)$.

   a. Find the coordinates of the fourth vertex of the square.

   b. Find the perimeter of the square.

   c. Find the area of the square.

3.2 Graphing Linear Equations

OBJECTIVES

1 Identify Linear Equations.

2 Graph a Linear Equation by Finding and Plotting Ordered Pair Solutions.

OBJECTIVE

1 Identifying Linear Equations

In the previous section, we found that equations in two variables may have more than one solution. For example, both $(6, 0)$ and $(2, -2)$ are solutions of the equation $x - 2y = 6$. In fact, this equation has an infinite number of solutions. Other solutions include $(0, -3)$, $(4, -1)$, and $(-2, -4)$. If we graph these solutions, notice that a pattern appears.

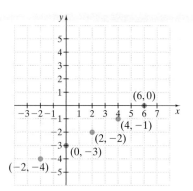

These solutions all appear to lie on the same line, which has been filled in below. It can be shown that every ordered pair solution of the equation corresponds to a point on this line, and every point on this line corresponds to an ordered pair solution. Thus, we say that this line is the **graph of the equation** $x - 2y = 6$.

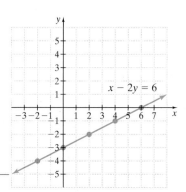

Helpful Hint

Notice that we can only show a part of a line on a graph. The arrowheads on each end of the line remind us that the line actually extends indefinitely in both directions.

The equation $x - 2y = 6$ is called a **linear equation in two variables** and **the graph of every linear equation in two variables is a line.**

Linear Equation in Two Variables

A linear equation in two variables is an equation that can be written in the form

$$Ax + By = C$$

where A, B, and C are real numbers and A and B are not both 0. **The graph of a linear equation in two variables is a straight line.**

The form $Ax + By = C$ is called **standard form**.

Helpful Hint

Notice in the form $Ax + By = C$, the understood exponent on both x and y is 1.

Examples of Linear Equations in Two Variables

$$2x + y = 8 \qquad -2x = 7y \qquad y = \frac{1}{3}x + 2 \qquad y = 7$$
(Standard Form)

Before we graph linear equations in two variables, let's practice identifying these equations.

EXAMPLE 1   Determine whether each equation is a linear equation in two variables.

a. $x - 1.5y = -1.6$ **b.** $y = -2x$ **c.** $x + y^2 = 9$ **d.** $x = 5$

Solution

a. This is a linear equation in two variables because it is written in the form $Ax + By = C$ with $A = 1$, $B = -1.5$, and $C = -1.6$.

b. This is a linear equation in two variables because it can be written in the form $Ax + By = C$.

$$y = -2x$$
$$2x + y = 0 \qquad \text{Add } 2x \text{ to both sides.}$$

c. This is *not* a linear equation in two variables because y is squared.

d. This is a linear equation in two variables because it can be written in the form $Ax + By = C$.

$$x = 5$$
$$x + 0y = 5 \qquad \text{Add } 0 \cdot y. \qquad \square$$

PRACTICE

1   Determine whether each equation is a linear equation in two variables.

a. $3x + 2.7y = -5.3$ **b.** $x^2 + y = 8$

c. $y = 12$ **d.** $5x = -3y$ ■

OBJECTIVE

2   Graphing Linear Equations by Plotting Ordered Pair Solutions

From geometry, we know that a straight line is determined by just two points. Graphing a linear equation in two variables, then, requires that we find just two of its infinitely many solutions. Once we do so, we plot the solution points and draw the line connecting the points. Usually, we find a third solution as well, as a check.

EXAMPLE 2   Graph the linear equation $2x + y = 5$.

Solution   Find three ordered pair solutions of $2x + y = 5$. To do this, choose a value for one variable, x or y, and solve for the other variable. For example, let $x = 1$. Then $2x + y = 5$ becomes

$$2x + y = 5$$
$$2(1) + y = 5 \qquad \text{Replace } x \text{ with 1.}$$
$$2 + y = 5 \qquad \text{Multiply.}$$
$$y = 3 \qquad \text{Subtract 2 from both sides.}$$

Since $y = 3$ when $x = 1$, the ordered pair $(1, 3)$ is a solution of $2x + y = 5$. Next, let $x = 0$.

$$2x + y = 5$$
$$2(0) + y = 5 \qquad \text{Replace } x \text{ with 0.}$$
$$0 + y = 5$$
$$y = 5$$

The ordered pair $(0, 5)$ is a second solution.

The two solutions found so far allow us to draw the straight line that is the graph of all solutions of $2x + y = 5$. However, we find a third ordered pair as a check. Let $y = -1$.

$$2x + y = 5$$
$$2x + (-1) = 5 \quad \text{Replace } y \text{ with } -1.$$
$$2x - 1 = 5$$
$$2x = 6 \quad \text{Add 1 to both sides.}$$
$$x = 3 \quad \text{Divide both sides by 2.}$$

The third solution is $(3, -1)$. These three ordered pair solutions are listed in table form as shown. The graph of $2x + y = 5$ is the line through the three points.

x	y
1	3
0	5
3	-1

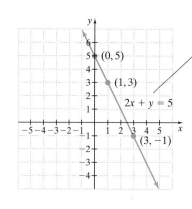

> **Helpful Hint**
>
> All three points should fall on the same straight line. If not, check your ordered pair solutions for a mistake.

PRACTICE
2 Graph the linear equation $x + 3y = 9$.

EXAMPLE 3 Graph the linear equation $-5x + 3y = 15$.

Solution Find three ordered pair solutions of $-5x + 3y = 15$.

Let $x = 0$.	**Let $y = 0$.**	**Let $x = -2$.**
$-5x + 3y = 15$	$-5x + 3y = 15$	$-5x + 3y = 15$
$-5 \cdot 0 + 3y = 15$	$-5x + 3 \cdot 0 = 15$	$-5(-2) + 3y = 15$
$0 + 3y = 15$	$-5x + 0 = 15$	$10 + 3y = 15$
$3y = 15$	$-5x = 15$	$3y = 5$
$y = 5$	$x = -3$	$y = \dfrac{5}{3}$

The ordered pairs are $(0, 5)$, $(-3, 0)$, and $\left(-2, \dfrac{5}{3}\right)$. The graph of $-5x + 3y = 15$ is the line through the three points.

x	y
0	5
-3	0
-2	$\dfrac{5}{3} = 1\dfrac{2}{3}$

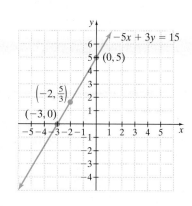

PRACTICE
3 Graph the linear equation $3x - 4y = 12$.

EXAMPLE 4   Graph the linear equation $y = 3x$.

Solution To graph this linear equation, we find three ordered pair solutions. Since this equation is solved for y, choose three x-values.

If $x = 2$, $y = 3 \cdot 2 = 6$.
If $x = 0$, $y = 3 \cdot 0 = 0$.
If $x = -1$, $y = 3 \cdot -1 = -3$.

x	y
2	6
0	0
−1	−3

Next, graph the ordered pair solutions listed in the table above and draw a line through the plotted points as shown below. The line is the graph of $y = 3x$. Every point on the graph represents an ordered pair solution of the equation and every ordered pair solution is a point on this line.

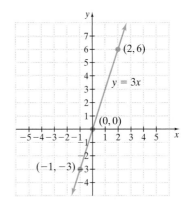

PRACTICE
4   Graph the linear equation $y = -2x$.

Helpful Hint

When graphing a linear equation in two variables, if it is

- solved for y, it may be easier to find ordered pair solutions by choosing x-values. If it is
- solved for x, it may be easier to find ordered pair solutions by choosing y-values.

EXAMPLE 5   Graph the linear equation $y = -\dfrac{1}{3}x + 2$.

Solution Find three ordered pair solutions, graph the solutions, and draw a line through the plotted solutions. To avoid fractions, choose x-values that are multiples of 3 to substitute in the equation. When a multiple of 3 is multiplied by $-\dfrac{1}{3}$, the result is an integer. See the calculations below used to fill in the table.

If $x = 6$, then $y = -\dfrac{1}{3} \cdot 6 + 2 = -2 + 2 = 0$

If $x = 0$, then $y = -\dfrac{1}{3} \cdot 0 + 2 = 0 + 2 = 2$

If $x = -3$, then $y = -\dfrac{1}{3} \cdot -3 + 2 = 1 + 2 = 3$

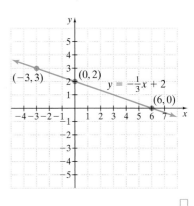

x	y
6	0
0	2
−3	3

PRACTICE
5   Graph the linear equation $y = \dfrac{1}{2}x + 3$.

Let's compare the graphs in Examples 4 and 5. The graph of $y = 3x$ tilts upward (as we follow the line from left to right) and the graph of $y = -\dfrac{1}{3}x + 2$ tilts downward (as we follow the line from left to right). We will learn more about the tilt, or slope, of a line in Section 3.4.

EXAMPLE 6 Graph the linear equation $y = -2$.

Solution The equation $y = -2$ can be written in standard form as $0x + y = -2$. No matter what value we replace x with, y is always -2.

x	y
0	-2
3	-2
-2	-2

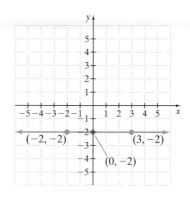

Notice that the graph of $y = -2$ is a horizontal line. □

PRACTICE

6 Graph the linear equation $x = -2$. ■

EXAMPLE 7 Graph the linear equation $y = 3x + 6$ and compare this graph with the graph of $y = 3x$ in Example 4.

Solution Find ordered pair solutions, graph the solutions, and draw a line through the plotted solutions. We choose x-values and substitute in the equation $y = 3x + 6$.

If $x = -3$, then $y = 3(-3) + 6 = -3$.
If $x = 0$, then $y = 3(0) + 6 = 6$.
If $x = 1$, then $y = 3(1) + 6 = 9$.

x	y
-3	-3
0	6
1	9

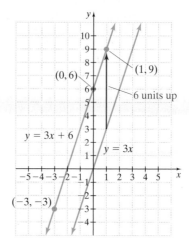

The most startling similarity is that both graphs appear to have the same upward tilt as we move from left to right. Also, the graph of $y = 3x$ crosses the y-axis at the origin, while the graph of $y = 3x + 6$ crosses the y-axis at 6. In fact, the graph of $y = 3x + 6$ is the same as the graph of $y = 3x$ moved vertically upward 6 units. □

PRACTICE
7 Graph the linear equation $y = -2x + 3$ and compare this graph with the graph of $y = -2x$ in Practice 4. ■

Notice that the graph of $y = 3x + 6$ crosses the y-axis at 6. This happens because when $x = 0$, $y = 3x + 6$ becomes $y = 3 \cdot 0 + 6 = 6$. The graph contains the point $(0, 6)$, which is on the y-axis.

In general, if a linear equation in two variables is solved for y, we say that it is written in the form $y = mx + b$. The graph of this equation contains the point $(0, b)$ because when $x = 0$, $y = mx + b$ is $y = m \cdot 0 + b = b$.

> The graph of $y = mx + b$ crosses the y-axis at $(0, b)$.

We will review this again in Section 3.5.

Linear equations are often used to model real data as seen in the next example.

EXAMPLE 8 **Estimating the Number of Registered Nurses**

The occupation expected to have the most employment growth in the next few years is registered nurse. The number of people y (in thousands) employed as registered nurses in the United States can be estimated by the linear equation $y = 58.1x + 2619$, where x is the number of years after the year 2008. (*Source:* U.S. Bureau of Labor Statistics)

a. Graph the equation.

b. Use the graph to predict the number of registered nurses in the year 2018.

Solution

a. To graph $y = 58.1x + 2619$, choose x-values and substitute in the equation.

If $x = 0$, then $y = 58.1(0) + 2619 = 2619$.
If $x = 2$, then $y = 58.1(2) + 2619 = 2735.2$.
If $x = 5$, then $y = 58.1(5) + 2619 = 2909.5$.

x	y
0	2619
2	2735.2
5	2909.5

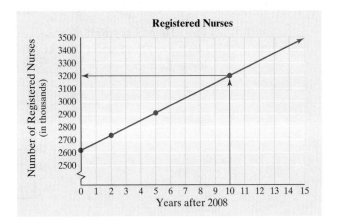

b. To use the graph to *predict* the number of registered nurses in the year 2018, we need to find the y-coordinate that corresponds to $x = 10$. (10 years after 2008 is the year 2018.) To do so, find 10 on the x-axis. Move vertically upward to the graphed line and then horizontally to the left. We approximate the number on the y-axis to be 3200. Thus, in the year 2018, we predict that there will be 3200 thousand registered nurses. (The actual value, using 10 for x, is 3200.) □

(Continued on next page)

8   One of the occupations expected to have a large growth in employment in the next few years is computer software application engineers. The number of people y (in thousands) employed as computer software application engineers in the United States can be estimated by the linear equation $y = 17.5x + 515$, where x is the number of years after 2008. (*Source:* Based on data from the Bureau of Labor Statistics)

a. Graph the equation.

b. Use the graph to predict the number of computer software application engineers in the year 2020.

> **Helpful Hint**
>
> Make sure you understand that models are mathematical approximations of the data for the known years. (For example, see the model in Example 8.) Any number of unknown factors can affect future years, so be cautious when using models to predict.

Graphing Calculator Explorations

In this section, we begin an optional study of graphing calculators and graphing software packages for computers. These graphers use the same point plotting technique that was introduced in this section. The advantage of this graphing technology is, of course, that graphing calculators and computers can find and plot ordered pair solutions much faster than we can. Note, however, that the features described in these boxes may not be available on all graphing calculators.

The rectangular screen where a portion of the rectangular coordinate system is displayed is called a **window.** We call it a **standard window** for graphing when both the x- and y-axes show coordinates between -10 and 10. This information is often displayed in the window menu on a graphing calculator as

$$\text{Xmin} = -10$$
$$\text{Xmax} = 10$$
$$\text{Xscl} = 1 \quad \text{The scale on the } x\text{-axis is one unit per tick mark.}$$
$$\text{Ymin} = -10$$
$$\text{Ymax} = 10$$
$$\text{Yscl} = 1 \quad \text{The scale on the } y\text{-axis is one unit per tick mark.}$$

To use a graphing calculator to graph the equation $y = 2x + 3$, press the $\boxed{Y =}$ key and enter the keystrokes $\boxed{2}\ \boxed{x}\ \boxed{+}\ \boxed{3}$. The top row should now read $Y_1 = 2x + 3$. Next press the $\boxed{\text{GRAPH}}$ key, and the display should look like this:

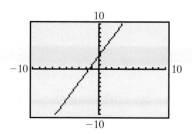

Use a standard window and graph the following linear equations. (Unless otherwise stated, use a standard window when graphing.)

1. $y = -3x + 7$ **2.** $y = -x + 5$ **3.** $y = 2.5x - 7.9$

4. $y = -1.3x + 5.2$ **5.** $y = -\dfrac{3}{10}x + \dfrac{32}{5}$ **6.** $y = \dfrac{2}{9}x - \dfrac{22}{3}$

✔ Vocabulary, Readiness & Video Check

Martin-Gay Interactive Videos

See Video 3.2 🍎

Watch the section lecture video and answer the following questions.

OBJECTIVE 1
1. Exponents aren't mentioned in the definition of a linear equation in two variables. However, in determining whether Example 3 is a linear equation in two variables, the exponents or powers on the variables are discussed. Explain.

OBJECTIVE 2
2. In the lecture before Example 5, it's mentioned that you need only two points to determine a line. Why then are three ordered pair solutions found in Examples 5–7?

OBJECTIVE 2
3. What does a graphed line represent as discussed at the end of Examples 5 and 7?

3.2 Exercise Set MyMathLab®

Determine whether each equation is a linear equation in two variables. See Example 1.

1. $-x = 3y + 10$
2. $y = x - 15$
3. $x = y$
4. $x = y^3$
5. $x^2 + 2y = 0$
6. $0.01x - 0.2y = 8.8$
7. $y = -1$
8. $x = 25$

For each equation, find three ordered pair solutions by completing the table. Then use the ordered pairs to graph the equation. See Examples 2 through 7.

9. $x - y = 6$

x	y
	0
4	
	-1

10. $x - y = 4$

x	y
	0
	2
	-1

11. $y = -4x$

x	y
1	
0	
-1	

12. $y = -5x$

x	y
1	
0	
-1	

13. $y = \frac{1}{3}x$

x	y
0	
6	
-3	

14. $y = \frac{1}{2}x$

x	y
0	
-4	
2	

15. $y = -4x + 3$

x	y
0	
1	
2	

16. $y = -5x + 2$

x	y
0	
1	
2	

MIXED PRACTICE

Graph each linear equation. See Examples 2 through 7.

17. $x + y = 1$
18. $x + y = 7$
19. $x - y = -2$
20. $-x + y = 6$
21. $x - 2y = 6$
22. $-x + 5y = 5$
23. $y = 6x + 3$
24. $y = -2x + 7$
25. $x = -4$
26. $y = 5$
27. $y = 3$
28. $x = -1$
29. $y = x$
30. $y = -x$
31. $x = -3y$
32. $x = -5y$
33. $x + 3y = 9$
34. $2x + y = 2$
35. $y = \frac{1}{2}x + 2$
36. $y = \frac{1}{4}x + 3$
37. $3x - 2y = 12$
38. $2x - 7y = 14$
39. $y = -3.5x + 4$
40. $y = -1.5x - 3$

Graph each pair of linear equations on the same set of axes. Discuss how the graphs are similar and how they are different. See Example 7.

41. $y = 5x; y = 5x + 4$
42. $y = 2x; y = 2x + 5$
43. $y = -2x; y = -2x - 3$
44. $y = x; y = x - 7$
45. $y = \frac{1}{2}x; y = \frac{1}{2}x + 2$
46. $y = -\frac{1}{4}x; y = -\frac{1}{4}x + 3$

The graph of $y = 5x$ is given below as well as Figures A–D. For Exercises 47 through 50, match each equation with its graph. Hint: Recall that if an equation is written in the form $y = mx + b$, its graph crosses the y-axis at $(0, b)$.

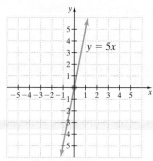

47. $y = 5x + 5$

48. $y = 5x - 4$

49. $y = 5x - 1$

50. $y = 5x + 2$

A.

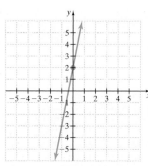

B.

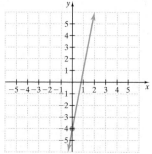

C.

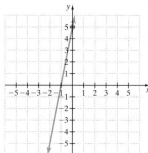

D.

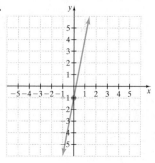

Solve. See Example 8.

51. Jogging is one of the few sports that has been consistently increasing over the past few years. The number of people jogging (in millions) from the years 2000 to 2009 is given by the equation $y = x + 23$, where x is the number of years after 2000. (*Source:* Based on data from the National Sporting Goods Association)

a. Use this equation or a graph of it to complete the ordered pair (8,   ).

b. Write a sentence explaining the meaning of the answer to part (a).

c. If this trend continues, how many joggers will there be in 2017?

52. The revenue y (in billions of dollars) for Home Depot stores during the years 2010 through 2014 is given by the equation $y = 3.2x + 65.2$, where x is the number of years after 2010. (*Source:* Based on data from Home Depot stores)

a. Use this equation or a graph of it to complete the ordered pair (3,   ).

b. Write a sentence explaining the meaning of the answer to part (a).

c. If this trend continues, predict the revenue for Home Depot stores for the year 2018.

53. One American rite of passage is a driver's license. The number of people y (in millions) who have a driver's license can be estimated by the linear equation $y = 2.2x + 190$, where x is the number of years after 2000. (*Source:* Federal Highway Administration)

a. Use this equation to complete the ordered pair (12,   ).

b. Write a sentence explaining the meaning of the ordered pair in part (a).

c. If this trend continues, predict the number of people with driver's licenses in 2020.

54. The percent of U.S. households y with at least one computer can be approximated by the linear equation $y = 2.4x + 51$, where x is the number of years since 2000. (*Source:* Pew Research)

a. Use the equation to complete the ordered pair (10,   ).

b. Write a sentence explaining the meaning of the ordered pair found in part (a).

c. If this trend continues, predict the percent of U.S. households that have at least one computer in 2018.

d. Explain any issues with your answer to part (c).

REVIEW AND PREVIEW

Solve. See Section 3.1.

△ **55.** The coordinates of three vertices of a rectangle are $(-2, 5)$, $(4, 5)$, and $(-2, -1)$. Find the coordinates of the fourth vertex.

△ **56.** The coordinates of two vertices of a square are $(-3, -1)$ and $(2, -1)$. Find the coordinates of two pairs of points possible for the third and fourth vertices.

Complete each table.

57. $x - y = -3$

x	y
0	
	0

58. $y - x = 5$

x	y
0	
	0

59. $y = 2x$

x	y
0	
	0

60. $x = -3y$

x	y
0	
	0

CONCEPT EXTENSIONS

Write each statement as an equation in two variables. Then graph the equation.

61. The y-value is 5 more than the x-value.

62. The y-value is twice the x-value.

63. Two times the x-value, added to three times the y-value is 6.

64. Five times the x-value, added to twice the y-value is -10.

Solve.

△ **65.** The perimeter of the trapezoid below is 22 centimeters. Write a linear equation in two variables for the perimeter. Find y if x is 3 cm.

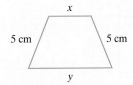

△ **66.** The perimeter of the rectangle below is 50 miles. Write a linear equation in two variables for this perimeter. Use this equation to find x when y is 20.

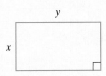

✎ **67.** Explain how to find ordered pair solutions of linear equations in two variables.

✎ **68.** If (a, b) is an ordered pair solution of $x + y = 5$, is (b, a) also a solution? Explain why or why not.

69. Graph the nonlinear equation $y = x^2$ by completing the table shown. Plot the ordered pairs and connect them with a smooth curve.

x	y
0	
1	
-1	
2	
-2	

70. Graph the nonlinear equation $y = |x|$ by completing the table shown. Plot the ordered pairs and connect them. This curve is "V" shaped.

x	y
0	
1	
-1	
2	
-2	

3.3 | Intercepts

OBJECTIVES

1 Identify Intercepts of a Graph.

2 Graph a Linear Equation by Finding and Plotting Intercepts.

3 Identify and Graph Vertical and Horizontal Lines.

OBJECTIVE
1 Identifying Intercepts

In this section, we graph linear equations in two variables by identifying intercepts. For example, the graph of $y = 4x - 8$ is shown on the right. Notice that this graph crosses the y-axis at the point $(0, -8)$. This point is called the **y-intercept.** Likewise, the graph crosses the x-axis at $(2, 0)$, and this point is called the **x-intercept.**

The intercepts are $(2, 0)$ and $(0, -8)$.

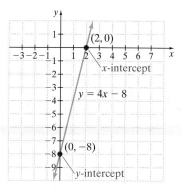

Helpful Hint

If a graph crosses the x-axis at $(-3, 0)$ and the y-axis at $(0, 7)$, then

$$(-3, 0) \qquad (0, 7)$$
$$\uparrow \qquad\qquad \uparrow$$
$$x\text{-intercept} \quad y\text{-intercept}$$

Notice that for the y-intercept, the x-value is 0 and for the x-intercept, the y-value is 0.
Note: Sometimes in mathematics, you may see just the number -3 stated as the x-intercept, and 7 stated as the y-intercept.

EXAMPLES   Identify the x- and y-intercepts.

1.

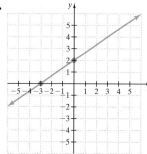

2.

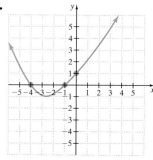

Solution

x-intercept: $(-3, 0)$
y-intercept: $(0, 2)$

Solution

x-intercepts: $(-4, 0)$, $(-1, 0)$
y-intercept: $(0, 1)$

Helpful Hint

Notice that any time $(0, 0)$ is a point of a graph, then it is an x-intercept and a y-intercept. Why? It is the only point that lies on both axes.

3.

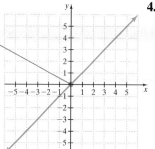

4.

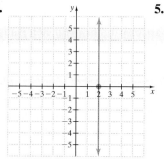

5.

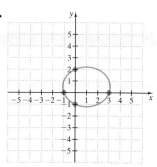

Solution

x-intercept: $(0, 0)$
y-intercept: $(0, 0)$

Solution

x-intercept: $(2, 0)$
y-intercept: none

Solution

x-intercepts:
$(-1, 0)$, $(3, 0)$
y-intercepts:
$(0, 2)$, $(0, -1)$

PRACTICE

1–5   Identify the *x*- and *y*-intercepts.

1.
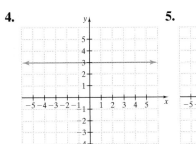

2.
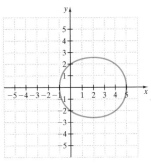

3.
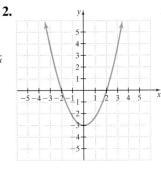

4.

5.

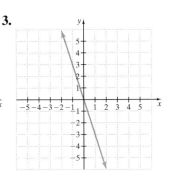

OBJECTIVE

2   Using Intercepts to Graph a Linear Equation

Given the equation of a line, intercepts are usually easy to find since one coordinate is 0.

One way to find the *y*-intercept of a line, given its equation, is to let $x = 0$, since a point on the *y*-axis has an *x*-coordinate of 0. To find the *x*-intercept of a line, let $y = 0$, since a point on the *x*-axis has a *y*-coordinate of 0.

Finding *x*- and *y*-intercepts

To find the *x*-intercept, let $y = 0$ and solve for *x*.

To find the *y*-intercept, let $x = 0$ and solve for *y*.

EXAMPLE 6   Graph $x - 3y = 6$ by finding and plotting intercepts.

Solution   Let $y = 0$ to find the *x*-intercept and let $x = 0$ to find the *y*-intercept.

Let $y = 0$	Let $x = 0$
$x - 3y = 6$	$x - 3y = 6$
$x - 3(0) = 6$	$0 - 3y = 6$
$x - 0 = 6$	$-3y = 6$
$x = 6$	$y = -2$

The *x*-intercept is $(6, 0)$ and the *y*-intercept is $(0, -2)$. We find a third ordered pair solution to check our work. If we let $y = -1$, then $x = 3$. Plot the points $(6, 0)$, $(0, -2)$, and $(3, -1)$. The graph of $x - 3y = 6$ is the line drawn through these points, as shown.

(Continued on next page)

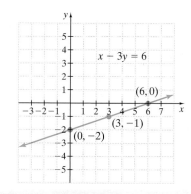

x	y
6	0
0	−2
3	−1

PRACTICE
6 Graph $x + 2y = -4$ by finding and plotting intercepts.

EXAMPLE 7 Graph $x = -2y$ by plotting intercepts.

Solution Let $y = 0$ to find the x-intercept and $x = 0$ to find the y-intercept.

$$\begin{array}{ll} \text{Let } y = 0 & \text{Let } x = 0 \\ x = -2y & x = -2y \\ x = -2(0) & 0 = -2y \\ x = 0 & 0 = y \end{array}$$

Both the x-intercept and y-intercept are $(0,0)$. In other words, when $x = 0$, then $y = 0$, which gives the ordered pair $(0,0)$. Also, when $y = 0$, then $x = 0$, which gives the same ordered pair $(0, 0)$. This happens when the graph passes through the origin. Since two points are needed to determine a line, we must find at least one more ordered pair that satisfies $x = -2y$. We will let $y = -1$ to find a second ordered pair solution and let $y = 1$ as a checkpoint.

$$\begin{array}{ll} \text{Let } y = -1 & \text{Let } y = 1 \\ x = -2(-1) & x = -2(1) \\ x = 2 & x = -2 \end{array}$$

The ordered pairs are $(0,0)$, $(2, -1)$, and $(-2, 1)$. Plot these points to graph $x = -2y$.

x	y
0	0
2	−1
−2	1

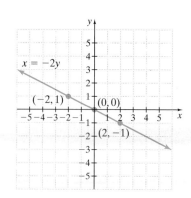

PRACTICE
7 Graph $x = 3y$ by plotting intercepts.

EXAMPLE 8   Graph: $4x = 3y - 9$

Solution   Find the x- and y-intercepts, and then choose $x = 2$ to find a checkpoint.

Let $y = 0$	Let $x = 0$	Let $x = 2$
$4x = 3(0) - 9$	$4 \cdot 0 = 3y - 9$	$4(2) = 3y - 9$
$4x = -9$	$9 = 3y$	$8 = 3y - 9$
Solve for x.	Solve for y.	Solve for y.
$x = -\dfrac{9}{4}$ or $-2\dfrac{1}{4}$	$3 = y$	$17 = 3y$
		$\dfrac{17}{3} = y$ or $y = 5\dfrac{2}{3}$

The ordered pairs are $\left(-2\dfrac{1}{4}, 0\right)$, $(0, 3)$, and $\left(2, 5\dfrac{2}{3}\right)$. The equation $4x = 3y - 9$ is graphed as follows.

x	y
$-2\dfrac{1}{4}$	0
0	3
2	$5\dfrac{2}{3}$

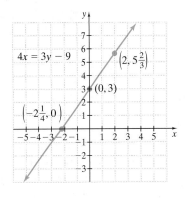

PRACTICE
8   Graph: $3x = 2y + 4$

OBJECTIVE
3   Graphing Vertical and Horizontal Lines

The equation $x = c$, where c is a real number constant, is a linear equation in two variables because it can be written in the form $x + 0y = c$. The graph of this equation is a vertical line as shown in the next example.

EXAMPLE 9   Graph: $x = 2$

Solution   The equation $x = 2$ can be written as $x + 0y = 2$. For any y-value chosen, notice that x is 2. No other value for x satisfies $x + 0y = 2$. Any ordered pair whose x-coordinate is 2 is a solution of $x + 0y = 2$. We will use the ordered pair solutions $(2, 3), (2, 0)$, and $(2, -3)$ to graph $x = 2$.

x	y
2	3
2	0
2	-3

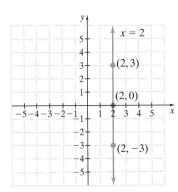

(Continued on next page)

The graph is a vertical line with x-intercept $(2, 0)$. Note that this graph has no y-intercept because x is never 0. ☐

PRACTICE
9 Graph: $x = -2$ ■

Vertical Lines

The graph of $x = c$, where c is a real number, is a vertical line with x-intercept $(c, 0)$.

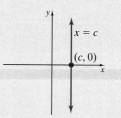

EXAMPLE 10 Graph: $y = -3$

Solution The equation $y = -3$ can be written as $0x + y = -3$. For any x-value chosen, y is -3. If we choose 4, 1, and -2 as x-values, the ordered pair solutions are $(4, -3)$, $(1, -3)$, and $(-2, -3)$. Use these ordered pairs to graph $y = -3$. The graph is a horizontal line with y-intercept $(0, -3)$ and no x-intercept.

x	y
4	-3
1	-3
-2	-3

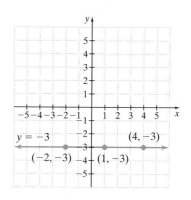

☐

PRACTICE
10 Graph: $y = 2$ ■

Horizontal Lines

The graph of $y = c$, where c is a real number, is a horizontal line with y-intercept $(0, c)$.

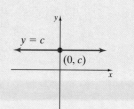

Graphing Calculator Explorations

You may have noticed that to use the $\boxed{Y =}$ key on a grapher to graph an equation, the equation must be solved for y. For example, to graph $2x + 3y = 7$, we solve this equation for y.

$$2x + 3y = 7$$
$$3y = -2x + 7 \quad \text{Subtract } 2x \text{ from both sides.}$$
$$\frac{3y}{3} = -\frac{2x}{3} + \frac{7}{3} \quad \text{Divide both sides by 3.}$$
$$y = -\frac{2}{3}x + \frac{7}{3} \quad \text{Simplify.}$$

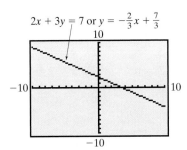

To graph $2x + 3y = 7$ or $y = -\frac{2}{3}x + \frac{7}{3}$, press the $\boxed{Y =}$ key and enter

$$Y_1 = -\frac{2}{3}x + \frac{7}{3}$$

Graph each linear equation.

1. $x = 3.78y$　　　　**2.** $-2.61y = x$　　　　**3.** $3x + 7y = 21$

4. $-4x + 6y = 21$　　**5.** $-2.2x + 6.8y = 15.5$　　**6.** $5.9x - 0.8y = -10.4$

✔ **Vocabulary, Readiness & Video Check**

Use the choices below to fill in each blank. Some choices may be used more than once. Exercises 1 and 2 come from Section 3.2.

x	vertical	x-intercept	linear
y	horizontal	y-intercept	standard

1. An equation that can be written in the form $Ax + By = C$ is called a(n) _____ equation in two variables.

2. The form $Ax + By = C$ is called _____ form.

3. The graph of the equation $y = -1$ is a _____ line.

4. The graph of the equation $x = 5$ is a _____ line.

5. A point where a graph crosses the y-axis is called a(n) _____.

6. A point where a graph crosses the x-axis is called a(n) _____.

7. Given an equation of a line, to find the x-intercept (if there is one), let _____ = 0 and solve for _____.

8. Given an equation of a line, to find the y-intercept (if there is one), let _____ = 0 and solve for _____.

Martin-Gay Interactive Videos

See Video 3.3 ◉

Watch the section lecture video and answer the following questions.

OBJECTIVE 1

9. At the end of ▦ Example 2, patterns are discussed. What reason is given for why x-intercepts have y-values of 0? For why y-intercepts have x-values of 0?

OBJECTIVE 2

10. In ▦ Example 3, the goal is to use the x- and y-intercepts to graph a line. Yet once the two intercepts are found, a third point is also found before the line is graphed. Why do you think this practice of finding a third point is continued?

OBJECTIVE 3

11. From ▦ Examples 5 and 6, what can you say about the coefficient of x when the equation of a horizontal line is written as $Ax + By = C$? What about the coefficient of y when the equation of a vertical line is written as $Ax + By = C$?

3.3 Exercise Set MyMathLab®

Identify the intercepts. See Examples 1 through 5.

1.

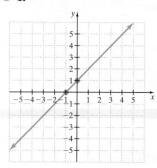

2.

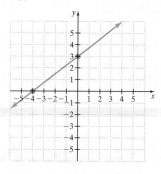

3.

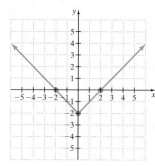

4.

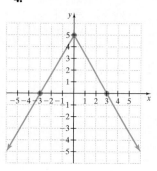

5.

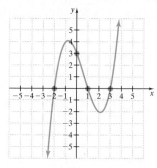

6.

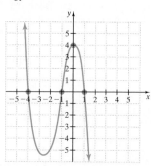

7.

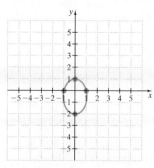

8.

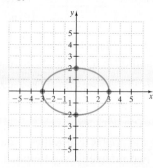

Solve. See Examples 1 through 5.

9. What is the greatest number of intercepts for a line?

10. What is the least number of intercepts for a line?

11. What is the least number of intercepts for a circle?

12. What is the greatest number of intercepts for a circle?

Graph each linear equation by finding and plotting its intercepts. See Examples 6 through 8.

13. $x - y = 3$ **14.** $x - y = -4$ **15.** $x = 5y$

16. $x = 2y$ **17.** $-x + 2y = 6$ **18.** $x - 2y = -8$

19. $2x - 4y = 8$ **20.** $2x + 3y = 6$ **21.** $y = 2x$

22. $y = -2x$ **23.** $y = 3x + 6$ **24.** $y = 2x + 10$

Graph each linear equation. See Examples 9 and 10.

25. $x = -1$ **26.** $y = 5$ **27.** $y = 0$

28. $x = 0$ **29.** $y + 7 = 0$ **30.** $x - 2 = 0$

31. $x + 3 = 0$ **32.** $y - 6 = 0$

MIXED PRACTICE

Graph each linear equation. See Examples 6 through 10.

33. $x = y$ **34.** $x = -y$

35. $x + 8y = 8$ **36.** $x + 3y = 9$

37. $5 = 6x - y$ **38.** $4 = x - 3y$

39. $-x + 10y = 11$ **40.** $-x + 9y = 10$

41. $x = -4\frac{1}{2}$ **42.** $x = -1\frac{3}{4}$

43. $y = 3\frac{1}{4}$ **44.** $y = 2\frac{1}{2}$

45. $y = -\frac{2}{3}x + 1$ **46.** $y = -\frac{3}{5}x + 3$

47. $4x - 6y + 2 = 0$ **48.** $9x - 6y + 3 = 0$

For Exercises 49 through 54, match each equation with its graph. See graphs A–F below and on the next page.

49. $y = 3$ **50.** $y = 2x + 2$

51. $x = -1$ **52.** $x = 3$

53. $y = 2x + 3$ **54.** $y = -2x$

A.

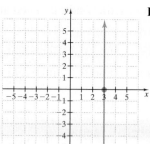

B.

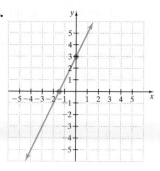

C.

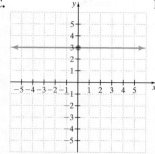

D.

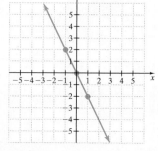

E.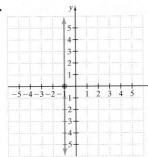

F.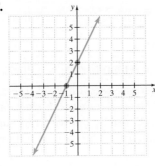

REVIEW AND PREVIEW

Simplify. See Sections 1.4 through 1.7.

55. $\dfrac{-6 - 3}{2 - 8}$

56. $\dfrac{4 - 5}{-1 - 0}$

57. $\dfrac{-8 - (-2)}{-3 - (-2)}$

58. $\dfrac{12 - 3}{10 - 9}$

59. $\dfrac{0 - 6}{5 - 0}$

60. $\dfrac{2 - 2}{3 - 5}$

CONCEPT EXTENSIONS

Answer the following true or false.

61. All lines have an x-intercept *and* a y-intercept.

62. The graph of $y = 4x$ contains the point $(0, 0)$.

63. The graph of $x + y = 5$ has an x-intercept of $(5, 0)$ and a y-intercept of $(0, 5)$.

64. The graph of $y = 5x$ contains the point $(5, 1)$.

The production supervisor at Alexandra's Office Products finds that it takes 3 hours to manufacture a particular office chair and 6 hours to manufacture an office desk. A total of 1200 hours is available to produce office chairs and desks of this style. The linear equation that models this situation is $3x + 6y = 1200$, where x represents the number of chairs produced and y the number of desks manufactured. Use this information for Exercises 65 through 68.

65. Complete the ordered pair solution $(0, \ )$ of this equation. Describe the manufacturing situation that corresponds to this solution.

66. Complete the ordered pair solution $(\ , 0)$ of this equation. Describe the manufacturing situation that corresponds to this solution.

67. If 50 desks are manufactured, find the greatest number of chairs that can be made.

68. If 50 chairs are manufactured, find the greatest number of desks that can be made.

Solve.

69. Since 2009, the number of analog theater screens has been on the decline in the U.S. The number of analog movie screens y each year can be estimated by the equation $y = -7000x + 31{,}800$, where x represents the number of years since 2009. (*Source:* MPAA)

a. Find the x-intercept of this equation. Round to the nearest tenth.

b. What does this x-intercept mean?

c. Use part (b) to comment on your opinion of the limitations of using equations to model real data.

70. The price of admission to a movie theater has been steadily increasing. The price of regular admission y (in dollars) to a movie theater may be represented by the equation $y = 0.24x + 5.28$, where x is the number of years after 2000. (*Source:* Based on data from Motion Picture Association of America)

a. Find the x-intercept of this equation.

b. What does this x-intercept mean?

c. Use part (b) to comment on your opinion of the limitations of using equations to model real data.

Two lines in the same plane that do not intersect are called **parallel lines.**

71. Draw a line parallel to the line $x = 5$ that intersects the x-axis at $(1, 0)$. What is the equation of this line?

72. Draw a line parallel to the line $y = -1$ that intersects the y-axis at $(0, -4)$. What is the equation of this line?

73. Discuss whether a vertical line ever has a y-intercept.

74. Explain why it is a good idea to use three points to graph a linear equation.

75. Discuss whether a horizontal line ever has an x-intercept.

76. Explain how to find intercepts.

3.4 | Slope and Rate of Change

OBJECTIVE

1   Finding the Slope of a Line Given Two Points of the Line

Thus far, much of this chapter has been devoted to graphing lines. You have probably noticed by now that a key feature of a line is its slant or steepness. In mathematics, the slant or steepness of a line is formally known as its **slope.** We measure the slope of a line by the ratio of vertical change to the corresponding horizontal change as we move along the line.

On the line below, for example, suppose that we begin at the point $(1, 2)$ and move to the point $(4, 6)$. The vertical change is the change in y-coordinates: $6 - 2$ or 4 units. The corresponding horizontal change is the change in x-coordinates: $4 - 1 = 3$ units. The ratio of these changes is

$$\text{slope} = \frac{\text{change in } y \text{ (vertical change)}}{\text{change in } x \text{ (horizontal change)}} = \frac{4}{3}$$

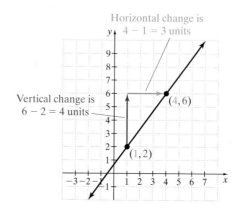

The slope of this line, then, is $\frac{4}{3}$. This means that for every 4 units of change in y-coordinates, there is a corresponding change of 3 units in x-coordinates.

Helpful Hint

It makes no difference what two points of a line are chosen to find its slope. The slope of a line is the same everywhere on the line.

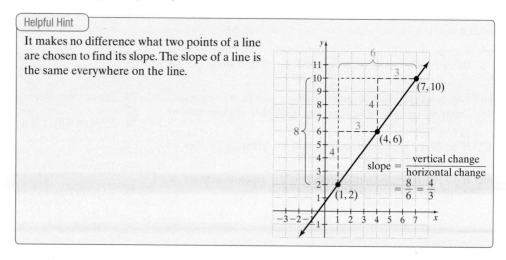

To find the slope of a line, then, choose two points of the line. Label the x-coordinates of the two points x_1 and x_2 (read "x sub one" and "x sub two"), and label the corresponding y-coordinates y_1 and y_2.

The vertical change or **rise** between these points is the difference in the y-coordinates: $y_2 - y_1$. The horizontal change or **run** between the points is the difference of the x-coordinates: $x_2 - x_1$. The slope of the line is the ratio of $y_2 - y_1$ to $x_2 - x_1$, and we traditionally use the letter m to denote slope: $m = \dfrac{y_2 - y_1}{x_2 - x_1}$.

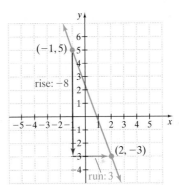

Slope of a Line

The slope m of the line containing the points (x_1, y_1) and (x_2, y_2) is given by

$$m = \frac{\text{rise}}{\text{run}} = \frac{\text{change in } y}{\text{change in } x} = \frac{y_2 - y_1}{x_2 - x_1}, \quad \text{as long as } x_2 \neq x_1$$

EXAMPLE I   Find the slope of the line through $(-1, 5)$ and $(2, -3)$. Graph the line.

Solution   If we let (x_1, y_1) be $(-1, 5)$, then $x_1 = -1$ and $y_1 = 5$. Also, let (x_2, y_2) be $(2, -3)$ so that $x_2 = 2$ and $y_2 = -3$. Then, by the definition of slope,

$$m = \frac{y_2 - y_1}{x_2 - x_1}$$

$$= \frac{-3 - 5}{2 - (-1)}$$

$$= \frac{-8}{3} = -\frac{8}{3}$$

The slope of the line is $-\dfrac{8}{3}$.

PRACTICE

1   Find the slope of the line through $(-4, 11)$ and $(2, 5)$.

Helpful Hint

When finding slope, it makes no difference which point is identified as (x_1, y_1) and which is identified as (x_2, y_2). Just remember that whatever y-value is first in the numerator, its corresponding x-value must be first in the denominator. Another way to calculate the slope in Example 1 is:

$$m = \frac{y_2 - y_1}{x_2 - x_1} = \frac{5 - (-3)}{-1 - 2} = \frac{8}{-3} \quad \text{or} \quad -\frac{8}{3} \quad \leftarrow \text{Same slope as found in Example 1.}$$

✔ **CONCEPT CHECK**

The points $(-2, -5)$, $(0, -2)$, $(4, 4)$, and $(10, 13)$ all lie on the same line. Work with a partner and verify that the slope is the same no matter which points are used to find slope.

Answer to Concept Check:

$$m = \frac{3}{2}$$

EXAMPLE 2   Find the slope of the line through $(-1, -2)$ and $(2, 4)$. Graph the line.

Solution   Let (x_1, y_1) be $(2, 4)$ and (x_2, y_2) be $(-1, -2)$.

$$m = \frac{y_2 - y_1}{x_2 - x_1}$$

$$= \frac{-2 - 4}{-1 - 2} \quad \begin{array}{l} y\text{-value} \\ \text{corresponding } x\text{-value} \end{array}$$

$$= \frac{-6}{-3} = 2$$

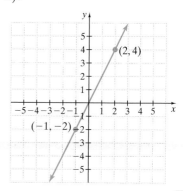

Helpful Hint

The slope for Example 2 is the same if we let (x_1, y_1) be $(-1, -2)$ and (x_2, y_2) be $(2, 4)$.

$$m = \frac{\overset{y\text{-value}}{4 - (-2)}}{\underset{\text{corresponding } x\text{-value}}{2 - (-1)}} = \frac{6}{3} = 2$$

PRACTICE

2   Find the slope of the line through $(-3, -1)$ and $(3, 1)$.

✔ **CONCEPT CHECK**

What is wrong with the following slope calculation for the points $(3, 5)$ and $(-2, 6)$?

$$m = \frac{5 - 6}{-2 - 3} = \frac{-1}{-5} = \frac{1}{5}$$

Notice that the slope of the line in Example 1 is negative, whereas the slope of the line in Example 2 is positive. Let your eye follow the line with negative slope from left to right and notice that the line "goes down." Following the line with positive slope from left to right, notice that the line "goes up." This is true in general.

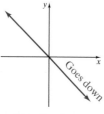

Negative slope

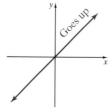

Positive slope

Helpful Hint

To decide whether a line "goes up" or "goes down," always follow the line from left to right.

OBJECTIVE

2   Finding the Slope of a Line Given Its Equation

As we have seen, the slope of a line is defined by two points on the line. Thus, if we know the equation of a line, we can find its slope by finding two of its points. For example, let's find the slope of the line

$$y = 3x + 2$$

To find two points, we can choose two values for x and substitute to find corresponding y-values. If $x = 0$, for example, $y = 3 \cdot 0 + 2$ or $y = 2$. If $x = 1, y = 3 \cdot 1 + 2$ or $y = 5$. This gives the ordered pairs $(0, 2)$ and $(1, 5)$. Using the definition for slope, we have

$$m = \frac{5 - 2}{1 - 0} = \frac{3}{1} = 3 \quad \text{The slope is 3.}$$

Notice that the slope, 3, is the same as the coefficient of x in the equation $y = 3x + 2$.

Also, recall from Section 3.2 that the graph of an equation of the form $y = mx + b$ has y-intercept $(0, b)$.

Answer to Concept Check:
The order in which the x- and y-values are used must be the same.

$$m = \frac{5 - 6}{3 - (-2)} = \frac{-1}{5} = -\frac{1}{5}$$

This means that the y-intercept of the graph of $y = 3x + 2$ is $(0, 2)$. This is true in general and the form $y = mx + b$ is appropriately called the **slope-intercept form.**

$$\underset{\text{slope}}{\uparrow} \quad \underset{\substack{y\text{-intercept} \\ (0, b)}}{\uparrow}$$

Slope-Intercept Form

When a linear equation in two variables is written in slope-intercept form,

$$y = mx + b$$

m is the slope of the line and $(0, b)$ is the y-intercept of the line.

EXAMPLE 3   Find the slope and y-intercept of the line whose equation is $y = \dfrac{3}{4}x + 6$

Solution   The equation is in slope-intercept form, $y = mx + b$.

$$y = \frac{3}{4}x + 6$$

The coefficient of x, $\dfrac{3}{4}$, is the slope and the constant term, 6, is the y-value of the y-intercept, $(0, 6)$.   □

PRACTICE
3   Find the slope and y-intercept of the line whose equation is $y = \dfrac{2}{3}x - 2$.   ■

EXAMPLE 4   Find the slope and the y-intercept of the line whose equation is $-y = 5x - 2$.

Solution   Remember, the equation must be solved for y (not $-y$) in order for it to be written in slope-intercept form.

To solve for y, let's divide both sides of the equation by -1.

$$-y = 5x - 2$$
$$\frac{-y}{-1} = \frac{5x}{-1} - \frac{2}{-1} \quad \text{Divide both sides by } -1.$$
$$y = -5x + 2 \quad \text{Simplify.}$$

The coefficient of x, -5, is the slope and the constant term, 2, is the y-value of the y-intercept, $(0, 2)$.   □

PRACTICE
4   Find the slope and y-intercept of the line whose equation is $-y = -6x + 5$.   ■

EXAMPLE 5   Find the slope and the y-intercept of the line whose equation is $3x - 4y = 4$.

Solution   Write the equation in slope-intercept form by solving for y.

$$3x - 4y = 4$$
$$-4y = -3x + 4 \quad \text{Subtract } 3x \text{ from both sides.}$$
$$\frac{-4y}{-4} = \frac{-3x}{-4} + \frac{4}{-4} \quad \text{Divide both sides by } -4.$$
$$y = \frac{3}{4}x - 1 \quad \text{Simplify.}$$

The coefficient of x, $\dfrac{3}{4}$, is the slope, and the y-intercept is $(0, -1)$.   □

(Continued on next page)

PRACTICE
5   Find the slope and the y-intercept of the line whose equation is $5x + 2y = 8$. ∎

OBJECTIVE

3   Finding Slopes of Horizontal and Vertical Lines

Recall that if a line tilts upward from left to right, its slope is positive. If a line tilts downward from left to right, its slope is negative. Let's now find the slopes of two special lines, horizontal and vertical lines.

EXAMPLE 6   Find the slope of the line $y = -1$.

Solution Recall that $y = -1$ is a horizontal line with y-intercept $(0, -1)$. To find the slope, find two ordered pair solutions of $y = -1$. Solutions of $y = -1$ must have a y-value of -1. Let's use points $(2, -1)$ and $(-3, -1)$, which are on the line.

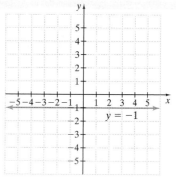

$$m = \frac{y_2 - y_1}{x_2 - x_1} = \frac{-1 - (-1)}{-3 - 2} = \frac{0}{-5} = 0$$

The slope of the line $y = -1$ is 0 and its graph is shown. □

PRACTICE
6   Find the slope of the line $y = 3$. ∎

Any two points of a horizontal line will have the same y-values. This means that the y-values will always have a difference of 0 for all horizontal lines. Thus, **all horizontal lines have a slope 0.**

EXAMPLE 7   Find the slope of the line $x = 5$.

Solution Recall that the graph of $x = 5$ is a vertical line with x-intercept $(5, 0)$.

To find the slope, find two ordered pair solutions of $x = 5$. Solutions of $x = 5$ must have an x-value of 5. Let's use points $(5, 0)$ and $(5, 4)$, which are on the line.

$$m = \frac{y_2 - y_1}{x_2 - x_1} = \frac{4 - 0}{5 - 5} = \frac{4}{0}$$

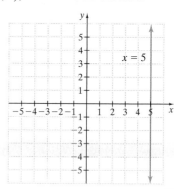

Since $\frac{4}{0}$ is undefined, we say the slope of the vertical line $x = 5$ is undefined, and its graph is shown. □

PRACTICE
7   Find the slope of the line $x = -4$. ∎

Any two points of a vertical line will have the same x-values. This means that the x-values will always have a difference of 0 for all vertical lines. Thus **all vertical lines have undefined slope.**

> **Helpful Hint**
>
> Slope of 0 and undefined slope are not the same. Vertical lines have undefined slope or no slope, while horizontal lines have a slope of 0.

Here is a general review of slope.

Summary of Slope

Slope m of the line through (x_1, y_1) and (x_2, y_2) is given by the equation $m = \dfrac{y_2 - y_1}{x_2 - x_1}$.

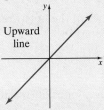

Upward line

Positive slope: $m > 0$

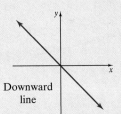

Downward line

Negative slope: $m < 0$

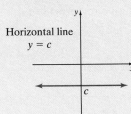

Horizontal line
$y = c$

Zero slope: $m = 0$

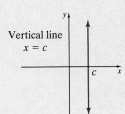

Vertical line
$x = c$

Undefined slope or no slope

OBJECTIVE

4 Slopes of Parallel and Perpendicular Lines

Two lines in the same plane are **parallel** if they do not intersect. Slopes of lines can help us determine whether lines are parallel. Parallel lines have the same steepness, so it follows that they have the same slope.

For example, the graphs of

$$y = -2x + 4$$

and

$$y = -2x - 3$$

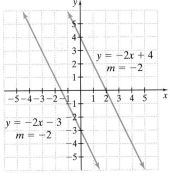

are shown. These lines have the same slope, -2. They also have different y-intercepts, so the lines are distinct and parallel. (If the y-intercepts were the same also, the lines would be the same.)

Parallel Lines

Nonvertical parallel lines have the same slope and different y-intercepts.

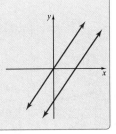

Two lines are **perpendicular** if they lie in the same plane and meet at a 90° (right) angle. How do the slopes of perpendicular lines compare? The product of the slopes of two perpendicular lines is -1.

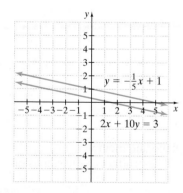

For example, the graphs of

$$y = 4x + 1$$

and

$$y = -\frac{1}{4}x - 3$$

are shown. The slopes of the lines are 4 and $-\frac{1}{4}$. Their product is $4\left(-\frac{1}{4}\right) = -1$, so the lines are perpendicular.

Perpendicular Lines

If the product of the slopes of two lines is -1, then the lines are perpendicular.

(Two nonvertical lines are perpendicular if the slope of one is the negative reciprocal of the slope of the other.)

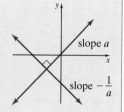

Helpful Hint

Here are examples of numbers that are negative (opposite) reciprocals.

Number	Negative Reciprocal	Their Product Is -1.
$\frac{2}{3}$	$-\frac{3}{2}$	$\frac{2}{3} \cdot -\frac{3}{2} = -\frac{6}{6} = -1$
-5 or $-\frac{5}{1}$	$\frac{1}{5}$	$-5 \cdot \frac{1}{5} = -\frac{5}{5} = -1$

Helpful Hint

Here are a few important facts about vertical and horizontal lines.

- Two distinct vertical lines are parallel.
- Two distinct horizontal lines are parallel.
- A horizontal line and a vertical line are always perpendicular.

EXAMPLE 8   Determine whether each pair of lines is parallel, perpendicular, or neither.

a. $y = -\frac{1}{5}x + 1$ **b.** $x + y = 3$ **c.** $3x + y = 5$

$2x + 10y = 3$ $-x + y = 4$ $2x + 3y = 6$

Solution

a. The slope of the line $y = -\frac{1}{5}x + 1$ is $-\frac{1}{5}$. We find the slope of the second line by solving its equation for y.

$$2x + 10y = 3$$
$$10y = -2x + 3 \qquad \text{Subtract } 2x \text{ from both sides.}$$
$$y = \frac{-2}{10}x + \frac{3}{10} \qquad \text{Divide both sides by 10.}$$
$$y = -\frac{1}{5}x + \frac{3}{10} \qquad \text{Simplify.}$$

The slope of this line is $-\frac{1}{5}$ also. Since the lines have the same slope and different y-intercepts, they are parallel, as shown in the margin.

b. To find each slope, we solve each equation for y.

$$x + y = 3 \qquad\qquad -x + y = 4$$
$$y = -x + 3 \qquad\qquad y = x + 4$$

The slope is -1.   The slope is 1.

The slopes are not the same, so the lines are not parallel. Next we check the product of the slopes: $(-1)(1) = -1$. Since the product is -1, the lines are perpendicular, as shown in the figure.

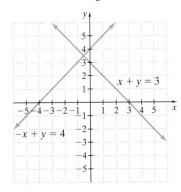

c. We solve each equation for y to find each slope. The slopes are -3 and $-\dfrac{2}{3}$.

The slopes are not the same and their product is not -1. Thus, the lines are neither parallel nor perpendicular.   □

PRACTICE
8   Determine whether each pair of lines is parallel, perpendicular, or neither.

a. $y = -5x + 1$ **b.** $x + y = 11$ **c.** $2x + 3y = 21$
      $x - 5y = 10$ $2x + y = 11$ $6y = -4x - 2$ ■

✔ **CONCEPT CHECK**

Consider the line $-6x + 2y = 1$.

a. Write the equations of two lines parallel to this line.
b. Write the equations of two lines perpendicular to this line.

OBJECTIVE
5   **Slope as a Rate of Change** ▶

Slope can also be interpreted as a rate of change. In other words, slope tells us how fast y is changing with respect to x. To see this, let's look at a few of the many real-world applications of slope. For example, the pitch of a roof, used by builders and architects,

is its slope. The pitch of the roof on the left is $\dfrac{7}{10}\left(\dfrac{\text{rise}}{\text{run}}\right)$. This means that the roof rises vertically 7 feet for every horizontal 10 feet. The rate of change for the roof is 7 vertical feet (y) per 10 horizontal feet (x).

The grade of a road is its slope written as a percent. A 7% grade, as shown below, means that the road rises (or falls) 7 feet for every horizontal 100 feet. $\left(\text{Recall that } 7\% = \dfrac{7}{100}.\right)$ Here, the slope of $\dfrac{7}{100}$ gives us the rate of change. The road rises (in our diagram) 7 vertical feet (y) for every 100 horizontal feet (x).

Answers to Concept Check:
a. any two lines with $m = 3$ and
y-intercept not $\left(0, \dfrac{1}{2}\right)$

b. any two lines with $m = -\dfrac{1}{3}$

$\dfrac{7}{100}$ = 7% grade   7 feet

100 feet

EXAMPLE 9   Finding the Grade of a Road

At one part of the road to the summit of Pikes Peak, the road rises at a rate of 15 vertical feet for a horizontal distance of 250 feet. Find the grade of the road.

Solution Recall that the grade of a road is its slope written as a percent.

$$\text{grade} = \frac{\text{rise}}{\text{run}} = \frac{15}{250} = 0.06 = 6\%$$

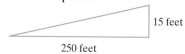

The grade is 6%.

PRACTICE
9   One part of the Mt. Washington (New Hampshire) cog railway rises about 1794 feet over a horizontal distance of 7176 feet. Find the grade of this part of the railway.

EXAMPLE 10   Finding the Slope of a Line

The following graph shows annual food and drink sales y (in billions of dollars) for year x.

a. Find the slope of the line and attach the proper units for the rate of change.

b. Then write a sentence explaining the meaning of the slope for this application.

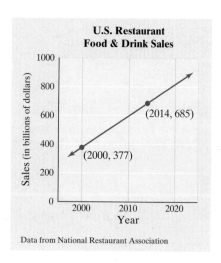

Solution

a. Use (2000, 377) and (2014, 685) to calculate slope.

$$m = \frac{685 - 377}{2014 - 2000} = \frac{308}{14} = \frac{22 \text{ billion dollars}}{1 \text{ year}}$$

b. This means that the rate of change of restaurant food and drink sales increases by 22 billion dollars every 1 year, or $22 billion per year.

PRACTICE
10   The following graph shows the cost y (in dollars) of having laundry done at the Wash-n-Fold, where x is the number of pounds of laundry.

a. Find the slope of the line, and attach the proper units for the rate of change.

b. Then write a sentence explaining the meaning of the slope for this application.

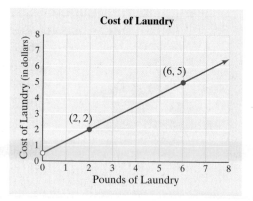

Graphing Calculator Explorations

It is possible to use a grapher to sketch the graph of more than one equation on the same set of axes. This feature can be used to confirm our findings from Section 3.2 when we learned that the graph of an equation written in the form $y = mx + b$ has a y-intercept of b. For example, graph the equations $y = \frac{2}{5}x$, $y = \frac{2}{5}x + 7$, and $y = \frac{2}{5}x - 4$

on the same set of axes. To do so, press the $\boxed{Y =}$ key and enter the equations on the first three lines.

$$Y_1 = \left(\frac{2}{5}\right)x$$

$$Y_2 = \left(\frac{2}{5}\right)x + 7$$

$$Y_3 = \left(\frac{2}{5}\right)x - 4$$

The screen should look like:

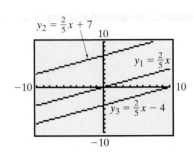

Notice that all three graphs appear to have the same positive slope. The graph of $y = \frac{2}{5}x + 7$ is the graph of $y = \frac{2}{5}x$ moved 7 units upward with a y-intercept of 7. Also, the graph of $y = \frac{2}{5}x - 4$ is the graph of $y = \frac{2}{5}x$ moved 4 units downward with a y-intercept of -4.

Graph the equations on the same set of axes. Describe the similarities and differences in their graphs. Use the standard window setting or any other convenient window setting.

1. $y = 3.8x, y = 3.8x - 3, y = 3.8x + 7$

2. $y = -4.9x, y = -4.9x + 1, y = -4.9x + 8$

3. $y = \frac{1}{4}x; y = \frac{1}{4}x + 5, y = \frac{1}{4}x - 8$

4. $y = -\frac{3}{4}x, y = -\frac{3}{4}x - 5, y = -\frac{3}{4}x + 6$

✔ **Vocabulary, Readiness & Video Check**

Use the choices below to fill in each blank. Not all choices will be used.

m	x	0	positive	undefined
b	y	slope	negative	

1. The measure of the steepness or tilt of a line is called _____.

2. If an equation is written in the form $y = mx + b$, the value of the letter _____ is the value of the slope of the graph.

3. The slope of a horizontal line is _____.

4. The slope of a vertical line is _____.

5. If the graph of a line moves upward from left to right, the line has _____ slope.

6. If the graph of a line moves downward from left to right, the line has _____ slope.

7. Given two points of a line, slope $= \dfrac{\text{change in} \underline{}}{\text{change in} \underline{}}$.

Martin-Gay Interactive Videos

See Video 3.4

Watch the section lecture video and answer the following questions.

OBJECTIVE
1

8. What important point is made during Example 1 having to do with the order of the points in the slope formula?

OBJECTIVE
2

9. From Example 5, how do you write an equation in "slope-intercept form"? Once the equation is in slope-intercept form, how do you identify the slope?

OBJECTIVE
3

10. In the lecture after Example 8, different slopes are summarized. What is the difference between zero slope and undefined slope? What does "no slope" mean?

OBJECTIVE
4

11. From Example 10, what form of the equations is best to determine if two lines are parallel or perpendicular? Why?

OBJECTIVE
5

12. Writing the slope as a rate of change in Example 11 gave real-life meaning to the slope. What step in the general strategy for problem solving does this correspond to?

3.4 Exercise Set MyMathLab

Find the slope of the line that passes through the given points. See Examples 1 and 2.

1. $(-1, 5)$ and $(6, -2)$ **2.** $(3, 1)$ and $(2, 6)$

3. $(-4, 3)$ and $(-4, 5)$ **4.** $(6, -6)$ and $(6, 2)$

5. $(-2, 8)$ and $(1, 6)$ **6.** $(4, -3)$ and $(2, 2)$

7. $(5, 1)$ and $(-2, 1)$ **8.** $(0, 13)$ and $(-4, 13)$

Find the slope of each line if it exists. See Examples 1 and 2.

9.

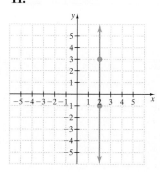

10.

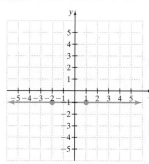

11.

12.

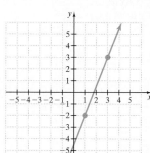

13.

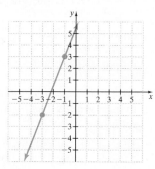

14.

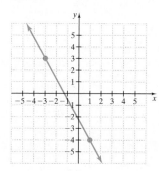

State whether the slope of the line is positive, negative, 0, or is undefined. See the top box on p. 215.

15.

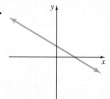

16.

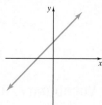

17.

18.

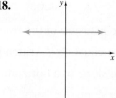

Decide whether a line with the given slope is upward, downward, horizontal, or vertical. See the top box on p. 215.

19. $m = \dfrac{7}{6}$ _____

20. $m = -3$ _____

21. $m = 0$ _____

22. m is undefined. _____

For each graph, determine which line has the greater slope. See the top box on p. 215.

23.

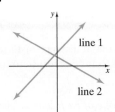

line 1
line 2

24.

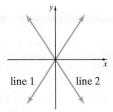

line 1   line 2

25.

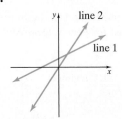

line 2
line 1

26.

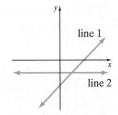

line 1
line 2

In Exercises 27 through 32, match each line with its slope. See Examples 1 and 2 and the top box on p. 215.

A. $m = 0$ **B.** undefined slope   **C.** $m = 3$

D. $m = 1$ **E.** $m = -\dfrac{1}{2}$ **F.** $m = -\dfrac{3}{4}$

27.

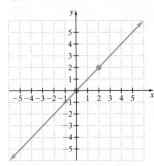

28.

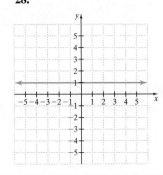

29.

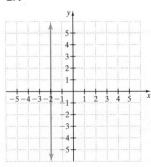

30.

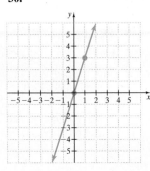

31.

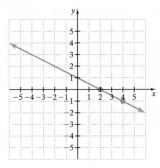

32.

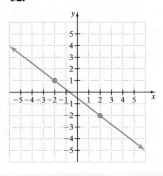

Find the slope of each line. See Examples 6 and 7.

33. $x = 6$ **34.** $y = 4$

35. $y = -4$ **36.** $x = 2$

37. $x = -3$ **38.** $y = -11$

39. $y = 0$ **40.** $x = 0$

MIXED PRACTICE

Find the slope of each line. See Examples 3 through 7.

41. $y = 5x - 2$ **42.** $y = -2x + 6$

43. $y = -0.3x + 2.5$ **44.** $y = -7.6x - 0.1$

▶ **45.** $2x + y = 7$ **46.** $-5x + y = 10$

▶ **47.** $2x - 3y = 10$ **48.** $3x - 5y = 1$

▶ **49.** $x = 1$ **50.** $y = -2$

51. $x = 2y$ **52.** $x = -4y$

▶ **53.** $y = -3$ **54.** $x = 5$

55. $-3x - 4y = 6$ **56.** $-4x - 7y = 9$

57. $20x - 5y = 1.2$ **58.** $24x - 3y = 5.7$

△ *Find the slope of the line that is (**a**) parallel and (**b**) perpendicular to the line through each pair of points. See Example 8.*

59. $(-3, -3)$ and $(0, 0)$

60. $(6, -2)$ and $(1, 4)$

61. $(-8, -4)$ and $(3, 5)$

62. $(6, -1)$ and $(-4, -10)$

△ *Determine whether each pair of lines is parallel, perpendicular, or neither. See Example 8.*

▶ **63.** $y = \dfrac{2}{9}x + 3$

     $y = -\dfrac{2}{9}x$

64. $y = \dfrac{1}{5}x + 20$

     $y = -\dfrac{1}{5}x$

65. $x - 3y = -6$

     $y = 3x - 9$

66. $y = 4x - 2$

     $4x + y = 5$

67. $6x = 5y + 1$

     $-12x + 10y = 1$

68. $-x + 2y = -2$

     $2x = 4y + 3$

69. $6 + 4x = 3y$

     $3x + 4y = 8$

▶ **70.** $10 + 3x = 5y$

     $5x + 3y = 1$

The pitch of a roof is its slope. Find the pitch of each roof shown. See Example 9. (Note: Pitch of a roof is a positive value.)

71.

72.

The grade of a road is its slope written as a percent. Find the grade of each road shown. See Example 9. (Note: Grade of a road is a positive value.)

73.

74.

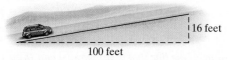

75. One of Japan's superconducting "bullet" trains is researched and tested at the Yamanashi Maglev Test Line near Otsuki City. The steepest section of the track has a rise of 2580 meters for a horizontal distance of 6450 meters. What is the grade of this section of track? (*Source:* Japan Railways Central Co.)

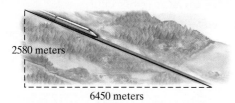

76. Professional plumbers suggest that a sewer pipe should rise 0.25 inch for every horizontal foot. Find the recommended slope for a sewer pipe. Round to the nearest hundredth.

77. There has been controversy over the past few years about the world's steepest street. The *Guinness Book of Records* actually listed Baldwin Street, in Dunedin, New Zealand, as the world's steepest street, but Canton Avenue in the Pittsburgh neighborhood of Beechview may be steeper. Calculate each grade to the nearest percent.

		Grade (%)
Canton Avenue	for every 30 meters of horizontal distance, the vertical change is 11 meters	
Baldwin Street	for every 2.86 meters of horizontal distance, the vertical change is 1 meter	

78. According to federal regulations, a wheelchair ramp should rise no more than 1 foot for a horizontal distance of 12 feet. Write the slope as a grade. Round to the nearest tenth of a percent.

For Exercises 79 through 82, find the slope of each line and write a sentence explaining the meaning of the slope as a rate of change. Don't forget to attach the proper units. See Example 10.

79. This graph approximates the number of U.S. households that have computers y (in millions) for year x. (*Source:* U.S. census and statistics)

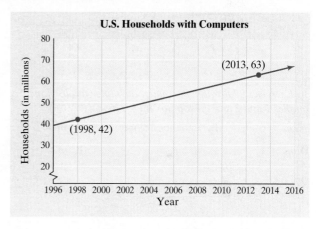

80. The graph approximates the amount of money y (in billions of dollars) spent worldwide on leisure travel and tourism for year x. (*Source:* World Travel and Tourism Council)

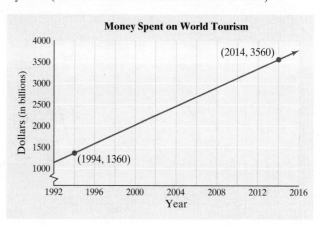

For Exercises 81 and 82, write the slope as a decimal.

81. The graph below shows the total cost y (in dollars) of owning and operating a compact car where x is the number of miles driven.

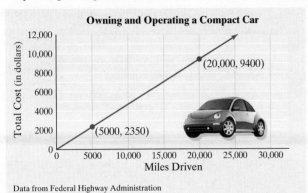

Owning and Operating a Compact Car

(20,000, 9400)

(5000, 2350)

Total Cost (in dollars) vs Miles Driven

Data from Federal Highway Administration

82. Americans are keeping their cars longer. The graph below shows the median age y (in years) of automobiles in the United States for the years shown. (*Source:* Bureau of Transportation Statistics)

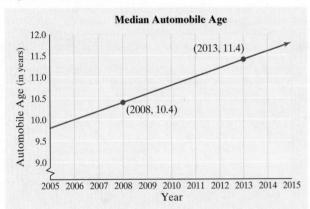

Median Automobile Age

(2013, 11.4)

(2008, 10.4)

Automobile Age (in years) vs Year

REVIEW AND PREVIEW

Solve each equation for y. See Section 2.6.

83. $y - (-6) = 2(x - 4)$

84. $y - 7 = -9(x - 6)$

85. $y - 1 = -6(x - (-2))$

86. $y - (-3) = 4(x - (-5))$

CONCEPT EXTENSIONS

Solve. See a Concept Check in this section.

87. Verify that the points $(2, 1)$, $(0, 0)$, $(-2, -1)$ and $(-4, -2)$ are all on the same line by computing the slope between each pair of points. (See the first Concept Check.)

88. Given the points $(2, 3)$ and $(-5, 1)$, can the slope of the line through these points be calculated by $\dfrac{1 - 3}{2 - (-5)}$? Why or why not? (See the second Concept Check.)

89. Write the equations of three lines parallel to $10x - 5y = -7$. (See the third Concept Check.)

90. Write the equations of two lines perpendicular to $10x - 5y = -7$. (See the third Concept Check.)

The following line graph shows the average fuel economy (in miles per gallon) of passenger automobiles produced during each of the model years shown. Use this graph to answer Exercises 91 through 96.

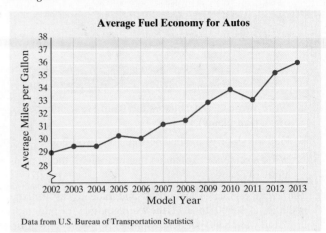

Average Fuel Economy for Autos

Average Miles per Gallon vs Model Year

Data from U.S. Bureau of Transportation Statistics

91. Between what two years shown was there a decrease in average fuel economy for automobiles?

92. What was the average fuel economy (in miles per gallon) for automobiles produced during 2008?

93. During which of the model years shown was average fuel economy the lowest? What was the average fuel economy that year?

94. During which of the model years shown was average fuel economy the highest? What was the average fuel economy for that year?

95. Of the following line segments, which has the greatest slope: from 2008 to 2009, 2009 to 2010, or 2011 to 2012?

96. Which line segment has a slope of 0?

Solve.

97. Find x so that the pitch of the roof is $\dfrac{1}{3}$.

18 feet

98. Find x so that the pitch of the roof is $\dfrac{2}{5}$.

4 feet

x

99. Approximately 27,000 organ transplants were performed in the United States in 2004. In 2014, the number rose to approximately 29,500. (*Source:* Organ Procurement and Transplantation Network)

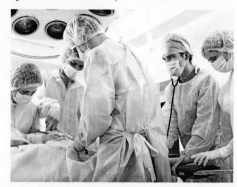

a. Write two ordered pairs of the form (year, number of organ transplants).

b. Find the slope of the line between the two points.

c. Write a sentence explaining the meaning of the slope as a rate of change.

100. The average price of an acre of midgrade Iowa farmland in 2008 was $2300. In 2012, the average price for midgrade farmland was $8300 per acre. (*Source:* National Agricultural Statistics Service)

a. Write two ordered pairs of the form (year, price of an acre).

b. Find the slope of the line through the two points.

c. Write a sentence explaining the meaning of the slope as a rate of change.

101. Show that a triangle with vertices at the points $(1, 1)$, $(-4, 4)$, and $(-3, 0)$ is a right triangle.

102. Show that the quadrilateral with vertices $(1, 3)$, $(2, 1)$, $(-4, 0)$, and $(-3, -2)$ is a parallelogram.

Find the slope of the line through the given points.

103. $(2.1, 6.7)$ and $(-8.3, 9.3)$

104. $(-3.8, 1.2)$ and $(-2.2, 4.5)$

105. $(2.3, 0.2)$ and $(7.9, 5.1)$

106. $(14.3, -10.1)$ and $(9.8, -2.9)$

107. The graph of $y = -\frac{1}{3}x + 2$ has a slope of $-\frac{1}{3}$. The graph of $y = -2x + 2$ has a slope of -2. The graph of $y = -4x + 2$ has a slope of -4. Graph all three equations on a single coordinate system. As the absolute value of the slope becomes larger, how does the steepness of the line change?

108. The graph of $y = \frac{1}{2}x$ has a slope of $\frac{1}{2}$. The graph of $y = 3x$ has a slope of 3. The graph of $y = 5x$ has a slope of 5. Graph all three equations on a single coordinate system. As slope becomes larger, how does the steepness of the line change?

Integrated Review Summary on Slope and Graphing Linear Equations

Sections 3.1–3.4

Find the slope of each line.

1.
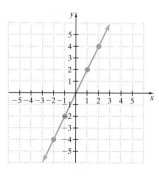

2.

3.
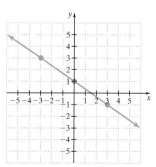

4.
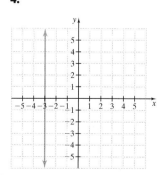

Graph each linear equation.

5. $y = -2x$

6. $x + y = 3$

7. $x = -1$

8. $y = 4$

9. $x - 2y = 6$

10. $y = 3x + 2$

11. $5x + 3y = 15$

12. $2x - 4y = 8$

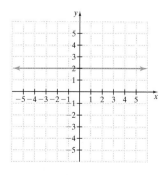

Determine whether the lines through the points are parallel, perpendicular, or neither.

13. $y = -\dfrac{1}{5}x + \dfrac{1}{3}$

$3x = -15y$

14. $x - y = \dfrac{1}{2}$

$3x - y = \dfrac{1}{2}$

15. In the years 2002 through 2013 the number of bridges on public roads (in thousands) in the United States can be modeled by the linear equation $y = 4.09x + 490$, where x is the number of years after 2002 and y is the number of bridges (in thousands). (*Source:* U.S. Dept. of Transportation)

    a. Find the y-intercept of the line.

    b. Write a sentence explaining the meaning of this intercept.

    c. Find the slope of this line.

    d. Write a sentence explaining the meaning of the slope as a rate of change.

16. Online advertising is a means of promoting products and services using the Internet. The revenue y (in billions of dollars) for online advertising for the years 2009 through 2014 is given by $y = 5.3x + 22.7$, where x is the number of years after 2009.

    a. Use this equation to complete the ordered pair (4,   )

    b. Write a sentence explaining the meaning of the answer to part (a).

Chapter 3 Vocabulary Check

Fill in each blank with one of the words listed below.

relation	function	domain	range	standard	slope-intercept
y-axis	x-axis	solution	linear	slope	point-slope
x-intercept	y-intercept	y	x		

1. An ordered pair is a(n) _____ of an equation in two variables if replacing the variables by the coordinates of the ordered pair results in a true statement.

2. The vertical number line in the rectangular coordinate system is called the _____.

3. A(n) _____ equation can be written in the form $Ax + By = C$.

4. A(n) _____ is a point of the graph where the graph crosses the x-axis.

5. The form $Ax + By = C$ is called _____ form.

6. A(n) _____ is a point of the graph where the graph crosses the y-axis.

7. The equation $y = 7x - 5$ is written in _____ form.

8. The equation $y + 1 = 7(x - 2)$ is written in _____ form.

9. To find an x-intercept of a graph, let _____ = 0.

10. The horizontal number line in the rectangular coordinate system is called the _____.

11. To find a y-intercept of a graph, let _____ = 0.

12. The _____ of a line measures the steepness or tilt of a line.

13. A set of ordered pairs that assigns to each x-value exactly one y-value is called a(n) _____.

14. The set of all x-coordinates of a relation is called the _____ of the relation.

15. The set of all y-coordinates of a relation is called the _____ of the relation.

16. A set of ordered pairs is called a(n) _____.

Chapter 3 Highlights

DEFINITIONS AND CONCEPTS	EXAMPLES

Section 3.1   Reading Graphs and the Rectangular Coordinate System

The **rectangular coordinate system** consists of a plane and a vertical and a horizontal number line intersecting at their 0 coordinates. The vertical number line is called the **y-axis** and the horizontal number line is called the **x-axis.** The point of intersection of the axes is called the **origin**.

To **plot** or **graph** an ordered pair means to find its corresponding point on a rectangular coordinate system.

To plot or graph an ordered pair such as $(3, -2)$, start at the origin. Move 3 units to the right and, from there, 2 units down.

To plot or graph $(-3, 4)$, start at the origin. Move 3 units to the left and, from there, 4 units up.

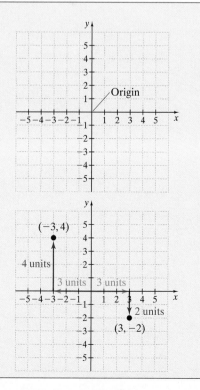

DEFINITIONS AND CONCEPTS	EXAMPLES

Section 3.1   Reading Graphs and the Rectangular Coordinate System (continued)

An ordered pair is a **solution** of an equation in two variables if replacing the variables by the coordinates of the ordered pair results in a true statement.

Determine whether $(-1, 5)$ is a solution of $2x + 3y = 13$.

$$2x + 3y = 13$$
$$2(-1) + 3 \cdot 5 = 13 \quad \text{Let } x = -1, y = 5$$
$$-2 + 15 = 13$$
$$13 = 13 \quad \text{True}$$

If one coordinate of an ordered pair solution is known, the other value can be determined by substitution.

Complete the ordered pair solution $(0, \ )$ for the equation $x - 6y = 12$.

$$x - 6y = 12$$
$$0 - 6y = 12 \quad \text{Let } x = 0.$$
$$\frac{-6y}{-6} = \frac{12}{-6} \quad \text{Divide by } -6.$$
$$y = -2$$

The ordered pair solution is $(0, -2)$.

Section 3.2   Graphing Linear Equations

A **linear equation in two variables** is an equation that can be written in the form $Ax + By = C$ where A and B are not both 0. The form $Ax + By = C$ is called **standard form.**

Linear Equations

$$3x + 2y = -6 \qquad x = -5$$
$$y = 3 \qquad y = -x + 10$$

$x + y = 10$ is in standard form.

To graph a linear equation in two variables, find three ordered pair solutions. Plot the solution points and draw the line connecting the points.

Graph $x - 2y = 5$.

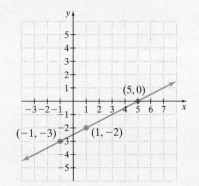

x	y
5	0
1	-2
-1	-3

Section 3.3   Intercepts

An **intercept** of a graph is a point where the graph intersects an axis. If a graph intersects the x-axis at a, then $(a, 0)$ is the **x-intercept.** If a graph intersects the y-axis at b, then $(0, b)$ is the **y-intercept.**

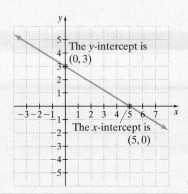

(continued)

DEFINITIONS AND CONCEPTS	EXAMPLES

Section 3.3 Intercepts (continued)

To find the x-intercept, let $y = 0$ and solve for x.

To find the y-intercept, let $x = 0$ and solve for y.

Graph $2x - 5y = -10$ by finding intercepts.

If $y = 0$, then   If $x = 0$, then

$2x - 5 \cdot 0 = -10$ $2 \cdot 0 - 5y = -10$

$2x = -10$ $-5y = -10$

$\dfrac{2x}{2} = \dfrac{-10}{2}$ $\dfrac{-5y}{-5} = \dfrac{-10}{-5}$

$x = -5$ $y = 2$

The x-intercept is $(-5, 0)$. The y-intercept is $(0, 2)$.

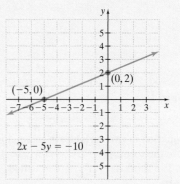

The graph of $x = c$ is a vertical line with x-intercept $(c, 0)$.

The graph of $y = c$ is a horizontal line with y-intercept $(0, c)$.

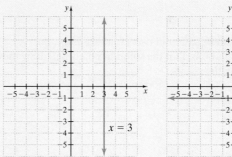

Section 3.4 Slope and Rate of Change

The **slope m** of the line through points (x_1, y_1) and (x_2, y_2) is given by

$$m = \frac{y_2 - y_1}{x_2 - x_1} \qquad \text{as long as } x_2 \neq x_1$$

A horizontal line has slope 0.
The slope of a vertical line is undefined.

Nonvertical parallel lines have the same slope.

Two nonvertical lines are perpendicular if the slope of one is the negative reciprocal of the slope of the other.

The slope of the line through points $(-1, 6)$ and $(-5, 8)$ is

$$m = \frac{y_2 - y_1}{x_2 - x_1} = \frac{8 - 6}{-5 - (-1)} = \frac{2}{-4} = -\frac{1}{2}$$

The slope of the line $y = -5$ is 0.
The line $x = 3$ has undefined slope.

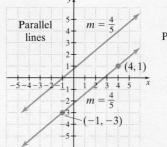

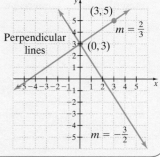

Chapter 3 Review

(3.1) *Plot the following ordered pairs on a Cartesian coordinate system.*

1. $(-7, 0)$

2. $\left(0, 4\frac{4}{5}\right)$

3. $(-2, -5)$

4. $(1, -3)$

5. $(0.7, 0.7)$

6. $(-6, 4)$

7. A local office supply store uses quantity pricing. The table shows the price per box of #10 security envelopes for different numbers of envelopes in a box purchased.

Price per Box of Envelopes (in dollars)	Number of Envelopes in Box
5.00	50
8.50	100
20.00	250
27.00	500

a. Write each paired data as an ordered pair of the form (price per box of envelopes, number of envelopes in box).

b. Create a scatter diagram of the paired data. Be sure to label the axes appropriately.

8. The table shows the annual overnight stays in national parks. (*Source:* National Park Service)

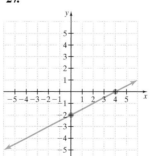

Year	Overnight Stays in National Parks (in millions)
2008	13.9
2009	14.6
2010	14.6
2011	14.0
2012	14.3
2013	13.5

a. Write each paired data as an ordered pair of the form (year, number of overnight stays).

b. Create a scatter diagram of the paired data. Be sure to label the axes properly.

Determine whether each ordered pair is a solution of the given equation.

9. $7x - 8y = 56$; $(0, 56), (8, 0)$

10. $-2x + 5y = 10$; $(-5, 0), (1, 1)$

11. $x = 13$; $(13, 5), (13, 13)$

12. $y = 2$; $(7, 2), (2, 7)$

Complete the ordered pairs so that each is a solution of the given equation.

13. $-2 + y = 6x$; $(7, \quad)$

14. $y = 3x + 5$; $\left(\quad, -8 \right)$

Complete the table of values for each given equation; then plot the ordered pairs. Use a single coordinate system for each exercise.

15. $9 = -3x + 4y$

x	y
	0
	3
9	

16. $x = 2y$

x	y
	0
	5
	-5

The cost in dollars of producing x compact disc holders is given by $y = 5x + 2000$. Use this equation for Exercises 17 and 18.

17. Complete the following table.

x	y
1	
100	
1000	

18. Find the number of compact disc holders that can be produced for $6430.

(3.2) *Graph each linear equation.*

19. $x - y = 1$

20. $x + y = 6$

21. $x - 3y = 12$

22. $5x - y = -8$

23. $x = 3y$

24. $y = -2x$

25. $2x - 3y = 6$

26. $4x - 3y = 12$

(3.3) *Identify the intercepts.*

27.

28.

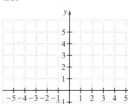

29.

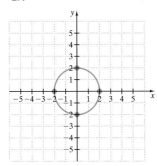

30.

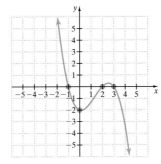

Graph each linear equation by finding its intercepts.

31. $x - 3y = 12$

32. $-4x + y = 8$

33. $y = -3$

34. $x = 5$

35. $y = -3x$

36. $x = 5y$

37. $x - 2 = 0$

38. $y + 6 = 0$

(3.4) Find the slope of each line.

39.

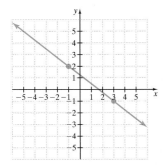

40.

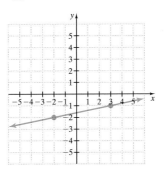

For Exercises 41 through 44, match each slope with its line.

A.

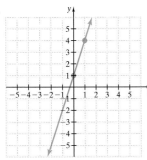

B.

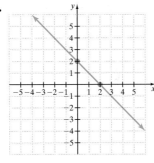

C.

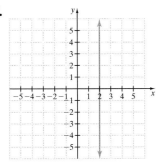

D.

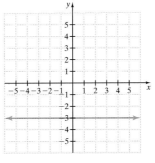

41. $m = 0$

42. $m = -1$

43. undefined slope

44. $m = 3$

Find the slope of the line that goes through the given points.

45. $(2, 5)$ and $(6, 8)$

46. $(4, 7)$ and $(1, 2)$

47. $(1, 3)$ and $(-2, -9)$

48. $(-4, 1)$ and $(3, -6)$

Find the slope of each line.

49. $y = 3x + 7$

50. $x - 2y = 4$

51. $y = -2$

52. $x = 0$

Determine whether each pair of lines is parallel, perpendicular, or neither.

53. $x - y = -6$
$x + y = 3$

54. $3x + y = 7$
$-3x - y = 10$

55. $y = 4x + \dfrac{1}{2}$
$4x + 2y = 1$

56. $x = 4$
$y = -2$

Find the slope of each line. Then write a sentence explaining the meaning of the slope as a rate of change. Don't forget to attach the proper units.

57. The graph below approximates the number of U.S. college students (in thousands) earning an associate's degree for each year x.

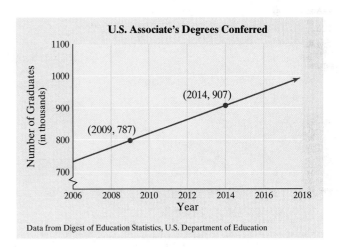

Data from Digest of Education Statistics, U.S. Department of Education

58. The graph below approximates the number of kidney transplants y in the United States for year x.

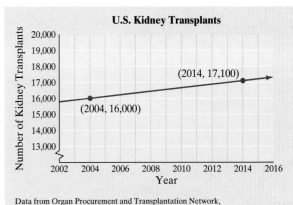

Data from Organ Procurement and Transplantation Network, U.S. Department of Health and Human Services

Chapter 3 Getting Ready for the Test

`1c`

MULTIPLE CHOICE *For Exercises 1 and 2, choose the ordered pair that is NOT a solution of the linear equation.*

1. $x - y = 5$

   A. $(7, 2)$ **B.** $(0, -5)$ **C.** $(-2, 3)$ **D.** $(-2, -7)$

2. $y = 4$

   A. $(4, 0)$ **B.** $(0, 4)$ **C.** $(2, 4)$ **D.** $(100, 4)$

3. What is the most and then the fewest number of intercepts a line may have?

   A. most: 2; fewest: 1 **B.** most: infinite number; fewest: 1 **C.** most: 2; fewest: 0

   D. most: infinite number; fewest: 0

4. Choose the linear equation:

   A. $\sqrt{x} - 3y = 7$ **B.** $2x = 6^2$ **C.** $4x^3 + 6y^3 = 5^3$ **D.** $y = |x|$

MATCHING *Match each graph in the rectangular system with its slope to the right. Each slope may be used only once.*

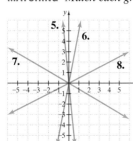

▶ **5.**   **A.** $m = 5$

▶ **6.**   **B.** $m = -10$

▶ **7.**   **C.** $m = \dfrac{1}{2}$

▶ **8.**   **D.** $m = -\dfrac{4}{7}$

MULTIPLE CHOICE *For Exercises 9 and 10, choose the best answer.*

▶ **9.** An ordered pair solution for the function $f(x)$ is $(0, 5)$. This solution using function notation is:

     A. $f(5) = 0$ **B.** $f(5) = f(0)$ **C.** $f(0) = 5$ **D.** $0 = 5$

▶ **10.** Given: $(2, 3)$ and $(0, 9)$. Final Answer: $y = -3x + 9$. Select the correct directions:

     A. Find the slope of the line through the two points.

     B. Find an equation of the line through the two points. Write the equation in standard form.

     C. Find an equation of the line through the two points. Write the equation in slope-intercept form.

MULTIPLE CHOICE *For Exercises 11–14, use the graph to fill in each blank using the choices below.*

     A. -2 **B.** 2   **C.** 4   **D.** 0   **E.** 3

▶ **11.** $f(0) = $ _____ .

▶ **12.** $f(4) = $ _____ .

▶ **13.** If $f(x) = 0$, then $x = $ _____ or $x = $ _____ .

▶ **14.** $f(1) = $ _____ .

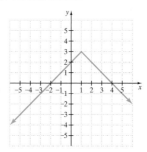

Chapter 3 Test   MyMathLab®   You Tube™

Graph the following.

▶ **1.** $y = \dfrac{1}{2}x$

▶ **2.** $2x + y = 8$

▶ **3.** $5x - 7y = 10$

▶ **4.** $y = -1$

▶ **5.** $x - 3 = 0$

For Exercises 6 through 10, find the slopes of the lines.

▶ **6.**   ▶ **7.**

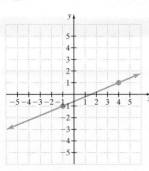 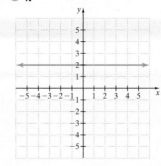

▶ **8.** Through $(6, -5)$ and $(-1, 2)$

▶ **9.** $-3x + y = 5$

▶ **10.** $x = 6$

▶ **11.** Determine the slope and the y-intercept of the graph of $7x - 3y = 2$.

▶ **12.** Determine whether the graphs of $y = 2x - 6$ and $-4x = 2y$ are parallel lines, perpendicular lines, or neither.

Find equations of the following lines. Write the equation in standard form.

▶ **13.** With slope of $-\dfrac{1}{4}$, through $(2, 2)$

▶ **14.** Through the origin and $(6, -7)$

▶ **15.** Through $(2, -5)$ and $(1, 3)$

▶ **16.** Through $(-5, -1)$ and parallel to $x = 7$

▶ **17.** With slope $\dfrac{1}{8}$ and y-intercept $(0, 12)$

Determine whether each graph is the graph of a function.

▶ **18.**   ▶ **19.**

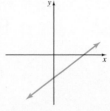 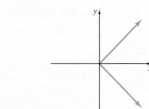

Given the following function, find the indicated function values.

  20. $h(x) = x^3 - x$

    a. $h(-1)$ **b.** $h(0)$ **c.** $h(4)$

21. Find the domain of $y = \dfrac{1}{x + 1}$.

For Exercises 22 and 23,

a. *Identify the x- and y-intercepts.*

b. *Find the domain and the range of each function graphed.*

22.   **23.**

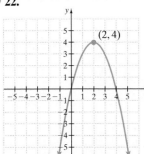 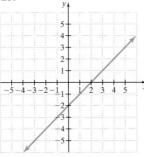

24. If $f(7) = 20$, write the corresponding ordered pair.

Use the bar graph below to answer Exercises 25 and 26.

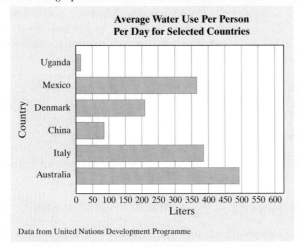

Data from United Nations Development Programme

25. Estimate the average water use per person per day in Denmark.

26. Estimate the average water use per person per day in Australia.

Use this graph to answer Exercises 27 through 29.

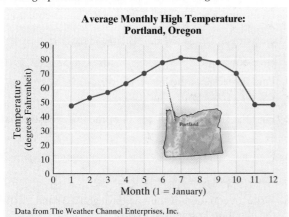

Data from The Weather Channel Enterprises, Inc.

27. During what month is the average high temperature the greatest?

28. Approximate the average high temperature for the month of April.

29. During what month(s) is the average high temperature below 60°F?

30. The table gives the number of Dish Network subscribers (in millions) for the years shown. (*Source:* Dish Network)

Year	Dish Network Subscribers (in millions)
2008	13.68
2009	14.10
2010	14.13
2011	13.97
2012	14.06
2013	14.06
2014	13.98

a. Write this data as a set of ordered pairs of the form (year, number of Dish Network subscribers in millions).

b. Create a scatter diagram of the data. Be sure to label the axes properly.

31. This graph approximates the number of movie ticket sales y (in millions) for the year x.

Data from National Association of Theater Owners

a. Find the slope of the line. Then write a sentence explaining the meaning of the slope as a rate of change. Don't forget to attach the proper units.

b. Write two ordered pairs of the form (years past 2000, number of tickets sold in millions).

c. Use the two ordered pairs from part (b) to write a linear equation. Write the equation in slope-intercept form.

d. Use the equation from part (c) to predict the number of movie tickets sold in 2020.

Chapter 3 Cumulative Review

1. Insert $<$, $>$, or $=$ in the space between each pair of numbers to make each statement true.
   a. 2   3   b. 7   4   c. 72   27

2. Write the fraction $\dfrac{56}{64}$ in lowest terms.

3. Multiply $\dfrac{2}{15}$ and $\dfrac{5}{13}$. Simplify the product if possible.

4. Add: $\dfrac{10}{3} + \dfrac{5}{21}$

5. Simplify: $\dfrac{3 + |4 - 3| + 2^2}{6 - 3}$

6. Simplify: $16 - 3 \cdot 3 + 2^4$

7. Add.
   a. $-8 + (-11)$ b. $-5 + 35$
   c. $0.6 + (-1.1)$ d. $-\dfrac{7}{10} + \left(-\dfrac{1}{10}\right)$
   e. $11.4 + (-4.7)$ f. $-\dfrac{3}{8} + \dfrac{2}{5}$

8. Simplify: $|9 + (-20)| + |-10|$

9. Simplify each expression.
   a. $-14 - 8 + 10 - (-6)$
   b. $1.6 - (-10.3) + (-5.6)$

10. Simplify: $-9 - (3 - 8)$

11. If $x = -2$ and $y = -4$, evaluate each expression.
    a. $5x - y$ b. $x^4 - y^2$
    c. $\dfrac{3x}{2y}$

12. Is -20 a solution of $\dfrac{x}{-10} = 2$?

13. Simplify each expression.
    a. $10 + (x + 12)$ b. $-3(7x)$

14. Simplify: $(12 + x) - (4x - 7)$

15. Identify the numerical coefficient of each term.
    a. $-3y$ b. $22z^4$ c. y
    d. $-x$ e. $\dfrac{x}{7}$

16. Multiply: $-5(x - 7)$

17. Solve: $y + 0.6 = -1.0$ for y

18. Solve: $5(3 + z) - (8z + 9) = -4$

19. Solve: $-\dfrac{2}{3}x = -\dfrac{5}{2}$

20. Solve: $\dfrac{x}{4} - 1 = -7$

21. If x is the first of three consecutive integers, express the sum of the three integers in terms of x. Simplify if possible.

22. Solve: $\dfrac{x}{3} - 2 = \dfrac{x}{3}$

23. Solve: $\dfrac{2(a + 3)}{3} = 6a + 2$

24. Solve: $x + 2y = 6$ for y

25. The 114th Congress began on January 3, 2015, and had a total of 435 Democratic and Republican representatives. There were 59 fewer Democratic representatives than Republican. Find the number of representatives from each party. (*Source:* congress.gov)

26. Solve $5(x + 4) \geq 4(2x + 3)$. Write the solution set in interval notation.

27. Charles Pecot can afford enough fencing to enclose a rectangular garden with a perimeter of 140 feet. If the width of his garden must be 30 feet, find the length.

28. Solve $-3 < 4x - 1 \leq 2$. Write the solution set in interval notation.

29. Solve: $y = mx + b$ for x

30. Complete the table for $y = -5x$.

x	y
0	
-1	
	-10

31. A chemist working on his doctoral degree at Massachusetts Institute of Technology needs 12 liters of a 50% acid solution for a lab experiment. The stockroom has only 40% and 70% solutions. How much of each solution should be mixed together to form 12 liters of a 50% solution?

32. Graph: $y = -3x + 5$

33. Graph: $x \geq -1$ Then write the solutions in interval notation.

34. Find the x- and y-intercepts of $2x + 4y = -8$.

35. Solve $-1 \leq 2x - 3 < 5$. Graph the solution set and write it in interval notation.

36. Graph $x = 2$ on a rectangular coordinate system.

37. Determine whether each ordered pair is a solution of the equation $x - 2y = 6$.
    a. $(6, 0)$ b. $(0, 3)$
    c. $\left(1, -\dfrac{5}{2}\right)$

38. Find the slope of the line through $(0, 5)$ and $(-5, 4)$.

39. Determine whether each equation is a linear equation in two variables.
    a. $x - 1.5y = -1.6$ b. $y = -2x$
    c. $x + y^2 = 9$ d. $x = 5$

40. Find the slope of the line $x = -10$.

41. Find the slope of the line $y = -1$.

42. Find the slope and y-intercept of the line whose equation is $2x - 5y = 10$.

43. Find an equation of the line with y-intercept $(0, -3)$ and slope of $\dfrac{1}{4}$.

44. Write an equation of the line through $(2, 3)$ and $(0, 0)$. Write the equation in standard form.

Exponents and Polynomials

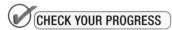

Recall from Chapter 1 that an exponent is a shorthand notation for repeated factors. This chapter explores additional concepts about exponents and exponential expressions. An especially useful type of exponential expression is a polynomial. Polynomials model many real-world phenomena. In this chapter, we focus on polynomials and operations on polynomials.

Can You Imagine a World Without the Internet?

In 1995, less than 1% of the world population was connected to the Internet. By 2015, that number had increased to 40%. Technology changes so fast that, if this trend continues, by the time you read this, far more than 40% of the world population will be connected to the Internet. The circle graph below shows Internet users by region of the world in 2015. In Section 5.2, Exercises 103 and 104, we explore more about the growth of Internet users.

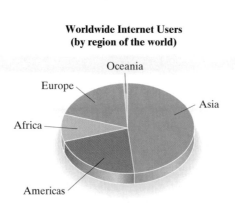

Worldwide Internet Users (by region of the world)

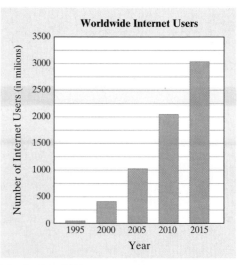

Data from International Telecommunication Union and United Nations Population Division

5.1 | Exponents

OBJECTIVES

1 Evaluate Exponential Expressions.

2 Use the Product Rule for Exponents.

3 Use the Power Rule for Exponents.

4 Use the Power Rules for Products and Quotients.

5 Use the Quotient Rule for Exponents, and Define a Number Raised to the 0 Power.

6 Decide Which Rule(s) to Use to Simplify an Expression.

OBJECTIVE

1   Evaluating Exponential Expressions

As we reviewed in Section 1.4, an exponent is a shorthand notation for repeated factors. For example, $2 \cdot 2 \cdot 2 \cdot 2 \cdot 2$ can be written as 2^5. The expression 2^5 is called an **exponential expression.** It is also called the fifth **power** of 2, or we say that 2 is **raised** to the fifth power.

$$5^6 = \underbrace{5 \cdot 5 \cdot 5 \cdot 5 \cdot 5 \cdot 5}_{6 \text{ factors; each factor is } 5} \quad \text{and} \quad (-3)^4 = \underbrace{(-3) \cdot (-3) \cdot (-3) \cdot (-3)}_{4 \text{ factors; each factor is } -3}$$

The **base** of an exponential expression is the repeated factor. The **exponent** is the number of times that the base is used as a factor.

$$5^6 \overset{\text{exponent}}{\underset{\text{base}}{}} \qquad (-3)^4 \overset{\text{exponent}}{\underset{\text{base}}{}}$$

EXAMPLE 1   Evaluate each expression.

a. 2^3 **b.** 3^1 **c.** $(-4)^2$ **d.** -4^2 **e.** $\left(\dfrac{1}{2}\right)^4$ **f.** $(0.5)^3$ **g.** $4 \cdot 3^2$

Solution

a. $2^3 = 2 \cdot 2 \cdot 2 = 8$

b. To raise 3 to the first power means to use 3 as a factor only once. Therefore, $3^1 = 3$. Also, when no exponent is shown, the exponent is assumed to be 1.

c. $(-4)^2 = (-4)(-4) = 16$ **d.** $-4^2 = -(4 \cdot 4) = -16$

e. $\left(\dfrac{1}{2}\right)^4 = \dfrac{1}{2} \cdot \dfrac{1}{2} \cdot \dfrac{1}{2} \cdot \dfrac{1}{2} = \dfrac{1}{16}$ **f.** $(0.5)^3 = (0.5)(0.5)(0.5) = 0.125$

g. $4 \cdot 3^2 = 4 \cdot 9 = 36$ □

PRACTICE

1   Evaluate each expression.

a. 3^3 **b.** 4^1 **c.** $(-8)^2$ **d.** -8^2

e. $\left(\dfrac{3}{4}\right)^3$ **f.** $(0.3)^4$ **g.** $3 \cdot 5^2$ ■

Notice how similar -4^2 is to $(-4)^2$ in the example above. The difference between the two is the parentheses. In $(-4)^2$, the parentheses tell us that the base, or repeated factor, is -4. In -4^2, only 4 is the base.

> **Helpful Hint**
>
> Be careful when identifying the base of an exponential expression. Pay close attention to the use of parentheses.
>
> $(-3)^2$ -3^2 $2 \cdot 3^2$
> The base is -3.   The base is 3.   The base is 3.
> $(-3)^2 = (-3)(-3) = 9$ $-3^2 = -(3 \cdot 3) = -9$ $2 \cdot 3^2 = 2 \cdot 3 \cdot 3 = 18$

An exponent has the same meaning whether the base is a number or a variable. If x is a real number and n is a positive integer, then x^n is the product of n factors, each of which is x.

$$x^n = \underbrace{x \cdot x \cdot x \cdot x \cdot x \cdot \ldots \cdot x}_{n \text{ factors of } x}$$

EXAMPLE 2 Evaluate each expression for the given value of x.

a. $2x^3$; x is 5

b. $\dfrac{9}{x^2}$; x is -3

Solution a. If x is 5, $2x^3 = 2 \cdot (5)^3$

$= 2 \cdot (5 \cdot 5 \cdot 5)$

$= 2 \cdot 125$

$= 250$

b. If x is -3, $\dfrac{9}{x^2} = \dfrac{9}{(-3)^2}$

$= \dfrac{9}{(-3)(-3)}$

$= \dfrac{9}{9}$

$= 1$

PRACTICE

2 Evaluate each expression for the given value of x.

a. $3x^4$; x is 3

b. $\dfrac{6}{x^2}$; x is -4

OBJECTIVE

2 Using the Product Rule ▶

Exponential expressions can be multiplied, divided, added, subtracted, and themselves raised to powers. By our definition of an exponent,

$$5^4 \cdot 5^3 = \underbrace{(5 \cdot 5 \cdot 5 \cdot 5)}_{4 \text{ factors of } 5} \cdot \underbrace{(5 \cdot 5 \cdot 5)}_{3 \text{ factors of } 5}$$

$$= \underbrace{5 \cdot 5 \cdot 5 \cdot 5 \cdot 5 \cdot 5 \cdot 5}_{7 \text{ factors of } 5}$$

$$= 5^7$$

Also,

$$x^2 \cdot x^3 = (x \cdot x) \cdot (x \cdot x \cdot x)$$

$$= x \cdot x \cdot x \cdot x \cdot x$$

$$= x^5$$

In both cases, notice that the result is exactly the same if the exponents are added.

$$5^4 \cdot 5^3 = 5^{4+3} = 5^7 \quad \text{and} \quad x^2 \cdot x^3 = x^{2+3} = x^5$$

This suggests the following rule.

Product Rule for Exponents

If m and n are positive integers and a is a real number, then

$$a^m \cdot a^n = a^{m+n} \leftarrow \text{Add exponents.}$$

Keep common base.

For example, $3^5 \cdot 3^7 = 3^{5+7} = 3^{12} \leftarrow$ Add exponents.

Keep common base.

Helpful Hint

Don't forget that

$$3^5 \cdot 3^7 \neq 9^{12} \leftarrow \text{Add exponents.}$$

Common base *not* kept.

$$3^5 \cdot 3^7 = \underbrace{3 \cdot 3 \cdot 3 \cdot 3 \cdot 3}_{5 \text{ factors of } 3} \cdot \underbrace{3 \cdot 3 \cdot 3 \cdot 3 \cdot 3 \cdot 3 \cdot 3}_{7 \text{ factors of } 3}$$

$$= 3^{12} \quad 12 \text{ factors of } 3, \textit{not } 9$$

In other words, to multiply two exponential expressions with the **same base,** we keep the base and add the exponents. We call this **simplifying** the exponential expression.

EXAMPLE 3 Use the product rule to simplify.

a. $4^2 \cdot 4^5$ b. $x^4 \cdot x^6$ c. $y^3 \cdot y$
d. $y^3 \cdot y^2 \cdot y^7$ e. $(-5)^7 \cdot (-5)^8$ f. $a^2 \cdot b^2$

Solution

a. $4^2 \cdot 4^5 = 4^{2+5} = 4^7$ ← Add exponents.
    ↳ **Keep** common base.

b. $x^4 \cdot x^6 = x^{4+6} = x^{10}$

c. $y^3 \cdot y = y^3 \cdot y^1$
    $= y^{3+1}$
    $= y^4$

> **Helpful Hint**
> Don't forget that if no exponent is written, it is assumed to be 1.

d. $y^3 \cdot y^2 \cdot y^7 = y^{3+2+7} = y^{12}$

e. $(-5)^7 \cdot (-5)^8 = (-5)^{7+8} = (-5)^{15}$

f. $a^2 \cdot b^2$ Cannot be simplified because a and b are different bases. □

PRACTICE
3 Use the product rule to simplify.

a. $3^4 \cdot 3^6$ b. $y^3 \cdot y^2$
c. $z \cdot z^4$ d. $x^3 \cdot x^2 \cdot x^6$
e. $(-2)^5 \cdot (-2)^3$ f. $b^3 \cdot t^5$

✔ **CONCEPT CHECK**
Where possible, use the product rule to simplify the expression.
a. $z^2 \cdot z^{14}$ b. $x^2 \cdot y^{14}$ c. $9^8 \cdot 9^3$ d. $9^8 \cdot 2^7$

EXAMPLE 4 Use the product rule to simplify $(2x^2)(-3x^5)$.

Solution Recall that $2x^2$ means $2 \cdot x^2$ and $-3x^5$ means $-3 \cdot x^5$.

$(2x^2)(-3x^5) = 2 \cdot x^2 \cdot -3 \cdot x^5$ Remove parentheses.
    $= 2 \cdot -3 \cdot x^2 \cdot x^5$ Group factors with common bases.
    $= -6x^7$ Simplify. □

PRACTICE
4 Use the product rule to simplify $(-5y^3)(-3y^4)$.

EXAMPLE 5 Simplify.

a. $(x^2y)(x^3y^2)$ b. $(-a^7b^4)(3ab^9)$

Solution

a. $(x^2y)(x^3y^2) = (x^2 \cdot x^3) \cdot (y^1 \cdot y^2)$ Group like bases and write y as y^1.
    $= x^5 \cdot y^3$ or x^5y^3 Multiply.

b. $(-a^7b^4)(3ab^9) = (-1 \cdot 3) \cdot (a^7 \cdot a^1) \cdot (b^4 \cdot b^9)$
    $= -3a^8b^{13}$ □

Answers to Concept Check:
a. z^{16} b. cannot be simplified
c. 9^{11} d. cannot be simplified

PRACTICE
5 Simplify.

a. $(y^7z^3)(y^5z)$ b. $(-m^4n^4)(7mn^{10})$

> **Helpful Hint**
>
> These examples will remind you of the difference between adding and multiplying terms.
>
> **Addition**
>
> $$5x^3 + 3x^3 = (5 + 3)x^3 = 8x^3 \quad \text{By the distributive property.}$$
> $$7x + 4x^2 = 7x + 4x^2 \qquad\qquad \text{Cannot be combined.}$$
>
> **Multiplication**
>
> $$(5x^3)(3x^3) = 5 \cdot 3 \cdot x^3 \cdot x^3 = 15x^{3+3} = 15x^6 \quad \text{By the product rule.}$$
> $$(7x)(4x^2) = 7 \cdot 4 \cdot x \cdot x^2 = 28x^{1+2} = 28x^3 \quad \text{By the product rule.}$$

OBJECTIVE

3 Using the Power Rule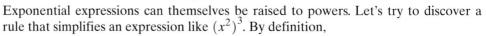

Exponential expressions can themselves be raised to powers. Let's try to discover a rule that simplifies an expression like $(x^2)^3$. By definition,

$$(x^2)^3 = \underbrace{(x^2)(x^2)(x^2)}_{3 \text{ factors of } x^2}$$

which can be simplified by the product rule for exponents.

$$(x^2)^3 = (x^2)(x^2)(x^2) = x^{2+2+2} = x^6$$

Notice that the result is exactly the same if we multiply the exponents.

$$(x^2)^3 = x^{2 \cdot 3} = x^6$$

The following property states this result.

Power Rule for Exponents

If m and n are positive integers and a is a real number, then

$$(a^m)^n = a^{mn} \leftarrow \text{Multiply exponents.}$$
$$\uparrow$$
$$\text{Keep common base.}$$

For example, $(7^2)^5 = 7^{2 \cdot 5} = 7^{10} \leftarrow$ Multiply exponents.
$\qquad\qquad\qquad\qquad\quad$ Keep common base.

To raise a power to a power, keep the base and multiply the exponents.

EXAMPLE 6   Use the power rule to simplify.

a. $(y^8)^2$ **b.** $(8^4)^5$ ▶ **c.** $[(-5)^3]^7$

Solution

a. $(y^8)^2 = y^{8 \cdot 2} = y^{16}$ **b.** $(8^4)^5 = 8^{4 \cdot 5} = 8^{20}$ **c.** $[(-5)^3]^7 = (-5)^{21}$ □

PRACTICE

6   Use the power rule to simplify.

a. $(z^3)^7$ **b.** $(4^9)^2$ **c.** $[(-2)^3]^5$ ∎

> **Helpful Hint**
>
> Take a moment to make sure that you understand when to apply the product rule and when to apply the power rule.
>
> | *Product Rule* → *Add Exponents* | *Power Rule* → *Multiply Exponents* |
> |---|---|
> | $x^5 \cdot x^7 = x^{5+7} = x^{12}$ | $(x^5)^7 = x^{5 \cdot 7} = x^{35}$ |
> | $y^6 \cdot y^2 = y^{6+2} = y^8$ | $(y^6)^2 = y^{6 \cdot 2} = y^{12}$ |

OBJECTIVE

4   Using the Power Rules for Products and Quotients

When the base of an exponential expression is a product, the definition of x^n still applies. To simplify $(xy)^3$, for example,

$$(xy)^3 = (xy)(xy)(xy) \quad \text{{\small $(xy)^3$ means 3 factors of (xy).}}$$
$$= x \cdot x \cdot x \cdot y \cdot y \cdot y \quad \text{{\small Group factors with common bases.}}$$
$$= x^3 y^3 \quad \text{{\small Simplify.}}$$

Notice that to simplify the expression $(xy)^3$, we raise each factor within the parentheses to a power of 3.

$$(xy)^3 = x^3 y^3$$

In general, we have the following rule.

Power of a Product Rule

If n is a positive integer and a and b are real numbers, then

$$(ab)^n = a^n b^n$$

For example, $(3x)^5 = 3^5 x^5$.

In other words, to raise a product to a power, we raise each factor to the power.

EXAMPLE 7   Simplify each expression.

    a. $(st)^4$ **b.** $(2a)^3$ **c.** $\left(\dfrac{1}{3}mn^3\right)^2$ **d.** $(-5x^2 y^3 z)^2$

Solution

    a. $(st)^4 = s^4 \cdot t^4 = s^4 t^4$ Use the power of a product rule.

    b. $(2a)^3 = 2^3 \cdot a^3 = 8a^3$ Use the power of a product rule.

    c. $\left(\dfrac{1}{3}mn^3\right)^2 = \left(\dfrac{1}{3}\right)^2 \cdot (m)^2 \cdot (n^3)^2 = \dfrac{1}{9}m^2 n^6$ Use the power of a product rule.

    d. $(-5x^2 y^3 z)^2 = (-5)^2 \cdot (x^2)^2 \cdot (y^3)^2 \cdot (z^1)^2$ Use the power of a product rule.

               $= 25x^4 y^6 z^2$ Use the power rule for exponents. □

PRACTICE

7   Simplify each expression.

    a. $(pr)^5$ **b.** $(6b)^2$ **c.** $\left(\dfrac{1}{4}x^2 y\right)^3$ **d.** $(-3a^3 b^4 c)^4$

Let's see what happens when we raise a quotient to a power. To simplify $\left(\dfrac{x}{y}\right)^3$, for example,

$$\left(\frac{x}{y}\right)^3 = \left(\frac{x}{y}\right)\left(\frac{x}{y}\right)\left(\frac{x}{y}\right) \quad \text{{\small $\left(\dfrac{x}{y}\right)^3$ means 3 factors of $\left(\dfrac{x}{y}\right)$}}$$
$$= \frac{x \cdot x \cdot x}{y \cdot y \cdot y} \quad \text{{\small Multiply fractions.}}$$
$$= \frac{x^3}{y^3} \quad \text{{\small Simplify.}}$$

Notice that to simplify the expression $\left(\dfrac{x}{y}\right)^3$, we raise both the numerator and the denominator to a power of 3.

$$\left(\frac{x}{y}\right)^3 = \frac{x^3}{y^3}$$

In general, we have the following.

> **Power of a Quotient Rule**
>
> If n is a positive integer and a and c are real numbers, then
> $$\left(\frac{a}{c}\right)^n = \frac{a^n}{c^n}, \quad c \neq 0$$

For example, $\left(\dfrac{y}{7}\right)^4 = \dfrac{y^4}{7^4}$.

In other words, to raise a quotient to a power, we raise both the numerator and the denominator to the power.

EXAMPLE 8   Simplify each expression.

    a. $\left(\dfrac{m}{n}\right)^7$ **b.** $\left(\dfrac{x^3}{3y^5}\right)^4$

Solution

    a. $\left(\dfrac{m}{n}\right)^7 = \dfrac{m^7}{n^7}, n \neq 0$ Use the power of a quotient rule.

    b. $\left(\dfrac{x^3}{3y^5}\right)^4 = \dfrac{(x^3)^4}{3^4 \cdot (y^5)^4}, y \neq 0$ Use the power of a product or quotient rule.

           $= \dfrac{x^{12}}{81y^{20}}$ Use the power rule for exponents.   □

PRACTICE
8   Simplify each expression.

    a. $\left(\dfrac{x}{y^2}\right)^5$ **b.** $\left(\dfrac{2a^4}{b^3}\right)^5$ ■

OBJECTIVE

5   **Using the Quotient Rule and Defining the Zero Exponent** ▶

Another pattern for simplifying exponential expressions involves quotients.

To simplify an expression like $\dfrac{x^5}{x^3}$, in which the numerator and the denominator have a common base, we can apply the fundamental principle of fractions and divide the numerator and the denominator by the common base factors. Assume for the remainder of this section that denominators are not 0.

$$\frac{x^5}{x^3} = \frac{x \cdot x \cdot x \cdot x \cdot x}{x \cdot x \cdot x}$$
$$= \frac{x \cdot x \cdot x \cdot x \cdot x}{x \cdot x \cdot x}$$
$$= x \cdot x$$
$$= x^2$$

Notice that the result is exactly the same if we subtract exponents of the common bases.

$$\frac{x^5}{x^3} = x^{5-3} = x^2$$

The quotient rule for exponents states this result in a general way.

Quotient Rule for Exponents

If m and n are positive integers and a is a real number, then

$$\frac{a^m}{a^n} = a^{m-n}$$

as long as a is not 0.

For example, $\dfrac{x^6}{x^2} = x^{6-2} = x^4$.

In other words, to divide one exponential expression by another with a common base, keep the base and subtract exponents.

EXAMPLE 9 Simplify each quotient.

a. $\dfrac{x^5}{x^2}$ **b.** $\dfrac{4^7}{4^3}$ **c.** $\dfrac{(-3)^5}{(-3)^2}$ **d.** $\dfrac{s^2}{t^3}$ **e.** $\dfrac{2x^5y^2}{xy}$

Solution

a. $\dfrac{x^5}{x^2} = x^{5-2} = x^3$ Use the quotient rule.

b. $\dfrac{4^7}{4^3} = 4^{7-3} = 4^4 = 256$ Use the quotient rule.

c. $\dfrac{(-3)^5}{(-3)^2} = (-3)^3 = -27$ Use the quotient rule.

d. $\dfrac{s^2}{t^3}$ Cannot be simplified because s and t are different bases.

e. Begin by grouping common bases.

$$\frac{2x^5y^2}{xy} = 2\cdot\frac{x^5}{x^1}\cdot\frac{y^2}{y^1}$$
$$= 2\cdot(x^{5-1})\cdot(y^{2-1})\quad\text{Use the quotient rule.}$$
$$= 2x^4y^1\quad\text{or}\quad 2x^4y$$

PRACTICE
9 Simplify each quotient.

a. $\dfrac{z^8}{z^4}$ **b.** $\dfrac{(-5)^5}{(-5)^3}$ **c.** $\dfrac{8^8}{8^6}$ **d.** $\dfrac{q^5}{t^2}$ **e.** $\dfrac{6x^3y^7}{xy^5}$

✔ **CONCEPT CHECK**
Suppose you are simplifying each expression. Tell whether you would _add_ the exponents, _subtract_ the exponents, _multiply_ the exponents, _divide_ the exponents, or _none of these_.

a. $(x^{63})^{21}$ **b.** $\dfrac{y^{15}}{y^3}$ **c.** $z^{16} + z^8$ **d.** $w^{45}\cdot w^9$

Let's now give meaning to an expression such as x^0. To do so, we will simplify $\dfrac{x^3}{x^3}$ in two ways and compare the results.

$$\frac{x^3}{x^3} = x^{3-3} = x^0\quad\text{Apply the quotient rule.}$$

$$\frac{x^3}{x^3} = \frac{x\cdot x\cdot x}{x\cdot x\cdot x} = 1\quad\text{Apply the fundamental principle for fractions.}$$

Answers to Concept Check:
a. multiply   **b.** subtract
c. none of these   **d.** add

Since $\dfrac{x^3}{x^3} = x^0$ and $\dfrac{x^3}{x^3} = 1$, we define that $x^0 = 1$ as long as x is not 0.

> **Zero Exponent**
>
> $a^0 = 1$, as long as a is not 0.

In other words, any base raised to the 0 power is 1 as long as the base is not 0.

EXAMPLE 10 Simplify each expression.

    a. 3^0 **b.** $(5x^3y^2)^0$ **c.** $(-5)^0$ **d.** -5^0 **e.** $\left(\dfrac{3}{100}\right)^0$ **f.** $4x^0$

Solution

    a. $3^0 = 1$

    b. Assume that neither x nor y is zero.
$$(5x^3y^2)^0 = 1$$

    c. $(-5)^0 = 1$

    d. $-5^0 = -1 \cdot 5^0 = -1 \cdot 1 = -1$

    e. $\left(\dfrac{3}{100}\right)^0 = 1$

    f. $4x^0 = 4 \cdot x^0 = 4 \cdot 1 = 4$ ☐

PRACTICE
10 Simplify the following expressions.

    a. -3^0 **b.** $(-3)^0$ **c.** 8^0 **d.** $(0.2)^0$

    e. $(7a^2y^4)^0$ **f.** $7y^0$ ■

OBJECTIVE
6 Deciding Which Rule to Use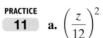

Let's practice deciding which rule(s) to use to simplify. We will continue this discussion with more examples in Section 5.5.

EXAMPLE 11 Simplify each expression.

    a. $x^7 \cdot x^4$ **b.** $\left(\dfrac{t}{2}\right)^4$ **c.** $(9y^5)^2$

Solution

    a. Here we have a product, so we use the product rule to simplify.
$$x^7 \cdot x^4 = x^{7+4} = x^{11}$$

    b. This is a quotient raised to a power, so we use the power of a quotient rule.
$$\left(\dfrac{t}{2}\right)^4 = \dfrac{t^4}{2^4} = \dfrac{t^4}{16}$$

    c. This is a product raised to a power, so we use the power of a product rule.
$$(9y^5)^2 = 9^2(y^5)^2 = 81y^{10}$$ ☐

PRACTICE
11   **a.** $\left(\dfrac{z}{12}\right)^2$ **b.** $(4x^6)^3$ **c.** $y^{10} \cdot y^3$ ■

EXAMPLE 12 Simplify each expression.

a. $4^2 - 4^0$ b. $(x^0)^3 + (2^0)^5$ c. $\left(\dfrac{3y^7}{6x^5}\right)^2$ d. $\dfrac{(2a^3b^4)^3}{-8a^9b^2}$

Solution

a. $4^2 - 4^0 = 16 - 1 = 15$ Remember that $4^0 = 1$.

b. $(x^0)^3 + (2^0)^5 = 1^3 + 1^5 = 1 + 1 = 2$

c. $\left(\dfrac{3y^7}{6x^5}\right)^2 = \dfrac{3^2(y^7)^2}{6^2(x^5)^2} = \dfrac{9 \cdot y^{14}}{36 \cdot x^{10}} = \dfrac{y^{14}}{4x^{10}}$

d. $\dfrac{(2a^3b^4)^3}{-8a^9b^2} = \dfrac{2^3(a^3)^3(b^4)^3}{-8a^9b^2} = \dfrac{8a^9b^{12}}{-8a^9b^2} = -1 \cdot (a^{9-9}) \cdot (b^{12-2})$

$= -1 \cdot a^0 \cdot b^{10} = -1 \cdot 1 \cdot b^{10} = -b^{10}$

PRACTICE
12 Simplify each expression.

a. $8^2 - 8^0$ b. $(z^0)^6 + (4^0)^5$ c. $\left(\dfrac{5x^3}{15y^4}\right)^2$ d. $\dfrac{(2z^8x^5)^4}{-16z^2x^{20}}$

✔ Vocabulary, Readiness & Video Check

Use the choices below to fill in each blank. Some choices may be used more than once.

0   base   add
1   exponent   multiply

1. Repeated multiplication of the same factor can be written using a(n) _____.
2. In 5^2, the 2 is called the _____ and the 5 is called the _____.
3. To simplify $x^2 \cdot x^7$, keep the base and _____ the exponents.
4. To simplify $(x^3)^6$, keep the base and _____ the exponents.
5. The understood exponent on the term y is _____.
6. If $x^\square = 1$, the exponent is _____.

Martin-Gay Interactive Videos

See Video 5.1 🔴

Watch the section lecture video and answer the following questions.

OBJECTIVE 1

7. 🎞 Examples 3 and 4 illustrate how to find the base of an exponential expression both with and without parentheses. Explain how identifying the base of 🎞 Example 7 is similar to identifying the base of 🎞 Example 4.

OBJECTIVE 2

8. Why were the commutative and associative properties applied in 🎞 Example 12? Were these properties used in another example?

OBJECTIVE 3

9. What point is made at the end of 🎞 Example 15?

OBJECTIVE 4

10. Although it's not especially emphasized in 🎞 Example 20, what is helpful to remind yourself about the -2 in the problem?

OBJECTIVE 5

11. In 🎞 Example 24, which exponent rule is used to show that any non-zero base raised to zero is 1?

OBJECTIVE 6

12. When simplifying an exponential expression that's a fraction, will you always use the quotient rule? Refer to 🎞 Example 30 for this objective to support your answer.

5.1 Exercise Set MyMathLab®

For each of the following expressions, state the exponent shown and its corresponding base.

1. 3^2

2. $(-3)^6$

3. -4^2

4. $5 \cdot 3^4$

5. $5x^2$

6. $(5x)^2$

Evaluate each expression. See Example 1.

7. 7^2

8. -3^2

9. $(-5)^1$

10. $(-3)^2$

11. -2^4

12. -4^3

13. $(-2)^4$

14. $(-4)^3$

15. $(0.1)^5$

16. $(0.2)^5$

17. $\left(\dfrac{1}{3}\right)^4$

18. $\left(-\dfrac{1}{9}\right)^2$

19. $7 \cdot 2^5$

20. $9 \cdot 1^7$

21. $-2 \cdot 5^3$

22. $-4 \cdot 3^3$

Evaluate each expression for the replacement values given. See Example 2.

23. $x^2; x = -2$

24. $x^3; x = -2$

25. $5x^3; x = 3$

26. $4x^2; x = -1$

27. $2xy^2; x = 3$ and $y = 5$

28. $-4x^2y^3; x = 2$ and $y = -1$

29. $\dfrac{2z^4}{5}; z = -2$

30. $\dfrac{10}{3y^3}; y = 5$

Use the product rule to simplify each expression. Write the results using exponents. See Examples 3 through 5

31. $x^2 \cdot x^5$

32. $y^2 \cdot y$

33. $(-3)^3 \cdot (-3)^9$

34. $(-5)^7 \cdot (-5)^6$

35. $(5y^4)(3y)$

36. $(-2z^3)(-2z^2)$

37. $(x^9y)(x^{10}y^5)$

38. $(a^2b)(a^{13}b^{17})$

39. $(-8mn^6)(9m^2n^2)$

40. $(-7a^3b^3)(7a^{19}b)$

41. $(4z^{10})(-6z^7)(z^3)$

42. $(12x^5)(-x^6)(x^4)$

△ **43.** The rectangle below has width $4x^2$ feet and length $5x^3$ feet. Find its area as an expression in x. ($A = l \cdot w$)

$4x^2$ feet

$5x^3$ feet

△ **44.** The parallelogram below has base length $9y^7$ meters and height $2y^{10}$ meters. Find its area as an expression in y. ($A = b \cdot h$)

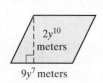

$2y^{10}$ meters

$9y^7$ meters

MIXED PRACTICE

Use the power rule and the power of a product or quotient rule to simplify each expression. See Examples 6 through 8.

45. $(x^9)^4$

46. $(y^7)^5$

47. $(pq)^8$

48. $(ab)^6$

49. $(2a^5)^3$

50. $(4x^6)^2$

51. $(x^2y^3)^5$

52. $(a^4b)^7$

53. $(-7a^2b^5c)^2$

54. $(-3x^7yz^2)^3$

55. $\left(\dfrac{r}{s}\right)^9$

56. $\left(\dfrac{q}{t}\right)^{11}$

57. $\left(\dfrac{mp}{n}\right)^5$

58. $\left(\dfrac{xy}{7}\right)^2$

59. $\left(\dfrac{-2xz}{y^5}\right)^2$

60. $\left(\dfrac{xy^4}{-3z^3}\right)^3$

△ **61.** The square shown has sides of length $8z^5$ decimeters. Find its area. ($A = s^2$)

$8z^5$
decimeters

△ **62.** Given the circle below with radius $5y$ centimeters, find its area. Do not approximate π. ($A = \pi r^2$)

$5y$ cm

△ **63.** The vault below is in the shape of a cube. If each side is $3y^4$ feet, find its volume. ($V = s^3$)

$3y^4$ feet

$3y^4$ feet

$3y^4$ feet

△ **64.** The silo shown is in the shape of a cylinder. If its radius is $4x$ meters and its height is $5x^3$ meters, find its volume. Do not approximate π. ($V = \pi r^2 h$)

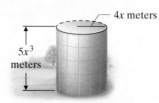

$4x$ meters

$5x^3$
meters

Use the quotient rule and simplify each expression. See Example 9.

65. $\dfrac{x^3}{x}$

66. $\dfrac{y^{10}}{y^9}$

67. $\dfrac{(-4)^6}{(-4)^3}$

68. $\dfrac{(-6)^{13}}{(-6)^{11}}$

69. $\dfrac{p^7 q^{20}}{pq^{15}}$

70. $\dfrac{x^8 y^6}{xy^5}$

71. $\dfrac{7x^2 y^6}{14x^2 y^3}$

72. $\dfrac{9a^4 b^7}{27ab^2}$

Simplify each expression. See Example 10.

73. 7^0

74. 23^0

75. $(2x)^0$

76. $(4y)^0$

77. $-7x^0$

78. $-2x^0$

79. $5^0 + y^0$

80. $-3^0 + 4^0$

MIXED PRACTICE

Simplify each expression. See Examples 1 through 12.

81. -9^2

82. $(-9)^2$

83. $\left(\dfrac{1}{4}\right)^3$

84. $\left(\dfrac{2}{3}\right)^3$

85. $b^4 b^2$

86. $y^4 y$

87. $a^2 a^3 a^4$

88. $x^2 x^{15} x^9$

89. $(2x^3)(-8x^4)$

90. $(3y^4)(-5y)$

91. $(a^7 b^{12})(a^4 b^8)$

92. $(y^2 z^2)(y^{15} z^{13})$

93. $(-2mn^6)(-13m^8 n)$

94. $(-3s^5 t)(-7st^{10})$

95. $(z^4)^{10}$

96. $(t^5)^{11}$

97. $(4ab)^3$

98. $(2ab)^4$

99. $(-6xyz^3)^2$

100. $(-3xy^2 a^3)^3$

101. $\dfrac{3x^5}{x^4}$

102. $\dfrac{5x^9}{x^3}$

103. $(9xy)^2$

104. $(2ab)^5$

105. $2^3 + 2^0$

106. $7^2 - 7^0$

107. $\left(\dfrac{3y^5}{6x^4}\right)^3$

108. $\left(\dfrac{2ab}{6yz}\right)^4$

109. $\dfrac{2x^3 y^2 z}{xyz}$

110. $\dfrac{x^{12} y^{13}}{x^5 y^7}$

111. $(5^0)^3 + (y^0)^7$

112. $(9^0)^4 + (z^0)^5$

113. $\left(\dfrac{5x^9}{10y^{11}}\right)^2$

114. $\left(\dfrac{3a^4}{9b^5}\right)^2$

115. $\dfrac{(2a^5 b^3)^4}{-16a^{20} b^7}$

116. $\dfrac{(2x^6 y^2)^5}{-32x^{20} y^{10}}$

REVIEW AND PREVIEW

Simplify each expression by combining any like terms. Use the distributive property to remove any parentheses. See Section 2.1.

117. $y - 10 + y$

118. $-6z + 20 - 3z$

119. $7x + 2 - 8x - 6$

120. $10y - 14 - y - 14$

121. $2(x - 5) + 3(5 - x)$

122. $-3(w + 7) + 5(w + 1)$

CONCEPT EXTENSIONS

Solve. See the Concept Checks in this section. For Exercises 123 through 126, match the expression with the operation needed to simplify each. A letter may be used more than once and a letter may not be used at all.

123. $(x^{14})^{23}$ **A.** Add the exponents

124. $x^{14} \cdot x^{23}$ **B.** Subtract the exponents

125. $x^{14} + x^{23}$ **C.** Multiply the exponents

126. $\dfrac{x^{35}}{x^{17}}$ **D.** Divide the exponents

               E. None of these

Fill in the boxes so that each statement is true. (More than one answer is possible for each exercise.)

127. $x^\square \cdot x^\square = x^{12}$

128. $(x^\square)^\square = x^{20}$

129. $\dfrac{y^\square}{y^\square} = y^7$

130. $(y^\square)^\square \cdot (y^\square)^\square = y^{30}$

131. The formula $V = x^3$ can be used to find the volume V of a cube with side length x. Find the volume of a cube with side length 7 meters. (Volume is measured in cubic units.)

132. The formula $S = 6x^2$ can be used to find the surface area S of a cube with side length x. Find the surface area of a cube with side length 5 meters. (Surface area is measured in square units.)

133. To find the amount of water that a swimming pool in the shape of a cube can hold, do we use the formula for volume of the cube or surface area of the cube? (See Exercises 131 and 132.)

134. To find the amount of material needed to cover an ottoman in the shape of a cube, do we use the formula for volume of the cube or surface area of the cube? (See Exercises 131 and 132.)

135. Explain why $(-5)^4 = 625$, while $-5^4 = -625$.

136. Explain why $5 \cdot 4^2 = 80$, while $(5 \cdot 4)^2 = 400$.

137. In your own words, explain why $5^0 = 1$.

138. In your own words, explain when $(-3)^n$ is positive and when it is negative.

Simplify each expression. Assume that variables represent positive integers.

139. $x^{5a} x^{4a}$

140. $b^{9a} b^{4a}$

141. $(a^b)^5$

142. $(2a^{4b})^4$

143. $\dfrac{x^{9a}}{x^{4a}}$

144. $\dfrac{y^{15b}}{y^{6b}}$

Solve. Round money amounts to 2 decimal places.

145. Suppose you borrow money for 6 months. If the interest is compounded monthly, the formula $A = P\left(1 + \dfrac{r}{12}\right)^6$ gives the total amount A to be repaid at the end of 6 months. For a loan of $P = \$1000$ and interest rate of 9% ($r = 0.09$), how much money is needed to pay off the loan?

146. Suppose you borrow money for 3 years. If the interest is compounded quarterly, the formula $A = P\left(1 + \dfrac{r}{4}\right)^{12}$ gives the total amount A to be repaid at the end of 3 years. For a loan of $\$10,000$ and interest rate of 8% ($r = 0.08$), how much money is needed to pay off the loan in 3 years?

5.2 | Adding and Subtracting Polynomials

OBJECTIVE

1 Defining Polynomial, Monomial, Binomial, Trinomial, and Degree

In this section, we introduce a special algebraic expression called a polynomial. Let's first review some definitions presented in Section 2.1.

Recall that a **term** is a number or the product of a number and variables raised to powers. The terms of the expression $4x^2 + 3x$ are $4x^2$ and $3x$.

The terms of the expression $9x^4 - 7x - 1$ are $9x^4$, $-7x$, and -1.

Expression	Terms
$4x^2 + 3x$	$4x^2, 3x$
$9x^4 - 7x - 1$	$9x^4, -7x, -1$
$7y^3$	$7y^3$
5	5

The **numerical coefficient** of a term, or simply the **coefficient**, is the numerical factor of each term. If no numerical factor appears in the term, then the coefficient is understood to be 1. If the term is a number only, it is called a **constant term** or simply a constant.

Term	Coefficient
x^5	1
$3x^2$	3
$-4x$	-4
$-x^2y$	-1
3 (constant)	3

Now we are ready to define a polynomial.

Polynomial

A **polynomial in x** is a finite sum of terms of the form ax^n, where a is a real number and n is a whole number.

For example,

$$x^5 - 3x^3 + 2x^2 - 5x + 1$$

is a polynomial. Notice that this polynomial is written in **descending powers** of x because the powers of x decrease from left to right. (Recall that the term 1 can be thought of as $1x^0$.)

On the other hand,

$$x^{-5} + 2x - 3$$

is **not** a polynomial because it contains an exponent, -5, that is not a whole number. (We study negative exponents in Section 5.5 of this chapter.)

Some polynomials are given special names.

Types of Polynomials

A **monomial** is a polynomial with exactly one term.

A **binomial** is a polynomial with exactly two terms.

A **trinomial** is a polynomial with exactly three terms.

The following are examples of monomials, binomials, and trinomials. Each of these examples is also a polynomial.

POLYNOMIALS

Monomials	*Binomials*	*Trinomials*	*More than Three Terms*
ax^2	$x + y$	$x^2 + 4xy + y^2$	$5x^3 - 6x^2 + 3x - 6$
$-3z$	$3p + 2$	$x^5 + 7x^2 - x$	$-y^5 + y^4 - 3y^3 - y^2 + y$
4	$4x^2 - 7$	$-q^4 + q^3 - 2q$	$x^6 + x^4 - x^3 + 1$

Each term of a polynomial has a **degree.**

Degree of a Term

The degree of a term is the sum of the exponents on the variables contained in the term.

EXAMPLE 1   Find the degree of each term.

   a. $-3x^2$ **b.** $5x^3yz$ **c.** 2

Solution

   a. The exponent on x is 2, so the degree of the term is 2.

   b. $5x^3yz$ can be written as $5x^3y^1z^1$. The degree of the term is the sum of the exponents on its variables, so the degree is $3 + 1 + 1$ or 5.

   c. The constant, 2, can be written as $2x^0$ (since $x^0 = 1$). The degree of 2 or $2x^0$ is 0.   ☐

PRACTICE
1   Find the degree of each term.

   a. $5y^3$ **b.** $-3a^2b^5c$ **c.** 8   ■

From the preceding, we can say that **the degree of a constant is 0.**
   Each polynomial also has a degree.

Degree of a Polynomial

The degree of a polynomial is the greatest degree of any term of the polynomial.

EXAMPLE 2   Find the degree of each polynomial and tell whether the polynomial is a monomial, binomial, trinomial, or none of these.

   ▶ **a.** $-2t^2 + 3t + 6$ **b.** $15x - 10$ **c.** $7x + 3x^3 + 2x^2 - 1$

Solution

   a. The degree of the trinomial $-2t^2 + 3t + 6$ is 2, the greatest degree of any of its terms.

   b. The degree of the binomial $15x - 10$ or $15x^1 - 10$ is 1.

   c. The degree of the polynomial $7x + 3x^3 + 2x^2 - 1$ is 3.   ☐

PRACTICE
2   Find the degree of each polynomial and tell whether the polynomial is a monomial, binomial, trinomial, or none of these.

   a. $5b^2 - 3b + 7$ **b.** $7t + 3$

   c. $5x^2 + 3x - 6x^3 + 4$ ■

EXAMPLE 3   Complete the table for the polynomial

$$7x^2y - 6xy + x^2 - 3y + 7$$

Use the table to give the degree of the polynomial.

Solution

Term	Numerical Coefficient	Degree of Term
$7x^2y$	7	3
$-6xy$	-6	2
x^2	1	2
$-3y$	-3	1
7	7	0

The degree of the polynomial is 3. ←

PRACTICE
3   Complete the table for the polynomial $-3x^3y^2 + 4xy^2 - y^2 + 3x - 2$.

Term	Numerical Coefficient	Degree of Term
$-3x^3y^2$		
$4xy^2$		
$-y^2$		
$3x$		
-2		

OBJECTIVE
2   Evaluating Polynomials ▶
Polynomials have different values depending on replacement values for the variables.

EXAMPLE 4   Find the value of each polynomial when $x = -2$.

   a. $-5x + 6$ **b.** $3x^2 - 2x + 1$

Solution

   a. $-5x + 6 = -5(-2) + 6$ Replace x with -2.
   $$= 10 + 6$$
   $$= 16$$

   b. $3x^2 - 2x + 1 = 3(-2)^2 - 2(-2) + 1$ Replace x with -2.
   $$= 3(4) + 4 + 1$$
   $$= 12 + 4 + 1$$
   $$= 17$$

PRACTICE
4   Find the value of each polynomial when $x = -3$.
   a. $-10x + 1$ **b.** $2x^2 - 5x + 3$

Many physical phenomena can be modeled by polynomials.

EXAMPLE 5   **Finding the Height of a Dropped Object**

The Swiss Re Building, in London, is a unique building. Londoners often refer to it as the "pickle building." The building is 592.1 feet tall. An object is dropped from the highest point of this building. Neglecting air resistance, the height in feet of the object above ground at time t seconds is given by the polynomial $-16t^2 + 592.1$. Find the height of the object when $t = 1$ second and when $t = 6$ seconds.

<u>*Solution*</u> To find each height, we evaluate the polynomial when $t = 1$ and when $t = 6$.

$$-16t^2 + 592.1 = -16(1)^2 + 592.1 \quad \text{Replace } t \text{ with 1.}$$
$$= -16(1) + 592.1$$
$$= -16 + 592.1$$
$$= 576.1$$

The height of the object at 1 second is 576.1 feet.

$$-16t^2 + 592.1 = -16(6)^2 + 592.1 \quad \text{Replace } t \text{ with 6.}$$
$$= -16(36) + 592.1$$
$$= -576 + 592.1 = 16.1$$

The height of the object at 6 seconds is 16.1 feet.

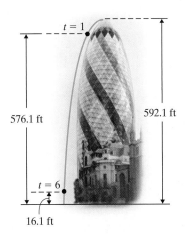

$t = 1$

576.1 ft   592.1 ft

$t = 6$

16.1 ft

PRACTICE

5   The cliff divers of Acapulco dive 130 feet into La Quebrada several times a day for the entertainment of the tourists. If a tourist is standing near the diving platform and drops his camera off the cliff, the height of the camera above the water at time t seconds is given by the polynomial $-16t^2 + 130$. Find the height of the camera when $t = 1$ second and when $t = 2$ seconds.

OBJECTIVE

3   Simplifying Polynomials by Combining Like Terms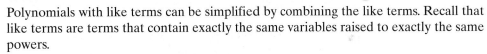

Polynomials with like terms can be simplified by combining the like terms. Recall that like terms are terms that contain exactly the same variables raised to exactly the same powers.

Like Terms	*Unlike Terms*
$5x^2, -7x^2$	$3x, 3y$
$y, 2y$	$-2x^2, -5x$
$\frac{1}{2}a^2b, -a^2b$	$6st^2, 4s^2t$

Only like terms can be combined. We combine like terms by applying the distributive property.

EXAMPLE 6   Simplify each polynomial by combining any like terms.

a. $-3x + 7x$
b. $x + 3x^2$
c. $9x^3 + x^3$
d. $11x^2 + 5 + 2x^2 - 7$
e. $\frac{2}{5}x^4 + \frac{2}{3}x^3 - x^2 + \frac{1}{10}x^4 - \frac{1}{6}x^3$

<u>*Solution*</u>

a. $-3x + 7x = (-3 + 7)x = 4x$
b. $x + 3x^2$ These terms cannot be combined because x and $3x^2$ are not like terms.
c. $9x^3 + x^3 = 9x^3 + 1x^3 = 10x^3$

(Continued on next page)

d. $11x^2 + 5 + 2x^2 - 7 = 11x^2 + 2x^2 + 5 - 7$
$= 13x^2 - 2$ Combine like terms.

e. $\dfrac{2}{5}x^4 + \dfrac{2}{3}x^3 - x^2 + \dfrac{1}{10}x^4 - \dfrac{1}{6}x^3$

$$= \left(\dfrac{2}{5} + \dfrac{1}{10}\right)x^4 + \left(\dfrac{2}{3} - \dfrac{1}{6}\right)x^3 - x^2$$

$$= \left(\dfrac{4}{10} + \dfrac{1}{10}\right)x^4 + \left(\dfrac{4}{6} - \dfrac{1}{6}\right)x^3 - x^2$$

$$= \dfrac{5}{10}x^4 + \dfrac{3}{6}x^3 - x^2$$

$$= \dfrac{1}{2}x^4 + \dfrac{1}{2}x^3 - x^2 \qquad \square$$

PRACTICE
6   Simplify each polynomial by combining any like terms.

a. $-4y + 2y$ **b.** $z + 5z^3$ **c.** $15x^3 - x^3$

d. $7a^2 - 5 - 3a^2 - 7$ **e.** $\dfrac{3}{8}x^3 - x^2 + \dfrac{5}{6}x^4 + \dfrac{1}{12}x^3 - \dfrac{1}{2}x^4$

✔ CONCEPT CHECK

When combining like terms in the expression $5x - 8x^2 - 8x$, which of the following is the proper result?

a. $-11x^2$ **b.** $-8x^2 - 3x$ **c.** $-11x$ **d.** $-11x^4$

EXAMPLE 7   Combine like terms to simplify.

$$-9x^2 + 3xy - 5y^2 + 7yx$$

Solution

$$-9x^2 + 3xy - 5y^2 + 7yx = -9x^2 + (3 + 7)xy - 5y^2$$
$$= -9x^2 + 10xy - 5y^2 \qquad \square$$

Helpful Hint
This term can be written as $7yx$ or $7xy$.

PRACTICE
7   Combine like terms to simplify: $9xy - 3x^2 - 4yx + 5y^2$

EXAMPLE 8   Write a polynomial that describes the total area of the squares and rectangles shown below. Then simplify the polynomial.

Solution

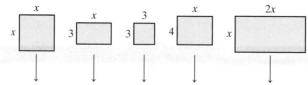

Area: $x \cdot x$ + $3 \cdot x$ + $3 \cdot 3$ + $4 \cdot x$ + $x \cdot 2x$ Recall that the area of a rectangle is length times width.
$= x^2 + 3x + 9 + 4x + 2x^2$
$= 3x^2 + 7x + 9$ Combine like terms. $\quad \square$

PRACTICE
8   Write a polynomial that describes the total area of the squares and rectangles shown below. Then simplify the polynomial.

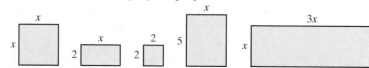

OBJECTIVE

4 Adding and Subtracting Polynomials

We now practice adding and subtracting polynomials.

Adding Polynomials

To add polynomials, combine all like terms.

EXAMPLE 9 Add $(-2x^2 + 5x - 1)$ and $(-2x^2 + x + 3)$.

Solution

$$(-2x^2 + 5x - 1) + (-2x^2 + x + 3) = -2x^2 + 5x - 1 - 2x^2 + x + 3$$
$$= (-2x^2 - 2x^2) + (5x + 1x) + (-1 + 3)$$
$$= -4x^2 + 6x + 2 \qquad \square$$

PRACTICE

9 Add $(-3x^2 - 4x + 9)$ and $(2x^2 - 2x)$.

EXAMPLE 10 Add: $(4x^3 - 6x^2 + 2x + 7) + (5x^2 - 2x)$

Solution

$$(4x^3 - 6x^2 + 2x + 7) + (5x^2 - 2x) = 4x^3 - 6x^2 + 2x + 7 + 5x^2 - 2x$$
$$= 4x^3 + (-6x^2 + 5x^2) + (2x - 2x) + 7$$
$$= 4x^3 - x^2 + 7 \qquad \square$$

PRACTICE

10 Add: $(-3x^3 + 7x^2 + 3x - 4) + (3x^2 - 9x)$

Polynomials can be added vertically if we line up like terms underneath one another.

EXAMPLE 11 Add $(7y^3 - 2y^2 + 7)$ and $(6y^2 + 1)$ using the vertical format.

Solution Vertically line up like terms and add.

$$\begin{array}{r} 7y^3 - 2y^2 + 7 \\ 6y^2 + 1 \\ \hline 7y^3 + 4y^2 + 8 \end{array} \qquad \square$$

PRACTICE

11 Add $(5z^3 + 3z^2 + 4z)$ and $(5z^2 + 4z)$ using the vertical format.

To subtract one polynomial from another, recall the definition of subtraction. To subtract a number, we add its opposite: $a - b = a + (-b)$. To subtract a polynomial, we also add its opposite. Just as $-b$ is the opposite of b, $-(x^2 + 5)$ is the opposite of $(x^2 + 5)$.

EXAMPLE 12 Subtract: $(5x - 3) - (2x - 11)$

Solution From the definition of subtraction, we have

$$(5x - 3) - (2x - 11) = (5x - 3) + [-(2x - 11)] \quad \text{Add the opposite.}$$
$$= (5x - 3) + (-2x + 11) \quad \text{Apply the distributive property.}$$
$$= (5x - 2x) + (-3 + 11)$$
$$= 3x + 8 \qquad \square$$

PRACTICE

12 Subtract $(8x - 7) - (3x - 6)$

> **Subtracting Polynomials**
> To subtract two polynomials, change the signs of the terms of the polynomial being subtracted and then add.

EXAMPLE 13   Subtract: $(2x^3 + 8x^2 - 6x) - (2x^3 - x^2 + 1)$

Solution   Change the sign of each term of the second polynomial and then add.

Helpful Hint
Notice the sign of each term is changed.

$$(2x^3 + 8x^2 - 6x) - (2x^3 - x^2 + 1) = (2x^3 + 8x^2 - 6x) + (-2x^3 + x^2 - 1)$$
$$= 2x^3 - 2x^3 + 8x^2 + x^2 - 6x - 1$$
$$= 9x^2 - 6x - 1 \quad \text{Combine like terms.} \quad \square$$

PRACTICE
13   Subtract: $(3x^3 - 5x^2 + 4x) - (x^3 - x^2 + 6)$ ∎

EXAMPLE 14   Subtract $(5y^2 + 2y - 6)$ from $(-3y^2 - 2y + 11)$ using the vertical format.

Solution   Arrange the polynomials in vertical format, lining up like terms.

$$
\begin{array}{r}
-3y^2 - 2y + 11 \\
-(5y^2 + 2y - 6) \\
\hline
\end{array}
\qquad
\begin{array}{r}
-3y^2 - 2y + 11 \\
-5y^2 - 2y + 6 \\
\hline
-8y^2 - 4y + 17
\end{array}
\qquad \square
$$

PRACTICE
14   Subtract $(6z^2 + 3z - 7)$ from $(-2z^2 - 8z + 5)$ using the vertical format.

∎

EXAMPLE 15   Subtract $(5z - 7)$ from the sum of $(8z + 11)$ and $(9z - 2)$.

Solution   Notice that $(5z - 7)$ is to be subtracted **from** a sum. The translation is

$$[(8z + 11) + (9z - 2)] - (5z - 7)$$
$$= 8z + 11 + 9z - 2 - 5z + 7 \quad \text{Remove grouping symbols.}$$
$$= 8z + 9z - 5z + 11 - 2 + 7 \quad \text{Group like terms.}$$
$$= 12z + 16 \quad \text{Combine like terms.} \quad \square$$

PRACTICE
15   Subtract $(3x + 5)$ from the sum of $(8x - 11)$ and $(2x + 5)$.   ∎

EXAMPLE 16   Add or subtract as indicated.
  a. $(3x^2 - 6xy + 5y^2) + (-2x^2 + 8xy - y^2)$
  b. $(9a^2b^2 + 6ab - 3ab^2) - (5b^2a + 2ab - 3 - 9b^2)$

Solution

  a. $(3x^2 - 6xy + 5y^2) + (-2x^2 + 8xy - y^2)$
$$= 3x^2 - 6xy + 5y^2 - 2x^2 + 8xy - y^2$$
$$= x^2 + 2xy + 4y^2 \quad \text{Combine like terms.}$$

  b. $(9a^2b^2 + 6ab - 3ab^2) - (5b^2a + 2ab - 3 - 9b^2)$ Change the sign of each term of the polynomial being subtracted.
$$= 9a^2b^2 + 6ab - 3ab^2 - 5b^2a - 2ab + 3 + 9b^2$$
$$= 9a^2b^2 + 4ab - 8ab^2 + 3 + 9b^2 \quad \text{Combine like terms.} \quad \square$$

PRACTICE

16 Add or subtract as indicated.

a. $(3a^2 - 4ab + 7b^2) + (-8a^2 + 3ab - b^2)$

b. $(5x^2y^2 - 6xy - 4xy^2) - (2x^2y^2 + 4xy - 5 + 6y^2)$

✔ **CONCEPT CHECK**

If possible, simplify each expression by performing the indicated operation.

a. $2y + y$ **b.** $2y \cdot y$ **c.** $-2y - y$ **d.** $(-2y)(-y)$ **e.** $2x + y$

Answers to Concept Check:

a. $3y$ **b.** $2y^2$ **c.** $-3y$ **d.** $2y^2$

e. cannot be simplified

 Vocabulary, Readiness & Video Check

Use the choices below to fill in each blank. Not all choices will be used.

least	monomial	trinomial	coefficient
greatest	binomial	constant	

1. A _____ is a polynomial with exactly two terms.

2. A _____ is a polynomial with exactly one term.

3. A _____ is a polynomial with exactly three terms.

4. The numerical factor of a term is called the _____.

5. A number term is also called a _____.

6. The degree of a polynomial is the _____ degree of any term of the polynomial.

Martin-Gay Interactive Videos

See Video 5.2

Watch the section lecture video and answer the following questions.

OBJECTIVE 1

7. For ▦ Example 2, why is the degree of each **term** found when the example asks for the degree of the **polynomial** only?

OBJECTIVE 2

8. From ▦ Example 3, what does the value of a polynomial depend on?

OBJECTIVE 3

9. When combining any like terms in a polynomial, as in ▦ Examples 4–6, what are we doing to the polynomial?

OBJECTIVE 4

10. From ▦ Example 7, when we simply remove parentheses and combine the like terms of two polynomials, what operation do we perform? Is this true of ▦ Examples 9–11?

5.2 Exercise Set MyMathLab ▷

Find the degree of each of the following polynomials and determine whether it is a monomial, binomial, trinomial, or none of these. See Examples 1 through 3.

1. $x + 2$

2. $-6y^2 + 4$

3. $9m^3 - 5m^2 + 4m - 8$

4. $a + 5a^2 + 3a^3 - 4a^4$

▷ **5.** $12x^4y - x^2y^2 - 12x^2y^4$

6. $7r^2s^2 + 2rs - 3rs^5$

7. $3 - 5x^8$

8. $5y^7 + 2$

In the second column, write the degree of the polynomial in the first column. See Examples 1 through 3.

	Polynomial	Degree
9.	$3xy^2 - 4$	
10.	$8x^2y^2$	
11.	$5a^2 - 2a + 1$	
12.	$4z^6 + 3z^2$	

Find the value of each polynomial when (a) $x = 0$ and (b) $x = -1$. See Examples 4 and 5.

13. $5x - 6$

14. $2x - 10$

15. $x^2 - 5x - 2$

16. $x^2 + 3x - 4$

17. $-x^3 + 4x^2 - 15x + 1$

18. $-2x^3 + 3x^2 - 6x + 1$

The CN Tower in Toronto, Ontario, is 1821 feet tall and is the world's tallest self-supporting structure. An object is dropped from the Skypod of the Tower, which is at 1150 feet. Neglecting air resistance, the height of the object at time t seconds is given by the polynomial $-16t^2 + 1150$. Find the height of the object at the given times.

	Time, t (in seconds)	Height $-16t^2 + 1150$
19.	1	
20.	7	
21.	3	
22.	6	

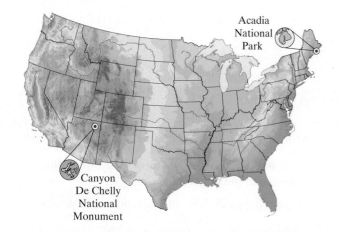

23. The polynomial $-7.5x^2 + 103x + 2000$ models the yearly number of visitors (in thousands) x years after 2006 at Acadia National Park in Maine. Use this polynomial to estimate the number of visitors to the park in 2016.

24. The polynomial $-0.13x^2 + x + 827$ models the yearly number of visitors (in thousand) x years after 2006 at Canyon De Chelly National Monument in Arizona. Use this polynomial to estimate the number of visitors to the park in 2010.

Simplify each of the following by combining like terms. See Examples 6 and 7.

25. $9x - 20x$

26. $14y - 30y$

27. $14x^2 + 9x^2$

28. $18x^3 - 4x^3$

29. $15x^2 - 3x^2 - y$

30. $12k^3 - 9k^3 + 11$

31. $8s - 5s + 4s$

32. $5y + 7y - 6y$

33. $0.1y^2 - 1.2y^2 + 6.7 - 1.9$

34. $7.6y + 3.2y^2 - 8y - 2.5y^2$

35. $\dfrac{2}{3}x^4 + 12x^3 + \dfrac{1}{6}x^4 - 19x^3 - 19$

36. $\dfrac{2}{5}x^4 - 23x^2 + \dfrac{1}{15}x^4 + 5x^2 - 5$

37. $\dfrac{2}{5}x^2 - \dfrac{1}{3}x^3 + x^2 - \dfrac{1}{4}x^3 + 6$

38. $\dfrac{1}{6}x^4 - \dfrac{1}{7}x^2 + 5 - \dfrac{1}{2}x^4 - \dfrac{3}{7}x^2 + 1$

39. $6a^2 - 4ab + 7b^2 - a^2 - 5ab + 9b^2$

40. $x^2y + xy - y + 10x^2y - 2y + xy$

Perform the indicated operations. See Examples 9 through 13.

41. $(8 + 2a) - (-a - 3)$

42. $(4 + 5a) - (-a - 5)$

43. $(2x^2 + 5) - (3x^2 - 9)$

44. $(5x^2 + 4) - (7x^2 - 6)$

45. $(-7x + 5) + (-3x^2 + 7x + 5)$

46. $(3x - 8) + (4x^2 - 3x + 3)$

47. $3x - (5x - 9)$

48. $4 - (-12y - 4)$

49. $(2x^2 + 3x - 9) - (-4x + 7)$

50. $(-7x^2 + 4x + 7) - (-8x + 2)$

Perform the indicated operations. See Examples 11, 14, and 15.

51.
$$\begin{array}{r} 3t^2 + 4 \\ + 5t^2 - 8 \\ \hline \end{array}$$

52.
$$\begin{array}{r} 7x^3 + 3 \\ + 2x^3 + 1 \\ \hline \end{array}$$

53.
$$\begin{array}{r} 4z^2 - 8z + 3 \\ -(6z^2 + 8z - 3) \\ \hline \end{array}$$

54.
$$\begin{array}{r} 7a^2 - 9a + 6 \\ -(11a^2 - 4a + 2) \\ \hline \end{array}$$

55.
$$\begin{array}{r} 5x^3 - 4x^2 + 6x - 2 \\ -(3x^3 - 2x^2 - x - 4) \\ \hline \end{array}$$

56.
$$\begin{array}{r} 5u^5 - 4u^2 + 3u - 7 \\ -(3u^5 + 6u^2 - 8u + 2) \\ \hline \end{array}$$

57. Subtract $(19x^2 + 5)$ from $(81x^2 + 10)$.

58. Subtract $(2x + xy)$ from $(3x - 9xy)$.

59. Subtract $(2x + 2)$ from the sum of $(8x + 1)$ and $(6x + 3)$.

60. Subtract $(-12x - 3)$ from the sum of $(-5x - 7)$ and $(12x + 3)$.

MIXED PRACTICE

Perform the indicated operations.

61. $(2y + 20) + (5y - 30)$

62. $(14y + 12) + (-3y - 5)$

63. $(x^2 + 2x + 1) - (3x^2 - 6x + 2)$

64. $(5y^2 - 3y - 1) - (2y^2 + y + 1)$

65. $(3x^2 + 5x - 8) + (5x^2 + 9x + 12) - (8x^2 - 14)$

66. $(2x^2 + 7x - 9) + (x^2 - x + 10) - (3x^2 - 30)$

67. $(-a^2 + 1) - (a^2 - 3) + (5a^2 - 6a + 7)$

68. $(-m^2 + 3) - (m^2 - 13) + (6m^2 - m + 1)$

TRANSLATING

Perform each indicated operation.

69. Subtract $4x$ from $(7x - 3)$.

70. Subtract y from $(y^2 - 4y + 1)$.

71. Add $(4x^2 - 6x + 1)$ and $(3x^2 + 2x + 1)$.

72. Add $(-3x^2 - 5x + 2)$ and $(x^2 - 6x + 9)$.

73. Subtract $(5x + 7)$ from $(7x^2 + 3x + 9)$.

74. Subtract $(5y^2 + 8y + 2)$ from $(7y^2 + 9y - 8)$.

75. Subtract $(4y^2 - 6y - 3)$ from the sum of $(8y^2 + 7)$ and $(6y + 9)$.

76. Subtract $(4x^2 - 2x + 2)$ from the sum of $(x^2 + 7x + 1)$ and $(7x + 5)$.

Find the area of each figure. Write a polynomial that describes the total area of the rectangles and squares shown in Exercises 77 and 78. Then simplify the polynomial. See Example 8.

△ **77.**

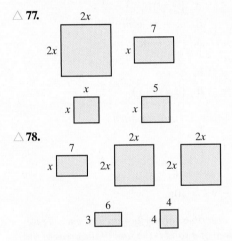

△ **78.**

Add or subtract as indicated. See Example 16.

79. $(9a + 6b - 5) + (-11a - 7b + 6)$

80. $(3x - 2 + 6y) + (7x - 2 - y)$

81. $(4x^2 + y^2 + 3) - (x^2 + y^2 - 2)$

82. $(7a^2 - 3b^2 + 10) - (-2a^2 + b^2 - 12)$

83. $(x^2 + 2xy - y^2) + (5x^2 - 4xy + 20y^2)$

84. $(a^2 - ab + 4b^2) + (6a^2 + 8ab - b^2)$

85. $(11r^2s + 16rs - 3 - 2r^2s^2) - (3sr^2 + 5 - 9r^2s^2)$

86. $(3x^2y - 6xy + x^2y^2 - 5) - (11x^2y^2 - 1 + 5yx^2)$

Simplify each polynomial by combining like terms.

87. $7.75x + 9.16x^2 - 1.27 - 14.58x^2 - 18.34$

88. $1.85x^2 - 3.76x + 9.25x^2 + 10.76 - 4.21x$

Perform each indicated operation.

89. $[(7.9y^4 - 6.8y^3 + 3.3y) + (6.1y^3 - 5)]$
$- (4.2y^4 + 1.1y - 1)$

90. $[(1.2x^2 - 3x + 9.1) - (7.8x^2 - 3.1 + 8)] + (1.2x - 6)$

REVIEW AND PREVIEW

Multiply. See Section 5.1.

91. $3x(2x)$ **92.** $-7x(x)$

93. $(12x^3)(-x^5)$ **94.** $6r^3(7r^{10})$

95. $10x^2(20xy^2)$ **96.** $-z^2y(11zy)$

CONCEPT EXTENSIONS

Recall that the perimeter of a figure is the sum of the lengths of its sides. For Exercises 97 through 100, find the perimeter of each figure. Write the perimeter as a simplified polynomial.

△ **97.** 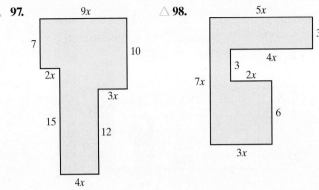 △ **98.**

△ **99.**

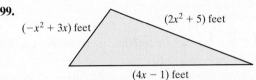

△ **100.**

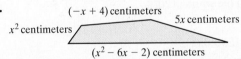

△ **101.** A wooden beam is $(4y^2 + 4y + 1)$ meters long. If a piece $(y^2 - 10)$ meters is cut, express the length of the remaining piece of beam as a polynomial in y.

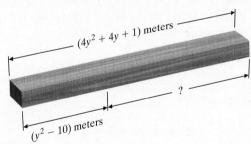

△ **102.** A piece of quarter-round molding is $(13x - 7)$ inches long. If a piece $(2x + 2)$ inches is removed, express the length of the remaining piece of molding as a polynomial in x.

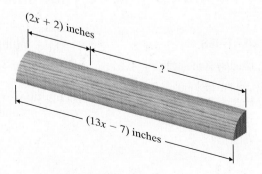

The number of worldwide Internet users (in millions) x years after the year 2000 is given by the polynomial $4.8x^2 + 104x + 431$ for the years 1995 through 2015. Use this polynomial for Exercises 103 and 104.

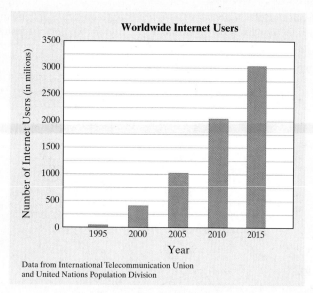

Worldwide Internet Users

Data from International Telecommunication Union and United Nations Population Division

103. Estimate the number of Internet users in the world in 2015.

104. Use the given polynomial to predict the number of Internet users in the world in 2020.

CONCEPT EXTENSIONS

105. Describe how to find the degree of a term.

106. Describe how to find the degree of a polynomial.

107. Explain why xyz is a monomial while $x + y + z$ is a trinomial.

108. Explain why the degree of the term $5y^3$ is 3 and the degree of the polynomial $2y + y + 2y$ is 1.

Match each expression on the left with its simplification on the right. Not all letters on the right must be used, and a letter may be used more than once.

109. $10y - 6y^2 - y$

110. $5x + 5x$

111. $(5x - 3) + (5x - 3)$

112. $(15x - 3) - (5x - 3)$

A. $3y$

B. $9y - 6y^2$

C. $10x$

D. $25x^2$

E. $10x - 6$

F. none of these

Simplify each expression by performing the indicated operation. Explain how you arrived at each answer. See the last Concept Check in this section.

113. a. $z + 3z$ **b.** $z \cdot 3z$
c. $-z - 3z$ **d.** $(-z)(-3z)$

114. a. $5y + y$ **b.** $5y \cdot y$
c. $-5y - y$ **d.** $(-5y)(-y)$

115. a. $m \cdot m \cdot m$ **b.** $m + m + m$
c. $(-m)(-m)(-m)$ **d.** $-m - m - m$

116. a. $x + x$ **b.** $x \cdot x$
c. $-x - x$ **d.** $(-x)(-x)$

Fill in the squares so that each is a true statement.

117. $3x^\square + 4x^2 = 7x^\square$

118. $9y^7 + 3y^\square = 12y^7$

119. $2x^\square + 3x^\square - 5x^\square + 4x^\square = 6x^4 - 2x^3$

120. $3y^\square + 7y^\square - 2y^\square - y^\square = 10y^5 - 3y^2$

Write a polynomial that describes the surface area of each figure. (Recall that the surface area of a solid is the sum of the areas of the faces or sides of the solid.)

△ **121.**

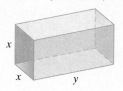

△ **122.**

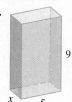

5.3 | Multiplying Polynomials

OBJECTIVES

1 Multiply Monomials.

2 Use the Distributive Property to Multiply Polynomials.

3 Multiply Polynomials Vertically.

OBJECTIVE

1 Multiplying Monomials

Recall from Section 5.1 that to multiply two monomials such as $(-5x^3)$ and $(-2x^4)$, we use the associative and commutative properties and regroup. Remember, also, that to multiply exponential expressions with a common base, we use the product rule for exponents and add exponents.

$$(-5x^3)(-2x^4) = (-5)(-2)(x^3)(x^4) = 10x^7$$

EXAMPLES   Multiply.

1. $6x \cdot 4x = (6 \cdot 4)(x \cdot x)$ Use the commutative and associative properties.

$= 24x^2$ Multiply.

2. $-7x^2 \cdot 0.2x^5 = (-7 \cdot 0.2)(x^2 \cdot x^5)$

$= -1.4x^7$

3. $\left(-\dfrac{1}{3}x^5\right)\left(-\dfrac{2}{9}x\right) = \left(-\dfrac{1}{3} \cdot -\dfrac{2}{9}\right) \cdot (x^5 \cdot x)$

$= \dfrac{2}{27}x^6$

PRACTICE

1–3   Multiply.

1. $5y \cdot 2y$ **2.** $(5z^3) \cdot (-0.4z^5)$ **3.** $\left(-\dfrac{1}{9}b^6\right)\left(-\dfrac{7}{8}b^3\right)$

✔ **CONCEPT CHECK**

Simplify.

a. $3x \cdot 2x$ **b.** $3x + 2x$

OBJECTIVE

2   Using the Distributive Property to Multiply Polynomials ▶

To multiply polynomials that are not monomials, use the distributive property.

EXAMPLE 4   Use the distributive property to find each product.

a. $5x(2x^3 + 6)$ **b.** $-3x^2(5x^2 + 6x - 1)$

Solution

a. $5x(2x^3 + 6) = 5x(2x^3) + 5x(6)$ Use the distributive property.

$= 10x^4 + 30x$ Multiply.

b. $-3x^2(5x^2 + 6x - 1)$

$= (-3x^2)(5x^2) + (-3x^2)(6x) + (-3x^2)(-1)$ Use the distributive property.

$= -15x^4 - 18x^3 + 3x^2$ Multiply.

PRACTICE

4   Use the distributive property to find each product.

a. $3x(9x^5 + 11)$ **b.** $-6x^3(2x^2 - 9x + 2)$

We also use the distributive property to multiply two binomials. To multiply $(x + 3)$ by $(x + 1)$, distribute the factor $(x + 3)$ first.

$(x + 3)(x + 1) = x(x + 1) + 3(x + 1)$ Distribute $(x + 3)$.

$= x(x) + x(1) + 3(x) + 3(1)$ Apply the distributive property a second time.

$= x^2 + x + 3x + 3$ Multiply.

$= x^2 + 4x + 3$ Combine like terms.

Answers to Concept Check:

a. $6x^2$ **b.** $5x$

This idea can be expanded so that we can multiply any two polynomials.

> **To Multiply Two Polynomials**
> Multiply each term of the first polynomial by each term of the second polynomial and then combine like terms.

EXAMPLE 5   Multiply: $(3x + 2)(2x - 5)$

Solution   Multiply each term of the first binomial by each term of the second.

$$(3x + 2)(2x - 5) = 3x(2x) + 3x(-5) + 2(2x) + 2(-5)$$
$$= 6x^2 - 15x + 4x - 10 \qquad \text{Multiply.}$$
$$= 6x^2 - 11x - 10 \qquad \text{Combine like terms.} \quad \square$$

PRACTICE
5   Multiply: $(5x - 2)(2x + 3)$

EXAMPLE 6   Multiply: $(2x - y)^2$

Solution   Recall that $a^2 = a \cdot a$, so $(2x - y)^2 = (2x - y)(2x - y)$. Multiply each term of the first polynomial by each term of the second.

$$(2x - y)(2x - y) = 2x(2x) + 2x(-y) + (-y)(2x) + (-y)(-y)$$
$$= 4x^2 - 2xy - 2xy + y^2 \qquad \text{Multiply.}$$
$$= 4x^2 - 4xy + y^2 \qquad \text{Combine like terms.} \quad \square$$

PRACTICE
6   Multiply: $(5x - 3y)^2$

✔ **CONCEPT CHECK**
Square where indicated. Simplify if possible.
a. $(4a)^2 + (3b)^2$ **b.** $(4a + 3b)^2$

EXAMPLE 7   Multiply $(t + 2)$ by $(3t^2 - 4t + 2)$.

Solution   Multiply each term of the first polynomial by each term of the second.

$$(t + 2)(3t^2 - 4t + 2) = t(3t^2) + t(-4t) + t(2) + 2(3t^2) + 2(-4t) + 2(2)$$
$$= 3t^3 - 4t^2 + 2t + 6t^2 - 8t + 4$$
$$= 3t^3 + 2t^2 - 6t + 4 \quad \text{Combine like terms.} \qquad \square$$

PRACTICE
7   Multiply $(y + 4)$ by $(2y^2 - 3y + 5)$.

EXAMPLE 8   Multiply: $(3a + b)^3$

Solution   Write $(3a + b)^3$ as $(3a + b)(3a + b)(3a + b)$.

$$(3a + b)(3a + b)(3a + b) = (9a^2 + 3ab + 3ab + b^2)(3a + b)$$
$$= (9a^2 + 6ab + b^2)(3a + b)$$
$$= 9a^2(3a + b) + 6ab(3a + b) + b^2(3a + b)$$
$$= 27a^3 + 9a^2b + 18a^2b + 6ab^2 + 3ab^2 + b^3$$
$$= 27a^3 + 27a^2b + 9ab^2 + b^3 \qquad \square$$

Answers to Concept Check:
a. $16a^2 + 9b^2$
b. $16a^2 + 24ab + 9b^2$

PRACTICE
8   Multiply: $(s + 2t)^3$

OBJECTIVE

3   Multiplying Polynomials Vertically

Another convenient method for multiplying polynomials is to use a vertical format similar to the format used to multiply real numbers. We demonstrate this method by multiplying $(3y^2 - 4y + 1)$ by $(y + 2)$.

EXAMPLE 9   Multiply $(3y^2 - 4y + 1)$ by $(y + 2)$. Use a vertical format.

Solution

$$
\begin{array}{r}
3y^2 - 4y + 1 \\
\times \quad\quad y + 2 \\
\hline
6y^2 - 8y + 2 \\
3y^3 - 4y^2 + \; y \quad\quad \\
\hline
3y^3 + 2y^2 - 7y + 2
\end{array}
$$

1st, multiply $3y^2 - 4y + 1$ by 2.
2nd, multiply $3y^2 - 4y + 1$ by y.
Line up like terms.
3rd, combine like terms.

> **Helpful Hint**
> Make sure like terms are lined up.

Thus, $(3y^2 - 4y + 1)(y + 2) = 3y^3 + 2y^2 - 7y + 2$. □

PRACTICE

9   Multiply $(5x^2 - 3x + 5)$ by $(x - 4)$. Use a vertical format. ■

When multiplying vertically, be careful if a power is missing; you may want to leave space in the partial products and take care that like terms are lined up.

EXAMPLE 10   Multiply $(2x^3 - 3x + 4)$ by $(x^2 + 1)$. Use a vertical format.

Solution

$$
\begin{array}{r}
2x^3 - 3x + 4 \\
\times \quad\quad x^2 + 1 \\
\hline
2x^3 \quad\quad - 3x + 4 \\
2x^5 - 3x^3 + 4x^2 \quad\quad\quad\quad \\
\hline
2x^5 - \; x^3 + 4x^2 - 3x + 4
\end{array}
$$

Leave space for missing powers of x.
← Line up like terms.
Combine like terms. □

PRACTICE

10   Multiply $(x^3 - 2x^2 + 1)$ by $(x^2 + 2)$ using a vertical format. ■

EXAMPLE 11   Find the product of $(2x^2 - 3x + 4)$ and $(x^2 + 5x - 2)$ using a vertical format.

Solution   First, we arrange the polynomials in a vertical format. Then we multiply each term of the second polynomial by each term of the first polynomial.

$$
\begin{array}{r}
2x^2 - \; 3x + 4 \\
\times \quad\quad x^2 + \; 5x - 2 \\
\hline
-4x^2 + \; 6x - 8 \\
10x^3 - 15x^2 + 20x \quad\quad\quad \\
2x^4 - \; 3x^3 + \; 4x^2 \quad\quad\quad\quad\quad \\
\hline
2x^4 + \; 7x^3 - 15x^2 + 26x - 8
\end{array}
$$

Multiply $2x^2 - 3x + 4$ by -2.
Multiply $2x^2 - 3x + 4$ by $5x$.
Multiply $2x^2 - 3x + 4$ by x^2.
Combine like terms. □

PRACTICE

11   Find the product of $(5x^2 + 2x - 2)$ and $(x^2 - x + 3)$ using a vertical format. ■

Vocabulary, Readiness & Video Check

Fill in each blank with the correct choice.

1. The expression $5x(3x + 2)$ equals $5x \cdot 3x + 5x \cdot 2$ by the _____ property.
   a. commutative   **b.** associative   **c.** distributive

2. The expression $(x + 4)(7x - 1)$ equals $x(7x - 1) + 4(7x - 1)$ by the _____ property.
   a. commutative   **b.** associative   **c.** distributive

3. The expression $(5y - 1)^2$ equals _____ .
   a. $2(5y - 1)$ **b.** $(5y - 1)(5y + 1)$ **c.** $(5y - 1)(5y - 1)$

4. The expression $9x \cdot 3x$ equals _____ .
   a. $27x$ **b.** $27x^2$ **c.** $12x$ **d.** $12x^2$

Martin-Gay Interactive Videos

See Video 5.3

Watch the section lecture video and answer the following questions.

OBJECTIVE
1
5. For Example 1, we use the product property to multiply the monomials. Is it possible to add the same two monomials? Why or why not?

OBJECTIVE
2
6. What property and what exponent rule is used in Examples 2–6?

OBJECTIVE
3
7. Would you say the vertical format used in Example 7 also applies the distributive property? Explain.

5.3 **Exercise Set** MyMathLab

Multiply. See Examples 1 through 3.

1. $-4n^3 \cdot 7n^7$

2. $9t^6(-3t^5)$

3. $(-3.1x^3)(4x^9)$

4. $(-5.2x^4)(3x^4)$

5. $\left(-\dfrac{1}{3}y^2\right)\left(\dfrac{2}{5}y\right)$

6. $\left(-\dfrac{3}{4}y^7\right)\left(\dfrac{1}{7}y^4\right)$

7. $(2x)(-3x^2)(4x^5)$

8. $(x)(5x^4)(-6x^7)$

Multiply. See Example 4.

9. $3x(2x + 5)$

10. $2x(6x + 3)$

11. $-2a(a + 4)$

12. $-3a(2a + 7)$

13. $3x(2x^2 - 3x + 4)$

14. $4x(5x^2 - 6x - 10)$

15. $-2a^2(3a^2 - 2a + 3)$

16. $-4b^2(3b^3 - 12b^2 - 6)$

17. $-y(4x^3 - 7x^2y + xy^2 + 3y^3)$

18. $-x(6y^3 - 5xy^2 + x^2y - 5x^3)$

19. $\dfrac{1}{2}x^2(8x^2 - 6x + 1)$

20. $\dfrac{1}{3}y^2(9y^2 - 6y + 1)$

Multiply. See Examples 5 and 6.

21. $(x + 4)(x + 3)$

22. $(x + 2)(x + 9)$

23. $(a + 7)(a - 2)$

24. $(y - 10)(y + 11)$

25. $\left(x + \dfrac{2}{3}\right)\left(x - \dfrac{1}{3}\right)$

26. $\left(x + \dfrac{3}{5}\right)\left(x - \dfrac{2}{5}\right)$

27. $(3x^2 + 1)(4x^2 + 7)$

28. $(5x^2 + 2)(6x^2 + 2)$

29. $(2y - 4)^2$

30. $(6x - 7)^2$

31. $(4x - 3)(3x - 5)$

32. $(8x - 3)(2x - 4)$

33. $(3x^2 + 1)^2$

34. $(x^2 + 4)^2$

35. Perform the indicated operations.
   a. $4y^2(-y^2)$
   b. $4y^2 - y^2$
   c. Explain the difference between the two expressions.

36. Perform the indicated operations.
   a. $9x^2(-10x^2)$
   b. $9x^2 - 10x^2$
   c. Explain the difference between the two expressions.

Multiply. See Example 7.

37. $(x - 2)(x^2 - 3x + 7)$

38. $(x + 3)(x^2 + 5x - 8)$

▶ **39.** $(x + 5)(x^3 - 3x + 4)$

40. $(a + 2)(a^3 - 3a^2 + 7)$

41. $(2a - 3)(5a^2 - 6a + 4)$

42. $(3 + b)(2 - 5b - 3b^2)$

Multiply. See Example 8.

43. $(x + 2)^3$

44. $(y - 1)^3$

45. $(2y - 3)^3$

46. $(3x + 4)^3$

Multiply vertically. See Examples 9 through 11.

47. $(2x - 11)(6x + 1)$

48. $(4x - 7)(5x + 1)$

▶ **49.** $(5x + 1)(2x^2 + 4x - 1)$

50. $(4x - 5)(8x^2 + 2x - 4)$

51. $(x^2 + 5x - 7)(2x^2 - 7x - 9)$

52. $(3x^2 - x + 2)(x^2 + 2x + 1)$

MIXED PRACTICE

Multiply. See Examples 1 through 11.

53. $-1.2y(-7y^6)$

54. $-4.2x(-2x^5)$

55. $-3x(x^2 + 2x - 8)$

56. $-5x(x^2 - 3x + 10)$

57. $(x + 19)(2x + 1)$

58. $(3y + 4)(y + 11)$

59. $\left(x + \dfrac{1}{7}\right)\left(x - \dfrac{3}{7}\right)$

60. $\left(m + \dfrac{2}{9}\right)\left(m - \dfrac{1}{9}\right)$

61. $(3y + 5)^2$

62. $(7y + 2)^2$

63. $(a + 4)(a^2 - 6a + 6)$

64. $(t + 3)(t^2 - 5t + 5)$

65. $(2x - 5)^3$

66. $(3y - 1)^3$

67. $(4x + 5)(8x^2 + 2x - 4)$

68. $(5x + 4)(x^2 - x + 4)$

69. $(3x^2 + 2x - 4)(2x^2 - 4x + 3)$

70. $(a^2 + 3a - 2)(2a^2 - 5a - 1)$

Express as the product of polynomials. Then multiply.

△ **71.** Find the area of the rectangle.

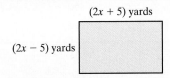

(2x + 5) yards

(2x − 5) yards

△ **72.** Find the area of the square field.

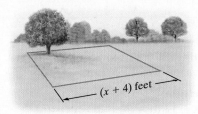

(x + 4) feet

△ **73.** Find the area of the triangle.

(Triangle Area $= \dfrac{1}{2} \cdot$ base $\cdot$ height)

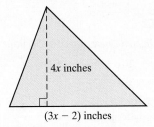

4x inches

(3x − 2) inches

△ **74.** Find the volume of the cube.

(Volume = length · width · height)

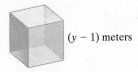

(y − 1) meters

REVIEW AND PREVIEW

In this section, we review operations on monomials. Study the box below, then proceed. See Sections 2.1, 5.1, and 5.2. (Continued on next page)

Operations on Monomials	
Multiply	Review the product rule for exponents.
Divide	Review the quotient rule for exponents.
Add or Subtract	Remember, we may only combine like terms.

Perform the operations on the monomials if possible. The first two rows have been completed for you.

Monomials	Add	Subtract	Multiply	Divide
$6x, 3x$	$6x + 3x = 9x$	$6x - 3x = 3x$	$6x \cdot 3x = 18x^2$	$\dfrac{6x}{3x} = 2$
$-12x^2, 2x$	$-12x^2 + 2x$, can't be simplified	$-12x^2 - 2x$, can't be simplified	$-12x^2 \cdot 2x = -24x^3$	$\dfrac{-12x^2}{2x} = -6x$
75. $5a, 15a$				
76. $4y^7, 4y^3$				
77. $-3y^5, 9y^4$				
78. $-14x^2, 2x^2$				

CONCEPT EXTENSIONS

79. Perform each indicated operation. Explain the difference between the two expressions.
   a. $(3x + 5) + (3x + 7)$
   b. $(3x + 5)(3x + 7)$

80. Perform each indicated operation. Explain the difference between the two expressions.
   a. $(8x - 3) - (5x - 2)$
   b. $(8x - 3)(5x - 2)$

MIXED PRACTICE

Perform the indicated operations. See Sections 5.2 and 5.3.

81. $(3x - 1) + (10x - 6)$
82. $(2x - 1) + (10x - 7)$
83. $(3x - 1)(10x - 6)$
84. $(2x - 1)(10x - 7)$
85. $(3x - 1) - (10x - 6)$
86. $(2x - 1) - (10x - 7)$

CONCEPT EXTENSIONS

87. The area of the larger rectangle on the right is $x(x + 3)$. Find another expression for this area by finding the sum of the areas of the two smaller rectangles.

88. Write an expression for the area of the larger rectangle on the right in two different ways.

89. The area of the figure on the right is $(x + 2)(x + 3)$. Find another expression for this area by finding the sum of the areas of the four smaller rectangles.

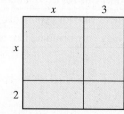

90. Write an expression for the area of the figure in two different ways.

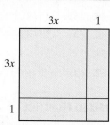

Simplify. See the Concept Checks in this section.

91. $5a + 6a$ **92.** $5a \cdot 6a$

Square where indicated. Simplify if possible.

93. $(5x)^2 + (2y)^2$ **94.** $(5x + 2y)^2$

95. Multiply each of the following polynomials.
   a. $(a + b)(a - b)$
   b. $(2x + 3y)(2x - 3y)$
   c. $(4x + 7)(4x - 7)$
   d. Can you make a general statement about all products of the form $(x + y)(x - y)$?

96. Evaluate each of the following.
   a. $(2 + 3)^2; 2^2 + 3^2$
   b. $(8 + 10)^2; 8^2 + 10^2$
   c. Does $(a + b)^2 = a^2 + b^2$ no matter what the values of a and b are? Why or why not?

97. Write a polynomial that describes the area of the shaded region. (Find the area of the larger square minus the area of the smaller square.)

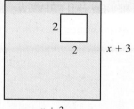

98. Write a polynomial that describes the area of the shaded region. (See Exercise 97.)

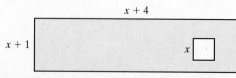

5.4 Special Products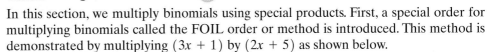

OBJECTIVES

1 Multiply Two Binomials Using the FOIL Method.

2 Square a Binomial.

3 Multiply the Sum and Difference of Two Terms.

4 Use Special Products to Multiply Binomials.

OBJECTIVE

1 Using the FOIL Method

In this section, we multiply binomials using special products. First, a special order for multiplying binomials called the FOIL order or method is introduced. This method is demonstrated by multiplying $(3x + 1)$ by $(2x + 5)$ as shown below.

The FOIL Method

F stands for the product of the **First** terms. $(3x + 1)(2x + 5)$

$$(3x)(2x) = 6x^2 \quad \textbf{F}$$

O stands for the product of the **Outer** terms. $(3x + 1)(2x + 5)$

$$(3x)(5) = 15x \quad \textbf{O}$$

I stands for the product of the **Inner** terms. $(3x + 1)(2x + 5)$

$$(1)(2x) = 2x \quad \textbf{I}$$

L stands for the product of the **Last** terms. $(3x + 1)(2x + 5)$

$$(1)(5) = 5 \quad \textbf{L}$$

$$
\begin{array}{cccc}
\text{F} & \text{O} & \text{I} & \text{L}
\end{array}
$$
$$(3x + 1)(2x + 5) = 6x^2 + 15x + 2x + 5$$
$$= 6x^2 + 17x + 5 \qquad \text{Combine like terms.}$$

✔ **CONCEPT CHECK**

Multiply $(3x + 1)(2x + 5)$ using methods from the last section. Show that the product is still $6x^2 + 17x + 5$.

EXAMPLE 1 Multiply $(x - 3)(x + 4)$ by the FOIL method.

Solution

$$
\begin{array}{cccc}
& \text{F} & \text{O} & \text{I} & \text{L}
\end{array}
$$
$$(x - 3)(x + 4) = (x)(x) + (x)(4) + (-3)(x) + (-3)(4)$$

$$= x^2 + 4x - 3x - 12$$
$$= x^2 + x - 12 \qquad \text{Combine like terms.} \qquad \square$$

Helpful Hint

Remember that the FOIL order for multiplying can be used only for the product of two binomials.

PRACTICE

1 Multiply $(x + 2)(x - 5)$ by the FOIL method.

EXAMPLE 2 Multiply $(5x - 7)(x - 2)$ by the FOIL method.

Solution

$$
\begin{array}{cccc}
& \text{F} & \text{O} & \text{I} & \text{L}
\end{array}
$$
$$(5x - 7)(x - 2) = 5x(x) + 5x(-2) + (-7)(x) + (-7)(-2)$$

$$= 5x^2 - 10x - 7x + 14$$
$$= 5x^2 - 17x + 14 \qquad \text{Combine like terms.} \qquad \square$$

Answer to Concept Check:
Multiply and simplify.
$3x(2x + 5) + 1(2x + 5)$

PRACTICE

2 Multiply $(4x - 9)(x - 1)$ by the FOIL method.

EXAMPLE 3 Multiply: $2(y + 6)(2y - 1)$

$$\quad\quad\quad\quad\quad\quad\quad\quad F\quad O\quad I\quad L$$

Solution $\ 2(y + 6)(2y - 1) = 2(2y^2 - 1y + 12y - 6)$

$$= 2(2y^2 + 11y - 6)\quad\text{Simplify inside parentheses.}$$

$$= 4y^2 + 22y - 12\quad\text{Now use the distributive property.}\ \square$$

PRACTICE
3 Multiply: $3(x + 5)(3x - 1)$

OBJECTIVE

2 Squaring Binomials ▶

Now, try squaring a binomial using the FOIL method.

EXAMPLE 4 Multiply: $(3y + 1)^2$

Solution $(3y + 1)^2 = (3y + 1)(3y + 1)$

$$\quad\quad\quad\quad\quad\quad F\quad\quad\quad O\quad\quad\quad I\quad\quad\quad L$$

$$= (3y)(3y) + (3y)(1) + 1(3y) + 1(1)$$

$$= 9y^2 + 3y + 3y + 1$$

$$= 9y^2 + 6y + 1\quad\quad\quad\quad\quad\quad\quad\square$$

PRACTICE
4 Multiply: $(4x - 1)^2$

Notice the pattern that appears in Example 4.

$$(3y + 1)^2 = 9y^2 + 6y + 1$$

▶ $9y^2$ is the first term of the binomial squared. $(3y)^2 = 9y^2$.

▶ $6y$ is 2 times the product of both terms of the binomial. $(2)(3y)(1) = 6y$.

▶ 1 is the second term of the binomial squared. $(1)^2 = 1$.

This pattern leads to the following, which can be used when squaring a binomial. We call these **special products.**

Squaring a Binomial

A binomial squared is equal to the square of the first term plus or minus twice the product of both terms plus the square of the second term.

$$(a + b)^2 = a^2 + 2ab + b^2$$

$$(a - b)^2 = a^2 - 2ab + b^2$$

This product can be visualized geometrically.

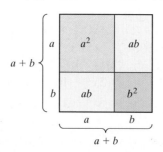

The area of the large square is side · side.

$$\text{Area} = (a + b)(a + b) = (a + b)^2$$

The area of the large square is also the sum of the areas of the smaller rectangles.

$$\text{Area} = a^2 + ab + ab + b^2 = a^2 + 2ab + b^2$$

Thus, $(a + b)^2 = a^2 + 2ab + b^2$.

EXAMPLE 5   Use a special product to square each binomial.

a. $(t + 2)^2$ **b.** $(p - q)^2$ **c.** $(2x + 5)^2$ **d.** $(x^2 - 7y)^2$

Solution

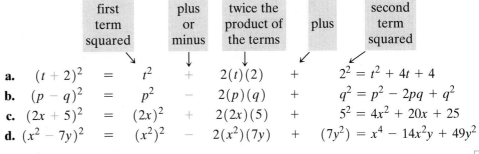

			first term squared	plus or minus	twice the product of the terms	plus	second term squared	

a. $(t + 2)^2$ $=$ t^2 $+$ $2(t)(2)$ $+$ $2^2 = t^2 + 4t + 4$
b. $(p - q)^2$ $=$ p^2 $-$ $2(p)(q)$ $+$ $q^2 = p^2 - 2pq + q^2$
c. $(2x + 5)^2$ $=$ $(2x)^2$ $+$ $2(2x)(5)$ $+$ $5^2 = 4x^2 + 20x + 25$
d. $(x^2 - 7y)^2$ $=$ $(x^2)^2$ $-$ $2(x^2)(7y)$ $+$ $(7y^2) = x^4 - 14x^2y + 49y^2$

☐

PRACTICE

5   Use a special product to square each binomial.

a. $(b + 3)^2$ **b.** $(x - y)^2$
c. $(3y + 2)^2$ **d.** $(a^2 - 5b)^2$

■

> **Helpful Hint**
>
> Notice that
>
> $$(a + b)^2 \neq a^2 + b^2 \quad \text{The middle term } 2ab \text{ is missing.}$$
> $$(a + b)^2 = (a + b)(a + b) = a^2 + 2ab + b^2$$
>
> Likewise,
>
> $$(a - b)^2 \neq a^2 - b^2$$
> $$(a - b)^2 = (a - b)(a - b) = a^2 - 2ab + b^2$$

OBJECTIVE

3   Multiplying the Sum and Difference of Two Terms

Another special product is the product of the sum and difference of the same two terms, such as $(x + y)(x - y)$. Finding this product by the FOIL method, we see a pattern emerge.

$$(x + y)(x - y) = x^2 - xy + xy - y^2$$

$$= x^2 - y^2$$

Notice that the middle two terms subtract out. This is because the **O**uter product is the opposite of the **I**nner product. Only the **difference of squares** remains.

> **Multiplying the Sum and Difference of Two Terms**
>
> The product of the sum and difference of two terms is the square of the first term minus the square of the second term.
>
> $$(a + b)(a - b) = a^2 - b^2$$

EXAMPLE 6 Use a special product to multiply.

a. $4(x + 4)(x - 4)$ b. $(6t + 7)(6t - 7)$ c. $\left(x - \dfrac{1}{4}\right)\left(x + \dfrac{1}{4}\right)$

d. $(2p - q)(2p + q)$ e. $(3x^2 - 5y)(3x^2 + 5y)$

Solution

first term squared	minus	second term squared

a. $4(x + 4)(x - 4) = 4(x^2 - 4^2) = 4(x^2 - 16) = 4x^2 - 64$

b. $(6t + 7)(6t - 7) = (6t)^2 - 7^2 = 36t^2 - 49$

c. $\left(x - \dfrac{1}{4}\right)\left(x + \dfrac{1}{4}\right) = x^2 - \left(\dfrac{1}{4}\right)^2 = x^2 - \dfrac{1}{16}$

d. $(2p - q)(2p + q) = (2p)^2 - q^2 = 4p^2 - q^2$

e. $(3x^2 - 5y)(3x^2 + 5y) = (3x^2)^2 - (5y)^2 = 9x^4 - 25y^2$

PRACTICE
6 Use a special product to multiply.

a. $3(x + 5)(x - 5)$ b. $(4b - 3)(4b + 3)$

c. $\left(x + \dfrac{2}{3}\right)\left(x - \dfrac{2}{3}\right)$ d. $(5s + t)(5s - t)$

e. $(2y - 3z^2)(2y + 3z^2)$

✔ **CONCEPT CHECK**

Match expression number 1 and number 2 to the equivalent expression or expressions in the list below.

1. $(a + b)^2$ **2.** $(a + b)(a - b)$

A. $(a + b)(a + b)$ **B.** $a^2 - b^2$ **C.** $a^2 + b^2$ **D.** $a^2 - 2ab + b^2$ **E.** $a^2 + 2ab + b^2$

OBJECTIVE
4 **Using Special Products** ▶

Let's now practice multiplying polynomials in general. If possible, use a special product.

EXAMPLE 7 Use a special product to multiply, if possible.

a. $(x - 5)(3x + 4)$ b. $(7x + 4)^2$ c. $(y - 0.6)(y + 0.6)$

d. $\left(y^4 + \dfrac{2}{5}\right)\left(3y^2 - \dfrac{1}{5}\right)$ e. $(a - 3)(a^2 + 2a - 1)$

Solution

a. $(x - 5)(3x + 4) = 3x^2 + 4x - 15x - 20$ FOIL.
$\quad = 3x^2 - 11x - 20$

b. $(7x + 4)^2 = (7x)^2 + 2(7x)(4) + 4^2$ Squaring a binomial.
$\quad = 49x^2 + 56x + 16$

c. $(y - 0.6)(y + 0.6) = y^2 - (0.6)^2 = y^2 - 0.36$ Multiplying the sum and difference of 2 terms.

d. $\left(y^4 + \dfrac{2}{5}\right)\left(3y^2 - \dfrac{1}{5}\right) = 3y^6 - \dfrac{1}{5}y^4 + \dfrac{6}{5}y^2 - \dfrac{2}{25}$ FOIL.

e. I've inserted this product as a reminder that since it is not a binomial times a binomial, the FOIL order may not be used.

$$(a - 3)(a^2 + 2a - 1) = a(a^2 + 2a - 1) - 3(a^2 + 2a - 1)$$

Multiplying each term of the binomial by each term of the trinomial.

$$= a^3 + 2a^2 - a - 3a^2 - 6a + 3$$

$$= a^3 - a^2 - 7a + 3$$

☐

PRACTICE
7   Use a special product to multiply, if possible.

a. $(4x + 3)(x - 6)$

b. $(7b - 2)^2$

c. $(x + 0.4)(x - 0.4)$

d. $\left(x^2 - \dfrac{3}{7}\right)\left(3x^4 + \dfrac{2}{7}\right)$

e. $(x + 1)(x^2 + 5x - 2)$

■

Helpful Hint

• When multiplying two binomials, you may always use the FOIL order or method.
• When multiplying any two polynomials, you may always use the distributive property to find the product.

✓ Vocabulary, Readiness & Video Check

Answer each exercise true or false.

1. $(x + 4)^2 = x^2 + 16$

2. For $(x + 6)(2x - 1)$ the product of the first terms is $2x^2$.

3. $(x + 4)(x - 4) = x^2 + 16$

4. The product $(x - 1)(x^3 + 3x - 1)$ is a polynomial of degree 5.

Martin-Gay Interactive Videos

See Video 5.4 ⬤

Watch the section lecture video and answer the following questions.

OBJECTIVE 1   **5.** From 🎞 Examples 1–3, for what type of multiplication problem is the FOIL order of multiplication used?

OBJECTIVE 2   **6.** Name at least one other method you can use to multiply 🎞 Example 4.

OBJECTIVE 3   **7.** From 🎞 Example 5, why does multiplying the sum and difference of the same two terms always give you a binomial answer?

OBJECTIVE 4   **8.** Why was the FOIL method not used for 🎞 Example 10?

5.4   Exercise Set   MyMathLab® ▶

Multiply using the FOIL method. See Examples 1 through 3.

1. $(x + 3)(x + 4)$

2. $(x + 5)(x - 1)$

3. $(x - 5)(x + 10)$

4. $(y - 12)(y + 4)$

5. $(5x - 6)(x + 2)$

6. $(3y - 5)(2y - 7)$

7. $5(y - 6)(4y - 1)$

8. $2(x - 11)(2x - 9)$

9. $(2x + 5)(3x - 1)$

10. $(6x + 2)(x - 2)$

11. $\left(x - \dfrac{1}{3}\right)\left(x + \dfrac{2}{3}\right)$

12. $\left(x - \dfrac{2}{5}\right)\left(x + \dfrac{1}{5}\right)$

Multiply. See Examples 4 and 5.

13. $(x + 2)^2$

14. $(x + 7)^2$

15. $(2x - 1)^2$

16. $(7x - 3)^2$

17. $(3a - 5)^2$

18. $(5a + 2)^2$

19. $(5x + 9)^2$

20. $(6s - 2)^2$

Multiply. See Example 6.

21. $(a - 7)(a + 7)$

22. $(b + 3)(b - 3)$

23. $(3x - 1)(3x + 1)$

24. $(4x - 5)(4x + 5)$

25. $\left(3x - \dfrac{1}{2}\right)\left(3x + \dfrac{1}{2}\right)$

26. $\left(10x + \dfrac{2}{7}\right)\left(10x - \dfrac{2}{7}\right)$

27. $(9x + y)(9x - y)$

28. $(2x - y)(2x + y)$

29. $(2x + 0.1)(2x - 0.1)$

30. $(5x - 1.3)(5x + 1.3)$

MIXED PRACTICE

Multiply. See Example 7.

31. $(a + 5)(a + 4)$

32. $(a - 5)(a - 7)$

33. $(a + 7)^2$

34. $(b - 2)^2$

35. $(4a + 1)(3a - 1)$

36. $(6a + 7)(6a + 5)$

37. $(x + 2)(x - 2)$

38. $(x - 10)(x + 10)$

39. $(3a + 1)^2$

40. $(4a - 2)^2$

41. $(x^2 + y)(4x - y^4)$

42. $(x^3 - 2)(5x + y)$

43. $(x + 3)(x^2 - 6x + 1)$

44. $(x - 2)(x^2 - 4x + 2)$

45. $(2a - 3)^2$

46. $(5b - 4x)^2$

47. $(5x - 6z)(5x + 6z)$

48. $(11x - 7y)(11x + 7y)$

49. $(x^5 - 3)(x^5 - 5)$

50. $(a^4 + 5)(a^4 + 6)$

51. $(x + 0.8)(x - 0.8)$

52. $(y - 0.9)(y + 0.9)$

53. $(a^3 + 11)(a^4 - 3)$

54. $(x^5 + 5)(x^2 - 8)$

55. $3(x - 2)^2$

56. $2(3b + 7)^2$

57. $(3b + 7)(2b - 5)$

58. $(3y - 13)(y - 3)$

59. $(7p - 8)(7p + 8)$

60. $(3s - 4)(3s + 4)$

61. $\left(\dfrac{1}{3}a^2 - 7\right)\left(\dfrac{1}{3}a^2 + 7\right)$

62. $\left(\dfrac{2}{3}a - b^2\right)\left(\dfrac{2}{3}a + b^2\right)$

63. $5x^2(3x^2 - x + 2)$

64. $4x^3(2x^2 + 5x - 1)$

65. $(2r - 3s)(2r + 3s)$

66. $(6r - 2x)(6r + 2x)$

67. $(3x - 7y)^2$

68. $(4s - 2y)^2$

69. $(4x + 5)(4x - 5)$

70. $(3x + 5)(3x - 5)$

71. $(8x + 4)^2$

72. $(3x + 2)^2$

73. $\left(a - \dfrac{1}{2}y\right)\left(a + \dfrac{1}{2}y\right)$

74. $\left(\dfrac{a}{2} + 4y\right)\left(\dfrac{a}{2} - 4y\right)$

75. $\left(\dfrac{1}{5}x - y\right)\left(\dfrac{1}{5}x + y\right)$

76. $\left(\dfrac{y}{6} - 8\right)\left(\dfrac{y}{6} + 8\right)$

77. $(a + 1)(3a^2 - a + 1)$

78. $(b + 3)(2b^2 + b - 3)$

Express each as a product of polynomials in x. Then multiply and simplify.

△ **79.** Find the area of the square rug shown if its side is $(2x + 1)$ feet.

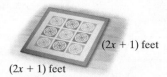

$(2x + 1)$ feet

$(2x + 1)$ feet

△ **80.** Find the area of the rectangular canvas if its length is $(3x - 2)$ inches and its width is $(x - 4)$ inches.

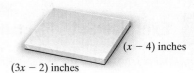

$(x - 4)$ inches

$(3x - 2)$ inches

REVIEW AND PREVIEW

Simplify each expression. See Section 5.1.

81. $\dfrac{50b^{10}}{70b^5}$

82. $\dfrac{x^3 y^6}{xy^2}$

83. $\dfrac{8a^{17}b^{15}}{-4a^7 b^{10}}$

84. $\dfrac{-6a^8 y}{3a^4 y}$

85. $\dfrac{2x^4 y^{12}}{3x^4 y^4}$

86. $\dfrac{-48ab^6}{32ab^3}$

Find the slope of each line. See Section 3.4.

87.

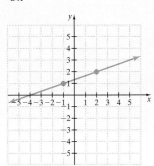

88.

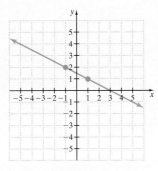

89.

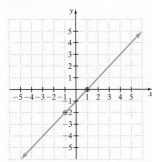

90.

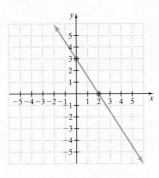

CONCEPT EXTENSIONS

Match each expression on the left to the equivalent expression on the right. See the second Concept Check in this section.

91. $(a - b)^2$

92. $(a - b)(a + b)$

93. $(a + b)^2$

94. $(a + b)^2(a - b)^2$

A. $a^2 - b^2$

B. $a^2 + b^2$

C. $a^2 - 2ab + b^2$

D. $a^2 + 2ab + b^2$

E. none of these

Fill in the squares so that a true statement forms.

95. $(x^{\square} + 7)(x^{\square} + 3) = x^4 + 10x^2 + 21$

96. $(5x^{\square} - 2)^2 = 25x^6 - 20x^3 + 4$

Find the area of the shaded figure. To do so, subtract the area of the smaller square(s) from the area of the larger geometric figure.

△ **97.**

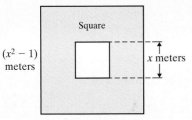

△ **98.**

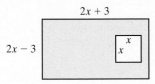

99.

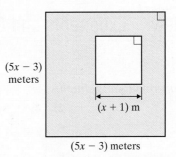

△ **100.**

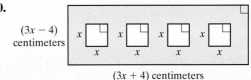

For Exercises 101 and 102, find the area of the shaded figure.

△ **101.**

△ **102.**

103. In your own words, describe the different methods that can be used to find the product $(2x - 5)(3x + 1)$.

104. In your own words, describe the different methods that can be used to find the product $(5x + 1)^2$.

105. Suppose that a classmate asked you why $(2x + 1)^2$ is **not** $(4x^2 + 1)$. Write down your response to this classmate.

106. Suppose that a classmate asked you why $(2x + 1)^2$ **is** $(4x^2 + 4x + 1)$. Write down your response to this classmate.

107. Using your own words, explain how to square a binomial such as $(a + b)^2$.

108. Explain how to find the product of two binomials using the FOIL method.

Find each product. For example,

$$[(a + b) - 2][(a + b) + 2] = (a + b)^2 - 2^2$$
$$= a^2 + 2ab + b^2 - 4$$

109. $[(x + y) - 3][(x + y) + 3]$

110. $[(a + c) - 5][(a + c) + 5]$

111. $[(a - 3) + b][(a - 3) - b]$

112. $[(x - 2) + y][(x - 2) - y]$

Integrated Review Exponents and Operations on Polynomials

Sections 5.1–5.4

Perform the indicated operations and simplify.

1. $(5x^2)(7x^3)$

2. $(4y^2)(8y^7)$

3. -4^2

4. $(-4)^2$

5. $(x-5)(2x+1)$

6. $(3x-2)(x+5)$

7. $(x-5)+(2x+1)$

8. $(3x-2)+(x+5)$

9. $\dfrac{7x^9y^{12}}{x^3y^{10}}$

10. $\dfrac{20a^2b^8}{14a^2b^2}$

11. $(12m^7n^6)^2$

12. $(4y^9z^{10})^3$

13. $3(4y-3)(4y+3)$

14. $2(7x-1)(7x+1)$

15. $(x^7y^5)^9$

16. $(3^1x^9)^3$

17. $(7x^2-2x+3)-(5x^2+9)$

18. $(10x^2+7x-9)-(4x^2-6x+2)$

19. $0.7y^2-1.2+1.8y^2-6y+1$

20. $7.8x^2-6.8x+3.3+0.6x^2-9$

21. $(x+4y)^2$

22. $(y-9z)^2$

23. $(x+4y)+(x+4y)$

24. $(y-9z)+(y-9z)$

25. $7x^2-6xy+4(y^2-xy)$

26. $5a^2-3ab+6(b^2-a^2)$

27. $(x-3)(x^2+5x-1)$

28. $(x+1)(x^2-3x-2)$

29. $(2x^3-7)(3x^2+10)$

30. $(5x^3-1)(4x^4+5)$

31. $(2x-7)(x^2-6x+1)$

32. $(5x-1)(x^2+2x-3)$

Perform the indicated operations and simplify if possible.

33. $5x^3+5y^3$

34. $(5x^3)(5y^3)$

35. $(5x^3)^3$

36. $\dfrac{5x^3}{5y^3}$

37. $x+x$

38. $x \cdot x$

5.5 Negative Exponents and Scientific Notation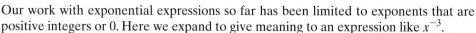

OBJECTIVES

1 Simplify Expressions Containing Negative Exponents.

2 Use All the Rules and Definitions for Exponents to Simplify Exponential Expressions.

3 Write Numbers in Scientific Notation.

4 Convert Numbers from Scientific Notation to Standard Form.

5 Perform Operations on Numbers Written in Scientific Notation.

OBJECTIVE

1 Simplifying Expressions Containing Negative Exponents

Our work with exponential expressions so far has been limited to exponents that are positive integers or 0. Here we expand to give meaning to an expression like x^{-3}.

Suppose that we wish to simplify the expression $\dfrac{x^2}{x^5}$. If we use the quotient rule for exponents, we subtract exponents:

$$\frac{x^2}{x^5} = x^{2-5} = x^{-3}, \quad x \neq 0$$

But what does x^{-3} mean? Let's simplify $\dfrac{x^2}{x^5}$ using the definition of x^n.

$$\frac{x^2}{x^5} = \frac{x \cdot x}{x \cdot x \cdot x \cdot x \cdot x}$$

$$= \frac{\overset{1}{\cancel{x}} \cdot \overset{1}{\cancel{x}}}{\cancel{x} \cdot \cancel{x} \cdot x \cdot x \cdot x} \quad \text{Divide numerator and denominator by common factors by applying the fundamental principle for fractions.}$$

$$= \frac{1}{x^3}$$

If the quotient rule is to hold true for negative exponents, then x^{-3} must equal $\dfrac{1}{x^3}$. From this example, we state the definition for negative exponents.

Negative Exponents

If a is a real number other than 0 and n is an integer, then

$$a^{-n} = \frac{1}{a^n}$$

For example, $x^{-3} = \frac{1}{x^3}$.

In other words, another way to write a^{-n} is to take its reciprocal and change the sign of its exponent.

EXAMPLE 1   Simplify by writing each expression with positive exponents only.

  a. 3^{-2} **b.** $2x^{-3}$ **c.** $2^{-1} + 4^{-1}$ **d.** $(-2)^{-4}$ **e.** y^{-4}

Solution

a. $3^{-2} = \dfrac{1}{3^2} = \dfrac{1}{9}$ Use the definition of negative exponents.

b. $2x^{-3} = 2 \cdot \dfrac{1}{x^3} = \dfrac{2}{x^3}$ Use the definition of negative exponents.

c. $2^{-1} + 4^{-1} = \dfrac{1}{2} + \dfrac{1}{4} = \dfrac{2}{4} + \dfrac{1}{4} = \dfrac{3}{4}$

d. $(-2)^{-4} = \dfrac{1}{(-2)^4} = \dfrac{1}{(-2)(-2)(-2)(-2)} = \dfrac{1}{16}$

e. $y^{-4} = \dfrac{1}{y^4}$

> **Helpful Hint**
>
> Don't forget that since there are no parentheses, only x is the base for the exponent -3.

PRACTICE

1   Simplify by writing each expression with positive exponents only.

  a. 5^{-3} **b.** $3y^{-4}$ **c.** $3^{-1} + 2^{-1}$ **d.** $(-5)^{-2}$ **e.** x^{-5}

> **Helpful Hint**
>
> A negative exponent *does not affect* the sign of its base.
> Remember: Another way to write a^{-n} is to take its reciprocal and change the sign of its exponent: $a^{-n} = \dfrac{1}{a^n}$. For example,
>
> $$x^{-2} = \frac{1}{x^2}, \qquad 2^{-3} = \frac{1}{2^3} \text{ or } \frac{1}{8}$$
>
> $$\frac{1}{y^{-4}} = \frac{1}{\frac{1}{y^4}} = y^4, \qquad \frac{1}{5^{-2}} = 5^2 \text{ or } 25$$

From the preceding Helpful Hint, we know that $x^{-2} = \dfrac{1}{x^2}$ and $\dfrac{1}{y^{-4}} = y^4$. We can use this to include another statement in our definition of negative exponents.

Negative Exponents

If a is a real number other than 0 and n is an integer, then

$$a^{-n} = \frac{1}{a^n} \quad \text{and} \quad \frac{1}{a^{-n}} = a^n$$

EXAMPLE 2 Simplify each expression. Write results using positive exponents only.

a. $\dfrac{1}{x^{-3}}$ **b.** $\dfrac{1}{3^{-4}}$ **c.** $\dfrac{p^{-4}}{q^{-9}}$ **d.** $\dfrac{5^{-3}}{2^{-5}}$

Solution

a. $\dfrac{1}{x^{-3}} = \dfrac{x^3}{1} = x^3$ **b.** $\dfrac{1}{3^{-4}} = \dfrac{3^4}{1} = 81$

c. $\dfrac{p^{-4}}{q^{-9}} = \dfrac{q^9}{p^4}$ **d.** $\dfrac{5^{-3}}{2^{-5}} = \dfrac{2^5}{5^3} = \dfrac{32}{125}$

PRACTICE

2 Simplify each expression. Write results using positive exponents only.

a. $\dfrac{1}{s^{-5}}$ **b.** $\dfrac{1}{2^{-3}}$ **c.** $\dfrac{x^{-7}}{y^{-5}}$ **d.** $\dfrac{4^{-3}}{3^{-2}}$

EXAMPLE 3 Simplify each expression. Write answers with positive exponents.

a. $\dfrac{y}{y^{-2}}$ **b.** $\dfrac{3}{x^{-4}}$ **c.** $\dfrac{x^{-5}}{x^7}$ **d.** $\left(\dfrac{2}{3}\right)^{-3}$

Solution

a. $\dfrac{y}{y^{-2}} = \dfrac{y^1}{y^{-2}} = y^{1-(-2)} = y^3$ Remember that $\dfrac{a^m}{a^n} = a^{m-n}$.

b. $\dfrac{3}{x^{-4}} = 3 \cdot \dfrac{1}{x^{-4}} = 3 \cdot x^4$ or $3x^4$

c. $\dfrac{x^{-5}}{x^7} = x^{-5-7} = x^{-12} = \dfrac{1}{x^{12}}$

d. $\left(\dfrac{2}{3}\right)^{-3} = \dfrac{2^{-3}}{3^{-3}} = \dfrac{3^3}{2^3} = \dfrac{27}{8}$

PRACTICE

3 Simplify each expression. Write answers with positive exponents.

a. $\dfrac{x^{-3}}{x^2}$ **b.** $\dfrac{5}{y^{-7}}$ **c.** $\dfrac{z}{z^{-4}}$ **d.** $\left(\dfrac{5}{9}\right)^{-2}$

OBJECTIVE

2 Simplifying Exponential Expressions

All the previously stated rules for exponents apply for negative exponents also. Here is a summary of the rules and definitions for exponents.

Summary of Exponent Rules

If m and n are integers and a, b, and c are real numbers, then:

Product rule for exponents: $a^m \cdot a^n = a^{m+n}$

Power rule for exponents: $(a^m)^n = a^{m \cdot n}$

Power of a product: $(ab)^n = a^n b^n$

Power of a quotient: $\left(\dfrac{a}{c}\right)^n = \dfrac{a^n}{c^n}, \quad c \neq 0$

Quotient rule for exponents: $\dfrac{a^m}{a^n} = a^{m-n}, \quad a \neq 0$

Zero exponent: $a^0 = 1, \quad a \neq 0$

Negative exponent: $a^{-n} = \dfrac{1}{a^n}, \quad a \neq 0$

EXAMPLE 4   Simplify the following expressions. Write each result using positive exponents only.

a. $(y^{-3}z^6)^{-6}$ **b.** $\dfrac{(2x^3)^4 x}{x^7}$ **c.** $\left(\dfrac{3a^2}{b}\right)^{-3}$ **d.** $\dfrac{4^{-1}x^{-3}y}{4^{-3}x^2 y^{-6}}$ **e.** $\left(\dfrac{-2x^3 y}{xy^{-1}}\right)^3$

Solution

a. $(y^{-3}z^6)^{-6} = y^{18} \cdot z^{-36} = \dfrac{y^{18}}{z^{36}}$

b. $\dfrac{(2x^3)^4 x}{x^7} = \dfrac{2^4 \cdot x^{12} \cdot x}{x^7} = \dfrac{16 \cdot x^{12+1}}{x^7} = \dfrac{16x^{13}}{x^7} = 16x^{13-7} = 16x^6$ Use the power rule.

c. $\left(\dfrac{3a^2}{b}\right)^{-3} = \dfrac{3^{-3}(a^2)^{-3}}{b^{-3}}$ Raise each factor in the numerator and the denominator to the -3 power.

$= \dfrac{3^{-3}a^{-6}}{b^{-3}}$ Use the power rule.

$= \dfrac{b^3}{3^3 a^6}$ Use the negative exponent rule.

$= \dfrac{b^3}{27a^6}$ Write 3^3 as 27.

d. $\dfrac{4^{-1}x^{-3}y}{4^{-3}x^2 y^{-6}} = 4^{-1-(-3)}x^{-3-2}y^{1-(-6)} = 4^2 x^{-5}y^7 = \dfrac{4^2 y^7}{x^5} = \dfrac{16y^7}{x^5}$

e. $\left(\dfrac{-2x^3 y}{xy^{-1}}\right)^3 = \dfrac{(-2)^3 x^9 y^3}{x^3 y^{-3}} = \dfrac{-8x^9 y^3}{x^3 y^{-3}} = -8x^{9-3}y^{3-(-3)} = -8x^6 y^6$ □

PRACTICE
4   Simplify the following expressions. Write each result using positive exponents only.

a. $(a^4 b^{-3})^{-5}$ **b.** $\dfrac{x^2(x^5)^3}{x^7}$ **c.** $\left(\dfrac{5p^8}{q}\right)^{-2}$

d. $\dfrac{6^{-2}x^{-4}y^{-7}}{6^{-3}x^3 y^{-9}}$ **e.** $\left(\dfrac{-3x^4 y}{x^2 y^{-2}}\right)^3$

OBJECTIVE
3   Writing Numbers in Scientific Notation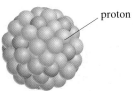

Both very large and very small numbers frequently occur in many fields of science. For example, the distance between the Sun and the dwarf planet Pluto is approximately 5,906,000,000 kilometers, and the mass of a proton is approximately 0.000000000000000000000000165 gram. It can be tedious to write these numbers in this standard decimal notation, so **scientific notation** is used as a convenient shorthand for expressing very large and very small numbers.

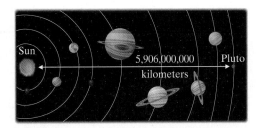

Mass of proton is approximately
0.000 000 000 000 000 000 000 001 65 gram

Scientific Notation

A positive number is written in scientific notation if it is written as the product of a number a, where $1 \le a < 10$, and an integer power r of 10:

$$a \times 10^r$$

The numbers below are written in scientific notation. The $\times$ sign for multiplication is used as part of the notation.

$$2.03 \times 10^2 \qquad 7.362 \times 10^7 \qquad 5.906 \times 10^9 \quad \text{(Distance between the Sun and Pluto)}$$
$$1 \times 10^{-3} \qquad 8.1 \times 10^{-5} \qquad 1.65 \times 10^{-24} \quad \text{(Mass of a proton)}$$

The following steps are useful when writing numbers in scientific notation.

To Write a Number in Scientific Notation

Step 1. Move the decimal point in the original number to the left or right so that the new number has a value between 1 and 10 (including 1).

Step 2. Count the number of decimal places the decimal point is moved in Step 1. If the original number is 10 or greater, the count is positive. If the original number is less than 1, the count is negative.

Step 3. Multiply the new number in Step 1 by 10 raised to an exponent equal to the count found in Step 2.

EXAMPLE 5 Write each number in scientific notation.

a. 367,000,000   **b.** 0.000003   **c.** 20,520,000,000   **d.** 0.00085

Solution

a. Step 1. Move the decimal point until the number is between 1 and 10.

367,000,000.
       8 places

Step 2. The decimal point is moved 8 places, and the original number is 10 or greater, so the count is positive 8.

Step 3. $367{,}000{,}000 = 3.67 \times 10^8$.

b. Step 1. Move the decimal point until the number is between 1 and 10.

0.000003
       6 places

Step 2. The decimal point is moved 6 places, and the original number is less than 1, so the count is -6.

Step 3. $0.000003 = 3.0 \times 10^{-6}$

c. $20{,}520{,}000{,}000 = 2.052 \times 10^{10}$

d. $0.00085 = 8.5 \times 10^{-4}$

PRACTICE

5 Write each number in scientific notation.

a. 0.000007   **b.** 20,700,000

c. 0.0043   **d.** 812,000,000

OBJECTIVE

4 Converting Numbers to Standard Form ▶

A number written in scientific notation can be rewritten in standard form. For example, to write 8.63×10^3 in standard form, recall that $10^3 = 1000$.

$$8.63 \times 10^3 = 8.63(1000) = 8630$$

Notice that the exponent on the 10 is positive 3, and we moved the decimal point 3 places to the right.

To write 7.29×10^{-3} in standard form, recall that $10^{-3} = \dfrac{1}{10^3} = \dfrac{1}{1000}$.

$$7.29 \times 10^{-3} = 7.29\left(\frac{1}{1000}\right) = \frac{7.29}{1000} = 0.00729$$

The exponent on the 10 is negative 3, and we moved the decimal to the left 3 places.

In general, **to write a scientific notation number in standard form,** move the decimal point the same number of places as the exponent on 10. If the exponent is positive, move the decimal point to the right; if the exponent is negative, move the decimal point to the left.

EXAMPLE 6   Write each number in standard notation, without exponents.

a. 1.02×10^5 b. 7.358×10^{-3} c. 8.4×10^7 d. 3.007×10^{-5}

Solution

a. Move the decimal point 5 places to the right.

$$1.02 \times 10^5 = 102,000.$$

b. Move the decimal point 3 places to the left.

$$7.358 \times 10^{-3} = 0.007358$$

c. $8.4 \times 10^7 = 84,000,000.$ 7 places to the right

d. $3.007 \times 10^{-5} = 0.00003007$ 5 places to the left

PRACTICE
6   Write each number in standard notation, without exponents.

a. 3.67×10^{-4} b. 8.954×10^6

c. 2.009×10^{-5} d. 4.054×10^3

✔ **CONCEPT CHECK**

Which number in each pair is larger?

a. 7.8×10^3 or 2.1×10^5 b. 9.2×10^{-2} or 2.7×10^4 c. 5.6×10^{-4} or 6.3×10^{-5}

OBJECTIVE

5   Performing Operations with Scientific Notation

Performing operations on numbers written in scientific notation uses the rules and definitions for exponents.

EXAMPLE 7   Perform each indicated operation. Write each result in standard decimal notation.

a. $(8 \times 10^{-6})(7 \times 10^3)$ b. $\dfrac{12 \times 10^2}{6 \times 10^{-3}}$

Solution

a. $(8 \times 10^{-6})(7 \times 10^3) = (8 \cdot 7) \times (10^{-6} \cdot 10^3)$
$$= 56 \times 10^{-3}$$
$$= 0.056$$

b. $\dfrac{12 \times 10^2}{6 \times 10^{-3}} = \dfrac{12}{6} \times 10^{2-(-3)} = 2 \times 10^5 = 200,000$

PRACTICE
7   Perform each indicated operation. Write each result in standard decimal notation.

a. $(5 \times 10^{-4})(8 \times 10^6)$ b. $\dfrac{64 \times 10^3}{32 \times 10^{-7}}$

Calculator Explorations

Scientific Notation

To enter a number written in scientific notation on a scientific calculator, locate the scientific notation key, which may be marked $\boxed{\text{EE}}$ or $\boxed{\text{EXP}}$. To enter 3.1×10^7, press $\boxed{3.1}$ $\boxed{\text{EE}}$ $\boxed{7}$. The display should read $\boxed{3.1 \quad 07}$.

Enter each number written in scientific notation on your calculator.

1. 5.31×10^3 **2.** -4.8×10^{14}

3. 6.6×10^{-9} **4.** -9.9811×10^{-2}

Multiply each of the following on your calculator. Notice the form of the result.

5. $3,000,000 \times 5,000,000$

6. $230,000 \times 1000$

Multiply each of the following on your calculator. Write the product in scientific notation.

7. $(3.26 \times 10^6)(2.5 \times 10^{13})$

8. $(8.76 \times 10^{-4})(1.237 \times 10^9)$

✔ **Vocabulary, Readiness & Video Check**

Fill in each blank with the correct choice.

1. The expression x^{-3} equals _____.

  a. $-x^3$ **b.** $\dfrac{1}{x^3}$ **c.** $\dfrac{-1}{x^3}$ **d.** $\dfrac{1}{x^{-3}}$

2. The expression 5^{-4} equals _____.

  a. -20 **b.** -625 **c.** $\dfrac{1}{20}$ **d.** $\dfrac{1}{625}$

3. The number 3.021×10^{-3} is written in _____.

  a. standard form   **b.** expanded form

  c. scientific notation

4. The number 0.0261 is written in _____.

  a. standard form   **b.** expanded form

  c. scientific notation

Martin-Gay Interactive Videos

See Video 5.5

Watch the section lecture video and answer the following questions.

OBJECTIVE 1   **5.** What important reminder is made at the end of ▦ Example 1?

OBJECTIVE 2   **6.** Name all the rules and definitions used to simplify ▦ Example 8.

OBJECTIVE 3   **7.** From ▦ Examples 9 and 10, explain how the movement of the decimal point in step 1 suggests the sign of the exponent on the number 10.

OBJECTIVE 4   **8.** From ▦ Example 11, what part of a number written in scientific notation is key in telling you how to write the number in standard form?

OBJECTIVE 5   **9.** For ▦ Example 13, what exponent rules were needed to evaluate?

5.5   **Exercise Set**   MyMathLab

Simplify each expression. Write each result using positive exponents only. See Examples 1 through 3.

1. 4^{-3} **2.** 6^{-2} **3.** $(-3)^{-4}$

4. $(-3)^{-5}$ **5.** $7x^{-3}$ **6.** $(7x)^{-3}$

7. $\left(\dfrac{1}{2}\right)^{-5}$ **8.** $\left(\dfrac{1}{8}\right)^{-2}$ **9.** $\left(-\dfrac{1}{4}\right)^{-3}$

10. $\left(-\dfrac{1}{8}\right)^{-2}$ **11.** $3^{-1} + 5^{-1}$ **12.** $4^{-1} + 4^{-2}$

13. $\dfrac{1}{p^{-3}}$ **14.** $\dfrac{1}{q^{-5}}$ **15.** $\dfrac{p^{-5}}{q^{-4}}$

16. $\dfrac{r^{-5}}{s^{-2}}$ **17.** $\dfrac{x^{-2}}{x}$ **18.** $\dfrac{y}{y^{-3}}$

19. $\dfrac{z^{-4}}{z^{-7}}$ **20.** $\dfrac{x^{-4}}{x^{-1}}$ **21.** $3^{-2} + 3^{-1}$

22. $4^{-2} - 4^{-3}$ **23.** $\dfrac{-1}{p^{-4}}$ **24.** $\dfrac{-1}{y^{-6}}$

25. $-2^0 - 3^0$ **26.** $5^0 + (-5)^0$

MIXED PRACTICE

Simplify each expression. Write each result using positive exponents only. See Examples 1 through 4.

27. $\dfrac{x^2 x^5}{x^3}$ **28.** $\dfrac{y^4 y^5}{y^6}$ **29.** $\dfrac{p^2 p}{p^{-1}}$

30. $\dfrac{y^3 y}{y^{-2}}$ **31.** $\dfrac{(m^5)^4 m}{m^{10}}$ **32.** $\dfrac{(x^2)^8 x}{x^9}$

33. $\dfrac{r}{r^{-3}r^{-2}}$ **34.** $\dfrac{p}{p^{-3}q^{-5}}$ **35.** $(x^5 y^3)^{-3}$

36. $(z^5 x^5)^{-3}$ **37.** $\dfrac{(x^2)^3}{x^{10}}$ **38.** $\dfrac{(y^4)^2}{y^{12}}$

39. $\dfrac{(a^5)^2}{(a^3)^4}$ **40.** $\dfrac{(x^2)^5}{(x^4)^3}$ **41.** $\dfrac{8k^4}{2k}$

42. $\dfrac{27r^4}{3r^6}$ **43.** $\dfrac{-6m^4}{-2m^3}$

44. $\dfrac{15a^4}{-15a^5}$ **45.** $\dfrac{-24a^6 b}{6ab^2}$

46. $\dfrac{-5x^4 y^5}{15x^4 y^2}$ **47.** $(-2x^3 y^{-4})(3x^{-1}y)$

48. $(-5a^4 b^{-7})(-a^{-4}b^3)$ **49.** $(a^{-5}b^2)^{-6}$

50. $(4^{-1}x^5)^{-2}$ **51.** $\left(\dfrac{x^{-2}y^4}{x^3 y^7}\right)^2$

52. $\left(\dfrac{a^5 b}{a^7 b^{-2}}\right)^{-3}$ **53.** $\dfrac{4^2 z^{-3}}{4^3 z^{-5}}$

54. $\dfrac{3^{-1}x^4}{3^3 x^{-7}}$ **55.** $\dfrac{2^{-3}x^{-4}}{2^2 x}$

56. $\dfrac{5^{-1}z^7}{5^{-2}z^9}$ **57.** $\dfrac{7ab^{-4}}{7^{-1}a^{-3}b^2}$

58. $\dfrac{6^{-5}x^{-1}y^2}{6^{-2}x^{-4}y^4}$ **59.** $\left(\dfrac{a^{-5}b}{ab^3}\right)^{-4}$

60. $\left(\dfrac{r^{-2}s^{-3}}{r^{-4}s^{-3}}\right)^{-3}$ **61.** $\dfrac{(xy^3)^5}{(xy)^{-4}}$

62. $\dfrac{(rs)^{-3}}{(r^2 s^3)^2}$ **63.** $\dfrac{(-2xy^{-3})^{-3}}{(xy^{-1})^{-1}}$

64. $\dfrac{(-3x^2 y^2)^{-2}}{(xyz)^{-2}}$ **65.** $\dfrac{6x^2 y^3}{-7xy^5}$

66. $\dfrac{-8xa^2 b}{-5xa^5 b}$ **67.** $\dfrac{(a^4 b^{-7})^{-5}}{(5a^2 b^{-1})^{-2}}$

68. $\dfrac{(a^6 b^{-2})^4}{(4a^{-3}b^{-3})^3}$

Write each number in scientific notation. See Example 5.

69. 78,000   **70.** 9,300,000,000

71. 0.00000167   **72.** 0.00000017

73. 0.00635   **74.** 0.00194

75. 1,160,000   **76.** 700,000

77. More than 2,000,000,000 pencils are manufactured in the United States annually. Write this number in scientific notation. (*Source:* AbsoluteTrivia.com)

78. The temperature at the interior of the Earth is 20,000,000 degrees Celsius. Write 20,000,000 in scientific notation.

79. As of this writing, the world's largest optical telescope is the Gran Telescopio Canaris, located in La Palma, Canary Islands, Spain. The elevation of this telescope is 2400 meters above sea level. Write 2400 in scientific notation.

80. In March 2004, the European Space Agency launched the Rosetta spacecraft, whose mission was to deliver the Philae lander to explore comet 67P/Churyumov-Gerasimenko. The lander finally arrived on the comet in late 2014. This comet is currently more than 320,000,000 miles from Earth. Write 320,000,000 in scientific notation. (*Source:* European Space Agency)

Write each number in standard notation. See Example 6.

81. 8.673×10^{-10}

82. 9.056×10^{-4}

83. 3.3×10^{-2}

84. 4.8×10^{-6}

85. 2.032×10^4

86. 9.07×10^{10}

87. Each second, the Sun converts 7.0×10^8 tons of hydrogen into helium and energy in the form of gamma rays. Write this number in standard notation. (*Source:* Students for the Exploration and Development of Space)

88. In chemistry, Avogadro's number is the number of atoms in one mole of an element. Avogadro's number is $6.02214199 \times 10^{23}$. Write this number in standard notation. *(Source:* National Institute of Standards and Technology)

89. The distance light travels in 1 year is 9.46×10^{12} kilometers. Write this number in standard notation.

90. The population of the world is 7.3×10^9. Write this number in standard notation. (*Source:* UN World Population Clock)

MIXED PRACTICE

See Examples 5 and 6. Below are some interesting facts about selected countries' external debts at a certain time. These are public and private debts owed to nonresidents of that country. If a number is written in standard form, write it in scientific notation. If a number is written in scientific notation, write it in standard form. (Source: CIA World Factbook)

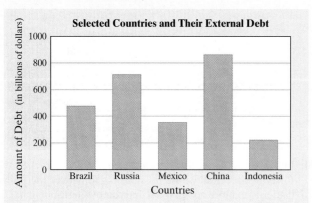

91. The external debt of Russia at a certain time was $714,000,000,000.

92. The amount by which Russia's debt was greater than Mexico's debt was $359,000,000,000.

93. At a certain time, China's external debt was $\$8.63 \times 10^{11}$.

94. At a certain time, the external debt of the United States was $\$1.5 \times 10^{13}$.

95. At a certain time, the estimated per person share of the United States external debt was $\$4.7 \times 10^4$.

96. The bar graph shows the external debt of five countries. Estimate the height of the tallest bar and the shortest bar in standard notation. Then write each number in scientific notation.

Evaluate each expression using exponential rules. Write each result in standard notation. See Example 7.

97. $(1.2 \times 10^{-3})(3 \times 10^{-2})$

98. $(2.5 \times 10^6)(2 \times 10^{-6})$

99. $(4 \times 10^{-10})(7 \times 10^{-9})$

100. $(5 \times 10^6)(4 \times 10^{-8})$

101. $\dfrac{8 \times 10^{-1}}{16 \times 10^5}$

102. $\dfrac{25 \times 10^{-4}}{5 \times 10^{-9}}$

103. $\dfrac{1.4 \times 10^{-2}}{7 \times 10^{-8}}$

104. $\dfrac{0.4 \times 10^5}{0.2 \times 10^{11}}$

REVIEW AND PREVIEW

Simplify the following. See Section 5.1.

105. $\dfrac{5x^7}{3x^4}$

106. $\dfrac{27y^{14}}{3y^7}$

107. $\dfrac{15z^4y^3}{21zy}$

108. $\dfrac{18a^7b^{17}}{30a^7b}$

Use the distributive property and multiply. See Sections 5.3 and 5.5.

109. $\dfrac{1}{y}(5y^2 - 6y + 5)$

110. $\dfrac{2}{x}(3x^5 + x^4 - 2)$

CONCEPT EXTENSIONS

111. Find the volume of the cube.

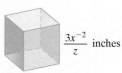

$\dfrac{3x^{-2}}{z}$ inches

112. Find the area of the triangle.

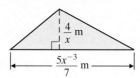

$\dfrac{4}{x}$ m

$\dfrac{5x^{-3}}{7}$ m

Simplify.

113. $(2a^3)^3a^4 + a^5a^8$

114. $(2a^3)^3a^{-3} + a^{11}a^{-5}$

Fill in the boxes so that each statement is true. (More than one answer may be possible for these exercises.)

115. $x^{\square} = \dfrac{1}{x^5}$

116. $7^{\square} = \dfrac{1}{49}$

117. $z^{\square} \cdot z^{\square} = z^{-10}$

118. $(x^{\square})^{\square} = x^{-15}$

119. Which is larger? See the Concept Check in this section.
   a. 9.7×10^{-2} or 1.3×10^1
   b. 8.6×10^5 or 4.4×10^7
   c. 6.1×10^{-2} or 5.6×10^{-4}

120. Determine whether each statement is true or false.
   a. $5^{-1} < 5^{-2}$
   b. $\left(\dfrac{1}{5}\right)^{-1} < \left(\dfrac{1}{5}\right)^{-2}$
   c. $a^{-1} < a^{-2}$ for all nonzero numbers.

121. It was stated earlier that for an integer n,

$$x^{-n} = \frac{1}{x^n}, \quad x \neq 0$$

Explain why x may not equal 0.

122. The quotient rule states that

$$\frac{a^m}{a^n} = a^{m-n}, a \neq 0.$$

Explain why a may not equal 0.

Simplify each expression. Assume that variables represent positive integers.

123. $a^{-4m} \cdot a^{5m}$

124. $(x^{-3s})^3$

125. $(3y^{2z})^3$

126. $a^{4m+1} \cdot a^4$

Simplify each expression. Write each result in standard notation.

127. $(2.63 \times 10^{12})(-1.5 \times 10^{-10})$

128. $(6.785 \times 10^{-4})(4.68 \times 10^{10})$

Light travels at a rate of 1.86×10^5 miles per second. Use this information and the distance formula $d = r \cdot t$ to answer Exercises 129 and 130.

129. If the distance from the moon to Earth is 238,857 miles, find how long it takes the reflected light of the moon to reach Earth. (Round to the nearest tenth of a second.)

130. If the distance from the Sun to Earth is 93,000,000 miles, find how long it takes the light of the Sun to reach Earth.

5.6 Dividing Polynomials

OBJECTIVES

1 Divide a Polynomial by a Monomial.

2 Use Long Division to Divide a Polynomial by Another Polynomial.

OBJECTIVE

1   Dividing by a Monomial

Now that we know how to add, subtract, and multiply polynomials, we practice dividing polynomials.

To divide a polynomial by a monomial, recall addition of fractions. Fractions that have a common denominator are added by adding the numerators:

$$\frac{a}{c} + \frac{b}{c} = \frac{a + b}{c}$$

If we read this equation from right to left and let a, b, and c be monomials, $c \neq 0$, we have the following:

Dividing a Polynomial by a Monomial

Divide each term of the polynomial by the monomial.

$$\frac{a + b}{c} = \frac{a}{c} + \frac{b}{c}, \quad c \neq 0$$

Throughout this section, we assume that denominators are not 0.

EXAMPLE 1   Divide $6m^2 + 2m$ by $2m$.

Solution We begin by writing the quotient in fraction form. Then we divide each term of the polynomial $6m^2 + 2m$ by the monomial $2m$.

$$\frac{6m^2 + 2m}{2m} = \frac{6m^2}{2m} + \frac{2m}{2m}$$

$$= 3m + 1 \quad \text{Simplify.}$$

Check: We know that if $\dfrac{6m^2 + 2m}{2m} = 3m + 1$, then $2m \cdot (3m + 1)$ must equal $6m^2 + 2m$. Thus, to check, we multiply.

$$2m(3m + 1) = 2m(3m) + 2m(1) = 6m^2 + 2m$$

The quotient $3m + 1$ checks.

PRACTICE

1   Divide $8t^3 + 4t^2$ by $4t^2$

EXAMPLE 2 Divide: $\dfrac{9x^5 - 12x^2 + 3x}{3x^2}$

Solution

$$\frac{9x^5 - 12x^2 + 3x}{3x^2} = \frac{9x^5}{3x^2} - \frac{12x^2}{3x^2} + \frac{3x}{3x^2} \quad \text{Divide each term by } 3x^2.$$

$$= 3x^3 - 4 + \frac{1}{x} \quad \text{Simplify.}$$

Notice that the quotient is not a polynomial because of the term $\dfrac{1}{x}$. This expression is called a rational expression—we will study rational expressions further in Chapter 7. Although the quotient of two polynomials is not always a polynomial, we may still check by multiplying.

Check: $3x^2\left(3x^3 - 4 + \dfrac{1}{x}\right) = 3x^2(3x^3) - 3x^2(4) + 3x^2\left(\dfrac{1}{x}\right)$

$$= 9x^5 - 12x^2 + 3x \qquad \square$$

PRACTICE
2 Divide: $\dfrac{16x^6 + 20x^3 - 12x}{4x^2}$

EXAMPLE 3 Divide: $\dfrac{8x^2y^2 - 16xy + 2x}{4xy}$

Solution

$$\frac{8x^2y^2 - 16xy + 2x}{4xy} = \frac{8x^2y^2}{4xy} - \frac{16xy}{4xy} + \frac{2x}{4xy} \quad \text{Divide each term by } 4xy.$$

$$= 2xy - 4 + \frac{1}{2y} \quad \text{Simplify.}$$

Check: $4xy\left(2xy - 4 + \dfrac{1}{2y}\right) = 4xy(2xy) - 4xy(4) + 4xy\left(\dfrac{1}{2y}\right)$

$$= 8x^2y^2 - 16xy + 2x \qquad \square$$

PRACTICE
3 Divide: $\dfrac{15x^4y^4 - 10xy + y}{5xy}$

✔ **CONCEPT CHECK**

In which of the following is $\dfrac{x + 5}{5}$ simplified correctly?

a. $\dfrac{x}{5} + 1$ **b.** x **c.** $x + 1$

OBJECTIVE
2 Using Long Division to Divide by a Polynomial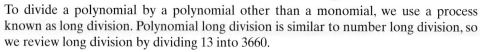

To divide a polynomial by a polynomial other than a monomial, we use a process known as long division. Polynomial long division is similar to number long division, so we review long division by dividing 13 into 3660.

Helpful Hint
Recall that 3660 is called the dividend.

$$\begin{array}{r} 281 \\ 13\overline{)3660} \\ \underline{26} \\ 106 \\ \underline{104} \\ 20 \\ \underline{13} \\ 7 \end{array}$$

$2 \cdot 13 = 26$
Subtract and bring down the next digit in the dividend.
$8 \cdot 13 = 104$
Subtract and bring down the next digit in the dividend.
$1 \cdot 13 = 13$
Subtract. There are no more digits to bring down, so the remainder is 7.

Answer to Concept Check:
a

The quotient is 281R7, which can be written as $281 \frac{7}{13}$. ← remainder ← divisor

Recall that division can be checked by multiplication. To check a division problem such as this one, we see that

$$13 \cdot 281 + 7 = 3660$$

Now we demonstrate long division of polynomials.

EXAMPLE 4   Divide $x^2 + 7x + 12$ by $x + 3$ using long division.

Solution

To subtract, change the signs of these terms and add.

$$
\begin{array}{r}
x \\
x + 3 \overline{)\, x^2 + 7x + 12} \\
x^2 \mp 3x \downarrow \\
\hline
4x + 12
\end{array}
$$

How many times does x divide x^2? $\frac{x^2}{x} = x$.
Multiply: $x(x + 3)$
Subtract and bring down the next term.

Now we repeat this process.

To subtract, change the signs of these terms and add.

$$
\begin{array}{r}
x + 4 \\
x + 3 \overline{)\, x^2 + 7x + 12} \\
x^2 \mp 3x \\
\hline
4x + 12 \\
4x \mp 12 \\
\hline
0
\end{array}
$$

How many times does x divide $4x$? $\frac{4x}{x} = 4$.

Multiply: $4(x + 3)$
Subtract. The remainder is 0.

The quotient is $x + 4$.

Check: We check by multiplying.

divisor	·	quotient	+	remainder	=	dividend
↓		↓		↓		↓
$(x + 3)$	·	$(x + 4)$	+	0	=	$x^2 + 7x + 12$

The quotient checks. ☐

PRACTICE
4   Divide $x^2 + 5x + 6$ by $x + 2$ using long division. ■

EXAMPLE 5   Divide $6x^2 + 10x - 5$ by $3x - 1$ using long division.

Solution

$$
\begin{array}{r}
2x + 4 \\
3x - 1 \overline{)\, 6x^2 + 10x - 5} \\
6x^2 \mp 2x \downarrow \\
\hline
12x - 5 \\
12x \mp 4 \\
\hline
-1
\end{array}
$$

$\frac{6x^2}{3x} = 2x$, so $2x$ is a term of the quotient.

Multiply $2x(3x - 1)$.
Subtract and bring down the next term.

$\frac{12x}{3x} = 4$, multiply $4(3x - 1)$

Subtract. The remainder is -1.

Thus $(6x^2 + 10x - 5)$ divided by $(3x - 1)$ is $(2x + 4)$ with a remainder of -1. This can be written as

$$\frac{6x^2 + 10x - 5}{3x - 1} = 2x + 4 + \frac{-1}{3x - 1} \quad \begin{array}{l} \leftarrow \text{remainder} \\ \leftarrow \text{divisor} \end{array}$$

Check: To check, we multiply $(3x - 1)(2x + 4)$. Then we add the remainder, -1, to this product.

$$(3x - 1)(2x + 4) + (-1) = (6x^2 + 12x - 2x - 4) - 1$$
$$= 6x^2 + 10x - 5$$

The quotient checks. ☐

PRACTICE
5   Divide $4x^2 + 8x - 7$ by $2x + 1$ using long division. ■

In Example 5, the degree of the divisor, $3x - 1$, is 1 and the degree of the remainder, -1, is 0. The division process is continued until the degree of the remainder polynomial is less than the degree of the divisor polynomial.

Writing the dividend and divisor in a form with descending order of powers and with no missing terms is helpful when dividing polynomials.

EXAMPLE 6   Divide: $\dfrac{4x^2 + 7 + 8x^3}{2x + 3}$

Solution Before we begin the division process, we rewrite

$$4x^2 + 7 + 8x^3 \quad \text{as} \quad 8x^3 + 4x^2 + 0x + 7$$

Notice that we have written the polynomial in descending order and have represented the missing x^1-term by $0x$.

$$
\require{enclose}
\begin{array}{r}
4x^2 - 4x + 6 \\
2x + 3 \enclose{longdiv}{8x^3 + 4x^2 + 0x + 7} \\
\underline{8x^3 + 12x^2} \\
-8x^2 + 0x \\
\underline{-8x^2 - 12x} \\
12x + 7 \\
\underline{12x + 18} \\
-11 \quad \text{Remainder}
\end{array}
$$

Thus, $\dfrac{4x^2 + 7 + 8x^3}{2x + 3} = 4x^2 - 4x + 6 + \dfrac{-11}{2x + 3}$.

PRACTICE
6   Divide: $\dfrac{11x - 3 + 9x^3}{3x + 2}$

EXAMPLE 7   Divide: $\dfrac{2x^4 - x^3 + 3x^2 + x - 1}{x^2 + 1}$

Solution Before dividing, rewrite the divisor polynomial

$$x^2 + 1 \quad \text{as} \quad x^2 + 0x + 1$$

The $0x$ term represents the missing x^1-term in the divisor.

$$
\require{enclose}
\begin{array}{r}
2x^2 - x + 1 \\
x^2 + 0x + 1 \enclose{longdiv}{2x^4 - x^3 + 3x^2 + x - 1} \\
\underline{2x^4 + 0x^3 + 2x^2} \\
-x^3 + x^2 + x \\
\underline{-x^3 + 0x^2 + x} \\
x^2 + 2x - 1 \\
\underline{x^2 + 0x + 1} \\
2x - 2 \quad \text{Remainder}
\end{array}
$$

Thus, $\dfrac{2x^4 - x^3 + 3x^2 + x - 1}{x^2 + 1} = 2x^2 - x + 1 + \dfrac{2x - 2}{x^2 + 1}$.

PRACTICE
7   Divide: $\dfrac{3x^4 - 2x^3 - 3x^2 + x + 4}{x^2 + 2}$

EXAMPLE 8   Divide $x^3 - 8$ by $x - 2$.

Solution: Notice that the polynomial $x^3 - 8$ is missing an x^2-term and an x-term. We'll represent these terms by inserting $0x^2$ and $0x$.

$$
\require{enclose}
\begin{array}{r}
x^2 + 2x + 4 \\
x - 2 \enclose{longdiv}{x^3 + 0x^2 + 0x - 8} \\
\underline{-x^3 \mp 2x^2} \\
2x^2 + 0x \\
\underline{-2x^2 \mp 4x} \\
4x - 8 \\
\underline{-4x \mp 8} \\
0
\end{array}
$$

Thus, $\dfrac{x^3 - 8}{x - 2} = x^2 + 2x + 4$.

Check: To check, see that $(x^2 + 2x + 4)(x - 2) = x^3 - 8$.

PRACTICE
8   Divide $x^3 + 27$ by $x + 3$.

✔ Vocabulary, Readiness & Video Check

Use the choices below to fill in each blank. Choices may be used more than once.

   dividend   divisor   quotient

1. In $\dfrac{3}{6\overline{)18}}$, the 18 is the _____, the 3 is the _____, and the 6 is the _____.

2. In $\dfrac{x+2}{x+1\overline{)x^2 + 3x + 2}}$, the $x + 1$ is the _____, the $x^2 + 3x + 2$ is the _____, and the $x + 2$ is the _____.

Simplify each expression mentally.

3. $\dfrac{a^6}{a^4}$ **4.** $\dfrac{p^8}{p^3}$ **5.** $\dfrac{y^2}{y}$ **6.** $\dfrac{a^3}{a}$

Martin-Gay Interactive Videos

See Video 5.6 🎥

Watch the section lecture video and answer the following questions.

OBJECTIVE 1
7. The lecture before 🎬 Example 1 begins with adding two fractions with the same denominator. From there, the lecture continues to a method for dividing a polynomial by a monomial. What role does the monomial play in the fraction example?

OBJECTIVE 2
8. In 🎬 Example 5, you're told that although you don't have to fill in missing powers in the divisor and the dividend, it really is a good idea to do so. Why?

5.6   Exercise Set   MyMathLab® ▶

Perform each division. See Examples 1 through 3.

1. $\dfrac{12x^4 + 3x^2}{x}$

2. $\dfrac{15x^2 - 9x^5}{x}$

3. $\dfrac{20x^3 - 30x^2 + 5x + 5}{5}$

4. $\dfrac{8x^3 - 4x^2 + 6x + 2}{2}$

5. $\dfrac{15p^3 + 18p^2}{3p}$

6. $\dfrac{14m^2 - 27m^3}{7m}$

7. $\dfrac{-9x^4 + 18x^5}{6x^5}$

8. $\dfrac{6x^5 + 3x^4}{3x^4}$

9. $\dfrac{-9x^5 + 3x^4 - 12}{3x^3}$

10. $\dfrac{6a^2 - 4a + 12}{-2a^2}$

11. $\dfrac{4x^4 - 6x^3 + 7}{-4x^4}$

12. $\dfrac{-12a^3 + 36a - 15}{3a}$

Find each quotient using long division. See Examples 4 and 5.

13. $\dfrac{x^2 + 4x + 3}{x + 3}$

14. $\dfrac{x^2 + 7x + 10}{x + 5}$

15. $\dfrac{2x^2 + 13x + 15}{x + 5}$

16. $\dfrac{3x^2 + 8x + 4}{x + 2}$

17. $\dfrac{2x^2 - 7x + 3}{x - 4}$

18. $\dfrac{3x^2 - x - 4}{x - 1}$

19. $\dfrac{9a^3 - 3a^2 - 3a + 4}{3a + 2}$

20. $\dfrac{4x^3 + 12x^2 + x - 14}{2x + 3}$

21. $\dfrac{8x^2 + 10x + 1}{2x + 1}$

22. $\dfrac{3x^2 + 17x + 7}{3x + 2}$

23. $\dfrac{2x^3 + 2x^2 - 17x + 8}{x - 2}$

24. $\dfrac{4x^3 + 11x^2 - 8x - 10}{x + 3}$

Find each quotient using long division. Don't forget to write the polynomials in descending order and fill in any missing terms. See Examples 6 through 8.

25. $\dfrac{x^2 - 36}{x - 6}$

26. $\dfrac{a^2 - 49}{a - 7}$

27. $\dfrac{x^3 - 27}{x - 3}$

28. $\dfrac{x^3 + 64}{x + 4}$

29. $\dfrac{1 - 3x^2}{x + 2}$

30. $\dfrac{7 - 5x^2}{x + 3}$

31. $\dfrac{-4b + 4b^2 - 5}{2b - 1}$

32. $\dfrac{-3y + 2y^2 - 15}{2y + 5}$

MIXED PRACTICE

Divide. If the divisor contains 2 or more terms, use long division. See Examples 1 through 8.

33. $\dfrac{a^2b^2 - ab^3}{ab}$

34. $\dfrac{m^3n^2 - mn^4}{mn}$

35. $\dfrac{8x^2 + 6x - 27}{2x - 3}$

36. $\dfrac{18w^2 + 18w - 8}{3w + 4}$

37. $\dfrac{2x^2y + 8x^2y^2 - xy^2}{2xy}$

38. $\dfrac{11x^3y^3 - 33xy + x^2y^2}{11xy}$

39. $\dfrac{2b^3 + 9b^2 + 6b - 4}{b + 4}$

40. $\dfrac{2x^3 + 3x^2 - 3x + 4}{x + 2}$

41. $\dfrac{5x^2 + 28x - 10}{x + 6}$

42. $\dfrac{2x^2 + x - 15}{x + 3}$

43. $\dfrac{10x^3 - 24x^2 - 10x}{10x}$

44. $\dfrac{2x^3 + 12x^2 + 16}{4x^2}$

45. $\dfrac{6x^2 + 17x - 4}{x + 3}$

46. $\dfrac{2x^2 - 9x + 15}{x - 6}$

47. $\dfrac{30x^2 - 17x + 2}{5x - 2}$

48. $\dfrac{4x^2 - 13x - 12}{4x + 3}$

49. $\dfrac{3x^4 - 9x^3 + 12}{-3x}$

50. $\dfrac{8y^6 - 3y^2 - 4y}{4y}$

51. $\dfrac{x^3 + 6x^2 + 18x + 27}{x + 3}$

52. $\dfrac{x^3 - 8x^2 + 32x - 64}{x - 4}$

53. $\dfrac{y^3 + 3y^2 + 4}{y - 2}$

54. $\dfrac{3x^3 + 11x + 12}{x + 4}$

55. $\dfrac{5 - 6x^2}{x - 2}$

56. $\dfrac{3 - 7x^2}{x - 3}$

Divide.

57. $\dfrac{x^5 + x^2}{x^2 + x}$

58. $\dfrac{x^6 - x^4}{x^3 + 1}$

REVIEW AND PREVIEW

Multiply each expression. See Section 5.3.

59. $2a(a^2 + 1)$

60. $-4a(3a^2 - 4)$

61. $2x(x^2 + 7x - 5)$

62. $4y(y^2 - 8y - 4)$

63. $-3xy(xy^2 + 7x^2y + 8)$

64. $-9xy(4xyz + 7xy^2z + 2)$

65. $9ab(ab^2c + 4bc - 8)$

66. $-7sr(6s^2r + 9sr^2 + 9rs + 8)$

CONCEPT EXTENSIONS

67. The perimeter of a square is $(12x^3 + 4x - 16)$ feet. Find the length of its side.

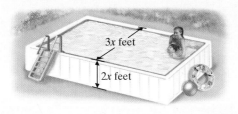

Perimeter is
$(12x^3 + 4x - 16)$ feet

△ **68.** The volume of the swimming pool shown is $(36x^5 - 12x^3 + 6x^2)$cubic feet. If its height is $2x$ feet and its width is $3x$ feet, find its length.

3x feet

2x feet

69. In which of the following is $\dfrac{a + 7}{7}$ simplified correctly? See the Concept Check in this section.

a. $a + 1$ **b.** a **c.** $\dfrac{a}{7} + 1$

70. In which of the following is $\dfrac{5x + 15}{5}$ simplified correctly? See the Concept Check in this section.

a. $x + 15$ **b.** $x + 3$ **c.** $x + 1$

✎ **71.** Explain how to check a polynomial long division result when the remainder is 0.

✎ **72.** Explain how to check a polynomial long division result when the remainder is not 0.

△ **73.** The area of the following parallelogram is $(10x^2 + 31x + 15)$ square meters. If its base is $(5x + 3)$ meters, find its height.

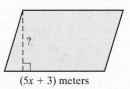

?

$(5x + 3)$ meters

△ **74.** The area of the top of the Ping-Pong table is $(49x^2 + 70x - 200)$ square inches. If its length is $(7x + 20)$ inches, find its width.

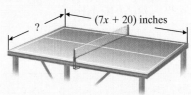

? $(7x + 20)$ inches

75. $(18x^{10a} - 12x^{8a} + 14x^{5a} - 2x^{3a}) \div 2x^{3a}$

76. $(25y^{11b} + 5y^{6b} - 20y^{3b} + 100y^b) \div 5y^b$

Chapter 5 Vocabulary Check

Fill in each blank with one of the words or phrases listed below.

term	coefficient	monomial	binomial	trinomial
polynomials	degree of a term	distributive	FOIL	degree of a polynomial

1. A _____ is a number or the product of numbers and variables raised to powers.
2. The _____ method may be used when multiplying two binomials.
3. A polynomial with exactly three terms is called a _____.
4. The _____ is the greatest degree of any term of the polynomial.
5. A polynomial with exactly two terms is called a _____.
6. The _____ of a term is its numerical factor.
7. The _____ is the sum of the exponents on the variables in the term.
8. A polynomial with exactly one term is called a _____.
9. Monomials, binomials, and trinomials are all examples of _____.
10. The _____ property is used to multiply $2x(x - 4)$.

Chapter 5 Highlights

DEFINITIONS AND CONCEPTS	EXAMPLES
Section 5.1	**Exponents**

a^n means the product of n factors, each of which is a.	$3^2 = 3 \cdot 3 = 9$ $(-5)^3 = (-5)(-5)(-5) = -125$ $\left(\dfrac{1}{2}\right)^4 = \dfrac{1}{2} \cdot \dfrac{1}{2} \cdot \dfrac{1}{2} \cdot \dfrac{1}{2} = \dfrac{1}{16}$
If m and n are integers and no denominators are 0,	
Product Rule: $a^m \cdot a^n = a^{m+n}$	$x^2 \cdot x^7 = x^{2+7} = x^9$
Power Rule: $(a^m)^n = a^{mn}$	$(5^3)^8 = 5^{3 \cdot 8} = 5^{24}$
Power of a Product Rule: $(ab)^n = a^n b^n$	$(7y)^4 = 7^4 y^4$
Power of a Quotient Rule: $\left(\dfrac{a}{b}\right)^n = \dfrac{a^n}{b^n}$	$\left(\dfrac{x}{8}\right)^3 = \dfrac{x^3}{8^3}$
Quotient Rule: $\dfrac{a^m}{a^n} = a^{m-n}$ Zero Exponent: $a^0 = 1, a \neq 0$.	$\dfrac{x^9}{x^4} = x^{9-4} = x^5$ $5^0 = 1, x^0 = 1, x \neq 0$

DEFINITIONS AND CONCEPTS	EXAMPLES

Section 5.2   Adding and Subtracting Polynomials

A **term** is a number or the product of numbers and variables raised to powers.

Terms

$-5x,\ 7a^2b,\ \dfrac{1}{4}y^4,\ 0.2$

The **numerical coefficient** or **coefficient** of a term is its numerical factor.

Term	**Coefficient**
$7x^2$	7
y	1
$-a^2b$	-1

A **polynomial** is a term or a finite sum of terms in which variables may appear in the numerator raised to whole number powers only.

Polynomials

$3x^2 - 2x + 1$	(Trinomial)
$-0.2a^2b - 5b^2$	(Binomial)
$\dfrac{5}{6}y^3$	(Monomial)

A **monomial** is a polynomial with exactly 1 term.
A **binomial** is a polynomial with exactly 2 terms.
A **trinomial** is a polynomial with exactly 3 terms.

The **degree of a term** is the sum of the exponents on the variables in the term.

Term	**Degree**
$-5x^3$	3
3 (or $3x^0$)	0
$2a^2b^2c$	5

The **degree of a polynomial** is the greatest degree of any term of the polynomial.

Polynomial	***Degree***
$5x^2 - 3x + 2$	2
$7y + 8y^2z^3 - 12$	$2 + 3 = 5$

To add polynomials, add or combine like terms.

Add:

$$(7x^2 - 3x + 2) + (-5x - 6) = 7x^2 - 3x + 2 - 5x - 6$$
$$= 7x^2 - 8x - 4$$

To subtract two polynomials, change the signs of the terms of the second polynomial, then add.

Subtract:

$$(17y^2 - 2y + 1) - (-3y^3 + 5y - 6)$$
$$= (17y^2 - 2y + 1) + (3y^3 - 5y + 6)$$
$$= 17y^2 - 2y + 1 + 3y^3 - 5y + 6$$
$$= 3y^3 + 17y^2 - 7y + 7$$

Section 5.3   Multiplying polynomials

To multiply two polynomials, multiply each term of one polynomial by each term of the other polynomial and then combine like terms.

Multiply:

$$(2x + 1)(5x^2 - 6x + 2)$$

$$= 2x(5x^2 - 6x + 2) + 1(5x^2 - 6x + 2)$$
$$= 10x^3 - 12x^2 + 4x + 5x^2 - 6x + 2$$
$$= 10x^3 - 7x^2 - 2x + 2$$

DEFINITIONS AND CONCEPTS	EXAMPLES

Section 5.4   Special Products

The **FOIL method** may be used when multiplying two binomials.

Multiply: $(5x - 3)(2x + 3)$

$$\underset{\text{Outer} \quad \text{Inner}}{(5x - 3)(2x + 3)} \overset{\text{First} \quad \text{Last}}{=} \overset{F \quad\quad O \quad\quad I \quad\quad L}{(5x)(2x) + (5x)(3) + (-3)(2x) + (-3)(3)}$$

$$= 10x^2 + 15x - 6x - 9$$

$$= 10x^2 + 9x - 9$$

Squaring a Binomial

$(a + b)^2 = a^2 + 2ab + b^2$

$(a - b)^2 = a^2 - 2ab + b^2$

Square each binomial.

$$(x + 5)^2 = x^2 + 2(x)(5) + 5^2$$
$$= x^2 + 10x + 25$$
$$(3x - 2y)^2 = (3x)^2 - 2(3x)(2y) + (2y)^2$$
$$= 9x^2 - 12xy + 4y^2$$

Multiplying the Sum and Difference of Two Terms

$(a + b)(a - b) = a^2 - b^2$

Multiply:

$$(6y + 5)(6y - 5) = (6y)^2 - 5^2$$
$$= 36y^2 - 25$$

Section 5.5   Negative Exponents and Scientific Notation

If $a \neq 0$ and n is an integer,

$$a^{-n} = \frac{1}{a^n}$$

Rules for exponents are true for positive and negative integers.

$$3^{-2} = \frac{1}{3^2} = \frac{1}{9}; \, 5x^{-2} = \frac{5}{x^2}$$

Simplify: $\left(\dfrac{x^{-2}y}{x^5}\right)^{-2} = \dfrac{x^4 y^{-2}}{x^{-10}}$

$$= x^{4-(-10)}y^{-2}$$
$$= \frac{x^{14}}{y^2}$$

A positive number is written in scientific notation if it is written as the product of a number a, $1 \leq a < 10$, and an integer power r of 10.

$$a \times 10^r$$

Write each number in scientific notation.

$$12{,}000 = 1.2 \times 10^4$$

$$0.00000568 = 5.68 \times 10^{-6}$$

Section 5.6   Dividing Polynomials

To divide a polynomial by a monomial:

$$\frac{a + b}{c} = \frac{a}{c} + \frac{b}{c}$$

Divide:

$$\frac{15x^5 - 10x^3 + 5x^2 - 2x}{5x^2} = \frac{15x^5}{5x^2} - \frac{10x^3}{5x^2} + \frac{5x^2}{5x^2} - \frac{2x}{5x^2}$$

$$= 3x^3 - 2x + 1 - \frac{2}{5x}$$

To divide a polynomial by a polynomial other than a monomial, use long division.

$$5x - 1 + \frac{-4}{2x + 3}$$

$$\begin{array}{r} 2x + 3 \overline{)10x^2 + 13x - 7} \\ \underline{10x^2 + 15x} \\ -2x - 7 \\ \underline{-2x - 3} \\ -4 \end{array}$$

Chapter 5 Review

(5.1) *State the base and the exponent for each expression.*

1. 7^9

2. $(-5)^4$

3. -5^4

4. x^6

Evaluate each expression.

5. 8^3

6. $(-6)^2$

7. -6^2

8. $-4^3 - 4^0$

9. $(3b)^0$

10. $\dfrac{8b}{8b}$

Simplify each expression.

11. $y^2 \cdot y^7$

12. $x^9 \cdot x^5$

13. $(2x^5)(-3x^6)$

14. $(-5y^3)(4y^4)$

15. $(x^4)^2$

16. $(y^3)^5$

17. $(3y^6)^4$

18. $(2x^3)^3$

19. $\dfrac{x^9}{x^4}$

20. $\dfrac{z^{12}}{z^5}$

21. $\dfrac{a^5b^4}{ab}$

22. $\dfrac{x^4y^6}{xy}$

23. $\dfrac{3x^4y^{10}}{12xy^6}$

24. $\dfrac{2x^7y^8}{8xy^2}$

25. $5a^7(2a^4)^3$

26. $(2x)^2(9x)$

27. $(-5a)^0 + 7^0 + 8^0$

28. $8x^0 + 9^0$

Simplify the given expression and choose the correct result.

29. $\left(\dfrac{3x^4}{4y}\right)^3$

   a. $\dfrac{27x^{64}}{64y^3}$
   b. $\dfrac{27x^{12}}{64y^3}$
   c. $\dfrac{9x^{12}}{12y^3}$
   d. $\dfrac{3x^{12}}{4y^3}$

30. $\left(\dfrac{5a^6}{b^3}\right)^2$

   a. $\dfrac{10a^{12}}{b^6}$
   b. $\dfrac{25a^{36}}{b^9}$
   c. $\dfrac{25a^{12}}{b^6}$
   d. $25a^{12}b^6$

(5.2) *Find the degree of each term.*

31. $-5x^4y^3$

32. $10x^3y^2z$

33. $35a^5bc^2$

34. $95xyz$

Find the degree of each polynomial.

35. $y^5 + 7x - 8x^4$

36. $9y^2 + 30y + 25$

37. $-14x^2y - 28x^2y^3 - 42x^2y^2$

38. $6x^2y^2z^2 + 5x^2y^3 - 12xyz$

39. The Glass Bridge Skywalk is suspended 4000 feet over the Colorado River at the very edge of the Grand Canyon. Neglecting air resistance, the height of an object dropped from the Skywalk at time t seconds is given by the polynomial $-16t^2 + 4000$. Find the height of the object at the given times. (See top of next column.)

t	0 seconds	1 second	3 seconds	5 seconds
$-16t^2 + 4000$				

△ **40.** The surface area of a box with a square base and a height of 5 units is given by the polynomial $2x^2 + 20x$. Fill in the table below by evaluating $2x^2 + 20x$ for the given values of x.

x	1	3	5.1	10
$2x^2 + 20x$				

Combine like terms in each expression.

41. $7a^2 - 4a^2 - a^2$

42. $9y + y - 14y$

43. $6a^2 + 4a + 9a^2$

44. $21x^2 + 3x + x^2 + 6$

45. $4a^2b - 3b^2 - 8q^2 - 10a^2b + 7q^2$

46. $2s^{14} + 3s^{13} + 12s^{12} - s^{10}$

Add or subtract as indicated.

47. $(3x^2 + 2x + 6) + (5x^2 + x)$

48. $(2x^5 + 3x^4 + 4x^3 + 5x^2) + (4x^2 + 7x + 6)$

49. $(-5y^2 + 3) - (2y^2 + 4)$

50. $(3x^2 - 7xy + 7y^2) - (4x^2 - xy + 9y^2)$

51. $(-9x^2 + 6x + 2) + (4x^2 - x - 1)$

52. $(8x^6 - 5xy - 10y^2) - (7x^6 - 9xy - 12y^2)$

TRANSLATING

Perform the indicated operations.

53. Subtract $(3x - y)$ from $(7x - 14y)$.

54. Subtract $(4x^2 + 8x - 7)$ from the sum of $(x^2 + 7x + 9)$ and $(x^2 + 4)$.

(5.3) *Multiply each expression.*

55. $4(2a + 7)$

56. $9(6a - 3)$

57. $-7x(x^2 + 5)$

58. $-8y(4y^2 - 6)$

59. $(3a^3 - 4a + 1)(-2a)$

60. $(6b^3 - 4b + 2)(7b)$

61. $(2x + 2)(x - 7)$

62. $(2x - 5)(3x + 2)$

63. $(x - 9)^2$

64. $(x - 12)^2$

65. $(4a - 1)(a + 7)$

66. $(6a - 1)(7a + 3)$

67. $(5x + 2)^2$

68. $(3x + 5)^2$

69. $(x + 7)(x^3 + 4x - 5)$

70. $(x + 2)(x^5 + x + 1)$

71. $(x^2 + 2x + 4)(x^2 + 2x - 4)$

72. $(x^3 + 4x + 4)(x^3 + 4x - 4)$

73. $(x + 7)^3$

74. $(2x - 5)^3$

(5.4) *Use special products to multiply each of the following.*

75. $(x + 7)^2$

76. $(x - 5)^2$

77. $(3x - 7)^2$

78. $(4x + 2)^2$

79. $(5x - 9)^2$

80. $(5x + 1)(5x - 1)$

81. $(7x + 4)(7x - 4)$

82. $(a + 2b)(a - 2b)$

83. $(2x - 6)(2x + 6)$

84. $(4a^2 - 2b)(4a^2 + 2b)$

Express each as a product of polynomials in x. Then multiply and simplify.

△ **85.** Find the area of the square if its side is $(3x - 1)$ meters.

(3x − 1) meters

△ **86.** Find the area of the rectangle.

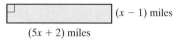

(x − 1) miles

(5x + 2) miles

(5.5) *Simplify each expression.*

87. 7^{-2} **88.** -7^{-2} **89.** $2x^{-4}$ **90.** $(2x)^{-4}$

91. $\left(\dfrac{1}{5}\right)^{-3}$ **92.** $\left(\dfrac{-2}{3}\right)^{-2}$

93. $2^0 + 2^{-4}$ **94.** $6^{-1} - 7^{-1}$

Simplify each expression. Write each answer using positive exponents only.

95. $\dfrac{x^5}{x^{-3}}$ **96.** $\dfrac{z^4}{z^{-4}}$

97. $\dfrac{r^{-3}}{r^{-4}}$ **98.** $\dfrac{y^{-2}}{y^{-5}}$

99. $\left(\dfrac{bc^{-2}}{bc^{-3}}\right)^4$ **100.** $\left(\dfrac{x^{-3}y^{-4}}{x^{-2}y^{-5}}\right)^{-3}$

101. $\dfrac{x^{-4}y^{-6}}{x^2y^7}$ **102.** $\dfrac{a^5b^{-5}}{a^{-5}b^5}$

103. $a^{6m}a^{5m}$ **104.** $\dfrac{(x^{5+h})^3}{x^5}$

105. $(3xy^{2z})^3$ **106.** $a^{m+2}a^{m+3}$

Write each number in scientific notation.

107. 0.00027 **108.** 0.8868

109. $80,800,000$ **110.** $868,000$

111. Google.com is an Internet search engine that handles 2,500,000,000 searches every day. Write 2,500,000,000 in scientific notation. (*Source:* Google, Inc.)

112. The approximate diameter of the Milky Way galaxy is 150,000 light years. Write this number in scientific notation. (*Source:* NASA IMAGE/POETRY Education and Public Outreach Program)

150,000 light years

Write each number in standard form.

113. 8.67×10^5 **114.** 3.86×10^{-3}

115. 8.6×10^{-4} **116.** 8.936×10^5

117. The volume of the planet Jupiter is 1.43128×10^{15} cubic kilometers. Write this number in standard notation. (*Source:* National Space Science Data Center)

118. An angstrom is a unit of measure, equal to 1×10^{-10} meter, used for measuring wavelengths or the diameters of atoms. Write this number in standard notation. (*Source:* National Institute of Standards and Technology)

Simplify. Express each result in standard form.

119. $(8 \times 10^4)(2 \times 10^{-7})$ **120.** $\dfrac{8 \times 10^4}{2 \times 10^{-7}}$

(5.6) Divide.

121. $\dfrac{x^2 + 21x + 49}{7x^2}$

122. $\dfrac{5a^3b - 15ab^2 + 20ab}{-5ab}$

123. $(a^2 - a + 4) \div (a - 2)$

124. $(4x^2 + 20x + 7) \div (x + 5)$

125. $\dfrac{a^3 + a^2 + 2a + 6}{a - 2}$

126. $\dfrac{9b^3 - 18b^2 + 8b - 1}{3b - 2}$

127. $\dfrac{4x^4 - 4x^3 + x^2 + 4x - 3}{2x - 1}$

128. $\dfrac{-10x^2 - x^3 - 21x + 18}{x - 6}$

△ **129.** The area of the rectangle below is $(15x^3 - 3x^2 + 60)$ square feet. If its length is $3x^2$ feet, find its width.

Area is $(15x^3 - 3x^2 + 60)$ sq feet

△ **130.** The perimeter of the equilateral triangle below is $(21a^3b^6 + 3a - 3)$ units. Find the length of a side.

Perimeter is $(21a^3b^6 + 3a - 3)$ units

MIXED REVIEW

Evaluate.

131. $\left(-\dfrac{1}{2}\right)^3$

Simplify each expression. Write each answer using positive exponents only.

132. $(4xy^2)(x^3y^5)$

133. $\dfrac{18x^9}{27x^3}$

134. $\left(\dfrac{3a^4}{b^2}\right)^3$

135. $(2x^{-4}y^3)^{-4}$

136. $\dfrac{a^{-3}b^6}{9^{-1}a^{-5}b^{-2}}$

Perform the indicated operations and simplify.

137. $(6x + 2) + (5x - 7)$

138. $(-y^2 - 4) + (3y^2 - 6)$

139. $(8y^2 - 3y + 1) - (3y^2 + 2)$

140. $(5x^2 + 2x - 6) - (-x - 4)$

141. $4x(7x^2 + 3)$

142. $(2x + 5)(3x - 2)$

143. $(x - 3)(x^2 + 4x - 6)$

144. $(7x - 2)(4x - 9)$

Use special products to multiply.

145. $(5x + 4)^2$

146. $(6x + 3)(6x - 3)$

Divide.

147. $\dfrac{8a^4 - 2a^3 + 4a - 5}{2a^3}$

148. $\dfrac{x^2 + 2x + 10}{x + 5}$

149. $\dfrac{4x^3 + 8x^2 - 11x + 4}{2x - 3}$

Chapter 5 Getting Ready for the Test

MATCHING *Match the expression with the exponent operation needed to simplify. Letters may be used more than once or not at all.*

1. $x^2 \cdot x^5$

2. $(x^2)^5$

3. $x^2 + x^5$

4. $\dfrac{x^5}{x^2}$

    A. multiply the exponents

    B. divide the exponents

    C. add the exponents

    D. subtract the exponents

    E. this expression will not simplify

MATCHING *Match the operation with the result when the operation is performed on the given terms. Letters may be used more than once or not at all.*

Given Terms: 20y and 4y

5. Add the terms
6. Subtract the terms
7. Multiply the terms
8. Divide the terms.

A. $80y$
B. $24y^2$
C. $16y$
D. 16

E. $80y^2$
F. $24y$
G. $16y^2$
H. $5y$
I. 5

9. **MULTIPLE CHOICE** *The expression 5^{-1} is equivalent to*

A. -5 B. 4 C. $\dfrac{1}{5}$ D. $-\dfrac{1}{5}$

10. **MULTIPLE CHOICE** *The expression 2^{-3} is equivalent to*

A. -6 B. -1 C. $-\dfrac{1}{6}$ D. $\dfrac{1}{8}$

MATCHING *Match each expression with its simplified form. Letters may be used more than once or not at all.*

11. $y + y + y$
12. $y \cdot y \cdot y$
13. $(-y)(-y)(-y)$
14. $-y - y - y$

A. $3y^3$
B. y^3
C. $3y$
D. $-3y$

E. $-3y^3$
F. $-y^3$

Chapter 5 Test   MyMathLab® YouTube™

Evaluate each expression.

1. 2^5 2. $(-3)^4$ 3. -3^4 4. 4^{-3}

Simplify each exponential expression. Write the result using only positive exponents.

5. $(3x^2)(-5x^9)$ 6. $\dfrac{y^7}{y^2}$

7. $\dfrac{r^{-8}}{r^{-3}}$ 8. $\left(\dfrac{x^2y^3}{x^3y^{-4}}\right)^2$

9. $\dfrac{6^2x^{-4}y^{-1}}{6^3x^{-3}y^7}$

Express each number in scientific notation.

10. 563,000 11. 0.0000863

Write each number in standard form.

12. 1.5×10^{-3} 13. 6.23×10^4

14. Simplify. Write the answer in standard form.

$$(1.2 \times 10^5)(3 \times 10^{-7})$$

15. **a.** Complete the table for the polynomial $4xy^2 + 7xyz + x^3y - 2$.

Term	Numerical Coefficient	Degree of Term
$4xy^2$		
$7xyz$		
x^3y		
-2		

b. What is the degree of the polynomial?

16. Simplify by combining like terms.

$$5x^2 + 4xy - 7x^2 + 11 + 8xy$$

Perform each indicated operation.

17. $(8x^3 + 7x^2 + 4x - 7) + (8x^3 - 7x - 6)$
18. $5x^3 + x^2 + 5x - 2 - (8x^3 - 4x^2 + x - 7)$
19. Subtract $(4x + 2)$ from the sum of $(8x^2 + 7x + 5)$ and $(x^3 - 8)$.

Multiply.

20. $(3x + 7)(x^2 + 5x + 2)$
21. $3x^2(2x^2 - 3x + 7)$
22. $(x + 7)(3x - 5)$
23. $\left(3x - \dfrac{1}{5}\right)\left(3x + \dfrac{1}{5}\right)$
24. $(4x - 2)^2$
25. $(8x + 3)^2$
26. $(x^2 - 9b)(x^2 + 9b)$

Solve.

27. The height of the Bank of China in Hong Kong is 1001 feet. Neglecting air resistance, the height of an object dropped from this building at time t seconds is given by

the polynomial $-16t^2 + 1001$. Find the height of the object at the given times below.

t	0 seconds	1 second	3 seconds	5 seconds
$-16t^2 + 1001$				

▶ **28.** Find the area of the top of the table. Express the area as a product, then multiply and simplify.

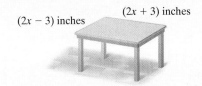

$(2x - 3)$ inches $(2x + 3)$ inches

Divide.

▶ **29.** $\dfrac{4x^2 + 24xy - 7x}{8xy}$

▶ **30.** $(x^2 + 7x + 10) \div (x + 5)$

▶ **31.** $\dfrac{27x^3 - 8}{3x + 2}$

Chapter 5 Cumulative Review

1. Tell whether each statement is true or false.
   a. $8 \geq 8$ **b.** $8 \leq 8$
   c. $23 \leq 0$ **d.** $23 \geq 0$

2. Find the absolute value of each number.
   a. $|-7.2|$ **b.** $|0|$ **c.** $\left|-\dfrac{1}{2}\right|$

3. Divide. Simplify all quotients if possible.
   a. $\dfrac{4}{5} \div \dfrac{5}{16}$ **b.** $\dfrac{7}{10} \div 14$ **c.** $\dfrac{3}{8} \div \dfrac{3}{10}$

4. Multiply. Write products in lowest terms.
   a. $\dfrac{3}{4} \cdot \dfrac{7}{21}$ **b.** $\dfrac{1}{2} \cdot 4\dfrac{5}{6}$

5. Evaluate the following.
   a. 3^2 **b.** 5^3 **c.** 2^4
   d. 7^1 **e.** $\left(\dfrac{3}{7}\right)^2$

6. Evaluate $\dfrac{2x - 7y}{x^2}$ for $x = 5$ and $y = 1$.

7. Add.
   a. $-3 + (-7)$ **b.** $-1 + (-20)$
   c. $-2 + (-10)$

8. Simplify: $8 + 3(2 \cdot 6 - 1)$

9. Subtract 8 from -4.

10. Is $x = 1$ a solution of $5x^2 + 2 = x - 8$?

11. Find the reciprocal of each number.
   a. 22   **b.** $\dfrac{3}{16}$
   c. -10 **d.** $-\dfrac{9}{13}$

12. Subtract.
   a. $7 - 40$ **b.** $-5 - (-10)$

13. Use an associative property to complete each statement.
   a. $5 + (4 + 6) = $ _____
   b. $(-1 \cdot 2) \cdot 5 = $ _____

14. Simplify: $\dfrac{4(-3) + (-8)}{5 + (-5)}$

15. Simplify each expression.
   a. $10 + (x + 12)$
   b. $-3(7x)$

16. Use the distributive property to write $-2(x + 3y - z)$ without parentheses.

17. Find each product by using the distributive property to remove parentheses.
   a. $5(3x + 2)$
   b. $-2(y + 0.3z - 1)$
   c. $-(9x + y - 2z + 6)$

18. Simplify: $2(6x - 1) - (x - 7)$

19. Solve $x - 7 = 10$ for x.

20. Write the phrase as an algebraic expression: double a number, subtracted from the sum of the number and seven

21. Solve: $\dfrac{5}{2}x = 15$

22. Solve: $2x + \dfrac{1}{8} = x - \dfrac{3}{8}$

23. Solve: $4(2x - 3) + 7 = 3x + 5$

24. Solve: $10 = 5j - 2$

25. Twice a number, added to seven, is the same as three subtracted from the number. Find the number.

26. Solve: $\dfrac{7x + 5}{3} = x + 3$

27. The length of a rectangular road sign is 2 feet less than three times its width. Find the dimensions if the perimeter is 28 feet.

28. Graph $x < 5$. Then write the solutions in interval notation.

29. Solve $F = \dfrac{9}{5}C + 32$ for C.

30. Find the slope of each line.
   a. $x = -1$
   b. $y = 7$

31. Graph $2 < x \leq 4$.

32. Recall that the grade of a road is its slope written as a percent. Find the grade of the road shown.

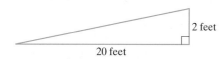

2 feet

20 feet

33. Complete the following ordered pair solutions for the equation $3x + y = 12$.

   a. $(0, \ )$

   b. $(\ , 6)$

   c. $(-1, \ )$

34. Solve the system: $\begin{cases} 3x + 2y = -8 \\ 2x - 6y = -9 \end{cases}$

35. Graph the linear equation $2x + y = 5$.

36. Solve the system: $\begin{cases} x = -3y + 3 \\ 2x + 9y = 5 \end{cases}$

37. Graph the linear equation $x = 2$.

38. Evaluate.

   a. $(-5)^2$

   b. -5^2

   c. $2 \cdot 5^2$

39. Find the slope of the line $x = 5$.

40. Simplify: $\dfrac{(z^2)^3 \cdot z^7}{z^9}$

41. Graph: $x + y < 7$

42. Subtract: $(5y^2 - 6) - (y^2 + 2)$

43. Use the product rule to simplify $(2x^2)(-3x^5)$.

44. Find the value of $-x^2$ when

   a. $x = 2$

   b. $x = -2$

45. Add $(-2x^2 + 5x - 1)$ and $(-2x^2 + x + 3)$.

46. Multiply: $(10x^2 - 3)(10x^2 + 3)$

47. Multiply: $(2x - y)^2$

48. Multiply: $(10x^2 + 3)^2$

49. Divide $6m^2 + 2m$ by $2m$.

50. Evaluate.

   a. 5^{-1}

   b. 7^{-2}

CHAPTER 6

Factoring Polynomials

✓ CHECK YOUR PROGRESS

Vocabulary Check

Chapter Highlights

Chapter Review

Getting Ready for the Test

Chapter Test

Cumulative Review

In Chapter 5, we learned how to multiply polynomials. This chapter deals with an operation that is the reverse process of multiplying, called *factoring*. Factoring is an important algebraic skill because this process allows us to write a sum as a product.

At the end of this chapter, we use factoring to help us solve equations other than linear equations, and in Chapter 7, we use factoring to simplify and perform arithmetic operations on rational expressions.

Why Are You in College?

There are probably as many answers as there are students. It may help you to know that college graduates have higher earnings and lower rates of unemployment. The double line graph below shows the increasing number of associate and bachelor degrees awarded over the years. It is also enlightening to know that an increasing number of high school graduates are looking to higher education.

In Exercise 110 of Section 6.1, we will explore how many students graduate from U.S. high schools each year, and how many of those may expect to go to college.

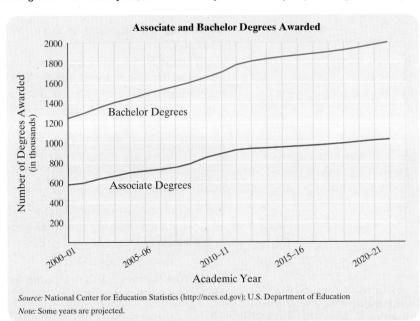

Associate and Bachelor Degrees Awarded

Source: National Center for Education Statistics (http://nces.ed.gov); U.S. Department of Education

Note: Some years are projected.

6.1 The Greatest Common Factor and Factoring by Grouping

OBJECTIVES

1 Find the Greatest Common Factor of a List of Integers.

2 Find the Greatest Common Factor of a List of Terms.

3 Factor Out the Greatest Common Factor from a Polynomial.

4 Factor a Polynomial by Grouping.

In the product $2 \cdot 3 = 6$, the numbers 2 and 3 are called **factors** of 6 and $2 \cdot 3$ is a **factored form** of 6. This is true of polynomials also. Since $(x + 2)(x + 3) = x^2 + 5x + 6$, $(x + 2)$ and $(x + 3)$ are factors of $x^2 + 5x + 6$, and $(x + 2)(x + 3)$ is a factored form of the polynomial.

$$\overbrace{2 \cdot 3}^{\text{a factored form of 6}} = 6$$
factor　factor　product

$$\overbrace{x^2 \cdot x^3}^{\text{a factored form of } x^5} = x^5$$
factor　factor　product

$$\overbrace{(x + 2)(x + 3)}^{\text{a factored form of } x^2 + 5x + 6} = x^2 + 5x + 6$$
factor　factor　product

The process of writing a polynomial as a product is called **factoring** the polynomial.

Do you see that factoring is the reverse process of multiplying?

$$x^2 + 5x + 6 = (x + 2)(x + 3)$$
factoring
multiplying

✔ **CONCEPT CHECK**

Multiply: $2(x - 4)$

What do you think the result of factoring $2x - 8$ would be? Why?

OBJECTIVE

1　Finding the Greatest Common Factor of a List of Integers

The first step in factoring a polynomial is to see whether the terms of the polynomial have a common factor. If there is one, we can write the polynomial as a product by **factoring out** the common factor. We will usually factor out the **greatest common factor (GCF).**

The GCF of a list of integers is the largest integer that is a factor of all the integers in the list. For example, the GCF of 12 and 20 is 4 because 4 is the largest integer that is a factor of both 12 and 20. With large integers, the GCF may not be found easily by inspection. When this happens, use the following steps.

Finding the GCF of a List of Integers

Step 1. Write each number as a product of prime numbers.

Step 2. Identify the common prime factors.

Step 3. The product of all common prime factors found in Step 2 is the greatest common factor. If there are no common prime factors, the greatest common factor is 1.

Recall from Section 1.3 that a prime number is a whole number other than 1 whose only factors are 1 and itself.

EXAMPLE 1   Find the GCF of each list of numbers.

    a. 28 and 40   **b.** 55 and 21   **c.** 15, 18, and 66

Solution

  a. Write each number as a product of primes.

$$28 = 2 \cdot 2 \cdot 7 = 2^2 \cdot 7$$
$$40 = 2 \cdot 2 \cdot 2 \cdot 5 = 2^3 \cdot 5$$

There are two common factors, each of which is 2, so the GCF is

$$\text{GCF} = 2 \cdot 2 = 4$$

  b. $55 = 5 \cdot 11$

     $21 = 3 \cdot 7$

There are no common prime factors; thus, the GCF is 1.

  c. $15 = 3 \cdot 5$

     $18 = 2 \cdot 3 \cdot 3 = 2 \cdot 3^2$

     $66 = 2 \cdot 3 \cdot 11$

The only prime factor common to all three numbers is 3, so the GCF is

$$\text{GCF} = 3$$

PRACTICE

1   Find the GCF of each list of numbers.

    a. 36 and 42   **b.** 35 and 44   **c.** 12, 16, and 40

OBJECTIVE

2   **Finding the Greatest Common Factor of a List of Terms**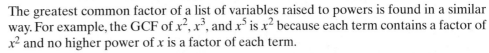

The greatest common factor of a list of variables raised to powers is found in a similar way. For example, the GCF of x^2, x^3, and x^5 is x^2 because each term contains a factor of x^2 and no higher power of x is a factor of each term.

$$x^2 = x \cdot x$$
$$x^3 = x \cdot x \cdot x$$
$$x^5 = x \cdot x \cdot x \cdot x \cdot x$$

There are two common factors, each of which is x, so the GCF $= x \cdot x$ or x^2.

    From this example, we see that **the GCF of a list of common variables raised to powers is the variable raised to the smallest exponent in the list.**

EXAMPLE 2   Find the GCF of each list of terms.

    a. x^3, x^7, and x^5 **b.** y, y^4, and y^7

Solution

  a. The GCF is x^3, since 3 is the smallest exponent to which x is raised.

  b. The GCF is y^1 or y, since 1 is the smallest exponent on y.

PRACTICE

2   Find the GCF of each list of terms.

    a. y^7, y^4, and y^6 **b.** x, x^4, and x^2

    In general, the **greatest common factor (GCF) of a list of terms** is the product of the GCF of the numerical coefficients and the GCF of the variable factors.

$$20x^2y^2 = 2 \cdot 2 \cdot 5 \cdot x \cdot x \cdot y \cdot y$$
$$6xy^3 = 2 \cdot 3 \cdot x \cdot y \cdot y \cdot y$$
$$\text{GCF} = 2 \cdot x \cdot y \cdot y = 2xy^2$$

Helpful Hint

Remember that the GCF of a list of terms contains the smallest exponent on each common variable.

The GCF of x^5y^6, x^2y^7, and x^3y^4 is x^2y^4.
— Smallest exponent on x
— Smallest exponent on y

EXAMPLE 3 Find the GCF of each list of terms.

a. $6x^2$, $10x^3$, and $-8x$ **b.** $-18y^2$, $-63y^3$, and $27y^4$ **c.** a^3b^2, a^5b, and a^6b^2

Solution

a. $6x^2 = 2 \cdot 3 \cdot x^2$
$10x^3 = 2 \cdot 5 \cdot x^3$ $\rightarrow$ The GCF of x^2, x^3, and x^1 is x^1 or x.
$-8x = -1 \cdot 2 \cdot 2 \cdot 2 \cdot x^1$
$\text{GCF} = 2 \cdot x^1$ or $2x$

b. $-18y^2 = -1 \cdot 2 \cdot 3 \cdot 3 \cdot y^2$
$-63y^3 = -1 \cdot 3 \cdot 3 \cdot 7 \cdot y^3$ $\rightarrow$ The GCF of y^2, y^3, and y^4 is y^2.
$27y^4 = 3 \cdot 3 \cdot 3 \cdot y^4$
$\text{GCF} = 3 \cdot 3 \cdot y^2$ or $9y^2$

c. The GCF of a^3, a^5, and a^6 is a^3.
The GCF of b^2, b, and b^2 is b. Thus,
the GCF of a^3b^2, a^5b, and a^6b^2 is a^3b. ☐

PRACTICE

3 Find the GCF of each list of terms.

a. $5y^4$, $15y^2$, and $-20y^3$ **b.** $4x^2$, x^3, and $3x^8$ **c.** a^4b^2, a^3b^5, and a^2b^3 ■

OBJECTIVE

3 Factoring Out the Greatest Common Factor ▶

The first step in factoring a polynomial is to find the GCF of its terms. Once we do so, we can write the polynomial as a product by **factoring out** the GCF.

The polynomial $8x + 14$, for example, contains two terms: $8x$ and 14. The GCF of these terms is 2. We factor out 2 from each term by writing each term as a product of 2 and the term's remaining factors.

$$8x + 14 = 2 \cdot 4x + 2 \cdot 7$$

Using the distributive property, we can write

$$8x + 14 = 2 \cdot 4x + 2 \cdot 7$$
$$= 2(4x + 7)$$

Thus, a factored form of $8x + 14$ is $2(4x + 7)$. We can check by multiplying:

$$2(4x + 7) = 2 \cdot 4x + 2 \cdot 7 = 8x + 14.$$

Helpful Hint

A factored form of $8x + 14$ is *not*

$$2 \cdot 4x + 2 \cdot 7$$

Although the *terms* have been factored (written as products), the *polynomial* $8x + 14$ has not been factored (written as a product).

A factored form of $8x + 14$ is the *product* $2(4x + 7)$.

✔ **CONCEPT CHECK**

Which of the following is/are factored form(s) of $7t + 21$?

a. 7   **b.** $7 \cdot t + 7 \cdot 3$ **c.** $7(t + 3)$ **d.** $7(t + 21)$

EXAMPLE 4   Factor each polynomial by factoring out the GCF.

a. $6t + 18$ **b.** $y^5 - y^7$

Solution

a. The GCF of terms $6t$ and 18 is 6.

$$6t + 18 = 6 \cdot t + 6 \cdot 3$$
$$= 6(t + 3) \qquad \text{Apply the distributive property.}$$

Our work can be checked by multiplying 6 and $(t + 3)$.

$$6(t + 3) = 6 \cdot t + 6 \cdot 3 = 6t + 18, \text{ the original polynomial.}$$

b. The GCF of y^5 and y^7 is y^5. Thus,

$$y^5 - y^7 = y^5(1) - y^5(y^2)$$
$$= y^5(1 - y^2)$$

> **Helpful Hint**
> Don't forget the 1.

PRACTICE
4   Factor each polynomial by factoring out the GCF.

a. $4t + 12$ **b.** $y^8 + y^4$

EXAMPLE 5   Factor: $-9a^5 + 18a^2 - 3a$

Solution

$$-9a^5 + 18a^2 - 3a = (3a)(-3a^4) + (3a)(6a) + (3a)(-1)$$
$$= 3a(-3a^4 + 6a - 1)$$

> **Helpful Hint**
> Don't forget the -1.

PRACTICE
5   Factor: $-8b^6 + 16b^4 - 8b^2$

In Example 5, we could have chosen to factor out a $-3a$ instead of $3a$. If we factor out a $-3a$, we have

$$-9a^5 + 18a^2 - 3a = (-3a)(3a^4) + (-3a)(-6a) + (-3a)(1)$$
$$= -3a(3a^4 - 6a + 1)$$

> **Helpful Hint**
> Notice the changes in signs when factoring out $-3a$.

EXAMPLES   Factor.

6. $6a^4 - 12a = 6a(a^3 - 2)$

7. $\dfrac{3}{7}x^4 + \dfrac{1}{7}x^3 - \dfrac{5}{7}x^2 = \dfrac{1}{7}x^2(3x^2 + x - 5)$

8. $15p^2q^4 + 20p^3q^5 + 5p^3q^3 = 5p^2q^3(3q + 4pq^2 + p)$

PRACTICE
6-8   Factor.

6. $5x^4 - 20x$ **7.** $\dfrac{5}{9}z^5 + \dfrac{1}{9}z^4 - \dfrac{2}{9}z^3$ **8.** $8a^2b^4 - 20a^3b^3 + 12ab^3$

EXAMPLE 9 Factor: $5(x + 3) + y(x + 3)$

Solution The binomial $(x + 3)$ is the greatest common factor. Use the distributive property to factor out $(x + 3)$.

$$5(x + 3) + y(x + 3) = (x + 3)(5 + y)$$ □

PRACTICE
9 Factor: $8(y - 2) + x(y - 2)$ ▪

EXAMPLE 10 Factor: $3m^2n(a + b) - (a + b)$

Solution The greatest common factor is $(a + b)$.

$$3m^2n(a + b) - 1(a + b) = (a + b)(3m^2n - 1)$$ □

PRACTICE
10 Factor: $7xy^3(p + q) - (p + q)$ ▪

OBJECTIVE

4 Factoring by Grouping ▶

Once the GCF is factored out, we can often continue to factor the polynomial, using a variety of techniques. We discuss here a technique for factoring polynomials called **factoring by grouping.**

EXAMPLE 11 Factor $xy + 2x + 3y + 6$ by grouping. Check by multiplying.

Solution The GCF of the first two terms is x, and the GCF of the last two terms is 3.

$$xy + 2x + 3y + 6 = (xy + 2x) + (3y + 6) \quad \text{Group terms.}$$
$$= x(y + 2) + 3(y + 2) \quad \text{Factor out GCF from each grouping.}$$

> **Helpful Hint**
> Notice that this form, $x(y + 2) + 3(y + 2)$, is _not_ a factored form of the original polynomial. It is a sum, not a product.

Next we factor out the common binomial factor, $(y + 2)$.

$$x(y + 2) + 3(y + 2) = (y + 2)(x + 3)$$

Now the result is a factored form because it is a product. We were able to write the polynomial as a product because of the common binomial factor, $(y + 2)$, that appeared. If this does not happen, try rearranging the terms of the original polynomial.

Check: Multiply: $(y + 2)$ by $(x + 3)$

$$(y + 2)(x + 3) = xy + 2x + 3y + 6,$$

the original polynomial.
Thus, a factored form of $xy + 2x + 3y + 6$ is the product $(y + 2)(x + 3)$. □

PRACTICE
11 Factor $xy + 3y + 4x + 12$ by grouping. Check by multiplying. ▪

You may want to try these steps when factoring by grouping.

To Factor a Four-Term Polynomial by Grouping

Step 1. Group the terms in two groups of two terms so that each group has a common factor.

Step 2. Factor out the GCF from each group.

Step 3. If there is now a common binomial factor in the groups, factor it out.

Step 4. If not, rearrange the terms and try these steps again.

EXAMPLES   Factor by grouping.

12. $15x^3 - 10x^2 + 6x - 4$

$= (15x^3 - 10x^2) + (6x - 4)$ Group the terms.

$= 5x^2(3x - 2) + 2(3x - 2)$ Factor each group.

$= (3x - 2)(5x^2 + 2)$ Factor out the common factor, $(3x - 2)$.

13. $3x^2 + 4xy - 3x - 4y$

$= (3x^2 + 4xy) + (-3x - 4y)$

$= x(3x + 4y) - 1(3x + 4y)$ Factor each group. A -1 is factored from the second pair of terms so that there is a common factor, $(3x + 4y)$.

$= (3x + 4y)(x - 1)$ Factor out the common factor, $(3x + 4y)$.

14. $2a^2 + 5ab + 2a + 5b$

$= (2a^2 + 5ab) + (2a + 5b)$

$= a(2a + 5b) + 1(2a + 5b)$ Factor each group. An understood 1 is written before $(2a + 5b)$ to help remember that $(2a + 5b)$ is $1(2a + 5b)$.

$= (2a + 5b)(a + 1)$ Factor out the common factor, $(2a + 5b)$. □

> **Helpful Hint**
> Notice the factor of 1 is written when $(2a + 5b)$ is factored out.

PRACTICE
12–14

12. Factor $40x^3 - 24x^2 + 15x - 9$ by grouping.

13. Factor $2xy + 3y^2 - 2x - 3y$ by grouping.

14. Factor $7a^3 + 5a^2 + 7a + 5$ by grouping.

EXAMPLES   Factor by grouping.

15. $3xy + 2 - 3x - 2y$

Notice that the first two terms have no common factor other than 1. However, if we rearrange these terms, a grouping emerges that does lead to a common factor.

$3xy + 2 - 3x - 2y$

$= (3xy - 3x) + (-2y + 2)$

$= 3x(y - 1) - 2(y - 1)$ Factor -2 from the second group so that there is a common factor, $(y - 1)$.

$= (y - 1)(3x - 2)$ Factor out the common factor, $(y - 1)$.

16. $5x - 10 + x^3 - x^2 = 5(x - 2) + x^2(x - 1)$

There is no common binomial factor that can now be factored out. No matter how we rearrange the terms, no grouping will lead to a common factor. Thus, this polynomial is not factorable by grouping. □

PRACTICE
15–16

15. Factor $4xy + 15 - 12x - 5y$ by grouping.

16. Factor $9y - 18 + y^3 - 4y^2$ by grouping.

> **Helpful Hint**
> One more reminder: When **factoring** a polynomial, make sure the polynomial is written as a **product.** For example, it is true that
>
> $$3x^2 + 4xy - 3x - 4y = \underbrace{x(3x + 4y) - 1(3x + 4y)}_{\text{but is not a factored form}},$$
>
> since it is a **sum (difference)**, not a **product.** A factored form of $3x^2 + 4xy - 3x - 4y$ is the product $(3x + 4y)(x - 1)$.

Factoring out a greatest common factor first makes factoring by any method easier, as we see in the next example.

EXAMPLE 17 Factor: $4ax - 4ab - 2bx + 2b^2$

Solution First, factor out the common factor 2 from all four terms.

$4ax - 4ab - 2bx + 2b^2$

$= 2(2ax - 2ab - bx + b^2)$ Factor out 2 from all four terms.

$= 2[2a(x - b) - b(x - b)]$ Factor each pair of terms. A "$-b$" is factored from the second pair so that there is a common factor, $x - b$.

$= 2(x - b)(2a - b)$ Factor out the common binomial.   □

PRACTICE
17   Factor: $3xy - 3ay - 6ax + 6a^2$ ▪

> **Helpful Hint**
> Throughout this chapter, we will be factoring polynomials. Even when the instructions do not so state, it is always a good idea to check your answers by multiplying.

✔ Vocabulary, Readiness & Video Check

Use the choices below to fill in each blank. Some choices may be used more than once and some may not be used at all.

greatest common factor   factors   factoring   true   false   least   greatest

1. Since $5 \cdot 4 = 20$, the numbers 5 and 4 are called _____ of 20.

2. The _____ of a list of integers is the largest integer that is a factor of all the integers in the list.

3. The greatest common factor of a list of common variables raised to powers is the variable raised to the _____ exponent in the list.

4. The process of writing a polynomial as a product is called _____.

5. True or false: A factored form of $7x + 21 + xy + 3y$ is $7(x + 3) + y(x + 3)$. _____

6. True or false: A factored form of $3x^3 + 6x + x^2 + 2$ is $3x(x^2 + 2)$. _____

Martin-Gay Interactive Videos

See Video 6.1 🔘

Watch the section lecture video and answer the following questions.

OBJECTIVE 1   7. Based on 🎞 Example 1, give a general definition for the greatest common factor (GCF) of a list of numbers.

OBJECTIVE 2   8. In 🎞 Example 3, why are the numbers factored out, but not the variables?

OBJECTIVE 3   9. From 🎞 Example 5, how can the number of terms in the other factor once you factor out the GCF help you determine if your factorization is correct?

OBJECTIVE 4   10. In 🎞 Examples 7 and 8, what are you reminded to always do first when factoring a polynomial? Also, explain how a polynomial looks that suggests it might be factored by grouping.

6.1 **Exercise Set** MyMathLab® ▶

Find the GCF for each list. See Examples 1 through 3.

1. 32, 36
▶ 2. 36, 90
3. 18, 42, 84
4. 30, 75, 135
5. 24, 14, 21
6. 15, 25, 27
7. y^2, y^4, y^7
▶ 8. x^3, x^2, x^5
9. z^7, z^9, z^{11}
10. y^8, y^{10}, y^{12}
11. $x^{10}y^2, xy^2, x^3y^3$
12. p^7q, p^8q^2, p^9q^3
13. $14x, 21$
14. $20y, 15$
▶ 15. $12y^4, 20y^3$
16. $32x^5, 18x^2$
17. $-10x^2, 15x^3$
18. $-21x^3, 14x$
19. $12x^3, -6x^4, 3x^5$
20. $15y^2, 5y^7, -20y^3$

21. $-18x^2y, 9x^3y^3, 36x^3y$

22. $7x^3y^3, -21x^2y^2, 14xy^4$

23. $20a^6b^2c^8, 50a^7b$

24. $40x^7y^2z, 64x^9y$

Factor out the GCF from each polynomial. See Examples 4 through 10.

25. $3a + 6$

26. $18a + 12$

▶ **27.** $30x - 15$

28. $42x - 7$

29. $x^3 + 5x^2$

30. $y^5 + 6y^4$

31. $6y^4 + 2y^3$

32. $5x^2 + 10x^6$

33. $4x - 8y + 4$

34. $7x + 21y - 7$

35. $6x^3 - 9x^2 + 12x$

36. $12x^3 + 16x^2 - 8x$

37. $a^7b^6 - a^3b^2 + a^2b^5 - a^2b^2$

38. $x^9y^6 + x^3y^5 - x^4y^3 + x^3y^3$

39. $8x^5 + 16x^4 - 20x^3 + 12$

40. $9y^6 - 27y^4 + 18y^2 + 6$

41. $\frac{1}{3}x^4 + \frac{2}{3}x^3 - \frac{4}{3}x^5 + \frac{1}{3}x$

42. $\frac{2}{5}y^7 - \frac{4}{5}y^5 + \frac{3}{5}y^2 - \frac{2}{5}y$

▶ **43.** $y(x^2 + 2) + 3(x^2 + 2)$

44. $x(y^2 + 1) - 3(y^2 + 1)$

45. $z(y + 4) - 3(y + 4)$

46. $8(x + 2) - y(x + 2)$

47. $r(z^2 - 6) + (z^2 - 6)$

48. $q(b^3 - 5) + (b^3 - 5)$

Factor a negative number or a GCF with a negative coefficient from each polynomial. See Example 5.

49. $-2x - 14$

50. $-7y - 21$

51. $-2x^5 + x^7$

52. $-5y^3 + y^6$

53. $-3a^4 + 9a^3 - 3a^2$

54. $-5m^6 + 10m^5 - 5m^3$

Factor each four-term polynomial by grouping. If this is not possible, write "not factorable by grouping." See Examples 11 through 17.

55. $x^3 + 2x^2 + 5x + 10$

56. $x^3 + 4x^2 + 3x + 12$

57. $5x + 15 + xy + 3y$

58. $xy + y + 2x + 2$

59. $6x^3 - 4x^2 + 15x - 10$

60. $16x^3 - 28x^2 + 12x - 21$

61. $5m^3 + 6mn + 5m^2 + 6n$

62. $8w^2 + 7wv + 8w + 7v$

63. $2y - 8 + xy - 4x$

64. $6x - 42 + xy - 7y$

65. $2x^3 - x^2 + 8x - 4$

66. $2x^3 - x^2 - 10x + 5$

67. $3x - 3 + x^3 - 4x^2$

68. $7x - 21 + x^3 - 2x^2$

69. $4x^2 - 8xy - 3x + 6y$

▶ **70.** $5xy - 15x - 6y + 18$

71. $5q^2 - 4pq - 5q + 4p$

72. $6m^2 - 5mn - 6m + 5n$

73. $2x^4 + 5x^3 + 2x^2 + 5x$

74. $4y^4 + y^2 + 20y^3 + 5y$

75. $12x^2y - 42x^2 - 4y + 14$

76. $90 + 15y^2 - 18x - 3xy^2$

MIXED PRACTICE

Factor. See Examples 4 through 17.

77. $32xy - 18x^2$

78. $10xy - 15x^2$

79. $y(x + 2) - 3(x + 2)$

80. $z(y - 4) + 3(y - 4)$

▶ **81.** $14x^3y + 7x^2y - 7xy$

82. $5x^3y - 15x^2y + 10xy$

83. $28x^3 - 7x^2 + 12x - 3$

84. $15x^3 + 5x^2 - 6x - 2$

85. $-40x^8y^6 - 16x^9y^5$

86. $-21x^3y - 49x^2y^2$

▶ **87.** $6a^2 + 9ab^2 + 6ab + 9b^3$

88. $16x^2 + 4xy^2 + 8xy + 2y^3$

REVIEW AND PREVIEW

Multiply. See Sections 5.3 and 5.4.

89. $(x + 2)(x + 5)$

90. $(y + 3)(y + 6)$

91. $(b + 1)(b - 4)$

92. $(x - 5)(x + 10)$

Fill in the chart by finding two numbers that have the given product and sum. The first column is filled in for you.

	93.	94.	95.	96.	97.	98.
Two Numbers	4, 7					
Their Product	28	12	20	8	16	-10	-24
Their Sum	11	8	9	-9	-10	3	-5

CONCEPT EXTENSIONS

See the Concept Checks in this section.

99. Which of the following is/are factored form(s) of $8a - 24$?

  a. $8 \cdot a - 24$ **b.** $8(a - 3)$

  c. $4(2a - 12)$ **d.** $8 \cdot a - 2 \cdot 12$

100. Which of the following is/are factored form(s) of $-2x + 14$?

  a. $-2(x + 7)$ **b.** $-2 \cdot x + 14$

  c. $-2(x - 14)$ **d.** $-2(x - 7)$

Determine whether the following expressions are factored.

101. $(a + 6)(a + 2)$

102. $(x + 5)(x + y)$

103. $5(2y + z) - b(2y + z)$

104. $3x(a + 2b) + 2(a + 2b)$

105. Construct a binomial whose greatest common factor is $5a^3$. (*Hint:* Multiply $5a^3$ by a binomial whose terms contain no common factor other than 1. $5a^3(\square + \square)$.)

106. Construct a trinomial whose greatest common factor is $2x^2$. See the hint for Exercise 105.

107. Explain how you can tell whether a polynomial is written in factored form.

108. Construct a four-term polynomial that can be factored by grouping.

109. The percent of total music industry revenues from streaming in the United States each year during 2007 through 2014 can be modeled by the polynomial $0.6x^2 - 0.6x + 3.6$, where x is the number of years since 2007. (*Source:* Recording Industry Association of America)

   a. Find the percent of music industry revenue derived from streaming in 2013. To do so, let $x = 6$ and evaluate $0.6x^2 - 0.6x + 3.6$. Round to the nearest percent.

   b. Use this expression to predict the percent revenue derived from streaming in 2018. Round to the nearest percent.

   c. Factor the polynomial $0.6x^2 - 0.6x + 3.6$ by factoring 0.6 from each term.

110. The number (in thousands) of students who graduated from U.S. high schools, both public and private, each year during 2000 through 2013 can be modeled by $-3x^2 + 78x + 2904$, where x is the number of years since 2000. (*Source:* National Center for Educational Statistics)

   a. Find the number of students who graduated from U.S. high schools in 2010. To do so, let $x = 10$ and evaluate $-3x^2 + 78x + 2904$.

   b. Use this expression to predict the number of students who will graduate from U.S. high schools in 2018.

   c. Factor the polynomial $-3x^2 + 78x + 2904$ by factoring -3 from each term.

   d. For the year 2010, the National Center for Higher Education determined that 62.5% of U.S. high school graduates went on to higher education. Using your answer from part **a**, determine how many of those graduating in 2010 pursued higher education.

Write an expression for the area of each shaded region. Then write the expression as a factored polynomial.

△ **111.**

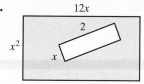

△ **112.**

*Write an expression for the length of each rectangle. (**Hint:** Factor the area binomial and recall that Area = width · length.)*

△ **113.** △ **114.**

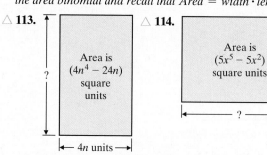

Factor each polynomial by grouping.

115. $x^{2n} + 2x^n + 3x^n + 6$
   (*Hint:* Don't forget that $x^{2n} = x^n \cdot x^n$.)

116. $x^{2n} + 6x^n + 10x^n + 60$

117. $3x^{2n} + 21x^n - 5x^n - 35$

118. $12x^{2n} - 10x^n - 30x^n + 25$

6.2 Factoring Trinomials of the Form $x^2 + bx + c$ ▶

OBJECTIVES

1 Factor Trinomials of the Form $x^2 + bx + c$. ▶

2 Factor Out the Greatest Common Factor and Then Factor a Trinomial of the Form $x^2 + bx + c$. ▶

OBJECTIVE

1 Factoring Trinomials of the Form $x^2 + bx + c$ ▶

In this section, we factor trinomials of the form $x^2 + bx + c$, such as

$$x^2 + 4x + 3, \quad x^2 - 8x + 15, \quad x^2 + 4x - 12, \quad r^2 - r - 42$$

Notice that for these trinomials, the coefficient of the squared variable is 1.

   Recall that factoring means to write as a product and that factoring and multiplying are reverse processes. Using the FOIL method of multiplying binomials, we have that

$$\overset{\text{F} \quad \text{O} \quad \text{I} \quad \text{L}}{(x + 3)(x + 1) = x^2 + 1x + 3x + 3}$$
$$= x^2 + 4x + 3$$

Thus, a factored form of $x^2 + 4x + 3$ is $(x + 3)(x + 1)$.

Notice that the product of the first terms of the binomials is $x \cdot x = x^2$, the first term of the trinomial. Also, the product of the last two terms of the binomials is $3 \cdot 1 = 3$, the third term of the trinomial. The sum of these same terms is $3 + 1 = 4$, the coefficient of the middle term, x, of the trinomial.

The product of these numbers is 3.

$$x^2 + 4x + 3 = (x + 3)(x + 1)$$

The sum of these numbers is 4.

Many trinomials, such as the one above, factor into two binomials. To factor $x^2 + 7x + 10$, let's assume that it factors into two binomials and begin by writing two pairs of parentheses. The first term of the trinomial is x^2, so we use x and x as the first terms of the binomial factors.

$$x^2 + 7x + 10 = (x + \square)(x + \square)$$

To determine the last term of each binomial factor, we look for two integers whose product is 10 and whose sum is 7. Since our numbers must have a positive product and a positive sum, we list pairs of positive integer factors of 10 only.

Positive Factors of 10	Sum of Factors
1, 10	$1 + 10 = 11$
2, 5	$2 + 5 = 7$

The correct pair of numbers is 2 and 5 because their product is 10 and their sum is 7. Now we can fill in the last terms of the binomial factors.

$$x^2 + 7x + 10 = (x + 2)(x + 5)$$

Check: To see if we have factored correctly, multiply.

$$(x + 2)(x + 5) = x^2 + 5x + 2x + 10$$
$$= x^2 + 7x + 10 \qquad \text{Combine like terms.}$$

Helpful Hint

Since multiplication is commutative, the factored form of $x^2 + 7x + 10$ can be written as either $(x + 2)(x + 5)$ or $(x + 5)(x + 2)$.

Factoring a Trinomial of the Form $x^2 + bx + c$

The factored form of $x^2 + bx + c$ is

The product of these numbers is c.

$$x^2 + bx + c = (x + \square)(x + \square)$$

The sum of these numbers is b.

EXAMPLE 1   Factor: $x^2 + 7x + 12$

Solution   We begin by writing the first terms of the binomial factors.

$$(x + \square)(x + \square)$$

Next we look for two numbers whose product is 12 and whose sum is 7. Since our numbers must have a positive product and a positive sum, we look at pairs of positive factors of 12 only.

(Continued on next page)

Positive Factors of 12	Sum of Factors
1, 12	13
2, 6	8
3, 4	7

Correct sum, so the numbers are 3 and 4.

Thus, $x^2 + 7x + 12 = (x + 3)(x + 4)$

Check: $(x + 3)(x + 4) = x^2 + 4x + 3x + 12 = x^2 + 7x + 12.$ □

PRACTICE
1 Factor: $x^2 + 5x + 6$ ■

EXAMPLE 2 Factor: $x^2 - 12x + 35$

Solution Again, we begin by writing the first terms of the binomials.

$$(x + \square)(x + \square)$$

Now we look for two numbers whose product is 35 and whose sum is −12. Since our numbers must have a positive product and a negative sum, we look at pairs of negative factors of 35 only.

Negative Factors of 35	Sum of Factors
−1, −35	−36
−5, −7	−12

Correct sum, so the numbers are −5 and −7.

Thus, $x^2 - 12x + 35 = (x - 5)(x - 7)$

Check: To check, multiply $(x - 5)(x - 7)$. □

PRACTICE
2 Factor: $x^2 - 17x + 70$ ■

EXAMPLE 3 Factor: $x^2 + 4x - 12$

Solution $x^2 + 4x - 12 = (x + \square)(x + \square)$

We look for two numbers whose product is −12 and whose sum is 4. Since our numbers must have a negative product, we look at pairs of factors with opposite signs.

Factors of −12	Sum of Factors
−1, 12	11
1, −12	−11
−2, 6	4
2, −6	−4
−3, 4	1
3, −4	−1

Correct sum, so the numbers are −2 and 6.

Thus, $x^2 + 4x - 12 = (x - 2)(x + 6)$ □

PRACTICE
3 Factor: $x^2 + 5x - 14$ ■

EXAMPLE 4   Factor: $r^2 - r - 42$

Solution Because the variable in this trinomial is r, the first term of each binomial factor is r.

$$r^2 - r - 42 = (r + \square)(r + \square)$$

Now we look for two numbers whose product is -42 and whose sum is -1, the numerical coefficient of r. The numbers are 6 and -7. Therefore,

$$r^2 - r - 42 = (r + 6)(r - 7)$$

PRACTICE
4   Factor: $p^2 - 2p - 63$

EXAMPLE 5   Factor: $a^2 + 2a + 10$

Solution Look for two numbers whose product is 10 and whose sum is 2. Neither 1 and 10 nor 2 and 5 give the required sum, 2. We conclude that $a^2 + 2a + 10$ is not factorable with integers. A polynomial such as $a^2 + 2a + 10$ is called a **prime polynomial.**

PRACTICE
5   Factor: $b^2 + 5b + 1$

EXAMPLE 6   Factor: $x^2 + 7xy + 6y^2$

Solution

$$x^2 + 7xy + 6y^2 = (x + \square)(x + \square)$$

Recall that the middle term $7xy$ is the same as $7yx$. Thus, we can see that $7y$ is the "coefficient" of x. We then look for two terms whose product is $6y^2$ and whose sum is $7y$. The terms are $6y$ and $1y$ or $6y$ and y because $6y \cdot y = 6y^2$ and $6y + y = 7y$. Therefore,

$$x^2 + 7xy + 6y^2 = (x + 6y)(x + y)$$

PRACTICE
6   Factor: $x^2 + 7xy + 12y^2$

EXAMPLE 7   Factor: $x^4 + 5x^2 + 6$

Solution As usual, we begin by writing the first terms of the binomials. Since the greatest power of x in this polynomial is x^4, we write

$$(x^2 + \square)(x^2 + \square) \quad \text{since } x^2 \cdot x^2 = x^4$$

Now we look for two factors of 6 whose sum is 5. The numbers are 2 and 3. Thus,

$$x^4 + 5x^2 + 6 = (x^2 + 2)(x^2 + 3)$$

PRACTICE
7   Factor: $x^4 + 13x^2 + 12$

If the terms of a polynomial are not written in descending powers of the variable, you may want to do so before factoring.

EXAMPLE 8   Factor: $40 - 13t + t^2$

Solution First, we rearrange terms so that the trinomial is written in descending powers of t.

$$40 - 13t + t^2 = t^2 - 13t + 40$$

(Continued on next page)

Next, try to factor.

$$t^2 - 13t + 40 = (t + \square)(t + \square)$$

Now we look for two factors of 40 whose sum is -13. The numbers are -8 and -5. Thus,

$$t^2 - 13t + 40 = (t - 8)(t - 5) \qquad \square$$

PRACTICE
8   Factor: $48 - 14x + x^2$

The following sign patterns may be useful when factoring trinomials.

Helpful Hint

A positive constant in a trinomial tells us to look for two numbers with the same sign. The sign of the coefficient of the middle term tells us whether the signs are both positive or both negative.

| both positive | same sign | | both negative | same sign |

$$x^2 + 10x + 16 = (x + 2)(x + 8) \qquad x^2 - 10x + 16 = (x - 2)(x - 8)$$

A negative constant in a trinomial tells us to look for two numbers with opposite signs.

| opposite signs | | opposite signs |

$$x^2 + 6x - 16 = (x + 8)(x - 2) \qquad x^2 - 6x - 16 = (x - 8)(x + 2)$$

OBJECTIVE

2   **Factoring Out the Greatest Common Factor** ▶

Remember that the first step in factoring any polynomial is to factor out the greatest common factor (if there is one other than 1 or -1).

EXAMPLE 9   Factor: $3m^2 - 24m - 60$

Solution First we factor out the greatest common factor, 3, from each term.

$$3m^2 - 24m - 60 = 3(m^2 - 8m - 20)$$

Now we factor $m^2 - 8m - 20$ by looking for two factors of -20 whose sum is -8. The factors are -10 and 2. Therefore, the complete factored form is

$$3m^2 - 24m - 60 = 3(m + 2)(m - 10) \qquad \square$$

Helpful Hint

Remember to write the common factor 3 as part of the factored form.

PRACTICE
9   Factor: $4x^2 - 24x + 36$

EXAMPLE 10   Factor: $2x^4 - 26x^3 + 84x^2$

Solution

$$\begin{aligned}
2x^4 - 26x^3 + 84x^2 &= 2x^2(x^2 - 13x + 42) &&\text{Factor out common factor, } 2x^2. \\
&= 2x^2(x - 6)(x - 7) &&\text{Factor } x^2 - 13x + 42. \qquad \square
\end{aligned}$$

PRACTICE
10   Factor: $3y^4 - 18y^3 - 21y^2$

✓ Vocabulary, Readiness & Video Check

Fill in each blank with "true" or "false."

1. To factor $x^2 + 7x + 6$, we look for two numbers whose product is 6 and whose sum is 7. _____

2. We can write the factorization $(y + 2)(y + 4)$ also as $(y + 4)(y + 2)$. _____

3. The factorization $(4x - 12)(x - 5)$ is completely factored. _____

4. The factorization $(x + 2y)(x + y)$ may also be written as $(x + 2y)^2$. _____

Complete each factored form.

5. $x^2 + 9x + 20 = (x + 4)(x \quad)$

6. $x^2 + 12x + 35 = (x + 5)(x \quad)$

7. $x^2 - 7x + 12 = (x - 4)(x \quad)$

8. $x^2 - 13x + 22 = (x - 2)(x \quad)$

9. $x^2 + 4x + 4 = (x + 2)(x \quad)$

10. $x^2 + 10x + 24 = (x + 6)(x \quad)$

Martin-Gay Interactive Videos

See Video 6.2

Watch the section lecture video and answer the following questions.

OBJECTIVE 1

11. In Example 2, why are only negative factors of 15 considered?

OBJECTIVE 2

12. In Example 5, we know we need a positive and a negative factor of -10. How do we determine which factor is negative?

6.2   Exercise Set   MyMathLab®

Factor each trinomial completely. If a polynomial can't be factored, write "prime." See Examples 1 through 8.

1. $x^2 + 7x + 6$

2. $x^2 + 6x + 8$

3. $y^2 - 10y + 9$

4. $y^2 - 12y + 11$

5. $x^2 - 6x + 9$

6. $x^2 - 10x + 25$

7. $x^2 - 3x - 18$

8. $x^2 - x - 30$

9. $x^2 + 3x - 70$

10. $x^2 + 4x - 32$

11. $x^2 + 5x + 2$

12. $x^2 - 7x + 5$

13. $x^2 + 8xy + 15y^2$

14. $x^2 + 6xy + 8y^2$

15. $a^4 - 2a^2 - 15$

16. $y^4 - 3y^2 - 70$

17. $13 + 14m + m^2$

18. $17 + 18n + n^2$

19. $10t - 24 + t^2$

20. $6q - 27 + q^2$

21. $a^2 - 10ab + 16b^2$

22. $a^2 - 9ab + 18b^2$

MIXED PRACTICE

Factor each trinomial completely. Some of these trinomials contain a greatest common factor (other than 1). Don't forget to factor out the GCF first. See Examples 1 through 10.

23. $2z^2 + 20z + 32$

24. $3x^2 + 30x + 63$

25. $2x^3 - 18x^2 + 40x$

26. $3x^3 - 12x^2 - 36x$

27. $x^2 - 3xy - 4y^2$

28. $x^2 - 4xy - 77y^2$

29. $x^2 + 15x + 36$

30. $x^2 + 19x + 60$

31. $x^2 - x - 2$

32. $x^2 - 5x - 14$

33. $r^2 - 16r + 48$

34. $r^2 - 10r + 21$

35. $x^2 + xy - 2y^2$

36. $x^2 - xy - 6y^2$

37. $3x^2 + 9x - 30$

38. $4x^2 - 4x - 48$

39. $3x^2 - 60x + 108$

40. $2x^2 - 24x + 70$

41. $x^2 - 18x - 144$

42. $x^2 + x - 42$

43. $r^2 - 3r + 6$

44. $x^2 + 4x - 10$

▶ **45.** $x^2 - 8x + 15$

46. $x^2 - 9x + 14$

47. $6x^3 + 54x^2 + 120x$

48. $3x^3 + 3x^2 - 126x$

49. $4x^2y + 4xy - 12y$

50. $3x^2y - 9xy + 45y$

51. $x^2 - 4x - 21$

52. $x^2 - 4x - 32$

53. $x^2 + 7xy + 10y^2$

54. $x^2 - 2xy - 15y^2$

55. $64 + 24t + 2t^2$

56. $50 + 20t + 2t^2$

57. $x^3 - 2x^2 - 24x$

58. $x^3 - 3x^2 - 28x$

59. $2t^5 - 14t^4 + 24t^3$

60. $3x^6 + 30x^5 + 72x^4$

▶ **61.** $5x^3y - 25x^2y^2 - 120xy^3$

62. $7a^3b - 35a^2b^2 + 42ab^3$

63. $162 - 45m + 3m^2$

64. $48 - 20n + 2n^2$

65. $-x^2 + 12x - 11$ (Factor out -1 first.)

66. $-x^2 + 8x - 7$ (Factor out -1 first.)

67. $\frac{1}{2}y^2 - \frac{9}{2}y - 11$ (Factor out $\frac{1}{2}$ first.)

68. $\frac{1}{3}y^2 - \frac{5}{3}y - 8$ (Factor out $\frac{1}{3}$ first.)

69. $x^3y^2 + x^2y - 20x$

70. $a^2b^3 + ab^2 - 30b$

REVIEW AND PREVIEW

Multiply. See Sections 5.3 and 5.4.

71. $(2x + 1)(x + 5)$

72. $(3x + 2)(x + 4)$

73. $(5y - 4)(3y - 1)$

74. $(4z - 7)(7z - 1)$

75. $(a + 3b)(9a - 4b)$

76. $(y - 5x)(6y + 5x)$

CONCEPT EXTENSIONS

77. Write a polynomial that factors as $(x - 3)(x + 8)$.

78. To factor $x^2 + 13x + 42$, think of two numbers whose _____ is 42 and whose _____ is 13.

Complete each sentence in your own words.

79. If $x^2 + bx + c$ is factorable and c is negative, then the signs of the last-term factors of the binomials are opposite because…

80. If $x^2 + bx + c$ is factorable and c is positive, then the signs of the last-term factors of the binomials are the same because…

Remember that perimeter means distance around. Write the perimeter of each rectangle as a simplified polynomial. Then factor the polynomial.

△ **81.**

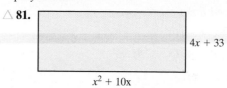

$4x + 33$

$x^2 + 10x$

△ **82.**

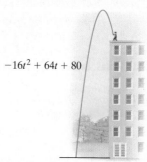

$12x^2$

$2x^3 + 16x$

83. An object is thrown upward from the top of an 80-foot building with an initial velocity of 64 feet per second. Neglecting air resistance, the height of the object after t seconds is given by $-16t^2 + 64t + 80$. Factor this polynomial.

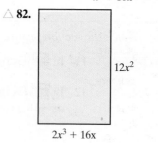

$-16t^2 + 64t + 80$

84. An object is thrown upward from the top of a 112-foot building with an initial velocity of 96 feet per second. Neglecting air resistance, the height of the object after t seconds is given by $-16t^2 + 96t + 112$. Factor this polynomial.

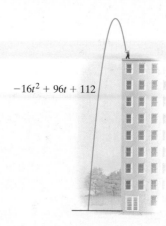

$-16t^2 + 96t + 112$

Factor each trinomial completely.

85. $x^2 + \dfrac{1}{2}x + \dfrac{1}{16}$

86. $x^2 + x + \dfrac{1}{4}$

87. $z^2(x + 1) - 3z(x + 1) - 70(x + 1)$

88. $y^2(x + 1) - 2y(x + 1) - 15(x + 1)$

Factor each trinomial. (**Hint:** *Notice that $x^{2n} + 4x^n + 3$ factors as* $(x^n + 1)(x^n + 3)$. **Remember:** $x^n \cdot x^n = x^{n+n}$ *or* x^{2n}.)

89. $x^{2n} + 8x^n - 20$

90. $x^{2n} + 5x^n + 6$

Find a positive value of c so that each trinomial is factorable.

91. $x^2 + 6x + c$

92. $t^2 + 8t + c$

93. $y^2 - 4y + c$

94. $n^2 - 16n + c$

Find a positive value of b so that each trinomial is factorable.

95. $x^2 + bx + 15$

96. $y^2 + by + 20$

97. $m^2 + bm - 27$

98. $x^2 + bx - 14$

6.3 Factoring Trinomials of the Form $ax^2 + bx + c$ and Perfect Square Trinomials ▶

OBJECTIVES

1 Factor Trinomials of the Form $ax^2 + bx + c$, Where $a \neq 1$. ▶

2 Factor Out the GCF Before Factoring a Trinomial of the Form $ax^2 + bx + c$. ▶

3 Factor Perfect Square Trinomials. ▶

OBJECTIVE

1 Factoring Trinomials of the Form $ax^2 + bx + c$ ▶

In this section, we factor trinomials of the form $ax^2 + bx + c$, such as

$$3x^2 + 11x + 6, \qquad 8x^2 - 22x + 5, \qquad \text{and} \qquad 2x^2 + 13x - 7$$

Notice that the coefficient of the squared variable in these trinomials is a number other than 1. We will factor these trinomials using a trial-and-check method based on our work in the last section.

To begin, let's review the relationship between the numerical coefficients of the trinomial and the numerical coefficients of its factored form. For example, since $(2x + 1)(x + 6) = 2x^2 + 13x + 6$,

a factored form of $2x^2 + 13x + 6$ is $(2x + 1)(x + 6)$

Notice that $2x$ and x are factors of $2x^2$, the first term of the trinomial. Also, 6 and 1 are factors of 6, the last term of the trinomial, as shown:

$$2x^2 + 13x + 6 = (2x + 1)(x + 6)$$

Also notice that $13x$, the middle term, is the sum of the following products:

$$2x^2 + 13x + 6 = (2x + 1)(x + 6)$$

$$1x$$
$$+12x$$
$$13x \qquad \text{Middle term}$$

Let's use this pattern to factor $5x^2 + 7x + 2$. First, we find factors of $5x^2$. Since all numerical coefficients in this trinomial are positive, we will use factors with positive numerical coefficients only. Thus, the factors of $5x^2$ are $5x$ and x. Let's try these factors as first terms of the binomials. Thus far, we have

$$5x^2 + 7x + 2 = (5x + \square)(x + \square)$$

Next, we need to find positive factors of 2. Positive factors of 2 are 1 and 2. Now we try possible combinations of these factors as second terms of the binomials until we obtain a middle term of $7x$.

$$(5x + 1)(x + 2) = 5x^2 + 11x + 2$$

$$\begin{array}{r} 1x \\ +10x \\ \hline 11x \end{array} \longrightarrow \text{Incorrect middle term}$$

Let's try switching factors 2 and 1.

$$(5x + 2)(x + 1) = 5x^2 + 7x + 2$$

$$\begin{array}{r} 2x \\ +5x \\ \hline 7x \end{array} \longrightarrow \text{Correct middle term}$$

Thus the factored form of $5x^2 + 7x + 2$ is $(5x + 2)(x + 1)$. To check, we multiply $(5x + 2)$ and $(x + 1)$. The product is $5x^2 + 7x + 2$.

EXAMPLE 1   Factor: $3x^2 + 11x + 6$

Solution Since all numerical coefficients are positive, we use factors with positive numerical coefficients. We first find factors of $3x^2$.

$$\text{Factors of } 3x^2: \quad 3x^2 = 3x \cdot x$$

If factorable, the trinomial will be of the form

$$3x^2 + 11x + 6 = (3x + \square)(x + \square)$$

Next we factor 6.

$$\text{Factors of 6:} \quad 6 = 1 \cdot 6, \quad 6 = 2 \cdot 3$$

Now we try combinations of factors of 6 until a middle term of $11x$ is obtained. Let's try 1 and 6 first.

$$(3x + 1)(x + 6) = 3x^2 + 19x + 6$$

$$\begin{array}{r} 1x \\ +18x \\ \hline 19x \end{array} \longrightarrow \textbf{Incorrect} \text{ middle term}$$

Now let's next try 6 and 1.

$$(3x + 6)(x + 1)$$

Before multiplying, notice that the terms of the factor $3x + 6$ have a common factor of 3. The terms of the original trinomial $3x^2 + 11x + 6$ have no common factor other than 1, so the terms of its factors will also contain no common factor other than 1. This means that $(3x + 6)(x + 1)$ is not a factored form.

Next let's try 2 and 3 as last terms.

$$(3x + 2)(x + 3) = 3x^2 + 11x + 6$$

$$\begin{array}{r} 2x \\ +9x \\ \hline 11x \end{array} \longrightarrow \textbf{Correct} \text{ middle term}$$

Thus a factored form of $3x^2 + 11x + 6$ is $(3x + 2)(x + 3)$. □

PRACTICE

1   Factor: $2x^2 + 11x + 15$

> **Helpful Hint**
> If the terms of a trinomial have no common factor (other than 1), then the terms of neither of its binomial factors will contain a common factor (other than 1).

✔ **CONCEPT CHECK**

Do the terms of $3x^2 + 29x + 18$ have a common factor? Without multiplying, decide which of the following factored forms could not be a factored form of $3x^2 + 29x + 18$.

a. $(3x + 18)(x + 1)$ **b.** $(3x + 2)(x + 9)$ **c.** $(3x + 6)(x + 3)$ **d.** $(3x + 9)(x + 2)$

EXAMPLE 2   Factor: $8x^2 - 22x + 5$

Solution Factors of $8x^2$: $8x^2 = 8x \cdot x$, $8x^2 = 4x \cdot 2x$

We'll try $8x$ and x.

$$8x^2 - 22x + 5 = (8x + \square)(x + \square)$$

Since the middle term, $-22x$, has a negative numerical coefficient, we factor 5 into negative factors.

$$\text{Factors of 5: } 5 = -1 \cdot -5$$

Let's try -1 and -5.

$$(8x - 1)(x - 5) = 8x^2 - 41x + 5$$

$$
\begin{array}{r}
-1x \\
+(-40x) \\
\hline
-41x
\end{array}
\longrightarrow \text{Incorrect middle term}
$$

Now let's try -5 and -1.

$$(8x - 5)(x - 1) = 8x^2 - 13x + 5$$

$$
\begin{array}{r}
-5x \\
+(-8x) \\
\hline
-13x
\end{array}
\longrightarrow \text{Incorrect middle term}
$$

Don't give up yet! We can still try other factors of $8x^2$. Let's try $4x$ and $2x$ with -1 and -5.

$$(4x - 1)(2x - 5) = 8x^2 - 22x + 5$$

$$
\begin{array}{r}
-2x \\
+(-20x) \\
\hline
-22x
\end{array}
\longrightarrow \text{Correct middle term}
$$

A factored form of $8x^2 - 22x + 5$ is $(4x - 1)(2x - 5)$.   □

PRACTICE
2   Factor: $15x^2 - 22x + 8$

EXAMPLE 3   Factor: $2x^2 + 13x - 7$

Solution Factors of $2x^2$: $2x^2 = 2x \cdot x$

   Factors of -7: $-7 = -1 \cdot 7$, $-7 = 1 \cdot -7$

Answers to Concept Check:
no; a, c, d

We try possible combinations of these factors:

$$(2x + 1)(x - 7) = 2x^2 - 13x - 7 \quad \text{Incorrect middle term}$$
$$(2x - 1)(x + 7) = 2x^2 + 13x - 7 \quad \text{Correct middle term}$$

A factored form of $2x^2 + 13x - 7$ is $(2x - 1)(x + 7)$.

PRACTICE
3 Factor: $4x^2 + 11x - 3$

EXAMPLE 4 Factor: $10x^2 - 13xy - 3y^2$

Solution Factors of $10x^2$: $\quad 10x^2 = 10x \cdot x, \quad 10x^2 = 2x \cdot 5x$

Factors of $-3y^2$: $\quad -3y^2 = -3y \cdot y, \quad -3y^2 = 3y \cdot -y$

We try some combinations of these factors:

$$\begin{array}{c} \quad\quad\quad\quad\quad\quad \text{Correct} \quad\quad \text{Correct} \\ \quad\quad\quad\quad\quad\quad \downarrow \quad\quad\quad\quad \downarrow \end{array}$$

$$(10x - 3y)(x + y) = 10x^2 + 7xy - 3y^2$$
$$(x + 3y)(10x - y) = 10x^2 + 29xy - 3y^2$$
$$(5x + 3y)(2x - y) = 10x^2 + xy - 3y^2$$
$$(2x - 3y)(5x + y) = 10x^2 - 13xy - 3y^2 \quad \text{Correct middle term}$$

A factored form of $10x^2 - 13xy - 3y^2$ is $(2x - 3y)(5x + y)$.

PRACTICE
4 Factor: $21x^2 + 11xy - 2y^2$

EXAMPLE 5 Factor: $3x^4 - 5x^2 - 8$

Solution Factors of $3x^4$: $\quad 3x^4 = 3x^2 \cdot x^2$

Factors of -8: $\quad -8 = -2 \cdot 4, \ -8 = 2 \cdot -4, \ -8 = -1 \cdot 8, \ -8 = 1 \cdot -8$

Try combinations of these factors:

$$\begin{array}{c} \quad\quad\quad\quad\quad\quad \text{Correct} \quad\quad\quad \text{Correct} \\ \quad\quad\quad\quad\quad\quad \downarrow \quad\quad\quad\quad\quad \downarrow \end{array}$$

$$(3x^2 - 2)(x^2 + 4) = 3x^4 + 10x^2 - 8$$
$$(3x^2 + 4)(x^2 - 2) = 3x^4 - 2x^2 - 8$$
$$(3x^2 + 8)(x^2 - 1) = 3x^4 + 5x^2 - 8 \quad \text{Incorrect sign on middle term, so}$$
$$(3x^2 - 8)(x^2 + 1) = 3x^4 - 5x^2 - 8 \quad \begin{array}{l}\text{switch signs in binomial factors.} \\ \text{Correct middle term.}\end{array}$$

A factored form of $3x^4 - 5x^2 - 8$ is $(3x^2 - 8)(x^2 + 1)$.

PRACTICE
5 Factor: $2x^4 - 5x^2 - 7$

Helpful Hint

Study the last two lines of Example 5. If a factoring attempt gives you a middle term whose numerical coefficient is the opposite of the desired numerical coefficient, try switching the signs of the last terms in the binomials.

Switched signs $\Big\langle$

$$(3x^2 + 8)(x^2 - 1) = 3x^4 + 5x^2 - 8 \quad \text{Middle term: } +5x^2$$
$$(3x^2 - 8)(x^2 + 1) = 3x^4 - 5x^2 - 8 \quad \text{Middle term: } -5x^2$$

OBJECTIVE

2   Factoring out the Greatest Common Factor

Don't forget that the first step in factoring any polynomial is to look for a greatest common factor to factor out.

EXAMPLE 6   Factor: $24x^4 + 40x^3 + 6x^2$

Solution   Notice that all three terms have a greatest common factor of $2x^2$. Thus we factor out $2x^2$ from all three terms first.

$$24x^4 + 40x^3 + 6x^2 = 2x^2(12x^2 + 20x + 3)$$

Next we factor $12x^2 + 20x + 3$.

Factors of $12x^2$: $12x^2 = 4x \cdot 3x,$ $12x^2 = 12x \cdot x,$ $12x^2 = 6x \cdot 2x$

Since all terms in the trinomial have positive numerical coefficients, we factor 3 using positive factors only.

Factors of 3: $3 = 1 \cdot 3$

We try some combinations of the factors.

$$2x^2(4x + 3)(3x + 1) = 2x^2(12x^2 + 13x + 3)$$
$$2x^2(12x + 1)(x + 3) = 2x^2(12x^2 + 37x + 3)$$
$$2x^2(2x + 3)(6x + 1) = 2x^2(12x^2 + 20x + 3) \quad \text{Correct middle term}$$

> **Helpful Hint**
> Don't forget to include the greatest common factor in the factored form.

A factored form of $24x^4 + 40x^3 + 6x^2$ is $2x^2(2x + 3)(6x + 1)$.   □

PRACTICE

6   Factor: $3x^3 + 17x^2 + 10x$ ▪

When the term containing the squared variable has a negative coefficient, you may want to first factor out a common factor of -1.

EXAMPLE 7   Factor: $-6x^2 - 13x + 5$

Solution   We begin by factoring out a common factor of -1.

$$-6x^2 - 13x + 5 = -1(6x^2 + 13x - 5) \quad \text{Factor out } -1.$$
$$= -1(3x - 1)(2x + 5) \quad \text{Factor } 6x^2 + 13x - 5.$$ □

PRACTICE

7   Factor: $-8x^2 + 2x + 3$ ▪

OBJECTIVE

3   Factoring Perfect Square Trinomials ▶

A trinomial that is the square of a binomial is called a **perfect square trinomial.** For example,

$$(x + 3)^2 = (x + 3)(x + 3)$$
$$= x^2 + 6x + 9$$

Thus $x^2 + 6x + 9$ is a perfect square trinomial.

In Chapter 5, we discovered special product formulas for squaring binomials.

$$(a + b)^2 = a^2 + 2ab + b^2 \quad \text{and} \quad (a - b)^2 = a^2 - 2ab + b^2$$

Because multiplication and factoring are reverse processes, we can now use these special products to help us factor perfect square trinomials. If we reverse these equations, we have the following.

> **Factoring Perfect Square Trinomials**
>
> $$a^2 + 2ab + b^2 = (a + b)^2$$
> $$a^2 - 2ab + b^2 = (a - b)^2$$

Helpful Hint

Notice that for both given forms of a perfect square trinomial, the last term is positive. This is because the last term is a square.

To use these equations to help us factor, we must first be able to recognize a perfect square trinomial. A trinomial is a perfect square when

1. two terms, a^2 and b^2, are squares and
2. the remaining term is $2 \cdot a \cdot b$ or $-2 \cdot a \cdot b$. That is, this term is twice the product of a and b, or its opposite.

When a trinomial fits this description, its factored form is $(a + b)^2$ or $(a - b)^2$.

EXAMPLE 8   Factor: $x^2 + 12x + 36$

Solution   First, is this a perfect square trinomial?

$$x^2 + 12x + 36$$

1. $x^2 = (x)^2$ and $36 = 6^2$.
2. Is the middle term $2 \cdot x \cdot 6$? Yes, $2 \cdot x \cdot 6 = 12x$, the middle term.

Thus, $x^2 + 12x + 36$ factors as $(x + 6)^2$. □

PRACTICE
8   Factor: $x^2 + 14x + 49$

EXAMPLE 9   Factor: $25x^2 + 25xy + 4y^2$

Solution   Is this a perfect square trinomial?

$$25x^2 + 25xy + 4y^2$$

1. $25x^2 = (5x)^2$ and $4y^2 = (2y)^2$.
2. Is the middle term $2 \cdot 5x \cdot 2y$? **No**, $2 \cdot 5x \cdot 2y = 20xy$, **not the middle term** $25xy$.

Helpful Hint

A perfect square trinomial can also be factored by other methods.

Therefore, $25x^2 + 25xy + 4y^2$ is not a perfect square trinomial. It is factorable, though. Using earlier techniques, we find that $25x^2 + 25xy + 4y^2$ factors as $(5x + 4y)(5x + y)$. □

PRACTICE
9   Factor: $4x^2 + 20xy + 9y^2$

EXAMPLE 10   Factor: $4m^4 - 4m^2 + 1$

Solution   Is this a perfect square trinomial?

$$4m^4 - 4m^2 + 1$$

1. $4m^4 = (2m^2)^2$ and $1 = 1^2$.
2. Is the middle term $2 \cdot 2m^2 \cdot 1$ or $-2 \cdot 2m^2 \cdot 1$? Yes, $-2 \cdot 2m^2 \cdot 1 = -4m^2$, the middle term.

Thus, $4m^4 - 4m^2 + 1$ factors as $(2m^2 - 1)^2$. □

PRACTICE
10   Factor: $36n^4 - 12n^2 + 1$

EXAMPLE 11 Factor: $162x^3 - 144x^2 + 32x$

Solution Don't forget to look first for a common factor. There is a greatest common factor of $2x$ in this trinomial.

$$162x^3 - 144x^2 + 32x = 2x(81x^2 - 72x + 16)$$
$$= 2x[(9x)^2 - 2 \cdot 9x \cdot 4 + 4^2]$$
$$= 2x(9x - 4)^2$$

PRACTICE
11 Factor: $12x^3 - 84x^2 + 147x$

✔ Vocabulary, Readiness & Video Check

Use the choices below to fill in each blank. Some choices will be used more than once and some not used at all.

$5y^2$	$(x + 5y)^2$
$(5y)^2$	$(x - 5y)^2$

perfect square trinomial
perfect square binomial

1. A _____ is a trinomial that is the square of a binomial.

2. The term $25y^2$ written as a square is _____.

3. The expression $x^2 + 10xy + 25y^2$ is called a _____.

4. The factorization $(x + 5y)(x + 5y)$ may also be written as _____.

Complete each factorization.

5. $2x^2 + 5x + 3$ factors as $(2x + 3)(\ ?\ )$.

  a. $(x + 3)$ **b.** $(2x + 1)$ **c.** $(3x + 4)$ **d.** $(x + 1)$

6. $7x^2 + 9x + 2$ factors as $(7x + 2)(\ ?\ )$.

  a. $(3x + 1)$ **b.** $(x + 1)$ **c.** $(x + 2)$ **d.** $(7x + 1)$

Martin-Gay Interactive Videos

See Video 6.3 ⊙

Watch the section lecture video and answer the following questions.

OBJECTIVE 1
7. From ▥ Example 1, explain in general terms how you would go about factoring a trinomial with a first-term coefficient $\neq 1$.

OBJECTIVE 2
8. From ▥ Examples 3 and 5, how can factoring the GCF from a trinomial help you save time when trying to factor the remaining trinomial?

OBJECTIVE 3
9. Describe in words the special patterns that the trinomials in ▥ Examples 7 and 8 have that identify them as perfect square trinomials.

6.3 Exercise Set MyMathLab ▶

Complete each factored form. See Examples 1 through 5, and 8 through 10.

1. $5x^2 + 22x + 8 = (5x + 2)$

2. $2y^2 + 27y + 25 = (2y + 25)$

3. $50x^2 + 15x - 2 = (5x + 2)$

4. $6y^2 + 11y - 10 = (2y + 5)$

5. $25x^2 - 20x + 4 = (5x - 2)$

6. $4y^2 - 20y + 25 = (2y - 5)$

Factor completely. See Examples 1 through 5.

7. $2x^2 + 13x + 15$

8. $3x^2 + 8x + 4$

9. $8y^2 - 17y + 9$

10. $21x^2 - 31x + 10$

11. $2x^2 - 9x - 5$

12. $36r^2 - 5r - 24$

13. $20r^2 + 27r - 8$

14. $3x^2 + 20x - 63$

15. $10x^2 + 31x + 3$

16. $12x^2 + 17x + 5$

17. $2m^2 + 17m + 10$

18. $3n^2 + 20n + 5$

19. $6x^2 - 13xy + 5y^2$

20. $8x^2 - 14xy + 3y^2$

21. $15m^2 - 16m - 15$

22. $25n^2 - 5n - 6$

Factor completely. See Examples 1 through 7.

23. $12x^3 + 11x^2 + 2x$

24. $8a^3 + 14a^2 + 3a$

25. $21b^2 - 48b - 45$

26. $12x^2 - 14x - 10$

27. $7z + 12z^2 - 12$

28. $16t + 15t^2 - 15$

29. $6x^2y^2 - 2xy^2 - 60y^2$

30. $8x^2y + 34xy - 84y$

31. $4x^2 - 8x - 21$

32. $6x^2 - 11x - 10$

33. $-x^2 + 2x + 24$

34. $-x^2 + 4x + 21$

35. $4x^3 - 9x^2 - 9x$

36. $6x^3 - 31x^2 + 5x$

37. $24x^2 - 58x + 9$

38. $36x^2 + 55x - 14$

Factor each perfect square trinomial completely. See Examples 8 through 11.

39. $x^2 + 22x + 121$

40. $x^2 + 18x + 81$

41. $x^2 - 16x + 64$

42. $x^2 - 12x + 36$

43. $16a^2 - 24a + 9$

44. $25x^2 - 20x + 4$

45. $x^4 + 4x^2 + 4$

46. $m^4 + 10m^2 + 25$

47. $2n^2 - 28n + 98$

48. $3y^2 - 6y + 3$

49. $16y^2 + 40y + 25$

50. $9y^2 + 48y + 64$

MIXED PRACTICE

Factor each trinomial completely. See Examples 1 through 11 and Section 6.2.

51. $2x^2 - 7x - 99$

52. $2x^2 + 7x - 72$

53. $24x^2 + 41x + 12$

54. $24x^2 - 49x + 15$

55. $3a^2 + 10ab + 3b^2$

56. $2a^2 + 11ab + 5b^2$

57. $-9x + 20 + x^2$

58. $-7x + 12 + x^2$

59. $p^2 + 12pq + 36q^2$

60. $m^2 + 20mn + 100n^2$

61. $x^2y^2 - 10xy + 25$

62. $x^2y^2 - 14xy + 49$

63. $40a^2b + 9ab - 9b$

64. $24y^2x + 7yx - 5x$

65. $30x^3 + 38x^2 + 12x$

66. $6x^3 - 28x^2 + 16x$

67. $6y^3 - 8y^2 - 30y$

68. $12x^3 - 34x^2 + 24x$

69. $10x^4 + 25x^3y - 15x^2y^2$

70. $42x^4 - 99x^3y - 15x^2y^2$

71. $-14x^2 + 39x - 10$

72. $-15x^2 + 26x - 8$

73. $16p^4 - 40p^3 + 25p^2$

74. $9q^4 - 42q^3 + 49q^2$

75. $x + 3x^2 - 2$

76. $y + 8y^2 - 9$

77. $8x^2 + 6xy - 27y^2$

78. $54a^2 + 39ab - 8b^2$

79. $1 + 6x^2 + x^4$

80. $1 + 16x^2 + x^4$

81. $9x^2 - 24xy + 16y^2$

82. $25x^2 - 60xy + 36y^2$

83. $18x^2 - 9x - 14$

84. $42a^2 - 43a + 6$

85. $-27t + 7t^2 - 4$

86. $-3t + 4t^2 - 7$

87. $49p^2 - 7p - 2$

88. $3r^2 + 10r - 8$

89. $m^3 + 18m^2 + 81m$

90. $y^3 + 12y^2 + 36y$

91. $5x^2y^2 + 20xy + 1$

92. $3a^2b^2 + 12ab + 1$

93. $6a^5 + 37a^3b^2 + 6ab^4$

94. $5m^5 + 26m^3h^2 + 5mh^4$

REVIEW AND PREVIEW

Multiply the following. See Sections 5.3 and 5.4.

95. $(x - 2)(x + 2)$

96. $(y^2 + 3)(y^2 - 3)$

97. $(a + 3)(a^2 - 3a + 9)$

98. $(z - 2)(z^2 + 2z + 4)$

The following graph shows the percent of online adults who participate in various social media sites. See Section 3.1.

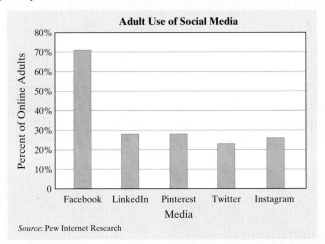

Adult Use of Social Media

Source: Pew Internet Research

99. Which social medium has the highest percent of online adult users?

100. Which social medium has the lowest percent of online adult users?

101. Describe any trend you see.

102. Why don't the percents shown in the graph add up to 100%?

CONCEPT EXTENSIONS

See the Concept Check in this section.

103. Do the terms of $4x^2 + 19x + 12$ have a common factor (other than 1)?

104. Without multiplying, decide which of the following factored forms is not a factored form of $4x^2 + 19x + 12$.

  a. $(2x + 4)(2x + 3)$ **b.** $(4x + 4)(x + 3)$

  c. $(4x + 3)(x + 4)$ **d.** $(2x + 2)(2x + 6)$

105. Describe a perfect square trinomial.

106. Write the perfect square trinomial that factors as $(x + 3y)^2$.

Write the perimeter of each figure as a simplified polynomial. Then factor the polynomial.

107.

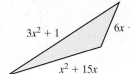

$3x^2 + 1$ $6x + 4$

$x^2 + 15x$

108.

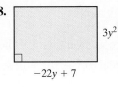

$3y^2$

$-22y + 7$

Factor each trinomial completely.

109. $4x^2 + 2x + \dfrac{1}{4}$

110. $27x^2 + 2x - \dfrac{1}{9}$

111. $4x^2(y - 1)^2 + 10x(y - 1)^2 + 25(y - 1)^2$

112. $3x^2(a + 3)^3 - 10x(a + 3)^3 + 25(a + 3)^3$

113. Fill in the blank so that $x^2 +$ _____ $x + 16$ is a perfect square trinomial.

114. Fill in the blank so that $9x^2 +$ _____ $x + 25$ is a perfect square trinomial.

The area of the largest square in the figure is $(a + b)^2$. Use this figure to answer Exercises 115 and 116.

△ **115.** Write the area of the largest square as the sum of the areas of the smaller squares and rectangles.

△ **116.** What factoring formula from this section is visually represented by this square?

Find a positive value of b so that each trinomial is factorable.

117. $3x^2 + bx - 5$ **118.** $2y^2 + by + 3$

Find a positive value of c so that each trinomial is factorable.

119. $5x^2 + 7x + c$ **120.** $11y^2 - 40y + c$

Factor completely. Don't forget to first factor out the greatest common factor.

121. $-12x^3y^2 + 3x^2y^2 + 15xy^2$

122. $-12r^3x^2 + 38r^2x^2 + 14rx^2$

123. $4x^2(y - 1)^2 + 20x(y - 1)^2 + 25(y - 1)^2$

124. $3x^2(a + 3)^3 - 28x(a + 3)^3 + 25(a + 3)^3$

Factor.

125. $3x^{2n} + 17x^n + 10$

126. $2x^{2n} + 5x^n - 12$

127. In your own words, describe the steps you will use to factor a trinomial.

6.4 **Factoring Trinomials of the Form $ax^2 + bx + c$ by Grouping**

OBJECTIVE

1 Use the Grouping Method to Factor Trinomials of the Form $ax^2 + bx + c$.

OBJECTIVE

1   Using the Grouping Method

There is an alternative method that can be used to factor trinomials of the form $ax^2 + bx + c, a \neq 1$. This method is called the **grouping method** because it uses factoring by grouping as we learned in Section 6.1.

To see how this method works, recall from Section 6.2 that to factor a trinomial such as $x^2 + 11x + 30$, we find two numbers such that

Product is 30
↓
$$x^2 + 11x + 30$$
↓
Sum is 11.

To factor a trinomial such as $2x^2 + 11x + 12$ by grouping, we use an extension of the method in Section 6.2. Here we look for two numbers such that

Product is $2 \cdot 12 = 24$
↓
$$2x^2 + 11x + 12$$
↓
Sum is 11.

This time, we use the two numbers to write

$2x^2 + 11x + 12$ as
$$= 2x^2 + \square x + \square x + 12$$

Then we factor by grouping. Since we want a positive product, 24, and a positive sum, 11, we consider pairs of positive factors of 24 only.

Factors of 24	Sum of Factors	
1, 24	25	
2, 12	14	
3, 8	11	Correct sum

The factors are 3 and 8. Now we use these factors to write the middle term $11x$ as $3x + 8x$ (or $8x + 3x$). We replace $11x$ with $3x + 8x$ in the original trinomial and then we can factor by grouping.

$$2x^2 + 11x + 12 = 2x^2 + 3x + 8x + 12$$
$$= (2x^2 + 3x) + (8x + 12) \quad \text{Group the terms.}$$
$$= x(2x + 3) + 4(2x + 3) \quad \text{Factor each group.}$$
$$= (2x + 3)(x + 4) \quad \text{Factor out } (2x + 3).$$

In general, we have the following procedure.

To Factor Trinomials by Grouping

Step 1. Factor out the greatest common factor if there is one other than 1.

Step 2. For the resulting trinomial $ax^2 + bx + c$, find two numbers whose product is $a \cdot c$ and whose sum is b.

Step 3. Write the middle term, bx, using the factors found in Step 2.

Step 4. Factor by grouping.

EXAMPLE I   Factor $3x^2 + 31x + 10$ by grouping.

Solution

Step 1. The terms of this trinomial contain no greatest common factor other than 1 (or −1).

Step 2. In $3x^2 + 31x + 10$, $a = 3$, $b = 31$, and $c = 10$.

Let's find two numbers whose product is $a \cdot c$ or $3(10) = 30$ and whose sum is b or 31. The numbers are 1 and 30, as shown in the table below.

Factors of 30	Sum of Factors	
5, 6	11	
3, 10	13	
2, 15	17	
1, 30	31	Correct sum

Step 3. Write $31x$ as $1x + 30x$ so that $3x^2 + 31x + 10 = 3x^2 + 1x + 30x + 10$.

Step 4. Factor by grouping.
$$3x^2 + 1x + 30x + 10 = x(3x + 1) + 10(3x + 1)$$
$$= (3x + 1)(x + 10) \qquad \square$$

PRACTICE
1   Factor $5x^2 + 61x + 12$ by grouping. ■

EXAMPLE 2   Factor $8x^2 - 14x + 5$ by grouping.

Solution

Step 1. The terms of this trinomial contain no greatest common factor other than 1.

Step 2. This trinomial is of the form $ax^2 + bx + c$ with $a = 8$, $b = -14$, and $c = 5$. Find two numbers whose product is $a \cdot c$ or $8 \cdot 5 = 40$, and whose sum is b or -14.
The numbers are -4 and -10, as shown in the table below.

Factors of 40	Sum of Factors	
$-40, -1$	-41	
$-20, -2$	-22	
$-10, -4$	-14	Correct sum

Step 3. Write $-14x$ as $-4x - 10x$ so that
$$8x^2 - 14x + 5 = 8x^2 - 4x - 10x + 5$$

Step 4. Factor by grouping.
$$8x^2 - 4x - 10x + 5 = 4x(2x - 1) - 5(2x - 1)$$
$$= (2x - 1)(4x - 5) \qquad \square$$

PRACTICE
2   Factor $12x^2 - 19x + 5$ by grouping. ■

EXAMPLE 3   Factor $6x^2 - 2x - 20$ by grouping.

Solution

Step 1. First factor out the greatest common factor, 2.
$$6x^2 - 2x - 20 = 2(3x^2 - x - 10)$$

Step 2. Next, notice that $a = 3$, $b = -1$, and $c = -10$ in the resulting trinomial. Find two numbers whose product is $a \cdot c$ or $3(-10) = -30$ and whose sum is b, -1. The numbers are -6 and 5.

Step 3. $3x^2 - x - 10 = 3x^2 - 6x + 5x - 10$

(Continued on the next page)

Step 4. $3x^2 - 6x + 5x - 10 = 3x(x - 2) + 5(x - 2)$

$$= (x - 2)(3x + 5)$$

The factored form of $6x^2 - 2x - 20 = 2(x - 2)(3x + 5)$.

⌐ Don't forget to include the GCF, 2. □

PRACTICE
3 Factor $30x^2 - 14x - 4$ by grouping. ■

EXAMPLE 4 Factor $18y^4 + 21y^3 - 60y^2$ by grouping.

Solution

Step 1. First factor out the greatest common factor, $3y^2$.

$$18y^4 + 21y^3 - 60y^2 = 3y^2(6y^2 + 7y - 20)$$

Step 2. Notice that $a = 6, b = 7$, and $c = -20$ in the resulting trinomial. Find two numbers whose product is $a \cdot c$ or $6(-20) = -120$ and whose sum is 7. It may help to factor -120 as a product of primes and -1.

$$-120 = 2 \cdot 2 \cdot 2 \cdot 3 \cdot 5 \cdot (-1)$$

Then choose pairings of factors until you have a pairing whose sum is 7.

$$\underbrace{\underbrace{2 \cdot 2 \cdot 2}_{\textstyle -8} \cdot 3 \cdot 5 \cdot (-1)}_{}$$

15   The numbers are -8 and 15.

Step 3. $6y^2 + 7y - 20 = 6y^2 - 8y + 15y - 20$

Step 4. $6y^2 - 8y + 15y - 20 = 2y(3y - 4) + 5(3y - 4)$

$$= (3y - 4)(2y + 5)$$

The factored form of $18y^4 + 21y^3 - 60y^2$ is $3y^2(3y - 4)(2y + 5)$.

⌐ Don't forget to include the GCF, $3y^2$ from **Step 1**. □

PRACTICE
4 Factor $40m^4 + 5m^3 - 35m^2$ by grouping. ■

EXAMPLE 5 Factor $4x^2 + 20x + 25$ by grouping.

Solution

Step 1. The terms of this trinomial contain no greatest common factor other than 1 (or -1).

Step 2. In $4x^2 + 20x + 25, a = 4, b = 20$, and $c = 25$. Find two numbers whose product is $a \cdot c$ or $4 \cdot 25 = 100$ and whose sum is 20. The numbers are 10 and 10.

Step 3. Write $20x$ as $10x + 10x$ so that

$$4x^2 + 20x + 25 = 4x^2 + 10x + 10x + 25$$

Step 4. Factor by grouping.

$$4x^2 + 10x + 10x + 25 = 2x(2x + 5) + 5(2x + 5)$$

$$= (2x + 5)(2x + 5)$$

The factored form of $4x^2 + 20x + 25$ is $(2x + 5)(2x + 5)$ or $(2x + 5)^2$. □

PRACTICE
5 Factor $16x^2 + 24x + 9$ by grouping. ■

A trinomial that is the square of a binomial, such as the trinomial in Example 5, is called a **perfect square trinomial.** From Chapter 5, there are special product formulas we can use to help us recognize and factor these trinomials. To study these formulas further, see Section 6.3, Objective 3.

> **Helpful Hint**
>
> **Remember:** A perfect square trinomial, such as the one in Example 5, may be factored by special product formulas or by other methods of factoring trinomials, such as by grouping.

✔ Vocabulary, Readiness & Video Check

For each trinomial $ax^2 + bx + c$, choose two numbers whose product is $a \cdot c$ and whose sum is b.

1. $x^2 + 6x + 8$
   a. 4, 2   **b.** 7, 1   **c.** 6, 2   **d.** 6, 8

2. $x^2 + 11x + 24$
   a. 6, 4   **b.** 24, 1   **c.** 8, 3   **d.** 2, 12

3. $2x^2 + 13x + 6$
   a. 2, 6   **b.** 12, 1   **c.** 13, 1   **d.** 3, 4

4. $4x^2 + 8x + 3$
   a. 4, 3   **b.** 4, 4   **c.** 12, 1   **d.** 2, 6

Martin-Gay Interactive Videos

See Video 6.4

Watch the section lecture video and answer the following question.

OBJECTIVE
1   **5.** In the lecture following ▤ Example 1, why does writing a term as the sum or difference of two terms suggest we'd then try to factor by grouping?

6.4   Exercise Set   MyMathLab®

Factor each polynomial by grouping. Notice that Step 3 has already been done in these exercises. See Examples 1 through 5.

1. $x^2 + 3x + 2x + 6$

2. $x^2 + 5x + 3x + 15$

3. $y^2 + 8y - 2y - 16$

4. $z^2 + 10z - 7z - 70$

5. $8x^2 - 5x - 24x + 15$

6. $4x^2 - 9x - 32x + 72$

7. $5x^4 - 3x^2 + 25x^2 - 15$

8. $2y^4 - 10y^2 + 7y^2 - 35$

MIXED PRACTICE

Factor each trinomial by grouping. Exercises 9–12 are broken into parts to help you get started. See Examples 1 through 5.

9. $6x^2 + 11x + 3$
   a. Find two numbers whose product is $6 \cdot 3 = 18$ and whose sum is 11.

   b. Write $11x$ using the factors from part **a.**
   c. Factor by grouping.

10. $8x^2 + 14x + 3$
   a. Find two numbers whose product is $8 \cdot 3 = 24$ and whose sum is 14.
   b. Write $14x$ using the factors from part **a.**
   c. Factor by grouping.

11. $15x^2 - 23x + 4$
   a. Find two numbers whose product is $15 \cdot 4 = 60$ and whose sum is -23.
   b. Write $-23x$ using the factors from part **a.**
   c. Factor by grouping.

12. $6x^2 - 13x + 5$
   a. Find two numbers whose product is $6 \cdot 5 = 30$ and whose sum is -13.
   b. Write $-13x$ using the factors from part **a.**
   c. Factor by grouping.

13. $21y^2 + 17y + 2$

14. $15x^2 + 11x + 2$

15. $7x^2 - 4x - 11$

16. $8x^2 - x - 9$

17. $10x^2 - 9x + 2$

18. $30x^2 - 23x + 3$

19. $2x^2 - 7x + 5$

20. $2x^2 - 7x + 3$

21. $12x + 4x^2 + 9$

22. $20x + 25x^2 + 4$

23. $4x^2 - 8x - 21$

24. $6x^2 - 11x - 10$

25. $10x^2 - 23x + 12$

26. $21x^2 - 13x + 2$

27. $2x^3 + 13x^2 + 15x$

28. $3x^3 + 8x^2 + 4x$

29. $16y^2 - 34y + 18$

30. $4y^2 - 2y - 12$

31. $-13x + 6 + 6x^2$

32. $-25x + 12 + 12x^2$

33. $54a^2 - 9a - 30$

34. $30a^2 + 38a - 20$

35. $20a^3 + 37a^2 + 8a$

36. $10a^3 + 17a^2 + 3a$

37. $12x^3 - 27x^2 - 27x$

38. $30x^3 - 155x^2 + 25x$

39. $3x^2y + 4xy^2 + y^3$

40. $6r^2t + 7rt^2 + t^3$

41. $20z^2 + 7z + 1$

42. $36z^2 + 6z + 1$

43. $5x^2 + 50xy + 125y^2$

44. $3x^2 + 42xy + 147y^2$

45. $24a^2 - 6ab - 30b^2$

46. $30a^2 + 5ab - 25b^2$

47. $15p^4 + 31p^3q + 2p^2q^2$

48. $20s^4 + 61s^3t + 3s^2t^2$

49. $162a^4 - 72a^2 + 8$

50. $32n^4 - 112n^2 + 98$

51. $35 + 12x + x^2$

52. $33 + 14x + x^2$

53. $6 - 11x + 5x^2$

54. $5 - 12x + 7x^2$

REVIEW AND PREVIEW

Multiply. See Sections 5.3 and 5.4.

55. $(x - 2)(x + 2)$

56. $(y - 5)(y + 5)$

57. $(y + 4)(y + 4)$

58. $(x + 7)(x + 7)$

59. $(9z + 5)(9z - 5)$

60. $(8y + 9)(8y - 9)$

61. $(x - 3)(x^2 + 3x + 9)$

62. $(2z - 1)(4z^2 + 2z + 1)$

CONCEPT EXTENSIONS

Write the perimeter of each figure as a simplified polynomial. Then factor the polynomial.

63.

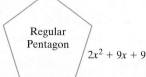

Regular Pentagon $2x^2 + 9x + 9$

64.

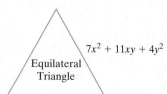

$7x^2 + 11xy + 4y^2$

Equilateral Triangle

Factor each polynomial by grouping.

65. $x^{2n} + 2x^n + 3x^n + 6$

(*Hint:* Don't forget that $x^{2n} = x^n \cdot x^n$.)

66. $x^{2n} + 6x^n + 10x^n + 60$

67. $3x^{2n} + 16x^n - 35$

68. $12x^{2n} - 40x^n + 25$

69. In your own words, explain how to factor a trinomial by grouping.

6.5 Factoring Binomials

OBJECTIVES

1 Factor the Difference of Two Squares.

2 Factor the Sum or Difference of Two Cubes.

OBJECTIVE

1 Factoring the Difference of Two Squares

When learning to multiply binomials in Chapter 5, we studied a special product, the product of the sum and difference of two terms, *a* and *b*:

$$(a + b)(a - b) = a^2 - b^2$$

For example, the product of $x + 3$ and $x - 3$ is

$$(x + 3)(x - 3) = x^2 - 9$$

The binomial $x^2 - 9$ is called a **difference of squares**. In this section, we reverse the pattern for the product of a sum and difference to factor the binomial difference of squares.

Factoring the Difference of Two Squares

$$a^2 - b^2 = (a + b)(a - b)$$

> **Helpful Hint**
>
> Since multiplication is commutative, remember that the order of factors does not matter. In other words,
>
> $$a^2 - b^2 = (a + b)(a - b) \text{ or } (a - b)(a + b)$$

EXAMPLE 1   Factor: $x^2 - 25$

Solution $x^2 - 25$ is the difference of two squares since $x^2 - 25 = x^2 - 5^2$. Therefore,

$$x^2 - 25 = x^2 - 5^2 = (x + 5)(x - 5)$$

Multiply to check.   □

PRACTICE
1   Factor: $x^2 - 81$ ■

EXAMPLE 2   Factor each difference of squares.

a. $4x^2 - 1$ b. $25a^2 - 9b^2$ c. $y^2 - \dfrac{4}{9}$

Solution

a. $4x^2 - 1 = (2x)^2 - 1^2 = (2x + 1)(2x - 1)$

b. $25a^2 - 9b^2 = (5a)^2 - (3b)^2 = (5a + 3b)(5a - 3b)$

c. $y^2 - \dfrac{4}{9} = y^2 - \left(\dfrac{2}{3}\right)^2 = \left(y + \dfrac{2}{3}\right)\left(y - \dfrac{2}{3}\right)$ □

PRACTICE
2   Factor each difference of squares.

a. $9x^2 - 1$ b. $36a^2 - 49b^2$ c. $p^2 - \dfrac{25}{36}$ ■

EXAMPLE 3   Factor: $x^4 - y^6$

Solution   This is a difference of squares since $x^4 = (x^2)^2$ and $y^6 = (y^3)^2$. Thus,

$$x^4 - y^6 = (x^2)^2 - (y^3)^2 = (x^2 + y^3)(x^2 - y^3)$$ □

PRACTICE
3   Factor: $p^4 - q^{10}$ ■

EXAMPLE 4   Factor each binomial.

a. $y^4 - 16$ b. $x^2 + 4$

Solution

a. $y^4 - 16 = (y^2)^2 - 4^2$

$= (y^2 + 4)\underbrace{(y^2 - 4)}$ Factor the difference of two squares.
                                          This binomial can be factored further
                                          since it is the difference of two squares.

$= (y^2 + 4)(y + 2)(y - 2)$ Factor the difference of two squares.

(Continued on the next page)

b. $x^2 + 4$

Note that the binomial $x^2 + 4$ is the *sum* of two squares since we can write $x^2 + 4$ as $x^2 + 2^2$. We might try to factor using $(x + 2)(x + 2)$ or $(x - 2)(x - 2)$. But when we multiply to check, we find that neither factoring is correct.

$$(x + 2)(x + 2) = x^2 + 4x + 4$$
$$(x - 2)(x - 2) = x^2 - 4x + 4$$

In both cases, the product is a trinomial, not the required binomial. In fact, $x^2 + 4$ is a prime polynomial. □

PRACTICE
4 Factor each binomial.

a. $z^4 - 81$ **b.** $m^2 + 49$ ■

Helpful Hint

When factoring, don't forget:
- See whether the terms have a greatest common factor (GCF) (other than 1) that can be factored out.
- Other than the GCF, the **sum** of two squares cannot be factored using real numbers.
- Factor completely. Always check to see whether any factors can be factored further.

EXAMPLES   Factor each binomial.

5. $4x^3 - 49x = x(4x^2 - 49)$ Factor out the GCF, x.

                $= x[(2x)^2 - 7^2]$

                $= x(2x + 7)(2x - 7)$ Factor the difference of two squares.

6. $162x^4 - 2 = 2(81x^4 - 1)$ Factor out the GCF, 2.

               $= 2(9x^2 + 1)(9x^2 - 1)$ Factor the difference of two squares.

               $= 2(9x^2 + 1)(3x + 1)(3x - 1)$ Factor the difference of two squares. □

PRACTICE
5–6 Factor each binomial.

5. $36y^3 - 25y$ **6.** $80y^4 - 5$ ■

EXAMPLE 7   Factor: $-49x^2 + 16$

Solution Factor as is, or, if you like, rearrange terms.

Factor as is: $-49x^2 + 16 = -1(49x^2 - 16)$ Factor out -1.

                      $= -1(7x + 4)(7x - 4)$ Factor the difference of two squares.

Helpful Hint

When rearranging terms, keep in mind that the sign of a term is in front of the term.

Rewrite binomial: $-49x^2 + 16 = 16 - 49x^2 = 4^2 - (7x)^2$

                       $= (4 + 7x)(4 - 7x)$

Both factorizations are correct and are equal. To see this, factor -1 from $(4 - 7x)$ in the second factorization. □

PRACTICE
7 Factor: $-9x^2 + 100$ ■

OBJECTIVE

2 Factoring the Sum or Difference of Two Cubes

Although the sum of two squares usually does not factor, the sum or difference of two cubes can be factored and reveals factoring patterns. The pattern for the sum of cubes is illustrated by multiplying the binomial $x + y$ and the trinomial $x^2 - xy + y^2$.

$$x^2 - xy + y^2$$
$$\underline{\qquad\qquad x + y}$$
$$x^2y - xy^2 + y^3$$
$$\underline{x^3 - x^2y + xy^2\qquad}$$
$$x^3 \qquad\qquad\qquad + y^3$$

Thus, $(x + y)(x^2 - xy + y^2) = x^3 + y^3$ Sum of cubes

The pattern for the difference of two cubes is illustrated by multiplying the binomial $x - y$ by the trinomial $x^2 + xy + y^2$. The result is

$$(x - y)(x^2 + xy + y^2) = x^3 - y^3$$ Difference of cubes

Factoring the Sum or Difference of Two Cubes

$$a^3 + b^3 = (a + b)(a^2 - ab + b^2)$$
$$a^3 - b^3 = (a - b)(a^2 + ab + b^2)$$

Recall that "factor" means "to write as a product." Above are patterns for writing sums and differences as products.

EXAMPLE 8   Factor: $x^3 + 8$

Solution First, write the binomial in the form $a^3 + b^3$.

$$x^3 + 8 = x^3 + 2^3$$ Write in the form $a^3 + b^3$.

If we replace a with x and b with 2 in the formula above, we have

$$x^3 + 2^3 = (x + 2)[x^2 - (x)(2) + 2^2]$$
$$= (x + 2)(x^2 - 2x + 4)$$

PRACTICE

8   Factor: $x^3 + 64$

Helpful Hint

When factoring sums or differences of cubes, notice the sign patterns.

same sign

$$x^3 + y^3 = (x + y)(x^2 - xy + y^2)$$

opposite signs   always positive

same sign

$$x^3 - y^3 = (x - y)(x^2 + xy + y^2)$$

opposite signs   always positive

EXAMPLE 9   Factor: $y^3 - 27$

Solution $y^3 - 27 = y^3 - 3^3$ Write in the form $a^3 - b^3$.
$$= (y - 3)[y^2 + (y)(3) + 3^2]$$
$$= (y - 3)(y^2 + 3y + 9)$$

PRACTICE

9   Factor: $x^3 - 125$

EXAMPLE 10 Factor: $64x^3 + 1$

Solution
$$64x^3 + 1 = (4x)^3 + 1^3$$
$$= (4x + 1)[(4x)^2 - (4x)(1) + 1^2]$$
$$= (4x + 1)(16x^2 - 4x + 1)$$

PRACTICE
10 Factor: $27y^3 + 1$

EXAMPLE 11 Factor: $54a^3 - 16b^3$

Solution Remember to factor out the greatest common factor first before using other factoring methods.

$$54a^3 - 16b^3 = 2(27a^3 - 8b^3) \qquad \text{Factor out the GCF, 2.}$$
$$= 2[(3a)^3 - (2b)^3] \quad \text{Difference of two cubes}$$
$$= 2(3a - 2b)[(3a)^2 + (3a)(2b) + (2b)^2]$$
$$= 2(3a - 2b)(9a^2 + 6ab + 4b^2)$$

PRACTICE
11 Factor: $32x^3 - 500y^3$

Graphing Calculator Explorations

Graphing

A graphing calculator is a convenient tool for evaluating an expression at a given replacement value. For example, let's evaluate $x^2 - 6x$ when $x = 2$. To do so, store the value 2 in the variable x and then enter and evaluate the algebraic expression.

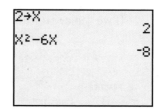

The value of $x^2 - 6x$ when $x = 2$ is -8. You may want to use this method for evaluating expressions as you explore the following.

We can use a graphing calculator to explore factoring patterns numerically. Use your calculator to evaluate $x^2 - 2x + 1$, $x^2 - 2x - 1$, and $(x - 1)^2$ for each value of x given in the table. What do you observe?

	$x^2 - 2x + 1$	$x^2 - 2x - 1$	$(x - 1)^2$
$x = 5$			
$x = -3$			
$x = 2.7$			
$x = -12.1$			
$x = 0$			

Notice in each case that $x^2 - 2x - 1 \neq (x - 1)^2$. Because for each x in the table the value of $x^2 - 2x + 1$ and the value of $(x - 1)^2$ are the same, we might guess that $x^2 - 2x + 1 = (x - 1)^2$. We can verify our guess algebraically with multiplication:

$$(x - 1)(x - 1) = x^2 - x - x + 1 = x^2 - 2x + 1$$

✓ Vocabulary, Readiness & Video Check

Use the choices below to fill in each blank. Some choices may be used more than once and some choices may not be used at all.

true	difference of two squares	sum of two cubes
false	difference of two cubes	

1. The expression $x^3 - 27$ is called a _____.
2. The expression $x^2 - 49$ is called a _____.
3. The expression $z^3 + 1$ is called a _____.
4. True or false: The binomial $y^2 + 9$ factors as $(y + 3)^2$. _____

Write each term as a square.

5. $49x^2$ **6.** $25y^4$

Write each term as a cube.

7. $8y^3$ **8.** x^6

Martin-Gay Interactive Videos

See Video 6.5 🍎

Watch the section lecture video and answer the following questions.

OBJECTIVE 1   **9.** In Examples 1 and 2, what are two reasons the original binomial is rewritten so that each term is a square?

OBJECTIVE 1   **10.** From Example 3, what is a prime polynomial?

OBJECTIVE 2   **11.** In Examples 6–8, what tips are given to remember how to factor the sum or difference of two cubes rather than memorizing the formulas?

6.5 Exercise Set MyMathLab® ▶

Factor each binomial completely. See Examples 1 through 7.

▶ **1.** $x^2 - 4$
2. $x^2 - 36$
3. $81p^2 - 1$
4. $49m^2 - 1$
5. $25y^2 - 9$
6. $49a^2 - 16$
▶ **7.** $121m^2 - 100n^2$
8. $169a^2 - 49b^2$
9. $x^2y^2 - 1$
10. $a^2b^2 - 16$
11. $x^2 - \dfrac{1}{4}$
12. $y^2 - \dfrac{1}{16}$
13. $-4r^2 + 1$
14. $-9t^2 + 1$
▶ **15.** $16r^2 + 1$
16. $49y^2 + 1$
17. $-36 + x^2$

18. $-1 + y^2$
19. $m^4 - 1$
20. $n^4 - 16$
21. $m^4 - n^{18}$
22. $n^4 - r^6$

Factor the sum or difference of two cubes. See Examples 8 through 11.

▶ **23.** $x^3 + 125$
24. $p^3 + 1$
25. $8a^3 - 1$
26. $27y^3 - 1$
27. $m^3 + 27n^3$
28. $y^3 + 64z^3$
29. $5k^3 + 40$
30. $6r^3 + 162$
▶ **31.** $x^3y^3 - 64$
32. $a^3b^3 - 8$
33. $250r^3 - 128t^3$
34. $24x^3 - 81y^3$

MIXED PRACTICE

Factor each binomial completely. See Examples 1 through 11.

35. $r^2 - 64$

36. $q^2 - 121$

37. $x^2 - 169y^2$

38. $x^2 - 225y^2$

39. $27 - t^3$

40. $125 - r^3$

41. $18r^2 - 8$

42. $32t^2 - 50$

43. $9xy^2 - 4x$

44. $36x^2y - 25y$

45. $8m^3 + 64$

46. $2x^3 + 54$

47. $xy^3 - 9xyz^2$

48. $x^3y - 4xy^3$

49. $36x^2 - 64y^2$

50. $225a^2 - 81b^2$

51. $144 - 81x^2$

52. $12x^2 - 27$

53. $x^3y^3 - z^6$

54. $a^3b^3 - c^9$

55. $49 - \dfrac{9}{25}m^2$

56. $100 - \dfrac{4}{81}n^2$

57. $t^3 + 343$

58. $s^3 + 216$

59. $n^3 + 49n$

60. $y^3 + 64y$

61. $x^6 - 81x^2$

62. $n^9 - n^5$

63. $64p^3q - 81pq^3$

64. $100x^3y - 49xy^3$

65. $27x^2y^3 + xy^2$

66. $8x^3y^3 + x^3y$

67. $125a^4 - 64ab^3$

68. $64m^4 - 27mn^3$

69. $16x^4 - 64x^2$

70. $25y^4 - 100y^2$

REVIEW AND PREVIEW

Solve each equation. See Section 2.4.

71. $x - 6 = 0$

72. $y + 5 = 0$

73. $2m + 4 = 0$

74. $3x - 9 = 0$

75. $5z - 1 = 0$

76. $4a + 2 = 0$

CONCEPT EXTENSIONS

Factor each expression completely.

77. $(x + 2)^2 - y^2$

78. $(y - 6)^2 - z^2$

79. $a^2(b - 4) - 16(b - 4)$

80. $m^2(n + 8) - 9(n + 8)$

81. $(x^2 + 6x + 9) - 4y^2$ (*Hint:* Factor the trinomial in parentheses first.)

82. $(x^2 + 2x + 1) - 36y^2$

83. $x^{2n} - 100$

84. $x^{2n} - 81$

85. What binomial multiplied by $(x - 6)$ gives the difference of two squares?

86. What binomial multiplied by $(5 + y)$ gives the difference of two squares?

87. In your own words, explain how to tell whether a binomial is a difference of squares. Then explain how to factor a difference of squares.

88. In your own words, explain how to tell whether a binomial is a sum of cubes. Then explain how to factor a sum of cubes.

89. The Toroweap Overlook, on the North Rim of the Grand Canyon, lies 3000 vertical feet above the Colorado River. The view is spectacular, and the sheer drop is dramatic. A film crew creating a documentary about the Grand Canyon has built a camera platform 136 feet above the Overlook. A camera filter comes loose and falls to the river below. The height of the filter above the river after t seconds is given by the expression $3136 - 16t^2$.

   a. Find the height of the filter above the river after 3 seconds.

   b. Find the height of the filter above the river after 10 seconds.

   c. To the nearest whole second, estimate when the filter lands in the river.

   d. Factor $3136 - 16t^2$.

90. An object is dropped from the top of Pittsburgh's USX Tower, which is 841 feet tall. (*Source: World Almanac* research) The height of the object after t seconds is given by the expression $841 - 16t^2$.

   a. Find the height of the object after 2 seconds.

   b. Find the height of the object after 5 seconds.

   c. To the nearest whole second, estimate when the object hits the ground.

   d. Factor $841 - 16t^2$.

841 feet

91. At this writing, the tallest completed building in the world is the Burj Khalifa, in Dubai, measuring a height of 2717 feet. (*Source:* Council on Tall Buildings and Urban Habitat) Suppose an action picture is being filmed there and a stunt man is making his way to the top of the spire. He sways in the wind and drops a clip from the height of 2704 feet. The height of the clip after t seconds is given by the expression $2704 - 16t^2$.

  a. Find the height of the clip after 3 seconds.

  b. Find the height of the clip after 7 seconds.

  c. To the nearest whole second, estimate when the clip will hit the ground.

  d. Factor $2704 - 16t^2$.

92. A performer with the Moscow Circus is planning a stunt involving a free fall from the top of the Moscow State University building, which is 784 feet tall. (*Source:* Council on Tall Buildings and Urban Habitat) Neglecting air resistance, the performer's height above gigantic cushions positioned at ground level after t seconds is given by the expression $784 - 16t^2$.

  a. Find the performer's height after 2 seconds.

  b. Find the performer's height after 5 seconds.

  c. To the nearest whole second, estimate when the performer reaches the cushions positioned at ground level.

  d. Factor $784 - 16t^2$.

Integrated Review Choosing a Factoring Strategy

Sections 6.1–6.5

The following steps may be helpful when factoring polynomials.

> **Factoring a Polynomial**
>
> **Step 1.** Are there any common factors? If so, factor out the GCF.
>
> **Step 2.** How many terms are in the polynomial?
>
>   **a.** If there are **two** terms, decide if one of the following can be applied.
>
>   **i.** Difference of two squares: $a^2 - b^2 = (a + b)(a - b)$.
>
>   **ii.** Difference of two cubes: $a^3 - b^3 = (a - b)(a^2 + ab + b^2)$.
>
>   **iii.** Sum of two cubes: $a^3 + b^3 = (a + b)(a^2 - ab + b^2)$.
>
>   **b.** If there are **three** terms, try one of the following.
>
>   **i.** Perfect square trinomial: $a^2 + 2ab + b^2 = (a + b)^2$
> $$a^2 - 2ab + b^2 = (a - b)^2.$$
>
>   **ii.** If not a perfect square trinomial, factor using the methods presented in Sections 6.2 through 6.4.
>
>   **c.** If there are **four** or more terms, try factoring by grouping.
>
> **Step 3.** See if any factors in the factored polynomial can be factored further.
>
> **Step 4.** Check by multiplying.

Study the next five examples to help you use the steps above.

EXAMPLE 1 Factor: $10t^2 - 17t + 3$

Solution

Step 1. The terms of this polynomial have no common factor (other than 1).

Step 2. There are three terms, so this polynomial is a trinomial. This trinomial is not a perfect square trinomial, so factor using methods from earlier sections.

$$\text{Factors of } 10t^2: \quad 10t^2 = 2t \cdot 5t, \qquad 10t^2 = t \cdot 10t$$

(Continued on next page)

Since the middle term, $-17t$, has a negative numerical coefficient, find negative factors of 3.

$$\text{Factors of 3:} \quad 3 = -1 \cdot -3$$

Try different combinations of these factors. The correct combination is

$$(2t - 3)(5t - 1) = 10t^2 - 17t + 3$$

$$-15t$$
$$-2t$$
$$\overline{-17t} \quad \text{Correct middle term}$$

Step 3. No factor can be factored further, so we have factored completely.

Step 4. To check, multiply $2t - 3$ and $5t - 1$.

$$(2t - 3)(5t - 1) = 10t^2 - 2t - 15t + 3 = 10t^2 - 17t + 3$$

The factored form of $10t^2 - 17t + 3$ is $(2t - 3)(5t - 1)$. □

PRACTICE
1 Factor: $6x^2 - 11x + 3$

EXAMPLE 2 Factor: $2x^3 + 3x^2 - 2x - 3$

Solution

Step 1. There are no factors common to all terms.

Step 2. Try factoring by grouping since this polynomial has four terms.

$$2x^3 + 3x^2 - 2x - 3 = x^2(2x + 3) - 1(2x + 3) \quad \text{Factor out the greatest common factor for each pair of terms.}$$

$$= (2x + 3)(x^2 - 1) \quad \text{Factor out } 2x + 3.$$

Step 3. The binomial $x^2 - 1$ can be factored further. It is the difference of two squares.

$$= (2x + 3)(x + 1)(x - 1) \quad \text{Factor } x^2 - 1 \text{ as a difference of squares.}$$

Step 4. Check by finding the product of the three binomials. The polynomial factored completely is $(2x + 3)(x + 1)(x - 1)$. □

PRACTICE
2 Factor: $3x^3 + x^2 - 12x - 4$

EXAMPLE 3 Factor: $12m^2 - 3n^2$

Solution

Step 1. The terms of this binomial contain a greatest common factor of 3.

$$12m^2 - 3n^2 = 3(4m^2 - n^2) \quad \text{Factor out the greatest common factor.}$$

Step 2. The binomial $4m^2 - n^2$ is a difference of squares.

$$= 3(2m + n)(2m - n) \quad \text{Factor the difference of squares.}$$

Step 3. No factor can be factored further.

Step 4. We check by multiplying.

$$3(2m + n)(2m - n) = 3(4m^2 - n^2) = 12m^2 - 3n^2$$

The factored form of $12m^2 - 3n^2$ is $3(2m + n)(2m - n)$. □

PRACTICE
3 Factor: $27x^2 - 3y^2$

EXAMPLE 4   Factor: $x^3 + 27y^3$

Solution

Step 1. The terms of this binomial contain no common factor (other than 1).

Step 2. This binomial is the sum of two cubes.

$$\begin{aligned} x^3 + 27y^3 &= (x)^3 + (3y)^3 \\ &= (x + 3y)[x^2 - x(3y) + (3y)^2] \\ &= (x + 3y)(x^2 - 3xy + 9y^2) \end{aligned}$$

Step 3. No factor can be factored further.

Step 4. We check by multiplying.

$$\begin{aligned} (x + 3y)(x^2 - 3xy + 9y^2) &= x(x^2 - 3xy + 9y^2) + 3y(x^2 - 3xy + 9y^2) \\ &= x^3 - 3x^2y + 9xy^2 + 3x^2y - 9xy^2 + 27y^3 \\ &= x^3 + 27y^3 \end{aligned}$$

Thus, $x^3 + 27y^3$ factored completely is $(x + 3y)(x^2 - 3xy + 9y^2)$.   □

PRACTICE

4   Factor: $8a^3 + b^3$ ■

EXAMPLE 5   Factor: $30a^2b^3 + 55a^2b^2 - 35a^2b$

Solution

Step 1. $30a^2b^3 + 55a^2b^2 - 35a^2b = 5a^2b(6b^2 + 11b - 7)$ Factor out the GCF.

Step 2. $= 5a^2b(2b - 1)(3b + 7)$ Factor the resulting trinomial.

Step 3. No factor can be factored further.

Step 4. Check by multiplying.

The trinomial factored completely is $5a^2b(2b - 1)(3b + 7)$.   □

PRACTICE

5   Factor: $60x^3y^2 - 66x^2y^2 - 36xy^2$ ■

Factor the following completely.

1. $x^2 + 2xy + y^2$

2. $x^2 - 2xy + y^2$

3. $a^2 + 11a - 12$

4. $a^2 - 11a + 10$

5. $a^2 - a - 6$

6. $a^2 - 2a + 1$

7. $x^2 + 2x + 1$

8. $x^2 + x - 2$

9. $x^2 + 4x + 3$

10. $x^2 + x - 6$

11. $x^2 + 7x + 12$

12. $x^2 + x - 12$

13. $x^2 + 3x - 4$

14. $x^2 - 7x + 10$

15. $x^2 + 2x - 15$

16. $x^2 + 11x + 30$

17. $x^2 - x - 30$

18. $x^2 + 11x + 24$

19. $2x^2 - 98$

20. $3x^2 - 75$

21. $x^2 + 3x + xy + 3y$

22. $3y - 21 + xy - 7x$

23. $x^2 + 6x - 16$

24. $x^2 - 3x - 28$

▶ **25.** $4x^3 + 20x^2 - 56x$

26. $6x^3 - 6x^2 - 120x$

27. $12x^2 + 34x + 24$

28. $8a^2 + 6ab - 5b^2$

29. $4a^2 - b^2$

30. $28 - 13x - 6x^2$

31. $20 - 3x - 2x^2$

32. $x^2 - 2x + 4$

33. $a^2 + a - 3$

34. $6y^2 + y - 15$

35. $4x^2 - x - 5$

36. $x^2y - y^3$

37. $4t^2 + 36$

38. $x^2 + x + xy + y$

39. $ax + 2x + a + 2$

40. $18x^3 - 63x^2 + 9x$

41. $12a^3 - 24a^2 + 4a$

42. $x^2 + 14x - 32$

43. $x^2 - 14x - 48$

44. $16a^2 - 56ab + 49b^2$

45. $25p^2 - 70pq + 49q^2$

46. $7x^2 + 24xy + 9y^2$

▶ **47.** $125 - 8y^3$

48. $64x^3 + 27$

49. $-x^2 - x + 30$

50. $-x^2 + 6x - 8$

51. $14 + 5x - x^2$

52. $3 - 2x - x^2$

53. $3x^4y + 6x^3y - 72x^2y$

54. $2x^3y + 8x^2y^2 - 10xy^3$

55. $5x^3y^2 - 40x^2y^3 + 35xy^4$

56. $4x^4y - 8x^3y - 60x^2y$

57. $12x^3y + 243xy$

58. $6x^3y^2 + 8xy^2$

59. $4 - x^2$

60. $9 - y^2$

61. $3rs - s + 12r - 4$

62. $x^3 - 2x^2 + 3x - 6$

63. $4x^2 - 8xy - 3x + 6y$

64. $4x^2 - 2xy - 7yz + 14xz$

65. $6x^2 + 18xy + 12y^2$

66. $12x^2 + 46xy - 8y^2$

67. $xy^2 - 4x + 3y^2 - 12$

68. $x^2y^2 - 9x^2 + 3y^2 - 27$

69. $5(x + y) + x(x + y)$

70. $7(x - y) + y(x - y)$

71. $14t^2 - 9t + 1$

72. $3t^2 - 5t + 1$

73. $3x^2 + 2x - 5$

74. $7x^2 + 19x - 6$

75. $x^2 + 9xy - 36y^2$

76. $3x^2 + 10xy - 8y^2$

77. $1 - 8ab - 20a^2b^2$

78. $1 - 7ab - 60a^2b^2$

79. $9 - 10x^2 + x^4$

80. $36 - 13x^2 + x^4$

81. $x^4 - 14x^2 - 32$

82. $x^4 - 22x^2 - 75$

83. $x^2 - 23x + 120$

84. $y^2 + 22y + 96$

85. $6x^3 - 28x^2 + 16x$

86. $6y^3 - 8y^2 - 30y$

87. $27x^3 - 125y^3$

88. $216y^3 - z^3$

89. $x^3y^3 + 8z^3$

90. $27a^3b^3 + 8$

91. $2xy - 72x^3y$

92. $2x^3 - 18x$

93. $x^3 + 6x^2 - 4x - 24$

94. $x^3 - 2x^2 - 36x + 72$

95. $6a^3 + 10a^2$

96. $4n^2 - 6n$

97. $a^2(a + 2) + 2(a + 2)$

98. $a - b + x(a - b)$

99. $x^3 - 28 + 7x^2 - 4x$

100. $a^3 - 45 - 9a + 5a^2$

CONCEPT EXTENSIONS

Factor.

101. $(x - y)^2 - z^2$

102. $(x + 2y)^2 - 9$

103. $81 - (5x + 1)^2$

104. $b^2 - (4a + c)^2$

105. Explain why it makes good sense to factor out the GCF first, before using other methods of factoring.

106. The sum of two squares usually does not factor. Is the sum of two squares $9x^2 + 81y^2$ factorable?

107. Which of the following are equivalent to $(x + 10)(x - 7)$?

   a. $(x - 7)(x + 10)$ **b.** $-1(x + 10)(x - 7)$

   c. $-1(x + 10)(7 - x)$ **d.** $-1(-x - 10)(7 - x)$

108. Which of the following are equivalent to $(x - 2)(x - 5)$?

   a. $-1(x + 2)(x + 5)$ **b.** $(x - 5)(x - 2)$

   c. $(5 - x)(2 - x)$ **d.** $-1(x + 2)(x - 5)$

6.6   Solving Quadratic Equations by Factoring

OBJECTIVES

1 Solve Quadratic Equations by Factoring.

2 Solve Equations with Degree Greater than 2 by Factoring.

3 Find the *x*-Intercepts of the Graph of a Quadratic Equation in Two Variables.

In this section, we introduce a new type of equation—the **quadratic equation**.

> **Quadratic Equation**
>
> A quadratic equation is one that can be written in the form
>
> $$ax^2 + bx + c = 0$$
>
> where a, b, and c are real numbers and $a \neq 0$.

Some examples of quadratic equations are shown below.

$$x^2 - 9x - 22 = 0 \qquad 4x^2 - 28 = -49 \qquad x(2x - 7) = 4$$

The form $ax^2 + bx + c = 0$ is called the **standard form** of a quadratic equation. The quadratic equation $x^2 - 9x - 22 = 0$ is the only equation above that is in standard form.

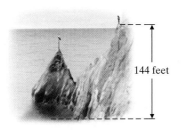

144 feet

Quadratic equations model many real-life situations. For example, let's suppose we want to know how long before a person diving from a 144-foot cliff reaches the ocean. The answer to this question is found by solving the quadratic equation $-16t^2 + 144 = 0$. (See Example 1 in Section 6.7.)

OBJECTIVE

1 Solving Quadratic Equations by Factoring

Some quadratic equations can be solved by making use of factoring and the **zero factor property.**

Zero Factor Property

If a and b are real numbers and if $ab = 0$, then $a = 0$ or $b = 0$.

This property states that if the product of two numbers is 0 then at least one of the numbers must be 0.

EXAMPLE 1 Solve: $(x - 3)(x + 1) = 0$

Solution If this equation is to be a true statement, then either the factor $x - 3$ must be 0 or the factor $x + 1$ must be 0. In other words, either

$$x - 3 = 0 \quad \text{or} \quad x + 1 = 0$$

If we solve these two linear equations, we have

$$x = 3 \quad \text{or} \quad x = -1$$

Thus, 3 and -1 are both solutions of the equation $(x - 3)(x + 1) = 0$. To check, we replace x with 3 in the original equation. Then we replace x with -1 in the original equation.

Check: Let $x = 3$.

$(x - 3)(x + 1) = 0$

$(3 - 3)(3 + 1) \stackrel{?}{=} 0$ Replace x with 3.

$0(4) = 0$ True

Let $x = -1$.

$(x - 3)(x + 1) = 0$

$(-1 - 3)(-1 + 1) \stackrel{?}{=} 0$ Replace x with -1.

$(-4)(0) = 0$ True

The solutions are 3 and -1, or we say that the solution set is $\{-1, 3\}$.   ☐

PRACTICE

1 Solve: $(x + 4)(x - 5) = 0$ ■

Helpful Hint

The zero factor property says that _if a product is 0, then a factor is 0._

If $a \cdot b = 0$, then $a = 0$ or $b = 0$.

If $x(x + 5) = 0$, then $x = 0$ or $x + 5 = 0$.

If $(x + 7)(2x - 3) = 0$, then $x + 7 = 0$ or $2x - 3 = 0$.

Use this property only when the product is 0.

For example, if $a \cdot b = 8$, we do not know the value of a or b. The values may be $a = 2, b = 4$ or $a = 8, b = 1$, or any other two numbers whose product is 8.

EXAMPLE 2 Solve: $(x - 5)(2x + 7) = 0$

Solution: The product is 0. By the zero factor property, this is true only when a factor is 0. To solve, we set each factor equal to 0 and solve the resulting linear equations.

$$(x - 5)(2x + 7) = 0$$

$$x - 5 = 0 \quad \text{or} \quad 2x + 7 = 0$$

$$x = 5 \quad \text{or} \quad 2x = -7$$

$$x = -\frac{7}{2}$$

(Continued on next page)

Check: Let $x = 5$.

$$(x - 5)(2x + 7) = 0$$
$$(5 - 5)(2 \cdot 5 + 7) \stackrel{?}{=} 0 \quad \text{Replace } x \text{ with } 5.$$
$$0 \cdot 17 \stackrel{?}{=} 0$$
$$0 = 0 \quad \text{True}$$

Let $x = -\dfrac{7}{2}$.

$$(x - 5)(2x + 7) = 0$$
$$\left(-\frac{7}{2} - 5\right)\left(2\left(-\frac{7}{2}\right) + 7\right) \stackrel{?}{=} 0 \quad \text{Replace } x \text{ with } -\frac{7}{2}.$$
$$\left(-\frac{17}{2}\right)(-7 + 7) \stackrel{?}{=} 0$$
$$\left(-\frac{17}{2}\right) \cdot 0 \stackrel{?}{=} 0$$
$$0 = 0 \quad \text{True}$$

The solutions are 5 and $-\dfrac{7}{2}$.   □

PRACTICE

2 Solve: $(x - 12)(4x + 3) = 0$ ■

EXAMPLE 3 Solve: $x(5x - 2) = 0$

Solution
$$x(5x - 2) = 0$$
$$x = 0 \quad \text{or} \quad 5x - 2 = 0 \quad \text{Use the zero factor property.}$$
$$5x = 2$$
$$x = \frac{2}{5}$$

Check: Let $x = 0$.

$$x(5x - 2) = 0$$
$$0(5 \cdot 0 - 2) \stackrel{?}{=} 0 \quad \text{Replace } x \text{ with } 0.$$
$$0(-2) \stackrel{?}{=} 0$$
$$0 = 0 \quad \text{True}$$

Let $x = \dfrac{2}{5}$.

$$x(5x - 2) = 0$$
$$\frac{2}{5}\left(5 \cdot \frac{2}{5} - 2\right) \stackrel{?}{=} 0 \quad \text{Replace } x \text{ with } \frac{2}{5}.$$
$$\frac{2}{5}(2 - 2) \stackrel{?}{=} 0$$
$$\frac{2}{5}(0) \stackrel{?}{=} 0$$
$$0 = 0 \quad \text{True}$$

The solutions are 0 and $\dfrac{2}{5}$.   □

PRACTICE

3 Solve: $x(7x - 6) = 0$ ■

EXAMPLE 4 Solve: $x^2 - 9x - 22 = 0$

Solution One side of the equation is 0. However, to use the zero factor property, one side of the equation must be 0 _and_ the other side must be written as a product (must be factored). Thus, we must first factor this polynomial.

$$x^2 - 9x - 22 = 0$$
$$(x - 11)(x + 2) = 0 \quad \text{Factor.}$$

Now we can apply the zero factor property.

$$x - 11 = 0 \quad \text{or} \quad x + 2 = 0$$
$$x = 11 \quad \text{or} \quad x = -2$$

Check: Let $x = 11$.   Let $x = -2$.

$$x^2 - 9x - 22 = 0 \qquad\qquad\qquad x^2 - 9x - 22 = 0$$
$$11^2 - 9 \cdot 11 - 22 \stackrel{?}{=} 0 \qquad\qquad (-2)^2 - 9(-2) - 22 \stackrel{?}{=} 0$$
$$121 - 99 - 22 \stackrel{?}{=} 0 \qquad\qquad\qquad 4 + 18 - 22 \stackrel{?}{=} 0$$
$$22 - 22 \stackrel{?}{=} 0 \qquad\qquad\qquad\qquad 22 - 22 \stackrel{?}{=} 0$$
$$0 = 0 \quad \text{True} \qquad\qquad\qquad\qquad 0 = 0 \quad \text{True}$$

The solutions are 11 and -2.

PRACTICE

4 Solve: $x^2 - 8x - 48 = 0$

EXAMPLE 5 Solve: $4x^2 - 28x = -49$

Solution First we rewrite the equation in standard form so that one side is 0. Then we factor the polynomial.

$$4x^2 - 28x = -49$$
$$4x^2 - 28x + 49 = 0 \qquad \text{Write in standard form by adding 49 to both sides.}$$
$$(2x - 7)(2x - 7) = 0 \qquad \text{Factor.}$$

Next we use the zero factor property and set each factor equal to 0. Since the factors are the same, the related equations will give the same solution.

$$2x - 7 = 0 \quad \text{or} \quad 2x - 7 = 0 \qquad \text{Set each factor equal to 0.}$$
$$2x = 7 \quad \text{or} \qquad 2x = 7 \qquad \text{Solve.}$$
$$x = \frac{7}{2} \quad \text{or} \qquad x = \frac{7}{2}$$

Check: Although $\frac{7}{2}$ occurs twice, there is a single solution. Check this solution in the original equation. The solution is $\frac{7}{2}$.

PRACTICE

5 Solve: $9x^2 - 24x = -16$

The following steps may be used to solve a quadratic equation by factoring.

To Solve Quadratic Equations by Factoring

Step 1. Write the equation in standard form so that one side of the equation is 0.

Step 2. Factor the quadratic expression completely.

Step 3. Set each factor containing a variable equal to 0.

Step 4. Solve the resulting equations.

Step 5. Check each solution in the original equation.

Since it is not always possible to factor a quadratic polynomial, not all quadratic equations can be solved by factoring. Other methods of solving quadratic equations are presented in Chapter 9.

EXAMPLE 6 Solve: $x(2x - 7) = 4$

Solution First we write the equation in standard form; then we factor.

$$x(2x - 7) = 4$$
$$2x^2 - 7x = 4 \qquad \text{Multiply.}$$
$$2x^2 - 7x - 4 = 0 \qquad \text{Write in standard form.}$$
$$(2x + 1)(x - 4) = 0 \qquad \text{Factor.}$$
$$2x + 1 = 0 \quad \text{or} \quad x - 4 = 0 \qquad \text{Set each factor equal to zero.}$$
$$2x = -1 \quad \text{or} \qquad x = 4 \qquad \text{Solve.}$$
$$x = -\frac{1}{2}$$

Check the solutions in the original equation. The solutions are $-\frac{1}{2}$ and 4. □

> **Helpful Hint**
>
> To solve the equation $x(2x - 7) = 4$, do **not** set each factor equal to 4. Remember that to apply the zero factor property, one side of the equation must be 0 and the other side of the equation must be in factored form.

PRACTICE

6 Solve: $x(3x + 7) = 6$ ■

✔ **CONCEPT CHECK**

Explain the error and solve the equation correctly.

$$(x - 3)(x + 1) = 5$$
$$x - 3 = 5 \quad \text{or} \quad x + 1 = 5$$
$$x = 8 \quad \text{or} \qquad x = 4$$

EXAMPLE 7 Solve: $-2x^2 - 4x + 30 = 0$

Solution The equation is in standard form, so we begin by factoring out the greatest common factor, -2.

$$-2x^2 - 4x + 30 = 0$$
$$-2(x^2 + 2x - 15) = 0 \qquad \text{Factor out } -2.$$
$$-2(x + 5)(x - 3) = 0 \qquad \text{Factor the quadratic.}$$

Next, set each factor **containing a variable** equal to 0.

$$x + 5 = 0 \qquad \text{or} \qquad x - 3 = 0 \qquad \text{Set each factor containing a variable equal to 0.}$$
$$x = -5 \qquad \text{or} \qquad x = 3 \qquad \text{Solve.}$$

Note: The factor -2 is a constant term containing no variables and can never equal 0. The solutions are -5 and 3. □

PRACTICE

7 Solve: $-3x^2 - 6x + 72 = 0$ ■

Answer to Concept Check:
To use the zero factor property, one side of the equation must be 0, not 5. Correctly, $(x - 3)(x + 1) = 5$, $x^2 - 2x - 3 = 5, x^2 - 2x - 8 = 0$, $(x - 4)(x + 2) = 0, x - 4 = 0$ or $x + 2 = 0, x = 4$ or $x = -2$.

OBJECTIVE

2 Solving Equations with Degree Greater than Two by Factoring

Some equations involving polynomials of degree higher than 2 may also be solved by factoring and then applying the zero factor property.

EXAMPLE 8   Solve: $3x^3 - 12x = 0$

Solution   Factor the left side of the equation. Begin by factoring out the greatest common factor, $3x$.

$$3x^3 - 12x = 0$$
$$3x(x^2 - 4) = 0 \quad \text{Factor out the GCF, } 3x.$$
$$3x(x + 2)(x - 2) = 0 \quad \text{Factor } x^2 - 4, \text{ a difference of squares.}$$

$3x = 0 \quad$ or $\quad x + 2 = 0 \quad$ or $\quad x - 2 = 0 \quad$ Set each factor equal to 0.

$x = 0 \quad$ or $\quad x = -2 \quad$ or $\quad x = 2 \quad$ Solve.

Thus, the equation $3x^3 - 12x = 0$ has three solutions: $0, -2$, and 2. To check, replace x with each solution in the original equation.

Let $x = 0$.	**Let $x = -2$.**	**Let $x = 2$.**
$3(0)^3 - 12(0) \stackrel{?}{=} 0$	$3(-2)^3 - 12(-2) \stackrel{?}{=} 0$	$3(2)^3 - 12(2) \stackrel{?}{=} 0$
$0 = 0$	$3(-8) + 24 \stackrel{?}{=} 0$	$3(8) - 24 \stackrel{?}{=} 0$
	$0 = 0$	$0 = 0$

Substituting $0, -2$, or 2 into the original equation results each time in a true equation. The solutions are $0, -2$, and 2. □

PRACTICE
8   Solve: $7x^3 - 63x = 0$

EXAMPLE 9   Solve: $(5x - 1)(2x^2 + 15x + 18) = 0$

Solution

$$(5x - 1)(2x^2 + 15x + 18) = 0$$
$$(5x - 1)(2x + 3)(x + 6) = 0 \quad \text{Factor the trinomial.}$$

$5x - 1 = 0 \quad$ or $\quad 2x + 3 = 0 \quad$ or $\quad x + 6 = 0 \quad$ Set each factor equal to 0.

$5x = 1 \quad$ or $\qquad 2x = -3 \quad$ or $\qquad x = -6 \quad$ Solve.

$$x = \frac{1}{5} \quad \text{or} \quad x = -\frac{3}{2}$$

The solutions are $\frac{1}{5}, -\frac{3}{2}$, and -6. Check by replacing x with each solution in the original equation. The solutions are $-6, -\frac{3}{2}$, and $\frac{1}{5}$. □

PRACTICE
9   Solve: $(3x - 2)(2x^2 - 13x + 15) = 0$

EXAMPLE 10   Solve: $2x^3 - 4x^2 - 30x = 0$

Solution   Begin by factoring out the GCF, $2x$.

$$2x^3 - 4x^2 - 30x = 0$$
$$2x(x^2 - 2x - 15) = 0 \quad \text{Factor out the GCF, } 2x.$$
$$2x(x - 5)(x + 3) = 0 \quad \text{Factor the quadratic.}$$

$2x = 0 \quad$ or $\quad x - 5 = 0 \quad$ or $\quad x + 3 = 0 \quad$ Set each factor containing a variable equal to 0.

$x = 0 \quad$ or $\qquad x = 5 \quad$ or $\qquad x = -3 \quad$ Solve.

Check by replacing x with each solution in the cubic equation. The solutions are $-3, 0$, and 5. □

PRACTICE
10   Solve: $5x^3 + 5x^2 - 30x = 0$

OBJECTIVE

3 Finding *x*-Intercepts of the Graph of a Quadratic Equation

In Chapter 3, we graphed linear equations in two variables, such as $y = 5x - 6$. Recall that to find the *x*-intercept of the graph of a linear equation, let $y = 0$ and solve for *x*. This is also how to find the *x*-intercepts of the graph of a **quadratic equation in two variables,** such as $y = x^2 - 5x + 4$.

EXAMPLE 11 Find the *x*-intercepts of the graph of $y = x^2 - 5x + 4$.

Solution Let $y = 0$ and solve for *x*.

$$y = x^2 - 5x + 4$$
$$0 = x^2 - 5x + 4 \qquad \text{Let } y = 0.$$
$$0 = (x - 1)(x - 4) \qquad \text{Factor.}$$
$$x - 1 = 0 \quad \text{or} \quad x - 4 = 0 \qquad \text{Set each factor equal to 0.}$$
$$x = 1 \quad \text{or} \quad x = 4 \qquad \text{Solve.}$$

The *x*-intercepts of the graph of $y = x^2 - 5x + 4$ are $(1, 0)$ and $(4, 0)$.
The graph of $y = x^2 - 5x + 4$ is shown in the margin.

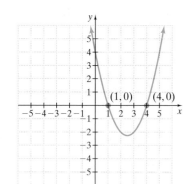

PRACTICE

11 Find the *x*-intercepts of the graph of $y = x^2 - 6x + 8$.

In general, a quadratic equation in two variables is one that can be written in the form $y = ax^2 + bx + c$ where $a \neq 0$. The graph of such an equation is called a **parabola** and will open up or down depending on the sign of *a*.

Notice that the *x*-intercepts of the graph of $y = ax^2 + bx + c$ are the real number solutions of $0 = ax^2 + bx + c$. Also, the real number solutions of $0 = ax^2 + bx + c$ are the *x*-intercepts of the graph of $y = ax^2 + bx + c$. We study more about graphs of quadratic equations in two variables in Chapter 9.

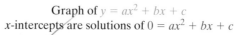

Graph of $y = ax^2 + bx + c$
x-intercepts are solutions of $0 = ax^2 + bx + c$

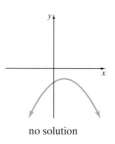 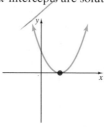 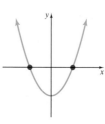 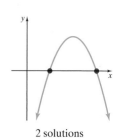

no solution   1 solution   2 solutions   2 solutions

Graphing Calculator Explorations

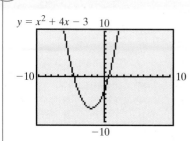

$y = x^2 + 4x - 3$

A grapher may be used to find solutions of a quadratic equation whether the related quadratic polynomial is factorable or not. For example, let's use a grapher to approximate the solutions of $0 = x^2 + 4x - 3$. To do so, graph $y_1 = x^2 + 4x - 3$. Recall that the *x*-intercepts of this graph are the solutions of $0 = x^2 + 4x - 3$.

Notice that the graph appears to have an *x*-intercept between -5 and -4 and one between 0 and 1. Many graphers contain a TRACE feature. This feature activates a graph cursor that can be used to *trace* along a graph while the corresponding *x*- and *y*-coordinates are shown on the screen. Use the TRACE feature to confirm that *x*-intercepts lie between -5 and -4 and between 0 and 1. To approximate the *x*-intercepts to the nearest tenth, use a ROOT or a ZOOM feature on your grapher or redefine the viewing window. (A ROOT feature calculates the *x*-intercept. A ZOOM feature magnifies the viewing window around a specific location such as

Y1=X2+4X-3

X=.63829787 Y=-.0393843

the graph cursor.) If we redefine the window to $[0, 1]$ on the x-axis and $[-1, 1]$ on the y-axis, the graph to the left is generated.

By using the TRACE feature, we can conclude that one x-intercept is approximately 0.6 to the nearest tenth. By repeating these steps for the other x-intercept, we find that it is approximately -4.6.

Use a grapher to approximate the real number solutions to the nearest tenth. If an equation has no real number solution, state so.

1. $3x^2 - 4x - 6 = 0$

2. $x^2 - x - 9 = 0$

3. $2x^2 + x + 2 = 0$

4. $-4x^2 - 5x - 4 = 0$

5. $-x^2 + x + 5 = 0$

6. $10x^2 + 6x - 3 = 0$

✔ Vocabulary, Readiness & Video Check

Use the choices below to fill in each blank. Not all choices will be used.

$-3, 5$	$a = 0$ or $b = 0$	0	linear
$3, -5$	quadratic	1	

1. An equation that can be written in the form $ax^2 + bx + c = 0$, with $a \neq 0$, is called a _____ equation.

2. If the product of two numbers is 0, then at least one of the numbers must be _____.

3. The solutions to $(x - 3)(x + 5) = 0$ are _____.

4. If $a \cdot b = 0$, then _____.

Martin-Gay Interactive Videos

Watch the section lecture video and answer the following questions.

OBJECTIVE 1

5. As shown in ▦ Examples 1–3, what two things have to be true in order to use the zero factor property?

OBJECTIVE 2

6. ▦ Example 4 implies that the zero factor property can be used with any number of factors on one side of the equation so long as the other side of the equation is zero. Why do you think this is true?

OBJECTIVE 3

7. From ▦ Example 5, how does finding the x-intercepts of the graph of a quadratic equation in two variables lead to solving a quadratic equation?

See Video 6.6 ⦿

6.6 Exercise Set MyMathLab® ▶

Solve each equation. See Examples 1 through 3.

1. $(x - 6)(x - 7) = 0$

2. $(x - 10)(x - 5) = 0$

3. $(x - 2)(x + 1) = 0$

4. $(x + 4)(x - 10) = 0$

5. $(x + 9)(x + 17) = 0$

6. $(x + 11)(x + 1) = 0$

7. $x(x + 6) = 0$

8. $x(x - 7) = 0$

9. $3x(x - 8) = 0$

10. $2x(x + 12) = 0$

▶ **11.** $(2x + 3)(4x - 5) = 0$

12. $(3x - 2)(5x + 1) = 0$

13. $(2x - 7)(7x + 2) = 0$

14. $(9x + 1)(4x - 3) = 0$

15. $\left(x - \dfrac{1}{2}\right)\left(x + \dfrac{1}{3}\right) = 0$

16. $\left(x + \dfrac{2}{9}\right)\left(x - \dfrac{1}{4}\right) = 0$

17. $(x + 0.2)(x + 1.5) = 0$

18. $(x + 1.7)(x + 2.3) = 0$

Solve. See Examples 4 through 7.

19. $x^2 - 13x + 36 = 0$

20. $x^2 + 2x - 63 = 0$

▶ **21.** $x^2 + 2x - 8 = 0$

22. $x^2 - 5x + 6 = 0$

23. $x^2 - 7x = 0$

24. $x^2 - 3x = 0$

25. $x^2 - 4x = 32$

26. $x^2 - 5x = 24$

27. $x^2 = 16$

28. $x^2 = 9$

29. $(x + 4)(x - 9) = 4x$

30. $(x + 3)(x + 8) = x$

▶ **31.** $x(3x - 1) = 14$

32. $x(4x - 11) = 3$

33. $-3x^2 + 75 = 0$

34. $-2y^2 + 72 = 0$

35. $24x^2 + 44x = 8$

36. $6x^2 + 57x = 30$

Solve each equation. See Examples 8 through 10.

37. $x^3 - 12x^2 + 32x = 0$

38. $x^3 - 14x^2 + 49x = 0$

39. $(4x - 3)(16x^2 - 24x + 9) = 0$

40. $(2x + 5)(4x^2 + 20x + 25) = 0$

41. $4x^3 - x = 0$ **42.** $4y^3 - 36y = 0$

43. $32x^3 - 4x^2 - 6x = 0$ **44.** $15x^3 + 24x^2 - 63x = 0$

MIXED PRACTICE

Solve each equation. See Examples 1 through 10. (A few exercises are linear equations.)

45. $(x + 3)(x - 2) = 0$ **46.** $(x - 6)(x + 7) = 0$

47. $x^2 + 20x = 0$ **48.** $x^2 + 15x = 0$

49. $4(x - 7) = 6$ **50.** $5(3 - 4x) = 9$

51. $4y^2 - 1 = 0$ **52.** $4y^2 - 81 = 0$

53. $(2x + 3)(2x^2 - 5x - 3) = 0$

54. $(2x - 9)(x^2 + 5x - 36) = 0$

55. $x^2 - 15 = -2x$ **56.** $x^2 - 26 = -11x$

57. $30x^2 - 11x - 30 = 0$ **58.** $12x^2 + 7x - 12 = 0$

59. $5x^2 - 6x - 8 = 0$ **60.** $9x^2 + 7x = 2$

61. $6y^2 - 22y - 40 = 0$ **62.** $3x^2 - 6x - 9 = 0$

63. $(y - 2)(y + 3) = 6$ **64.** $(y - 5)(y - 2) = 28$

65. $3x^3 + 19x^2 - 72x = 0$

66. $36x^3 + x^2 - 21x = 0$

67. $x^2 + 14x + 49 = 0$

68. $x^2 + 22x + 121 = 0$

69. $12y = 8y^2$

70. $9y = 6y^2$

71. $7x^3 - 7x = 0$

72. $3x^3 - 27x = 0$

73. $3x^2 + 8x - 11 = 13 - 6x$

74. $2x^2 + 12x - 1 = 4 + 3x$

75. $3x^2 - 20x = -4x^2 - 7x - 6$

76. $4x^2 - 20x = -5x^2 - 6x - 5$

Find the x-intercepts of the graph of each equation. See Example 11.

77. $y = (3x + 4)(x - 1)$

78. $y = (5x - 3)(x - 4)$

79. $y = x^2 - 3x - 10$

80. $y = x^2 + 7x + 6$

81. $y = 2x^2 + 11x - 6$

82. $y = 4x^2 + 11x + 6$

For Exercises 83 through 88, match each equation with its graph. See Example 11.

83. $y = (x + 2)(x - 1)$ **84.** $y = (x - 5)(x + 2)$

85. $y = x(x + 3)$ **86.** $y = x(x - 4)$

87. $y = 2x^2 - 8$ **88.** $y = 2x^2 - 2$

A.

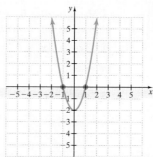

B.

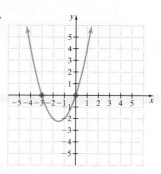

C.

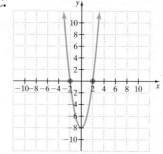

D.

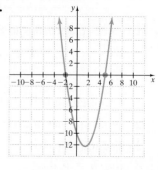

E.

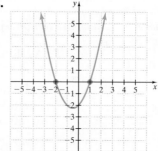

F.

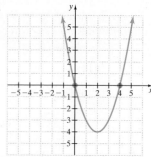

REVIEW AND PREVIEW

Perform the following operations. Write all results in lowest terms. See Section 1.3.

89. $\dfrac{3}{5} + \dfrac{4}{9}$ **90.** $\dfrac{2}{3} + \dfrac{3}{7}$

91. $\dfrac{7}{10} - \dfrac{5}{12}$ **92.** $\dfrac{5}{9} - \dfrac{5}{12}$

93. $\dfrac{7}{8} \div \dfrac{7}{15}$ **94.** $\dfrac{5}{12} - \dfrac{3}{10}$

95. $\dfrac{4}{5} \cdot \dfrac{7}{8}$ **96.** $\dfrac{3}{7} \cdot \dfrac{12}{17}$

CONCEPT EXTENSIONS

For Exercises 97 and 98, see the Concept Check in this section.

97. Explain the error and solve correctly:

$$x(x - 2) = 8$$
$$x = 8 \quad \text{or} \quad x - 2 = 8$$
$$x = 10$$

DEFINITIONS AND CONCEPTS	EXAMPLES

Section 6.3 Factoring Trinomials of the Form $ax^2 + bx + c$ and Perfect Square Trinomials

To factor $ax^2 + bx + c$, try various combinations of factors of ax^2 and c until a middle term of bx is obtained when checking.	Factor: $3x^2 + 14x - 5$ Factors of $3x^2$: $3x, x$ Factors of -5: $-1, 5$ and $1, -5$. $(3x - 1)(x + 5)$ $\quad -1x$ $\quad + 15x$ $\quad\quad 14x$ **Correct** middle term
A **perfect square trinomial** is a trinomial that is the square of some binomial.	Perfect square trinomial = square of binomial $x^2 + 4x + 4 = (x + 2)^2$ $25x^2 - 10x + 1 = (5x - 1)^2$
Factoring Perfect Square Trinomials $a^2 + 2ab + b^2 = (a + b)^2$ $a^2 - 2ab + b^2 = (a - b)^2$	Factor. $x^2 + 6x + 9 = x^2 + 2 \cdot x \cdot 3 + 3^2 = (x + 3)^2$ $4x^2 - 12x + 9 = (2x)^2 - 2 \cdot 2x \cdot 3 + 3^2 = (2x - 3)^2$

Section 6.4 Factoring Trinomials of the Form $ax^2 + bx + c$ by Grouping

To Factor $ax^2 + bx + c$ by Grouping **Step 1.** Find two numbers whose product is $a \cdot c$ and whose sum is b. **Step 2.** Rewrite bx, using the factors found in Step 1. **Step 3.** Factor by grouping.	Factor: $3x^2 + 14x - 5$ **Step 1.** Find two numbers whose product is $3 \cdot (-5)$ or -15 and whose sum is 14. They are 15 and -1. **Step 2.** $3x^2 + 14x - 5$ $\quad = 3x^2 + 15x - 1x - 5$ **Step 3.** $= 3x(x + 5) - 1(x + 5)$ $\quad = (x + 5)(3x - 1)$

Section 6.5 Factoring Binomials

Difference of Squares $a^2 - b^2 = (a + b)(a - b)$	Factor. $x^2 - 9 = x^2 - 3^2 = (x + 3)(x - 3)$
Sum or Difference of Cubes $a^3 + b^3 = (a + b)(a^2 - ab + b^2)$ $a^3 - b^3 = (a - b)(a^2 + ab + b^2)$	$y^3 + 8 = y^3 + 2^3 = (y + 2)(y^2 - 2y + 4)$ $125z^3 - 1 = (5z)^3 - 1^3 = (5z - 1)(25z^2 + 5z + 1)$

Integrated Review—Choosing a Factoring Strategy

To Factor a Polynomial
 	
 Step 1. Factor out the GCF.
 	
 Step 2.   **a.** If two terms
     i. $a^2 - b^2 = (a + b)(a - b)$
     ii. $a^3 - b^3 = (a - b)(a^2 + ab + b^2)$
     iii. $a^3 + b^3 = (a + b)(a^2 - ab + b^2)$
   b. If three terms
     i. $a^2 + 2ab + b^2 = (a + b)^2$
        $a^2 - 2ab + b^2 = (a - b)^2$
     ii. Methods in Sections 6.2 through 6.4
   c. If four or more terms, try factoring by grouping.
	Factor: $2x^4 - 6x^2 - 8$
	
	 Step 1. $2x^4 - 6x^2 - 8 = 2(x^4 - 3x^2 - 4)$
	
	 Step 2. b. ii. $\quad = 2(x^2 + 1)(x^2 - 4)$

9. In a right triangle, the side opposite the right angle is called the _____.

10. In a right triangle, each side adjacent to the right angle is called a _____.

11. The Pythagorean theorem states that $(\text{leg})^2 + (\text{leg})^2 = ($_____$)^2$.

Chapter 6 Highlights

DEFINITIONS AND CONCEPTS	EXAMPLES

Section 6.1   The Greatest Common Factor and Factoring by Grouping

Factoring is the process of writing an expression as a product.

Factor: $6 = 2 \cdot 3$
$$x^2 + 5x + 6 = (x + 2)(x + 3)$$

To Find the GCF of a List of Integers

Step 1. Write each number as a product of primes.

Step 2. Identify the common prime factors.

Step 3. The product of all common factors is the greatest common factor. If there are no common prime factors, the GCF is 1.

Find the GCF of 12, 36, and 48.

$12 = 2 \cdot 2 \cdot 3$
$36 = 2 \cdot 2 \cdot 3 \cdot 3$
$48 = 2 \cdot 2 \cdot 2 \cdot 2 \cdot 3$
$\text{GCF} = 2 \cdot 2 \cdot 3 = 12$

The GCF of a list of common variables raised to powers is the variable raised to the smallest exponent in the list.

The GCF of z^5, z^3, and z^{10} is z^3.

The GCF of a list of terms is the product of all common factors.

Find the GCF of $8x^2y$, $10x^3y^2$, and $26x^2y^3$.

The GCF of 8, 10, and 26 is 2.

The GCF of x^2, x^3, and x^2 is x^2.

The GCF of y, y^2, and y^3 is y.

The GCF of the terms is $2x^2y$.

To Factor by Grouping

Step 1. Arrange the terms so that the first two terms have a common factor and the last two have a common factor.

Step 2. For each pair of terms, factor out the pair's GCF.

Step 3. If there is now a common binomial factor, factor it out.

Step 4. If there is no common binomial factor, begin again, rearranging the terms differently. If no rearrangement leads to a common binomial factor, the polynomial cannot be factored by grouping.

Factor $10ax + 15a - 6xy - 9y$.

Step 1. $10ax + 15a - 6xy - 9y$

Step 2. $5a(2x + 3) - 3y(2x + 3)$

Step 3. $(2x + 3)(5a - 3y)$

Section 6.2   Factoring Trinomials of the Form $x^2 + bx + c$

The product of these numbers is c.
$$x^2 + bx + c = (x + \square)(x + \square)$$
The sum of these numbers is b.

Factor: $x^2 + 7x + 12$

$3 + 4 = 7 \qquad 3 \cdot 4 = 12$

$x^2 + 7x + 12 = (x + 3)(x + 4)$

Chapter 6 **Vocabulary Check**

Fill in each blank with one of the words or phrases listed below. Not all choices will be used and some choices may be used more than once.

factoring	quadratic equation	perfect square trinomial	0
greatest common factor	hypotenuse	sum of two cubes	1
difference of two cubes	difference of two squares	triangle	leg

1. An equation that can be written in the form $ax^2 + bx + c = 0$ (with a not 0) is called a(n) _____.

2. _____ is the process of writing an expression as a product.

3. The _____ of a list of terms is the product of all common factors.

4. A trinomial that is the square of some binomial is called a(n) _____.

5. The expression $a^2 - b^2$ is called a(n) _____.

6. The expression $a^3 - b^3$ is called a(n) _____.

7. The expression $a^3 + b^3$ is called a(n) _____.

8. By the zero factor property, if the product of two numbers is 0, then at least one of the numbers must be _____.

98. Explain the error and solve correctly:

$$(x - 4)(x + 2) = 0$$
$$x = -4 \quad \text{or} \quad x = 2$$

(with the "− 4" crossed out and "= −4" crossed out)

99. Write a quadratic equation that has two solutions, 6 and −1. Leave the polynomial in the equation in factored form.

100. Write a quadratic equation that has two solutions, 0 and −2. Leave the polynomial in the equation in factored form.

101. Write a quadratic equation in standard form that has two solutions, 5 and 7.

102. Write an equation that has three solutions, 0, 1, and 2.

103. A compass is accidentally thrown upward and out of an air balloon at a height of 300 feet. The height, y, of the compass at time x in seconds is given by the equation

$$y = -16x^2 + 20x + 300$$

300 ft

a. Find the height of the compass at the given times by filling in the table below.

time, x	0	1	2	3	4	5	6
height, y							

b. Use the table to determine when the compass strikes the ground.

c. Use the table to approximate the maximum height of the compass.

d. Plot the points (x, y) on a rectangular coordinate system and connect them with a smooth curve. Explain your results.

104. A rocket is fired upward from the ground with an initial velocity of 100 feet per second. The height, y, of the rocket at any time x is given by the equation

$$y = -16x^2 + 100x$$

y

a. Find the height of the rocket at the given times by filling in the table below.

time, x	0	1	2	3	4	5	6	7
height, y								

b. Use the table to approximate when the rocket strikes the ground to the nearest second.

c. Use the table to approximate the maximum height of the rocket.

d. Plot the points (x, y) on a rectangular coordinate system and connect them with a smooth curve. Explain your results.

Solve each equation. First, multiply the binomials.

To solve $(x - 6)(2x - 3) = (x + 2)(x + 9)$, see below.

$$(x - 6)(2x - 3) = (x + 2)(x + 9)$$
$$2x^2 - 15x + 18 = x^2 + 11x + 18$$
$$x^2 - 26x = 0$$
$$x(x - 26) = 0$$
$$x = 0 \quad \text{or} \quad x - 26 = 0$$
$$x = 26$$

105. $(x - 3)(3x + 4) = (x + 2)(x - 6)$

106. $(2x - 3)(x + 6) = (x - 9)(x + 2)$

107. $(2x - 3)(x + 8) = (x - 6)(x + 4)$

108. $(x + 6)(x - 6) = (2x - 9)(x + 4)$

DEFINITIONS AND CONCEPTS	EXAMPLES

Integrated Review—Choosing a Factoring Strategy (continued)

Step 3. See if any factors can be factored further.	**Step 3.** $= 2(x^2 + 1)(x + 2)(x - 2)$
Step 4. Check by multiplying.	**Step 4.** Check by multiplying.
	$2(x^2 + 1)(x + 2)(x - 2) = 2(x^2 + 1)(x^2 - 4)$
	$= 2(x^4 - 3x^2 - 4)$
	$= 2x^4 - 6x^2 - 8$

Section 6.6   Solving Quadratic Equations by Factoring

A **quadratic equation** is an equation that can be written in the form $ax^2 + bx + c = 0$ with a not 0.

The form $ax^2 + bx + c = 0$ is called the **standard form** of a quadratic equation.

Zero Factor Property

If a and b are real numbers and if $ab = 0$, then $a = 0$ or $b = 0$.

To Solve Quadratic Equations by Factoring

Step 1. Write the equation in standard form: $ax^2 + bx + c = 0$.

Step 2. Factor the quadratic.

Step 3. Set each factor containing a variable equal to 0.

Step 4. Solve the equations.

Step 5. Check in the original equation.

Quadratic Equation	***Standard Form***
$x^2 = 16$	$x^2 - 16 = 0$
$y = -2y^2 + 5$	$2y^2 + y - 5 = 0$

If $(x + 3)(x - 1) = 0$, then $x + 3 = 0$ or $x - 1 = 0$.

Solve: $3x^2 = 13x - 4$

Step 1. $3x^2 - 13x + 4 = 0$

Step 2. $(3x - 1)(x - 4) = 0$

Step 3. $3x - 1 = 0$ or $x - 4 = 0$

Step 4. $3x = 1$ or $x = 4$

$x = \dfrac{1}{3}$

Step 5. Check both $\dfrac{1}{3}$ and 4 in the original equation.

Chapter 6 Review

(6.1) *Complete the factoring.*

1. $6x^2 - 15x = 3x(\quad)$
2. $2x^3y + 6x^2y^2 + 8xy^3 = 2xy(\quad)$

Factor the GCF from each polynomial.

3. $20x^2 + 12x$
4. $6x^2y^2 - 3xy^3$
5. $3x(2x + 3) - 5(2x + 3)$
6. $5x(x + 1) - (x + 1)$

Factor each polynomial by grouping.

7. $3x^2 - 3x + 2x - 2$
8. $3a^2 + 9ab + 3b^2 + ab$
9. $10a^2 + 5ab + 7b^2 + 14ab$
10. $6x^2 + 10x - 3x - 5$

(6.2) *Factor each trinomial.*

11. $x^2 + 6x + 8$
12. $x^2 - 11x + 24$
13. $x^2 + x + 2$
14. $x^2 - x + 2$
15. $x^2 + 4xy - 12y^2$
16. $x^2 + 8xy + 15y^2$
17. $72 - 18x - 2x^2$
18. $32 + 12x - 4x^2$
19. $10a^3 - 110a^2 + 100a$
20. $5y^3 - 50y^2 + 120y$
21. To factor $x^2 + 2x - 48$, think of two numbers whose product is _____ and whose sum is _____.
22. What is the first step in factoring $3x^2 + 15x + 30$?

(6.3) *or* **(6.4)** *Factor each trinomial.*

23. $2x^2 + 13x + 6$
24. $4x^2 + 4x - 3$
25. $6x^2 + 5xy - 4y^2$
26. $18x^2 - 9xy - 20y^2$
27. $10y^3 + 25y^2 - 60y$
28. $60y^3 - 39y^2 + 6y$
29. $18x^2 - 60x + 50$
30. $4x^2 - 28xy + 49y^2$

(6.5) *Factor each binomial.*

31. $4x^2 - 9$
32. $9t^2 - 25s^2$
33. $16x^2 + y^2$
34. $x^3 - 8y^3$
35. $8x^3 + 27$
36. $2x^3 + 8x$
37. $54 - 2x^3y^3$
38. $9x^2 - 4y^2$
39. $16x^4 - 1$
40. $x^4 + 16$

(6.6) *Solve the following equations.*

41. $(x + 6)(x - 2) = 0$
42. $3x(x + 1)(7x - 2) = 0$
43. $4(5x + 1)(x + 3) = 0$
44. $x^2 + 8x + 7 = 0$
45. $x^2 - 2x - 24 = 0$
46. $x^2 + 10x = -25$

47. $x(x - 10) = -16$

48. $(3x - 1)(9x^2 - 6x + 1) = 0$

49. $56x^2 - 5x - 6 = 0$

50. $20x^2 - 7x - 6 = 0$

51. $5(3x + 2) = 4$

52. $6x^2 - 3x + 8 = 0$

53. $12 - 5t = -3$

54. $5x^3 + 20x^2 + 20x = 0$

55. $4t^3 - 5t^2 - 21t = 0$

56. Write a quadratic equation that has the two solutions 4 and 5.

Chapter 6 Getting Ready for the Test

lc

*All the exercises below are **Multiple Choice.** Choose the correct letter. Also, letters may be used more than once.*

1. The greatest common factor of the terms of $10x^4 - 70x^3 + 2x^2 - 14x$ is
   A. $2x^2$ **B.** $2x$ **C.** $7x^2$ **D.** $7x$

2. Choose the expression that is NOT a factored form of $9y^3 - 18y^2$.
   A. $9(y^3 - 2y^2)$ **B.** $9y(y^2 - 2y)$ **C.** $9y^2(y - 2)$ **D.** $9 \cdot y^3 - 18 \cdot y^2$

Identify each expression as:
   A. A factored expression or   **B.** Not a factored expression

3. $(x - 1)(x + 5)$

4. $z(z + 12)(z - 12)$

5. $y(x - 6) + 1(x - 6)$

6. $m \cdot m - 5 \cdot 5$

7. Choose the correct factored form for $4x^2 + 16$ or select "can't be factored."

    A. can't be factored   **B.** $4(x^2 + 4)$ **C.** $4(x + 2)^2$ **D.** $4(x + 2)(x - 2)$

8. Which of the binomials can't be factored using real numbers?

    A. $x^2 + 64$ **B.** $x^2 - 64$ **C.** $x^3 + 64$ **D.** $x^3 - 64$

9. To solve $x(x + 2) = 15$, which is an incorrect next step?

    A. $x^2 + 2x = 15$ **B.** $x(x + 2) - 15 = 0$ **C.** $x = 15$ and $x + 2 = 15$

Chapter 6 Test   MyMathLab®   You Tube

Factor each polynomial completely. If a polynomial cannot be factored, write "prime."

1. $x^2 + 11x + 28$
2. $49 - m^2$
3. $y^2 + 22y + 121$
4. $4(a + 3) - y(a + 3)$
5. $x^2 + 4$
6. $y^2 - 8y - 48$
7. $x^2 + x - 10$
8. $9x^3 + 39x^2 + 12x$
9. $3a^2 + 3ab - 7a - 7b$
10. $3x^2 - 5x + 2$
11. $x^2 + 14xy + 24y^2$
12. $180 - 5x^2$
13. $6t^2 - t - 5$
14. $xy^2 - 7y^2 - 4x + 28$
15. $x - x^5$
16. $-xy^3 - x^3y$
17. $64x^3 - 1$
18. $8y^3 - 64$

Solve each equation.

19. $(x - 3)(x + 9) = 0$
20. $x^2 + 5x = 14$
21. $x(x + 6) = 7$
22. $3x(2x - 3)(3x + 4) = 0$
23. $5t^3 - 45t = 0$

24. $t^2 - 2t - 15 = 0$
25. $6x^2 = 15x$

Solve each problem.

26. A deck for a home is in the shape of a triangle. The length of the base of the triangle is 9 feet longer than its altitude. If the area of the triangle is 68 square feet, find the length of the base.

27. The sum of two numbers is 17 and the sum of their squares is 145. Find the numbers.

28. An object is dropped from the top of the Woolworth Building on Broadway in New York City. The height h of the object after t seconds is given by the equation

$$h = -16t^2 + 784$$

Find how many seconds pass before the object reaches the ground.

29. Find the lengths of the sides of a right triangle if the hypotenuse is 10 centimeters longer than the shorter leg and 5 centimeters longer than the longer leg.

Chapter 6 Cumulative Review

1. Translate each sentence into a mathematical statement.

    a. Nine is less than or equal to eleven.

    b. Eight is greater than one.

    c. Three is not equal to four.

2. Insert $<$ or $>$ in the space to make each statement true.

    a. $|-5| \quad |-3|$

    b. $|0| \quad |-2|$

3. Simplify each fraction (write it in lowest terms).

    a. $\dfrac{42}{49}$ **b.** $\dfrac{11}{27}$ **c.** $\dfrac{88}{20}$

4. Evaluate $\dfrac{x}{y} + 5x$ if $x = 20$ and $y = 10$.

5. Simplify $\dfrac{8 + 2 \cdot 3}{2^2 - 1}$.

6. Evaluate $\dfrac{x}{y} + 5x$ if $x = -20$ and $y = 10$.

7. Add.
   a. $3 + (-7) + (-8)$
   b. $[7 + (-10)] + [-2 + |-4|]$

8. Evaluate $\dfrac{x}{y} + 5x$ if $x = -20$ and $y = -10$.

9. Multiply.
   a. $(-8)(4)$
   b. $14(-1)$
   c. $(-9)(-10)$

10. Simplify: $5 - 2(3x - 7)$

11. Simplify each expression by combining like terms.
   a. $7x - 3x$
   b. $10y^2 + y^2$
   c. $8x^2 + 2x - 3x$
   d. $9n^2 - 5n^2 + n^2$

12. Solve: $0.8y + 0.2(y - 1) = 1.8$

Solve.

13. $3 - x = 7$

14. $\dfrac{x}{-7} = -4$

15. $-3x = 33$

16. $-\dfrac{2}{3}x = -22$

17. $8(2 - t) = -5t$

18. $-z = \dfrac{7z + 3}{5}$

19. Balsa wood sticks are commonly used for building models (for example, bridge models). A 48-inch balsa wood stick is to be cut into two pieces so that the longer piece is 3 times the shorter. Find the length of each piece.

20. Solve $3x + 9 \le 5(x - 1)$. Write the solution set using interval notation.

21. Graph the linear equation $y = -\frac{1}{3}x + 2$.

22. Is the ordered pair $(-1, 2)$ a solution of $-7x - 8y = -9$?

23. Find the slope and the y-intercept of the line whose equation is $3x - 4y = 4$.

24. Find the slope of the line through $(5, -6)$ and $(5, 2)$.

25. Evaluate each expression for the given value of x.
   a. $2x^3$; x is 5
   b. $\dfrac{9}{x^2}$; x is -3

26. Find the slope and y-intercept of the line whose equation is $7x - 3y = 2$.

27. Find the degree of each term.
   a. $-3x^2$
   b. $5x^3yz$
   c. 2

28. Find an equation of the vertical line through $(0, 7)$.

29. Subtract $(2x^3 + 8x^2 - 6x) - (2x^3 - x^2 + 1)$.

30. Find an equation of the line with slope 4 and y-intercept $\left(0, \dfrac{1}{2}\right)$. Write the equation in standard form.

31. Multiply $(3x + 2)(2x - 5)$.

32. Write an equation of the line through $(-4, 0)$ and $(6, -1)$. Write the equation in standard form.

33. Multiply $(3y + 1)^2$.

34. Solve the system. $\begin{cases} -x + 3y = 18 \\ -3x + 2y = 19 \end{cases}$

35. Simplify by writing each expression with positive exponents only.
   a. 3^{-2}
   b. $2x^{-3}$
   c. $2^{-1} + 4^{-1}$
   d. $(-2)^{-4}$
   e. y^{-4}

36. Simplify: $\dfrac{(5a^7)^2}{a^5}$

37. Write each number in scientific notation.
   a. $367{,}000{,}000$
   b. 0.000003
   c. $20{,}520{,}000{,}000$
   d. 0.00085

38. Multiply $(3x - 7y)^2$.

39. Divide $x^2 + 7x + 12$ by $x + 3$ using long division.

40. Simplify: $\dfrac{(xy)^{-3}}{(x^5y^6)^3}$

41. Find the GCF of each list of terms.
   a. $x^3, x^7,$ and x^5
   b. $y, y^4,$ and y^7

Factor.

42. $z^3 + 7z + z^2 + 7$

43. $x^2 + 7x + 12$

44. $2x^3 + 2x^2 - 84x$

45. $8x^2 - 22x + 5$

46. $-4x^2 - 23x + 6$

47. $25a^2 - 9b^2$

48. $9xy^2 - 16x$

49. Solve: $(x - 3)(x + 1) = 0$

50. Solve $x^2 - 13x = -36$.

Rational Expressions

7.1 Simplifying Rational Expressions

7.2 Multiplying and Dividing Rational Expressions

Side Rear-View Mirror   Telescope   Magnifying Glass

Street Light Reflector   Sunglasses   Camera

What Do the Above Have in Common?

All the useful objects above contain convex mirrors or lenses or were made with convex mirrors or lenses. Basically, all of these objects were made using the rational equation below, called the Gaussian Mirror/Lens Formula. This equation or formula relates an object distance and image distance to the focal length. In general, the focal length is a measure of how strongly a lens converges or diverges light.

Of course, this is just one equation containing rational expressions. There are uses of rational expressions everywhere from health to sports statistics to driving safety. For some applications, see Section 7.1, Exercises 97 through 102, and Section 7.5, Exercises 43 through 52.

CHECK YOUR PROGRESS

Vocabulary Check
Chapter Highlights
Chapter Review
Getting Ready for the Test
Chapter Test
Cumulative Review

In this chapter, we expand our knowledge of algebraic expressions to include algebraic fractions, called *rational expressions*. We explore the operations of addition, subtraction, multiplication, and division using principles similar to the principles for numerical fractions.

Gaussian Mirror/Lens Formula

$$\frac{1}{o} + \frac{1}{i} = \frac{1}{f}$$

$$\frac{1}{\text{object distance}} + \frac{1}{\text{image distance}} = \frac{1}{\text{focal length}}$$

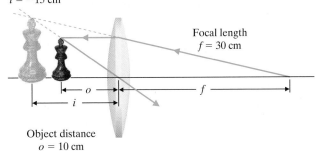

Image distance (negative because of location of image)
$i = -15$ cm

Focal length
$f = 30$ cm

Object distance
$o = 10$ cm

7.1 | Simplifying Rational Expressions

OBJECTIVES

1 Find the Value of a Rational Expression Given a Replacement Number.

2 Identify Values for Which a Rational Expression Is Undefined.

3 Simplify or Write Rational Expressions in Lowest Terms.

4 Write Equivalent Rational Expressions of the Form $-\dfrac{a}{b} = \dfrac{-a}{b} = \dfrac{a}{-b}$.

OBJECTIVE

1   Evaluating Rational Expressions

As we reviewed in Chapter 1, a rational number is a number that can be written as a quotient of integers. A **rational expression** is also a quotient; it is a quotient of polynomials.

> **Rational Expression**
>
> A rational expression is an expression that can be written in the form
> $$\frac{P}{Q},$$
> where P and Q are polynomials and $Q \neq 0$.

Rational Expressions

$$\frac{2}{3} \qquad \frac{3y^3}{8} \qquad \frac{-4p}{p^3 + 2p + 1} \qquad \frac{5x^2 - 3x + 2}{3x + 7}$$

Rational expressions have different values depending on what value replaces the variable. Next, we review the standard order of operations by finding values of rational expressions for given replacement values of the variable.

EXAMPLE 1   Find the value of $\dfrac{x + 4}{2x - 3}$ for the given replacement values.

   a. $x = 5$ **b.** $x = -2$

Solution

   a. Replace each x in the expression with 5 and then simplify.
$$\frac{x + 4}{2x - 3} = \frac{5 + 4}{2(5) - 3} = \frac{9}{10 - 3} = \frac{9}{7}$$

   b. Replace each x in the expression with -2 and then simplify.
$$\frac{x + 4}{2x - 3} = \frac{-2 + 4}{2(-2) - 3} = \frac{2}{-7} \quad \text{or} \quad -\frac{2}{7}$$

PRACTICE

1   Find the value of $\dfrac{x + 6}{3x - 2}$ for the given replacement values.

   a. $x = 3$ **b.** $x = -3$

In the example above, we wrote $\dfrac{2}{-7}$ as $-\dfrac{2}{7}$. For a negative fraction such as $\dfrac{2}{-7}$, recall from Section 1.7 that

$$\frac{2}{-7} = \frac{-2}{7} = -\frac{2}{7}$$

In general, for any fraction,

$$\frac{-a}{b} = \frac{a}{-b} = -\frac{a}{b}, \qquad b \neq 0$$

This is also true for rational expressions. For example,

$$\underbrace{\frac{-(x + 2)}{x}}_{\text{Notice the parentheses.}} = \frac{x + 2}{-x} = -\frac{x + 2}{x}$$

Helpful Hint

Do you recall why division by 0 is not defined? Remember, for example, that $\frac{8}{4} = 2$ because $2 \cdot 4 = 8$. Thus, if $\frac{8}{0} = a\ number$, then *the number* $\cdot\ 0 = 8$. There is no number that when multiplied by 0 equals 8; thus $\frac{8}{0}$ is undefined.

This is true in general for fractions and rational expressions.

OBJECTIVE

2 Identifying When a Rational Expression Is Undefined

In the definition of rational expression (see the first box in this section), notice that we wrote $Q \neq 0$ for the denominator Q. This is because the denominator of a rational expression must not equal 0 since division by 0 is not defined. (See the Helpful Hint.) This means we must be careful when replacing the variable in a rational expression by a number. For example, suppose we replace x with 5 in the rational expression $\frac{3 + x}{x - 5}$. The expression becomes

$$\frac{3 + x}{x - 5} = \frac{3 + 5}{5 - 5} = \frac{8}{0}$$

But division by 0 is undefined. Therefore, in this rational expression, we can allow x to be any real number *except* 5. **A rational expression is undefined for values that make the denominator 0.** Thus, to find values for which a rational expression is undefined, find values for which the denominator is 0.

EXAMPLE 2 Are there any values for x for which each rational expression is undefined?

a. $\dfrac{x}{x - 3}$ **b.** $\dfrac{x^2 + 2}{3x^2 - 5x + 2}$ **c.** $\dfrac{x^3 - 6x^2 - 10x}{3}$ **d.** $\dfrac{2}{x^2 + 1}$

Solution To find values for which a rational expression is undefined, find values that make the *denominator* 0.

a. The denominator of $\dfrac{x}{x - 3}$ is 0 when $x - 3 = 0$ or when $x = 3$. Thus, when $x = 3$, the expression $\dfrac{x}{x - 3}$ is undefined.

b. Set the denominator equal to zero.

$$3x^2 - 5x + 2 = 0$$
$$(3x - 2)(x - 1) = 0 \qquad\qquad \text{Factor.}$$
$$3x - 2 = 0 \quad\text{or}\quad x - 1 = 0 \quad \text{Set each factor equal to zero.}$$
$$3x = 2 \quad\text{or}\qquad x = 1 \quad \text{Solve.}$$
$$x = \frac{2}{3}$$

Thus, when $x = \dfrac{2}{3}$ or $x = 1$, the denominator $3x^2 - 5x + 2$ is 0. So the rational expression $\dfrac{x^2 + 2}{3x^2 - 5x + 2}$ is undefined when $x = \dfrac{2}{3}$ or when $x = 1$.

c. The denominator of $\dfrac{x^3 - 6x^2 - 10x}{3}$ is never 0, so there are no values of x for which this expression is undefined.

d. No matter which real number x is replaced by, the denominator $x^2 + 1$ does not equal 0, so there are no real numbers for which this expression is undefined. □

PRACTICE

2 Are there any values of x for which each rational expression is undefined?

a. $\dfrac{x}{x + 6}$ **b.** $\dfrac{x^4 - 3x^2 + 7x}{7}$ **c.** $\dfrac{x^2 - 5}{x^2 + 6x + 8}$ **d.** $\dfrac{3}{x^4 + 5}$

Note: Unless otherwise stated, we will now assume that variables in rational expressions are replaced only by values for which the expressions are defined.

OBJECTIVE

3   Simplifying Rational Expressions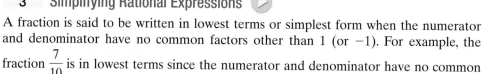

A fraction is said to be written in lowest terms or simplest form when the numerator and denominator have no common factors other than 1 (or −1). For example, the fraction $\dfrac{7}{10}$ is in lowest terms since the numerator and denominator have no common factors other than 1 (or −1).

The process of writing a rational expression in lowest terms or simplest form is called **simplifying** a rational expression.

Simplifying a rational expression is similar to simplifying a fraction. Recall that to simplify a fraction, we essentially "remove factors of 1." Our ability to do this comes from these facts:

- Any nonzero number over itself simplifies to 1

$$\left(\frac{5}{5} = 1, \frac{-7.26}{-7.26} = 1, \text{ or } \frac{c}{c} = 1 \text{ as long as } c \text{ is not } 0 \right), \text{and}$$

- The product of any number and 1 is that number

$$\left(19 \cdot 1 = 19, -8.9 \cdot 1 = -8.9, \frac{a}{b} \cdot 1 = \frac{a}{b} \right).$$

> **Helpful Hint**
>
> We use the Fundamental Principle of Fractions to simplify rational expressions. This process is also sometimes called
> - Dividing out common factors
>   or
> - Removing a factor of 1
> (See Section 1.3 for a review.)

In other words, we have the following:

Simplify: $\dfrac{15}{20}$

$\dfrac{15}{20} = \dfrac{3 \cdot 5}{2 \cdot 2 \cdot 5}$ Factor the numerator and the denominator.

$= \dfrac{3 \cdot 5}{2 \cdot 2 \cdot 5}$ Look for common factors.

$= \dfrac{3}{2 \cdot 2} \cdot \dfrac{5}{5}$ Common factors in the numerator and denominator form factors of 1.

$= \dfrac{3}{2 \cdot 2} \cdot 1$ Write $\dfrac{5}{5}$ as 1.

$= \dfrac{3}{2 \cdot 2} = \dfrac{3}{4}$ Multiply to remove a factor of 1.

Fundamental Principle of Fractions

$$\frac{a \cdot c}{b \cdot c} = \frac{a}{b} \cdot \frac{c}{c} = \frac{a}{b}$$

Since $\dfrac{a}{b} \cdot 1 = \dfrac{a}{b}$

Before we use the same technique to simplify a rational expression, remember that as long as the denominator is not 0, $\dfrac{a^3 b}{a^3 b} = 1, \dfrac{x+3}{x+3} = 1,$ and $\dfrac{7x^2 + 5x - 100}{7x^2 + 5x - 100} = 1.$

Simplify: $\dfrac{x^2 - 9}{x^2 + x - 6}$

$\dfrac{x^2 - 9}{x^2 + x - 6} = \dfrac{(x-3)(x+3)}{(x-2)(x+3)}$ Factor the numerator and the denominator.

$= \dfrac{(x-3)(x+3)}{(x-2)(x+3)}$ Look for common factors.

$= \dfrac{x-3}{x-2} \cdot \dfrac{x+3}{x+3}$

$= \dfrac{x-3}{x-2} \cdot 1$ Write $\dfrac{x+3}{x+3}$ as 1.

$= \dfrac{x-3}{x-2}$ Multiply to remove a factor of 1.

Just as for numerical fractions, we can use a shortcut notation. Remember that as long as exact factors in both the numerator and denominator are divided out, we are "removing a factor of 1." We will use the following notation to show this:

$$\frac{x^2 - 9}{x^2 + x - 6} = \frac{(x - 3)\,(x + 3)}{(x - 2)\,(x + 3)}$$ A factor of 1 is identified by the shading.

$$= \frac{x - 3}{x - 2}$$ Remove a factor of 1.

Thus, the rational expression $\dfrac{x^2 - 9}{x^2 + x - 6}$ has the same value as the rational expression $\dfrac{x - 3}{x - 2}$ for all values of x except 2 and -3. (Remember that when x is 2, the denominators of both rational expressions are 0 and when x is -3, the original rational expression has a denominator of 0.)

As we simplify rational expressions, we will assume that the simplified rational expression is equal to the original rational expression for all real numbers except those for which either denominator is 0. The following steps may be used to simplify rational expressions.

To Simplify a Rational Expression

Step 1. Completely factor the numerator and denominator.

Step 2. Divide out factors common to the numerator and denominator. (This is the same as "removing a factor of 1.")

EXAMPLE 3   Simplify: $\dfrac{5x - 5}{x^3 - x^2}$

Solution   To begin, we factor the numerator and denominator if possible. Then we look for common factors.

$$\frac{5x - 5}{x^3 - x^2} = \frac{5\,(x - 1)}{x^2\,(x - 1)} = \frac{5}{x^2}$$ □

PRACTICE 3   Simplify: $\dfrac{x^6 - x^5}{6x - 6}$ ▪

EXAMPLE 4   Simplify: $\dfrac{x^2 + 8x + 7}{x^2 - 4x - 5}$

Solution   We factor the numerator and denominator and then look for common factors.

$$\frac{x^2 + 8x + 7}{x^2 - 4x - 5} = \frac{(x + 7)\,(x + 1)}{(x - 5)\,(x + 1)} = \frac{x + 7}{x - 5}$$ □

PRACTICE 4   Simplify: $\dfrac{x^2 + 5x + 4}{x^2 + 2x - 8}$ ▪

EXAMPLE 5   Simplify: $\dfrac{x^2 + 4x + 4}{x^2 + 2x}$

Solution   We factor the numerator and denominator and then look for common factors.

$$\frac{x^2 + 4x + 4}{x^2 + 2x} = \frac{(x + 2)\,(x + 2)}{x\,(x + 2)} = \frac{x + 2}{x}$$ □

PRACTICE 5   Simplify: $\dfrac{x^3 + 9x^2}{x^2 + 18x + 81}$ ▪

> **Helpful Hint**
>
> When simplifying a rational expression, we look for **common *factors,* not common *terms.***
>
> $$\frac{x \cdot (x + 2)}{x \cdot x} = \frac{x + 2}{x}$$
>
> Common factors. These can be divided out.
>
> $$\frac{x + 2}{x}$$
>
> Common terms. There is no factor of 1 that can be generated.

✔ **CONCEPT CHECK**

Recall that we can remove only *factors* of 1. Which of the following are *not* true? Explain why.

a. $\dfrac{3 - 1}{3 + 5}$ simplifies to $-\dfrac{1}{5}$?

b. $\dfrac{2x + 10}{2}$ simplifies to $x + 5$?

c. $\dfrac{37}{72}$ simplifies to $\dfrac{3}{2}$?

d. $\dfrac{2x + 3}{2}$ simplifies to $x + 3$?

EXAMPLE 6   Simplify: $\dfrac{x + 9}{x^2 - 81}$

Solution We factor and then divide out common factors.

$$\frac{x + 9}{x^2 - 81} = \frac{x + 9}{(x + 9)(x - 9)} = \frac{1}{x - 9}$$

PRACTICE 6   Simplify: $\dfrac{x - 7}{x^2 - 49}$

EXAMPLE 7   Simplify each rational expression.

a. $\dfrac{x + y}{y + x}$ **b.** $\dfrac{x - y}{y - x}$

Solution

a. The expression $\dfrac{x + y}{y + x}$ can be simplified by using the commutative property of addition to rewrite the denominator $y + x$ as $x + y$.

$$\frac{x + y}{y + x} = \frac{x + y}{x + y} = 1$$

b. The expression $\dfrac{x - y}{y - x}$ can be simplified by recognizing that $y - x$ and $x - y$ are opposites. In other words, $y - x = -1(x - y)$. We proceed as follows:

$$\frac{x - y}{y - x} = \frac{1 \cdot (x - y)}{-1 \cdot (x - y)} = \frac{1}{-1} = -1$$

PRACTICE 7   Simplify each rational expression.

a. $\dfrac{s - t}{t - s}$ **b.** $\dfrac{2c + d}{d + 2c}$

EXAMPLE 8 Simplify: $\dfrac{4 - x^2}{3x^2 - 5x - 2}$

Solution

$$\dfrac{4 - x^2}{3x^2 - 5x - 2} = \dfrac{(2 - x)(2 + x)}{(x - 2)(3x + 1)} \qquad \text{Factor.}$$

$$= \dfrac{(-1)(x - 2)(2 + x)}{(x - 2)(3x + 1)} \qquad \text{Write } 2 - x \text{ as } -1(x - 2).$$

$$= \dfrac{(-1)(2 + x)}{3x + 1} \quad \text{or} \quad \dfrac{-2 - x}{3x + 1} \quad \text{Simplify.} \qquad \square$$

PRACTICE
8 Simplify: $\dfrac{2x^2 - 5x - 12}{16 - x^2}$

OBJECTIVE
4 Writing Equivalent Forms of Rational Expressions ▶

From Example 7(a), we have $y + x = x + y$. $y + x$ and $x + y$ are equivalent.
From Example 7(b), we have $y - x = -1(x - y)$. $y - x$ and $x - y$ are opposites.

Thus, $\dfrac{x + y}{y + x} = \dfrac{x + y}{x + y} = 1$ and $\dfrac{x - y}{y - x} = \dfrac{x - y}{-1(x - y)} = \dfrac{1}{-1} = -1$.

When performing operations on rational expressions, equivalent forms of answers often result. For this reason, it is very important to be able to recognize equivalent answers.

EXAMPLE 9 List some equivalent forms of $-\dfrac{5x - 1}{x + 9}$.

Solution To do so, recall that $-\dfrac{a}{b} = \dfrac{-a}{b} = \dfrac{a}{-b}$. Thus

$$-\dfrac{5x - 1}{x + 9} = \dfrac{-(5x - 1)}{x + 9} = \dfrac{-5x + 1}{x + 9} \quad \text{or} \quad \dfrac{1 - 5x}{x + 9}.$$

Also,

$$-\dfrac{5x - 1}{x + 9} = \dfrac{5x - 1}{-(x + 9)} = \dfrac{5x - 1}{-x - 9} \quad \text{or} \quad \dfrac{5x - 1}{-9 - x}$$

Thus $-\dfrac{5x - 1}{x + 9} = \dfrac{-(5x - 1)}{x + 9} = \dfrac{-5x + 1}{x + 9} = \dfrac{5x - 1}{-(x + 9)} = \dfrac{5x - 1}{-x - 9} \qquad \square$

PRACTICE
9 List some equivalent forms of $-\dfrac{x + 3}{6x - 11}$.

> **Helpful Hint**
>
> Remember, a negative sign in front of a fraction or rational expression may be moved to the numerator or the denominator, but *not* both.

Keep in mind that many rational expressions may look different but in fact be equivalent.

✔ Vocabulary, Readiness & Video Check

Use the choices below to fill in each blank. Not all choices will be used.

−1	0	simplifying
1	2	rational expression

$\dfrac{-a}{-b}$ $\dfrac{-a}{b}$ $\dfrac{a}{-b}$

1. A _____ is an expression that can be written in the form $\dfrac{P}{Q}$ where P and Q are polynomials and $Q \neq 0$.

2. The expression $\dfrac{x+3}{3+x}$ simplifies to _____.

3. The expression $\dfrac{x-3}{3-x}$ simplifies to _____.

4. A rational expression is undefined for values that make the denominator _____.

5. The expression $\dfrac{7x}{x-2}$ is undefined for $x =$ _____.

6. The process of writing a rational expression in lowest terms is called _____.

7. For a rational expression, $-\dfrac{a}{b} = \dfrac{}{} = \dfrac{}{}$.

Martin-Gay Interactive Videos

See Video 7.1 🔘

Watch the section lecture video and answer the following questions.

OBJECTIVE 1
8. From the lecture before ▦ Example 1, what do the different values of a rational expression depend on? How are these different values found?

OBJECTIVE 2
9. Why can't the denominators of rational expressions be zero? How can you find the numbers for which a rational expression is undefined?

OBJECTIVE 3
10. In ▦ Example 7, why isn't a factor of x divided out of the expression at the end?

OBJECTIVE 4
11. From ▦ Example 9, if you move a negative sign from in front of a rational expression to either the numerator or denominator, when would you need to use parentheses and why?

7.1 Exercise Set MyMathLab® ▶

Find the value of the following expressions when $x = 2$, $y = -2$, and $z = -5$. See Example 1.

1. $\dfrac{x+5}{x+2}$

2. $\dfrac{x+8}{x+1}$

3. $\dfrac{4z-1}{z-2}$

4. $\dfrac{7y-1}{y-1}$

5. $\dfrac{y^3}{y^2-1}$

6. $\dfrac{z}{z^2-5}$

7. $\dfrac{x^2+8x+2}{x^2-x-6}$

8. $\dfrac{x+5}{x^2+4x-8}$

Find any numbers for which each rational expression is undefined. See Example 2.

9. $\dfrac{7}{2x}$

10. $\dfrac{3}{5x}$

11. $\dfrac{x+3}{x+2}$

12. $\dfrac{5x+1}{x-9}$

13. $\dfrac{x-4}{2x-5}$

14. $\dfrac{x+1}{5x-2}$

15. $\dfrac{x^2-5x-2}{4}$

16. $\dfrac{9y^5+y^3}{9}$

17. $\dfrac{3x^2+9}{x^2-5x-6}$

18. $\dfrac{11x^2+1}{x^2-5x-14}$

19. $\dfrac{9x^3+4}{x^2+36}$

20. $\dfrac{19x^3+2}{x^2+4}$

21. $\dfrac{x}{3x^2+13x+14}$

22. $\dfrac{x}{2x^2+15x+27}$

Study Example 9. Then list four equivalent forms for each rational expression.

23. $-\dfrac{x-10}{x+8}$

24. $-\dfrac{x+11}{x-4}$

25. $-\dfrac{5y-3}{y-12}$

26. $-\dfrac{8y-1}{y-15}$

Simplify each expression. See Examples 3 through 8.

27. $\dfrac{x+7}{7+x}$

28. $\dfrac{y+9}{9+y}$

29. $\dfrac{x-7}{7-x}$

30. $\dfrac{y-9}{9-y}$

31. $\dfrac{2}{8x+16}$

32. $\dfrac{3}{9x+6}$

33. $\dfrac{x-2}{x^2-4}$

34. $\dfrac{x+5}{x^2-25}$

35. $\dfrac{2x-10}{3x-30}$

36. $\dfrac{3x-9}{4x-16}$

37. $\dfrac{-5a-5b}{a+b}$

38. $\dfrac{-4x-4y}{x+y}$

39. $\dfrac{7x+35}{x^2+5x}$

40. $\dfrac{9x+99}{x^2+11x}$

41. $\dfrac{x+5}{x^2-4x-45}$

42. $\dfrac{x-3}{x^2-6x+9}$

43. $\dfrac{5x^2+11x+2}{x+2}$

44. $\dfrac{12x^2+4x-1}{2x+1}$

45. $\dfrac{x^3+7x^2}{x^2+5x-14}$

46. $\dfrac{x^4-10x^3}{x^2-17x+70}$

47. $\dfrac{14x^2-21x}{2x-3}$

48. $\dfrac{4x^2+24x}{x+6}$

49. $\dfrac{x^2+7x+10}{x^2-3x-10}$

50. $\dfrac{2x^2+7x-4}{x^2+3x-4}$

51. $\dfrac{3x^2+7x+2}{3x^2+13x+4}$

52. $\dfrac{4x^2-4x+1}{2x^2+9x-5}$

53. $\dfrac{2x^2-8}{4x-8}$

54. $\dfrac{5x^2-500}{35x+350}$

55. $\dfrac{4-x^2}{x-2}$

56. $\dfrac{49-y^2}{y-7}$

57. $\dfrac{x^2-1}{x^2-2x+1}$

58. $\dfrac{x^2-16}{x^2-8x+16}$

59. $\dfrac{m^2-6m+9}{m^2-m-6}$

60. $\dfrac{m^2-4m+4}{m^2+m-6}$

61. $\dfrac{11x^2-22x^3}{6x-12x^2}$

62. $\dfrac{24y^2-8y^3}{15y-5y^2}$

Simplify. These expressions contain 4-term polynomials and sums and differences of cubes.

63. $\dfrac{x^2+xy+2x+2y}{x+2}$

64. $\dfrac{ab+ac+b^2+bc}{b+c}$

65. $\dfrac{5x+15-xy-3y}{2x+6}$

66. $\dfrac{xy-6x+2y-12}{y^2-6y}$

67. $\dfrac{x^3+8}{x+2}$

68. $\dfrac{x^3+64}{x+4}$

69. $\dfrac{x^3-1}{1-x}$

70. $\dfrac{3-x}{x^3-27}$

71. $\dfrac{2xy+5x-2y-5}{3xy+4x-3y-4}$

72. $\dfrac{2xy+2x-3y-3}{2xy+4x-3y-6}$

MIXED PRACTICE

Simplify each expression. Then determine whether the given answer is correct. See Examples 3 through 9.

73. $\dfrac{9-x^2}{x-3}$; Answer: $-3-x$

74. $\dfrac{100-x^2}{x-10}$; Answer: $-10-x$

75. $\dfrac{7-34x-5x^2}{25x^2-1}$; Answer: $\dfrac{x+7}{-5x-1}$

76. $\dfrac{2-15x-8x^2}{64x^2-1}$; Answer: $\dfrac{x+2}{-8x-1}$

REVIEW AND PREVIEW

Perform each indicated operation. See Section 1.3.

77. $\dfrac{1}{3}\cdot\dfrac{9}{11}$

78. $\dfrac{5}{27}\cdot\dfrac{2}{5}$

79. $\dfrac{1}{3}\div\dfrac{1}{4}$

80. $\dfrac{7}{8}\div\dfrac{1}{2}$

81. $\dfrac{13}{20}\div\dfrac{2}{9}$

82. $\dfrac{8}{15}\div\dfrac{5}{8}$

CONCEPT EXTENSIONS

Which of the following are incorrect and why? See the Concept Check in this section.

83. $\dfrac{5a-15}{5}$ simplifies to $a-3$?

84. $\dfrac{7m-9}{7}$ simplifies to $m-9$?

85. $\dfrac{1+2}{1+3}$ simplifies to $\dfrac{2}{3}$?

86. $\dfrac{46}{54}$ simplifies to $\dfrac{6}{5}$?

Determine whether each rational expression can be simplified. (Do not actually simplify.)

87. $\dfrac{x}{x+7}$

88. $\dfrac{3+x}{x+3}$

89. $\dfrac{5-x}{x-5}$

90. $\dfrac{x+2}{x+8}$

91. Explain how to write a fraction in lowest terms.

92. Explain how to write a rational expression in lowest terms.

93. Explain why the denominator of a fraction or a rational expression must not equal 0.

94. Does $\dfrac{(x-3)(x+3)}{x-3}$ have the same value as $x+3$ for all real numbers? Explain why or why not.

95. The total revenue R from the sale of a popular music compact disc is approximately given by the equation

$$R = \frac{150x^2}{x^2 + 3}$$

where x is the number of years since the CD has been released and revenue R is in millions of dollars.

a. Find the total revenue generated by the end of the first year.

b. Find the total revenue generated by the end of the second year.

c. Find the total revenue generated in the second year only.

96. For a certain model fax machine, the manufacturing cost C per machine is given by the equation

$$C = \frac{250x + 10,000}{x}$$

where x is the number of fax machines manufactured and cost C is in dollars per machine.

a. Find the cost per fax machine when manufacturing 100 fax machines.

b. Find the cost per fax machine when manufacturing 1000 fax machines.

c. Does the cost per machine decrease or increase when more machines are manufactured? Explain why this is so.

Solve.

97. The dose of medicine prescribed for a child depends on the child's age A in years and the adult dose D for the medication. Young's Rule is a formula used by pediatricians that gives a child's dose C as

$$C = \frac{DA}{A + 12}$$

Suppose that an 8-year-old child needs medication, and the normal adult dose is 1000 mg. What size dose should the child receive?

98. Calculating body-mass index is a way to gauge whether a person should lose weight. Doctors recommend that body-mass index values fall between 18.5 and 25. The formula for body-mass index B is

$$B = \frac{703w}{h^2}$$

where w is weight in pounds and h is height in inches. Should a 148-pound person who is 5 feet 6 inches tall lose weight?

99. Anthropologists and forensic scientists use a measure called the cephalic index to help classify skulls. The cephalic index of a skull with width W and length L from front to back is given by the formula

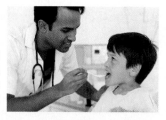

$$C = \frac{100W}{L} \quad \text{(Cont. in next column)}$$

A long skull has an index value less than 75, a medium skull has an index value between 75 and 85, and a broad skull has an index value over 85. Find the cephalic index of a skull that is 5 inches wide and 6.4 inches long. Classify the skull.

100. A company's gross profit margin P can be computed with the formula $P = \dfrac{R - C}{R}$, where R = the company's revenue and C = cost of goods sold. During a recent fiscal year, computer company Apple had revenues of $32.5 billion and cost of goods sold $21.3 billion. (*Source:* Apple, Inc.) What was Apple's gross profit margin in this year? Express the answer as a percent, rounded to the nearest tenth of a percent.

101. A baseball player's slugging average S can be calculated with the following formula:

$$S = \frac{h + d + 2t + 3r}{b}, \text{ where } h = \text{number of hits,}$$

d = number of doubles, t = number of triples, r = number of home runs, and b = number of at bats. In 2014, Jose Abreu of the Chicago White Sox led Major League Baseball in slugging average. During the 2014 season, Abreu had 556 at bats, 176 hits, 35 doubles, 2 triples, and 36 home runs. (*Source:* Major League Baseball) Calculate Abreu's slugging average. Round to three decimal places.

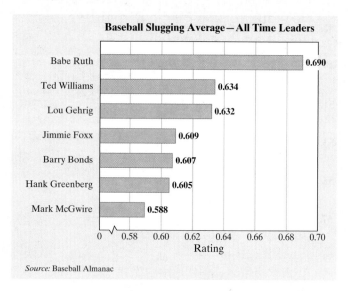

Source: Baseball Almanac

102. To calculate a quarterback's rating in NCAA football, you may use the formula $\dfrac{100C + 330T - 200I + 8.4Y}{A}$, where

C = the number of completed passes, A = the number of attempted passes, T = the number of touchdown passes, Y = the number of yards in the completed passes, and I = the number of interceptions. Marcus Mariota of the Oregon Ducks was selected as the 2014 winner of the Heisman Memorial Trophy as the Most Outstanding Football Player. Mariota, a junior quarterback, ended the season with 445 attempts, 304 completions, 4454 yards, 42 touchdowns, and only 4 interceptions. Calculate Mariota's quarterback rating for the 2014 season. (*Source:* NCAA) Round the answer to the nearest tenth.

How does the graph of $y = \dfrac{x^2 - 9}{x - 3}$ *compare to the graph of*

$y = x + 3$? *Recall that* $\dfrac{x^2 - 9}{x - 3} = \dfrac{(x + 3)(x - 3)}{x - 3} = x + 3$

as long as x is not 3. This means that the graph of $y = \dfrac{x^2 - 9}{x - 3}$

is the same as the graph of $y = x + 3$ *with* $x \neq 3$. *To graph*

$y = \dfrac{x^2 - 9}{x - 3}$, *then, graph the linear equation* $y = x + 3$ *and place*

an open dot on the graph at 3. This open dot or interruption of
the line at 3 means $x \neq 3$.

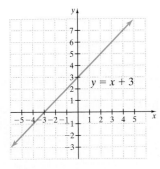

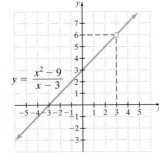

103. Graph $y = \dfrac{x^2 - 25}{x + 5}$.

104. Graph $y = \dfrac{x^2 - 16}{x - 4}$.

105. Graph $y = \dfrac{x^2 + x - 12}{x + 4}$.

106. Graph $y = \dfrac{x^2 - 6x + 8}{x - 2}$.

7.2 Multiplying and Dividing Rational Expressions

OBJECTIVES

1 Multiply Rational Expressions.

2 Divide Rational Expressions.

3 Multiply or Divide Rational Expressions.

4 Convert between Units of Measure.

OBJECTIVE

1 Multiplying Rational Expressions

Just as simplifying rational expressions is similar to simplifying number fractions, multiplying and dividing rational expressions is similar to multiplying and dividing number fractions.

Fractions	*Rational Expressions*
Multiply: $\dfrac{3}{5} \cdot \dfrac{10}{11}$	Multiply: $\dfrac{x - 3}{x + 5} \cdot \dfrac{2x + 10}{x^2 - 9}$

Multiply numerators and multiply denominators.

$$\dfrac{3}{5} \cdot \dfrac{10}{11} = \dfrac{3 \cdot 10}{5 \cdot 11} \qquad \dfrac{x - 3}{x + 5} \cdot \dfrac{2x + 10}{x^2 - 9} = \dfrac{(x - 3) \cdot (2x + 10)}{(x + 5) \cdot (x^2 - 9)}$$

Simplify by factoring numerators and denominators.

$$= \dfrac{3 \cdot 2 \cdot 5}{5 \cdot 11} \qquad = \dfrac{(x - 3) \cdot 2 (x + 5)}{(x + 5) (x + 3) (x - 3)}$$

Apply the fundamental principle.

$$= \dfrac{3 \cdot 2}{11} \quad \text{or} \quad \dfrac{6}{11} \qquad = \dfrac{2}{x + 3}$$

Multiplying Rational Expressions

If $\dfrac{P}{Q}$ and $\dfrac{R}{S}$ are rational expressions, then

$$\dfrac{P}{Q} \cdot \dfrac{R}{S} = \dfrac{PR}{QS}, \qquad Q \neq 0, S \neq 0$$

To multiply rational expressions, multiply the numerators and multiply the denominators.

Note: Recall that for Sections 7.1 through 7.4, we assume variables in rational expressions have only those replacement values for which the expressions are defined.

EXAMPLE 1 Multiply.

a. $\dfrac{25x}{2} \cdot \dfrac{1}{y^3}$

b. $\dfrac{-7x^2}{5y} \cdot \dfrac{3y^5}{14x^2}$

Solution To multiply rational expressions, multiply the numerators and multiply the denominators of both expressions. Then simplify if possible.

a. $\dfrac{25x}{2} \cdot \dfrac{1}{y^3} = \dfrac{25x \cdot 1}{2 \cdot y^3} = \dfrac{25x}{2y^3}$

The expression $\dfrac{25x}{2y^3}$ is in simplest form.

b. $\dfrac{-7x^2}{5y} \cdot \dfrac{3y^5}{14x^2} = \dfrac{-7x^2 \cdot 3y^5}{5y \cdot 14x^2}$ Multiply.

The expression $\dfrac{-7x^2 \cdot 3y^5}{5y \cdot 14x^2}$ is not in simplest form, so we factor the numerator and the denominator and divide out common factors.

$$= \dfrac{-1 \cdot 7 \cdot 3 \cdot x^2 \cdot y \cdot y^4}{5 \cdot 2 \cdot 7 \cdot x^2 \cdot y}$$

$$= -\dfrac{3y^4}{10}$$

> **Helpful Hint**
>
> It is the Fundamental Principle of Fractions that allows us to simplify.

PRACTICE
1 Multiply.

a. $\dfrac{4a}{5} \cdot \dfrac{3}{b^2}$

b. $\dfrac{-3p^4}{q^2} \cdot \dfrac{2q^3}{9p^4}$

When multiplying rational expressions, it is usually best to factor each numerator and denominator. This will help us when we divide out common factors to write the product in lowest terms.

EXAMPLE 2 Multiply: $\dfrac{x^2 + x}{3x} \cdot \dfrac{6}{5x + 5}$

Solution $\dfrac{x^2 + x}{3x} \cdot \dfrac{6}{5x + 5} = \dfrac{x(x + 1)}{3x} \cdot \dfrac{2 \cdot 3}{5(x + 1)}$ Factor numerators and denominators.

$$= \dfrac{x(x + 1) \cdot 2 \cdot 3}{3x \cdot 5 (x + 1)}$$ Multiply.

$$= \dfrac{2}{5}$$ Simplify by dividing out common factors.

PRACTICE
2 Multiply: $\dfrac{x^2 - x}{5x} \cdot \dfrac{15}{x^2 - 1}$

The following steps may be used to multiply rational expressions.

Multiplying Rational Expressions

Step 1. Completely factor numerators and denominators.

Step 2. Multiply numerators and multiply denominators.

Step 3. Simplify or write the product in lowest terms by dividing out common factors.

✔ **CONCEPT CHECK**

Which of the following is a true statement?

a. $\dfrac{1}{3} \cdot \dfrac{1}{2} = \dfrac{1}{5}$

b. $\dfrac{2}{x} \cdot \dfrac{5}{x} = \dfrac{10}{x}$

c. $\dfrac{3}{x} \cdot \dfrac{1}{2} = \dfrac{3}{2x}$

d. $\dfrac{x}{7} \cdot \dfrac{x+5}{4} = \dfrac{2x+5}{28}$

EXAMPLE 3 Multiply: $\dfrac{3x+3}{5x-5x^2} \cdot \dfrac{2x^2+x-3}{4x^2-9}$

Solution

$$\dfrac{3x+3}{5x-5x^2} \cdot \dfrac{2x^2+x-3}{4x^2-9} = \dfrac{3(x+1)}{5x(1-x)} \cdot \dfrac{(2x+3)(x-1)}{(2x-3)(2x+3)} \qquad \text{Factor.}$$

$$= \dfrac{3(x+1)(2x+3)(x-1)}{5x(1-x)(2x-3)(2x+3)} \qquad \text{Multiply.}$$

$$= \dfrac{3(x+1)(x-1)}{5x(1-x)(2x-3)} \qquad \text{Divide out common factors.}$$

Next, recall that $x-1$ and $1-x$ are opposites so that $x-1 = -1(1-x)$.

$$= \dfrac{3(x+1)(-1)(1-x)}{5x(1-x)(2x-3)} \qquad \text{Write } x-1 \text{ as } -1(1-x).$$

$$= \dfrac{-3(x+1)}{5x(2x-3)} \quad \text{or} \quad -\dfrac{3(x+1)}{5x(2x-3)} \qquad \text{Divide out common factors.} \quad \square$$

PRACTICE
3 Multiply: $\dfrac{6-3x}{6x+6x^2} \cdot \dfrac{3x^2-2x-5}{x^2-4}$

OBJECTIVE
2 Dividing Rational Expressions

We can divide by a rational expression in the same way we divide by a fraction. To divide by a fraction, multiply by its reciprocal.

Helpful Hint

Don't forget how to find reciprocals. The reciprocal of $\dfrac{a}{b}$ is $\dfrac{b}{a}$, $a \neq 0, b \neq 0$.

For example, to divide $\dfrac{3}{2}$ by $\dfrac{7}{8}$, multiply $\dfrac{3}{2}$ by $\dfrac{8}{7}$.

$$\dfrac{3}{2} \div \dfrac{7}{8} = \dfrac{3}{2} \cdot \dfrac{8}{7} = \dfrac{3 \cdot 4 \cdot 2}{2 \cdot 7} = \dfrac{12}{7}$$

Dividing Rational Expressions

If $\dfrac{P}{Q}$ and $\dfrac{R}{S}$ are rational expressions and $\dfrac{R}{S}$ is not 0, then

$$\dfrac{P}{Q} \div \dfrac{R}{S} = \dfrac{P}{Q} \cdot \dfrac{S}{R} = \dfrac{PS}{QR}$$

To divide two rational expressions, multiply the first rational expression by the reciprocal of the second rational expression.

EXAMPLE 4 Divide: $\dfrac{3x^3y^7}{40} \div \dfrac{4x^3}{y^2}$

Solution

$$\dfrac{3x^3y^7}{40} \div \dfrac{4x^3}{y^2} = \dfrac{3x^3y^7}{40} \cdot \dfrac{y^2}{4x^3} \qquad \text{Multiply by the reciprocal of } \dfrac{4x^3}{y^2}.$$

$$= \dfrac{3x^3y^9}{160x^3}$$

$$= \dfrac{3y^9}{160} \qquad \text{Simplify.} \qquad \square$$

PRACTICE
4   Divide: $\dfrac{5a^3b^2}{24} \div \dfrac{10a^5}{6}$ ■

EXAMPLE 5 Divide: $\dfrac{(x+2)^2}{10} \div \dfrac{2x+4}{5}$

Solution

$$\dfrac{(x+2)^2}{10} \div \dfrac{2x+4}{5} = \dfrac{(x+2)^2}{10} \cdot \dfrac{5}{2x+4} \qquad \text{Multiply by the reciprocal of } \dfrac{2x+4}{5}.$$

$$= \dfrac{(x+2)\,(x+2)\cdot 5}{5 \cdot 2 \cdot 2 \cdot (x+2)} \qquad \text{Factor and multiply.}$$

$$= \dfrac{x+2}{4} \qquad \text{Simplify.} \qquad \square$$

> **Helpful Hint**
> Remember, **to Divide by a Rational Expression**, multiply by its reciprocal.

PRACTICE
5   Divide: $\dfrac{(x-5)^2}{3}$ by $\dfrac{4x-20}{9}$ ■

The following may be used to divide by a rational expression.

Dividing by a Rational Expression

Multiply by its reciprocal.

EXAMPLE 6 Divide: $\dfrac{6x+2}{x^2-1} \div \dfrac{3x^2+x}{x-1}$

Solution

$$\dfrac{6x+2}{x^2-1} \div \dfrac{3x^2+x}{x-1} = \dfrac{6x+2}{x^2-1} \cdot \dfrac{x-1}{3x^2+x} \qquad \text{Multiply by the reciprocal.}$$

$$= \dfrac{2(3x+1)(x-1)}{(x+1)(x-1)\cdot x(3x+1)} \qquad \text{Factor and multiply.}$$

$$= \dfrac{2}{x(x+1)} \qquad \text{Simplify.} \qquad \square$$

PRACTICE
6   Divide: $\dfrac{10x-2}{x^2-9} \div \dfrac{5x^2-x}{x+3}$ ■

EXAMPLE 7   Divide: $\dfrac{2x^2 - 11x + 5}{5x - 25} \div \dfrac{4x - 2}{10}$

Solution

$$\dfrac{2x^2 - 11x + 5}{5x - 25} \div \dfrac{4x - 2}{10} = \dfrac{2x^2 - 11x + 5}{5x - 25} \cdot \dfrac{10}{4x - 2} \qquad \text{Multiply by the reciprocal.}$$

$$= \dfrac{(2x - 1)(x - 5) \cdot 2 \cdot 5}{5(x - 5) \cdot 2(2x - 1)} \qquad \text{Factor and multiply.}$$

$$= \dfrac{1}{1} \quad \text{or} \quad 1 \qquad \text{Simplify.} \qquad \square$$

PRACTICE
7   Divide: $\dfrac{3x^2 - 11x - 4}{2x - 8} \div \dfrac{9x + 3}{6}$ ∎

OBJECTIVE
3   **Multiplying or Dividing Rational Expressions**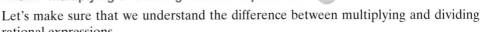

Let's make sure that we understand the difference between multiplying and dividing rational expressions.

Rational Expressions	
Multiplication	Multiply the numerators and multiply the denominators.
Division	Multiply by the reciprocal of the divisor.

EXAMPLE 8   Multiply or divide as indicated.

a. $\dfrac{x - 4}{5} \cdot \dfrac{x}{x - 4}$ **b.** $\dfrac{x - 4}{5} \div \dfrac{x}{x - 4}$ **c.** $\dfrac{x^2 - 4}{2x + 6} \cdot \dfrac{x^2 + 4x + 3}{2 - x}$

Solution

a. $\dfrac{x - 4}{5} \cdot \dfrac{x}{x - 4} = \dfrac{(x - 4) \cdot x}{5 \cdot (x - 4)} = \dfrac{x}{5}$

b. $\dfrac{x - 4}{5} \div \dfrac{x}{x - 4} = \dfrac{x - 4}{5} \cdot \dfrac{x - 4}{x} = \dfrac{(x - 4)^2}{5x}$

c. $\dfrac{x^2 - 4}{2x + 6} \cdot \dfrac{x^2 + 4x + 3}{2 - x} = \dfrac{(x - 2)(x + 2) \cdot (x + 1)(x + 3)}{2(x + 3) \cdot (2 - x)} \qquad \text{Factor and multiply.}$

$$= \dfrac{(x - 2)(x + 2) \cdot (x + 1)(x + 3)}{2(x + 3) \cdot (2 - x)}$$

$$= \dfrac{-1(x + 2)(x + 1)}{2} \qquad \begin{array}{l}\text{Divide out common}\\ \text{factors. Recall that}\\ \dfrac{x - 2}{2 - x} = -1\end{array}$$

$$= -\dfrac{(x + 2)(x + 1)}{2} \qquad \square$$

PRACTICE
8   Multiply or divide as indicated.

a. $\dfrac{y + 9}{8x} \cdot \dfrac{y + 9}{2x}$ **b.** $\dfrac{y + 9}{8x} \div \dfrac{y + 9}{2}$ **c.** $\dfrac{35x - 7x^2}{x^2 - 25} \cdot \dfrac{x^2 + 3x - 10}{x^2 + 4x}$ ∎

OBJECTIVE

4 Converting Between Units of Measure

How many square inches are in 1 square foot?

How many cubic feet are in a cubic yard?

If you have trouble answering these questions, this section will be helpful to you.

Now that we know how to multiply fractions and rational expressions, we can use this knowledge to help us convert between units of measure. To do so, we will use **unit fractions**. A unit fraction is a fraction that equals 1. For example, since 12 in. = 1 ft, we have the unit fractions

$$\frac{12 \text{ in.}}{1 \text{ ft}} = 1 \quad \text{and} \quad \frac{1 \text{ ft}}{12 \text{ in.}} = 1$$

EXAMPLE 9   18 square feet = _____ square yards

Solution   Let's multiply 18 square feet by a unit fraction that has square feet in the denominator and square yards in the numerator. From the diagram, you can see that

1 square yard = 9 square feet

Thus,

$$18 \text{ sq ft} = \frac{18 \text{ sq ft}}{1} \cdot 1 = \frac{\overset{2}{\cancel{18} \text{ sq ft}}}{1} \cdot \frac{1 \text{ sq yd}}{\underset{1}{\cancel{9} \text{ sq ft}}}$$

$$= \frac{2 \cdot 1}{1 \cdot 1} \text{ sq yd} = 2 \text{ sq yd}$$

1 yd = 3 ft

1 yd = 3 ft

Area: 1 sq yd or 9 sq ft

Thus, 18 sq ft = 2 sq yd.

Draw a diagram of 18 sq ft to help you see that this is reasonable.

PRACTICE

9   288 square inches = _____ square feet

EXAMPLE 10   5.2 square yards = _____ square feet

Solution

$$5.2 \text{ sq yd} = \frac{5.2 \text{ sq yd}}{1} \cdot 1 = \frac{5.2 \text{ sq yd}}{1} \cdot \frac{9 \text{ sq ft}}{1 \text{ sq yd}} \quad \begin{matrix} \leftarrow \text{Units converting to} \\ \leftarrow \text{Units given} \end{matrix}$$

$$= \frac{5.2 \cdot 9}{1 \cdot 1} \text{ sq ft}$$

$$= 46.8 \text{ sq ft}$$

Thus, 5.2 sq yd = 46.8 sq ft.

Draw a diagram to see that this is reasonable.

PRACTICE

10   3.5 square feet = _____ square inches

EXAMPLE 11   **Converting from Cubic Feet to Cubic Yards**

The largest building in the world by volume is The Boeing Company's Everett, Washington, factory complex, where Boeing's wide-body jetliners, the 747, 767, and 777, are built. The volume of this factory complex is 472,370,319 cubic feet. Find the volume of this Boeing facility in cubic yards. (_Source:_ The Boeing Company)

Solution There are 27 cubic feet in 1 cubic yard. (See the diagram.)

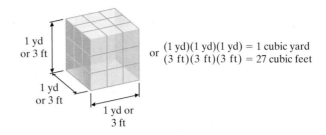

or (1 yd)(1 yd)(1 yd) = 1 cubic yard
(3 ft)(3 ft)(3 ft) = 27 cubic feet

$$472{,}370{,}319 \text{ cu ft} = 472{,}370{,}319 \text{ cu ft} \cdot \frac{1 \text{ cu yd}}{27 \text{ cu ft}}$$

$$= \frac{472{,}370{,}319}{27} \text{ cu yd}$$

$$= 17{,}495{,}197 \text{ cu yd}$$

PRACTICE
11 The largest casino in the world is the Venetian, in Macau, on the southern tip of China. The gaming area for this casino is approximately 61,000 _square yards_. Find the size of the gaming area in _square feet_. (_Source: USA Today_)

Helpful Hint

When converting among units of measurement, if possible write the unit fraction so that **the numerator contains the units you are converting to** and **the denominator contains the original units.**

Unit fraction

$$48 \text{ in.} = \frac{48 \text{ in.}}{1} \cdot \frac{1 \text{ ft}}{12 \text{ in.}} \quad \leftarrow \text{Units converting to} \\ \leftarrow \text{Original units}$$

$$= \frac{48}{12} \text{ ft} = 4 \text{ ft}$$

EXAMPLE 12 At the 2012 Summer Olympics, Jamaican athlete Usain Bolt won the gold medal in the men's 100-meter track event. He ran the distance at an average speed of 34.1 feet per second. Convert this speed to miles per hour. (_Source:_ International Olympic Committee)

Solution Recall that 1 mile = 5280 feet and 1 hour = 3600 seconds $(60 \cdot 60)$.

Unit fractions

$$34.1 \text{ feet/second} = \frac{34.1 \text{ feet}}{1 \text{ second}} \cdot \frac{3600 \text{ seconds}}{1 \text{ hour}} \cdot \frac{1 \text{ mile}}{5280 \text{ feet}}$$

$$= \frac{34.1 \cdot 3600}{5280} \text{ miles/hour}$$

$$\approx 23.3 \text{ miles/hour} \text{ (rounded to the nearest tenth)}$$

PRACTICE
12 The cheetah is the fastest land animal, being clocked at about 102.7 feet per second. Convert this to miles per hour. Round to the nearest tenth. (_Source: World Almanac and Book of Facts_)

✔ Vocabulary, Readiness & Video Check

Use one of the choices below to fill in the blank.

opposites   reciprocals

1. The expressions $\dfrac{x}{2y}$ and $\dfrac{2y}{x}$ are called _____ .

Multiply or divide as indicated.

2. $\dfrac{a}{b} \cdot \dfrac{c}{d} =$ _____

3. $\dfrac{a}{b} \div \dfrac{c}{d} =$ _____

4. $\dfrac{x}{7} \cdot \dfrac{x}{6} =$ _____

5. $\dfrac{x}{7} \div \dfrac{x}{6} =$ _____

Martin-Gay Interactive Videos

See Video 7.2 🔘

Watch the section lecture video and answer the following questions.

OBJECTIVE 1

6. Would you say a person needs to be quite comfortable with factoring polynomials in order to be successful with multiplying rational expressions? Explain, referencing 🎬 Example 2 in your answer.

OBJECTIVE 2

7. Based on the lecture before 🎬 Example 3, complete the following statements. Dividing rational expressions is exactly like dividing _____. Therefore, to divide by a rational expression, multiply by its _____.

OBJECTIVE 3

8. In 🎬 Examples 4 and 5, determining the operation is the first step in deciding how to simplify. Why do you think this is so?

OBJECTIVE 4

9. When converting between units of measurement, a unit fraction may be used. What units are used in the numerator and what units are used in the denominator of your unit fraction?

7.2   Exercise Set   MyMathLab® ▷

Find each product and simplify if possible. See Examples 1 through 3.

1. $\dfrac{3x}{y^2} \cdot \dfrac{7y}{4x}$

2. $\dfrac{9x^2}{y} \cdot \dfrac{4y}{3x^3}$

▶ **3.** $\dfrac{8x}{2} \cdot \dfrac{x^5}{4x^2}$

4. $\dfrac{6x^2}{10x^3} \cdot \dfrac{5x}{12}$

5. $-\dfrac{5a^2b}{30a^2b^2} \cdot b^3$

6. $-\dfrac{9x^3y^2}{18xy^5} \cdot y^3$

7. $\dfrac{x}{2x - 14} \cdot \dfrac{x^2 - 7x}{5}$

8. $\dfrac{4x - 24}{20x} \cdot \dfrac{5}{x - 6}$

9. $\dfrac{6x + 6}{5} \cdot \dfrac{10}{36x + 36}$

10. $\dfrac{x^2 + x}{8} \cdot \dfrac{16}{x + 1}$

11. $\dfrac{(m + n)^2}{m - n} \cdot \dfrac{m}{m^2 + mn}$

12. $\dfrac{(m - n)^2}{m + n} \cdot \dfrac{m}{m^2 - mn}$

13. $\dfrac{x^2 - 25}{x^2 - 3x - 10} \cdot \dfrac{x + 2}{x}$

14. $\dfrac{a^2 - 4a + 4}{a^2 - 4} \cdot \dfrac{a + 3}{a - 2}$

15. $\dfrac{x^2 + 6x + 8}{x^2 + x - 20} \cdot \dfrac{x^2 + 2x - 15}{x^2 + 8x + 16}$

16. $\dfrac{x^2 + 9x + 20}{x^2 - 15x + 44} \cdot \dfrac{x^2 - 11x + 28}{x^2 + 12x + 35}$

Find each quotient and simplify. See Examples 4 through 7.

17. $\dfrac{5x^7}{2x^5} \div \dfrac{15x}{4x^3}$

18. $\dfrac{9y^4}{6y} \div \dfrac{y^2}{3}$

19. $\dfrac{8x^2}{y^3} \div \dfrac{4x^2y^3}{6}$

20. $\dfrac{7a^2b}{3ab^2} \div \dfrac{21a^2b^2}{14ab}$

21. $\dfrac{(x - 6)(x + 4)}{4x} \div \dfrac{2x - 12}{8x^2}$

22. $\dfrac{(x + 3)^2}{5} \div \dfrac{5x + 15}{25}$

23. $\dfrac{3x^2}{x^2 - 1} \div \dfrac{x^5}{(x + 1)^2}$

24. $\dfrac{9x^5}{a^2 - b^2} \div \dfrac{27x^2}{3b - 3a}$

25. $\dfrac{m^2 - n^2}{m + n} \div \dfrac{m}{m^2 + nm}$

26. $\dfrac{(m - n)^2}{m + n} \div \dfrac{m^2 - mn}{m}$

▶ **27.** $\dfrac{x + 2}{7 - x} \div \dfrac{x^2 - 5x + 6}{x^2 - 9x + 14}$

28. $\dfrac{x - 3}{2 - x} \div \dfrac{x^2 + 3x - 18}{x^2 + 2x - 8}$

29. $\dfrac{x^2 + 7x + 10}{x - 1} \div \dfrac{x^2 + 2x - 15}{x - 1}$

30. $\dfrac{x + 1}{(x + 1)(2x + 3)} \div \dfrac{20x + 100}{2x + 3}$

MIXED PRACTICE

Multiply or divide as indicated. See Examples 1 through 8.

31. $\dfrac{5x - 10}{12} \div \dfrac{4x - 8}{8}$

32. $\dfrac{6x + 6}{5} \div \dfrac{9x + 9}{10}$

33. $\dfrac{x^2 + 5x}{8} \cdot \dfrac{9}{3x + 15}$

34. $\dfrac{3x^2 + 12x}{6} \cdot \dfrac{9}{2x + 8}$

35. $\dfrac{7}{6p^2 + q} \div \dfrac{14}{18p^2 + 3q}$

36. $\dfrac{3x + 6}{20} \div \dfrac{4x + 8}{8}$

37. $\dfrac{3x + 4y}{x^2 + 4xy + 4y^2} \cdot \dfrac{x + 2y}{2}$

38. $\dfrac{x^2 - y^2}{3x^2 + 3xy} \cdot \dfrac{3x^2 + 6x}{3x^2 - 2xy - y^2}$

39. $\dfrac{(x + 2)^2}{x - 2} \div \dfrac{x^2 - 4}{2x - 4}$

40. $\dfrac{x + 3}{x^2 - 9} \div \dfrac{5x + 15}{(x - 3)^2}$

41. $\dfrac{x^2 - 4}{24x} \div \dfrac{2 - x}{6xy}$

42. $\dfrac{3y}{3 - x} \div \dfrac{12xy}{x^2 - 9}$

43. $\dfrac{a^2 + 7a + 12}{a^2 + 5a + 6} \cdot \dfrac{a^2 + 8a + 15}{a^2 + 5a + 4}$

44. $\dfrac{b^2 + 2b - 3}{b^2 + b - 2} \cdot \dfrac{b^2 - 4}{b^2 + 6b + 8}$

45. $\dfrac{5x - 20}{3x^2 + x} \cdot \dfrac{3x^2 + 13x + 4}{x^2 - 16}$

46. $\dfrac{9x + 18}{4x^2 - 3x} \cdot \dfrac{4x^2 - 11x + 6}{x^2 - 4}$

47. $\dfrac{8n^2 - 18}{2n^2 - 5n + 3} \div \dfrac{6n^2 + 7n - 3}{n^2 - 9n + 8}$

48. $\dfrac{36n^2 - 64}{3n^2 + 10n + 8} \div \dfrac{3n^2 - 13n + 12}{n^2 - 5n - 14}$

49. Find the quotient of $\dfrac{x^2 - 9}{2x}$ and $\dfrac{x + 3}{8x^4}$.

50. Find the quotient of $\dfrac{4x^2 + 4x + 1}{4x + 2}$ and $\dfrac{4x + 2}{16}$.

Multiply or divide as indicated. Some of these expressions contain 4-term polynomials and sums and differences of cubes. See Examples 1 through 8.

51. $\dfrac{a^2 + ac + ba + bc}{a - b} \div \dfrac{a + c}{a + b}$

52. $\dfrac{x^2 + 2x - xy - 2y}{x^2 - y^2} \div \dfrac{2x + 4}{x + y}$

53. $\dfrac{3x^2 + 8x + 5}{x^2 + 8x + 7} \cdot \dfrac{x + 7}{x^2 + 4}$

54. $\dfrac{16x^2 + 2x}{16x^2 + 10x + 1} \cdot \dfrac{1}{4x^2 + 2x}$

55. $\dfrac{x^3 + 8}{x^2 - 2x + 4} \cdot \dfrac{4}{x^2 - 4}$

56. $\dfrac{9y}{3y - 3} \cdot \dfrac{y^3 - 1}{y^3 + y^2 + y}$

57. $\dfrac{a^2 - ab}{6a^2 + 6ab} \div \dfrac{a^3 - b^3}{a^2 - b^2}$

58. $\dfrac{x^3 + 27y^3}{6x} \div \dfrac{x^2 - 9y^2}{x^2 - 3xy}$

Convert as indicated. See Examples 9 through 12.

59. 10 square feet = _____ square inches.

60. 1008 square inches = _____ square feet.

61. 45 square feet = _____ square yards.

62. 2 square yards = _____ square inches.

63. 3 cubic yards = _____ cubic feet.

64. 2 cubic yards = _____ cubic inches.

65. 50 miles per hour = _____ feet per second (round to the nearest whole).

66. 10 feet per second = _____ miles per hour (round to the nearest tenth).

67. 6.3 square yards = _____ square feet.

68. 3.6 square yards = _____ square feet.

69. In January 2010, the Burj Khalifa Tower officially became the tallest building in the world. This tower has a curtain wall (the exterior skin of the building) that is approximately 133,500 square yards. Convert this to square feet. (*Source:* Burj Khalifa)

70. The Pentagon, headquarters for the Department of Defense, contains 3,705,793 square feet of office and storage space. Convert this to square yards. Round to the nearest square yard. (*Source:* U.S. Department of Defense)

71. On February 14, 2014, Brian Smith set a new stock car world speed record of 396.7 feet per second on the Space Shuttle landing runway at The John F. Kennedy Space Center. Convert this speed to miles per hour. Round to the nearest tenth. (*Source:* Vox Media)

72. On October 4, 2004, the rocket plane *SpaceShipOne* shot to an altitude of more than 100 km for the second time inside a week to claim the $10 million Ansari X-Prize. At one point in its flight, *SpaceShipOne* was traveling past Mach 1, about 930 miles per hour. Find this speed in feet per second. (*Source:* Space.com)

REVIEW AND PREVIEW

Perform each indicated operation. See Section 1.3.

73. $\dfrac{1}{5} + \dfrac{4}{5}$

74. $\dfrac{3}{15} + \dfrac{6}{15}$

75. $\dfrac{9}{9} - \dfrac{19}{9}$

76. $\dfrac{4}{3} - \dfrac{8}{3}$

77. $\dfrac{6}{5} + \left(\dfrac{1}{5} - \dfrac{8}{5}\right)$

78. $-\dfrac{3}{2} + \left(\dfrac{1}{2} - \dfrac{3}{2}\right)$

Graph each linear equation. See Section 3.2.

79. $x - 2y = 6$

80. $5x - y = 10$

CONCEPT EXTENSIONS

Identify each statement as true or false. If false, correct the multiplication. See the Concept Check in this section.

81. $\dfrac{4}{a} \cdot \dfrac{1}{b} = \dfrac{4}{ab}$

82. $\dfrac{2}{3} \cdot \dfrac{2}{4} = \dfrac{2}{7}$

83. $\dfrac{x}{5} \cdot \dfrac{x+3}{4} = \dfrac{2x+3}{20}$

84. $\dfrac{7}{a} \cdot \dfrac{3}{a} = \dfrac{21}{a}$

85. Find the area of the rectangle.

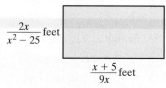

$\dfrac{2x}{x^2 - 25}$ feet

$\dfrac{x+5}{9x}$ feet

86. Find the area of the square.

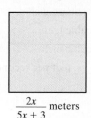

$\dfrac{2x}{5x+3}$ meters

Multiply or divide as indicated.

87. $\left(\dfrac{x^2 - y^2}{x^2 + y^2} \div \dfrac{x^2 - y^2}{3x} \right) \cdot \dfrac{x^2 + y^2}{6}$

88. $\left(\dfrac{x^2 - 9}{x^2 - 1} \cdot \dfrac{x^2 + 2x + 1}{2x^2 + 9x + 9} \right) \div \dfrac{2x + 3}{1 - x}$

89. $\left(\dfrac{2a + b}{b^2} \cdot \dfrac{3a^2 - 2ab}{ab + 2b^2} \right) \div \dfrac{a^2 - 3ab + 2b^2}{5ab - 10b^2}$

90. $\left(\dfrac{x^2y^2 - xy}{4x - 4y} \div \dfrac{3y - 3x}{8x - 8y} \right) \cdot \dfrac{y - x}{8}$

91. In your own words, explain how you multiply rational expressions.

92. Explain how dividing rational expressions is similar to dividing rational numbers.

Chapter 7 Vocabulary Check

Fill in each blank with one of the words or phrases listed below. Not all choices will be used.

least common denominator   simplifying   reciprocals   numerator $\dfrac{-a}{b}$ $\dfrac{a}{-b}$

cross products   ratio   proportion   inverse variation

rational expression   direct variation   complex fraction   denominator $\dfrac{-a}{-b}$

1. A(n) _____ is an expression that can be written in the form $\dfrac{P}{Q}$, where P and Q are polynomials and Q is not 0.

2. In a(n) _____ , the numerator or denominator or both may contain fractions.

3. For a rational expression, $-\dfrac{a}{b} =$ _____ $=$ _____ .

4. A rational expression is undefined when the _____ is 0.

5. The process of writing a rational expression in lowest terms is called _____ .

6. The expressions $\dfrac{2x}{7}$ and $\dfrac{7}{2x}$ are called _____ .

7. The _____ of a list of rational expressions is a polynomial of least degree whose factors include all factors of the denominators in the list.

8. A(n) _____ is the quotient of two numbers.

9. $\dfrac{x}{2} = \dfrac{7}{16}$ is an example of a(n) _____ .

10. If $\dfrac{a}{b} = \dfrac{c}{d}$, then ad and bc are called _____.

11. The equation $y = \dfrac{k}{x}$ is an example of _____.

12. The equation $y = kx$ is an example of _____.

Chapter 7 Highlights

DEFINITIONS AND CONCEPTS	EXAMPLES

Section 7.1   Simplifying Rational Expressions

A **rational expression** is an expression that can be written in the form $\dfrac{P}{Q}$, where P and Q are polynomials and Q does not equal 0.

$$\frac{7y^3}{4}, \frac{x^2 + 6x + 1}{x - 3}, \frac{-5}{s^3 + 8}$$

To find values for which a rational expression is undefined, find values for which the denominator is 0.

Find any values for which the expression $\dfrac{5y}{y^2 - 4y + 3}$ is undefined.

$$
\begin{aligned}
y^2 - 4y + 3 &= 0 && \text{Set the denominator equal to 0.} \\
(y - 3)(y - 1) &= 0 && \text{Factor.} \\
y - 3 = 0 \quad \text{or} \quad y - 1 &= 0 && \text{Set each factor equal to 0.} \\
y = 3 \qquad\qquad y &= 1 && \text{Solve.}
\end{aligned}
$$

The expression is undefined when y is 3 and when y is 1.

To Simplify a Rational Expression

Step 1. Factor the numerator and denominator.

Step 2. Divide out factors common to the numerator and denominator. (This is the same as removing a factor of 1.)

Simplify: $\dfrac{4x + 20}{x^2 - 25}$

$$\frac{4x + 20}{x^2 - 25} = \frac{4(x + 5)}{(x + 5)(x - 5)} = \frac{4}{x - 5}$$

Section 7.2   Multiplying and Dividing Rational Expressions

To Multiply Rational Expressions

Step 1. Factor numerators and denominators.

Step 2. Multiply numerators and multiply denominators.

Step 3. Write the product in simplest form.

$$\frac{P}{Q} \cdot \frac{R}{S} = \frac{PR}{QS}$$

Multiply: $\dfrac{4x + 4}{2x - 3} \cdot \dfrac{2x^2 + x - 6}{x^2 - 1}$

$$
\begin{aligned}
\frac{4x + 4}{2x - 3} \cdot \frac{2x^2 + x - 6}{x^2 - 1} &= \frac{4(x + 1)}{2x - 3} \cdot \frac{(2x - 3)(x + 2)}{(x + 1)(x - 1)} \\[4pt]
&= \frac{4(x + 1)(2x - 3)(x + 2)}{(2x - 3)(x + 1)(x - 1)} \\[4pt]
&= \frac{4(x + 2)}{x - 1}
\end{aligned}
$$

To Divide by a Rational Expression

To divide by a rational expression, multiply by the reciprocal.

$$\frac{P}{Q} \div \frac{R}{S} = \frac{P}{Q} \cdot \frac{S}{R} = \frac{PS}{QR}$$

Divide: $\dfrac{15x + 5}{3x^2 - 14x - 5} \div \dfrac{15}{3x - 12}$

$$
\begin{aligned}
\frac{15x + 5}{3x^2 - 14x - 5} \div \frac{15}{3x - 12} &= \frac{5(3x + 1)}{(3x + 1)(x - 5)} \cdot \frac{3(x - 4)}{3 \cdot 5} \\[4pt]
&= \frac{x - 4}{x - 5}
\end{aligned}
$$

Chapter 7 Review

(7.1) Find any real number for which each rational expression is undefined.

1. $\dfrac{x + 5}{x^2 - 4}$

2. $\dfrac{5x + 9}{4x^2 - 4x - 15}$

Find the value of each rational expression when $x = 5$, $y = 7$, and $z = -2$.

3. $\dfrac{2 - z}{z + 5}$

4. $\dfrac{x^2 + xy - y^2}{x + y}$

Simplify each rational expression.

5. $\dfrac{2x + 6}{x^2 + 3x}$

6. $\dfrac{3x - 12}{x^2 - 4x}$

7. $\dfrac{x + 2}{x^2 - 3x - 10}$

8. $\dfrac{x + 4}{x^2 + 5x + 4}$

9. $\dfrac{x^3 - 4x}{x^2 + 3x + 2}$

10. $\dfrac{5x^2 - 125}{x^2 + 2x - 15}$

11. $\dfrac{x^2 - x - 6}{x^2 - 3x - 10}$

12. $\dfrac{x^2 - 2x}{x^2 + 2x - 8}$

Simplify each expression. This section contains four-term polynomials and sums and differences of two cubes.

13. $\dfrac{x^2 + xa + xb + ab}{x^2 - xc + bx - bc}$

14. $\dfrac{x^2 + 5x - 2x - 10}{x^2 - 3x - 2x + 6}$

15. $\dfrac{4 - x}{x^3 - 64}$

16. $\dfrac{x^2 - 4}{x^3 + 8}$

(7.2) Perform each indicated operation and simplify.

17. $\dfrac{15x^3y^2}{z} \cdot \dfrac{z}{5xy^3}$

18. $\dfrac{-y^3}{8} \cdot \dfrac{9x^2}{y^3}$

19. $\dfrac{x^2 - 9}{x^2 - 4} \cdot \dfrac{x - 2}{x + 3}$

20. $\dfrac{2x + 5}{x - 6} \cdot \dfrac{2x}{-x + 6}$

21. $\dfrac{x^2 - 5x - 24}{x^2 - x - 12} \div \dfrac{x^2 - 10x + 16}{x^2 + x - 6}$

22. $\dfrac{4x + 4y}{xy^2} \div \dfrac{3x + 3y}{x^2y}$

23. $\dfrac{x^2 + x - 42}{x - 3} \cdot \dfrac{(x - 3)^2}{x + 7}$

24. $\dfrac{2a + 2b}{3} \cdot \dfrac{a - b}{a^2 - b^2}$

25. $\dfrac{2x^2 - 9x + 9}{8x - 12} \div \dfrac{x^2 - 3x}{2x}$

26. $\dfrac{x^2 - y^2}{x^2 + xy} \div \dfrac{3x^2 - 2xy - y^2}{3x^2 + 6x}$

27. $\dfrac{x - y}{4} \div \dfrac{y^2 - 2y - xy + 2x}{16x + 24}$

28. $\dfrac{5 + x}{7} \div \dfrac{xy + 5y - 3x - 15}{7y - 35}$

1c

Chapter 7 Getting Ready for the Test

MULTIPLE CHOICE *Select the correct choice.*

▶ 1. $\dfrac{x-8}{8-x}$ simplifies to

    A. 1   **B.** -1 **C.** -2 **D.** -8

▶ 2. $\dfrac{8}{x^2} \cdot \dfrac{4}{x^2} =$

    A. $\dfrac{32}{x^2}$ **B.** $\dfrac{2}{x^2}$ **C.** $\dfrac{32}{x^4}$ **D.** 2 **E.** $\dfrac{1}{2}$

▶ 3. $\dfrac{8}{x^2} \div \dfrac{4}{x^2} =$

    A. $\dfrac{32}{x^2}$ **B.** $\dfrac{2}{x^2}$ **C.** $\dfrac{32}{x^4}$ **D.** 2 **E.** $\dfrac{1}{2}$

▶ 4. $\dfrac{8}{x^2} + \dfrac{4}{x^2} =$

    A. $\dfrac{32}{x^2}$ **B.** $\dfrac{2}{x^2}$ **C.** $\dfrac{12}{x^4}$ **D.** $\dfrac{12}{x^2}$

▶ 5. $\dfrac{7x}{x-1} - \dfrac{5+2x}{x-1} =$

    A. 5 **B.** $\dfrac{9x-5}{x-1}$ **C.** $\dfrac{5}{x-1}$ **D.** $\dfrac{14}{x-1}$

▶ 6. The LCD of $\dfrac{9}{25x}$ and $\dfrac{z}{10x^3}$ is

    A. $250x^4$ **B.** $250x$ **C.** $50x^4$ **D.** $50x^3$

MULTIPLE CHOICE *Identify each as an **A.** expression or **B.** equation.*
Letters may be used more than once or not at all.

▶ 7. $\dfrac{5}{x} + \dfrac{1}{3}$ ▶ 8. $\dfrac{5}{x} + \dfrac{1}{3} = \dfrac{2}{x}$ ▶ 9. $\dfrac{a+5}{11} = 9$ ▶ 10. $\dfrac{a+5}{11} \cdot 9$

MULTIPLE CHOICE *Select the correct choice.*

▶ 11. Multiply the given equation through by the LCD of its terms. Choose the correct equivalent equation once this is done and terms are simplified.   Given Equation: $\dfrac{x+3}{4} + \dfrac{5}{6} = 3$

   A. $(x+3) + 5 = 3$ **B.** $3(x+3) + 2 \cdot 5 = 3$ **C.** $3(x+3) + 2 \cdot 5 = 12 \cdot 3$ **D.** $6(x+3) + 4 \cdot 5 = 3$

▶ 12. Translate to an equation. Let x be the unknown number. "The quotient of a number and 5 equals the sum of that number and 12."

   A. $\dfrac{x}{5} = x + 12$ **B.** $\dfrac{5}{x} = x + 12$ **C.** $\dfrac{x}{5} = x \cdot 12$ **D.** $\dfrac{x}{5} \cdot (x + 12)$

Chapter 7 Test   MyMathLab® YouTube

▶ **1.** Find any real numbers for which the following expression is undefined.

$$\frac{x+5}{x^2 + 4x + 3}$$

▶ **2.** For a certain computer desk, the average cost C (in dollars) per desk manufactured is

$$C = \frac{100x + 3000}{x}$$

where x is the number of desks manufactured.

   a. Find the average cost per desk when manufacturing 200 computer desks.

   b. Find the average cost per desk when manufacturing 1000 computer desks.

Simplify each rational expression.

▶ **3.** $\dfrac{3x - 6}{5x - 10}$

▶ **4.** $\dfrac{x + 6}{x^2 + 12x + 36}$

▶ **5.** $\dfrac{x + 3}{x^3 + 27}$

▶ **6.** $\dfrac{2m^3 - 2m^2 - 12m}{m^2 - 5m + 6}$

▶ **7.** $\dfrac{ay + 3a + 2y + 6}{ay + 3a + 5y + 15}$

▶ **8.** $\dfrac{y - x}{x^2 - y^2}$

Perform the indicated operation and simplify if possible.

▶ **9.** $\dfrac{3}{x - 1} \cdot (5x - 5)$

▶ **10.** $\dfrac{y^2 - 5y + 6}{2y + 4} \cdot \dfrac{y + 2}{2y - 6}$

▶ **11.** $\dfrac{15x}{2x + 5} - \dfrac{6 - 4x}{2x + 5}$

▶ **12.** $\dfrac{5a}{a^2 - a - 6} - \dfrac{2}{a - 3}$

▶ **13.** $\dfrac{6}{x^2 - 1} + \dfrac{3}{x + 1}$

▶ **14.** $\dfrac{x^2 - 9}{x^2 - 3x} \div \dfrac{xy + 5x + 3y + 15}{2x + 10}$

▶ **15.** $\dfrac{x + 2}{x^2 + 11x + 18} + \dfrac{5}{x^2 - 3x - 10}$

Solve each equation.

▶ **16.** $\dfrac{4}{y} - \dfrac{5}{3} = -\dfrac{1}{5}$

▶ **17.** $\dfrac{5}{y + 1} = \dfrac{4}{y + 2}$

▶ **18.** $\dfrac{a}{a - 3} = \dfrac{3}{a - 3} - \dfrac{3}{2}$

▶ **19.** $x - \dfrac{14}{x - 1} = 4 - \dfrac{2x}{x - 1}$

▶ **20.** $\dfrac{10}{x^2 - 25} = \dfrac{3}{x + 5} + \dfrac{1}{x - 5}$

Simplify each complex fraction.

▶ **21.** $\dfrac{\dfrac{5x^2}{yz^2}}{\dfrac{10x}{z^3}}$ ▶ **22.** $\dfrac{5 - \dfrac{1}{y^2}}{\dfrac{1}{y} + \dfrac{2}{y^2}}$ ▶ **23.** $\dfrac{\dfrac{b}{a} - \dfrac{a}{b}}{\dfrac{1}{b} + \dfrac{1}{a}}$

▶ **24.** y varies directly as x. If $y = 10$ when $x = 15$, find y when x is 42.

▶ **25.** y varies inversely as x^2. If $y = 8$ when $x = 5$, find y when x is 15.

▶ **26.** In a sample of 85 fluorescent bulbs, 3 were found to be defective. At this rate, how many defective bulbs should be found in 510 bulbs?

▶ **27.** One number plus five times its reciprocal is equal to six. Find the number.

28. A pleasure boat traveling down the Red River takes the same time to go 14 miles upstream as it takes to go 16 miles downstream. If the current of the river is 2 miles per hour, find the speed of the boat in still water.

29. An inlet pipe can fill a tank in 12 hours. A second pipe can fill the tank in 15 hours. If both pipes are used, find how long it takes to fill the tank.

30. Given that the two triangles are similar, find x.

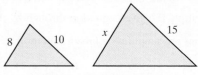

Chapter 7 Cumulative Review

TRANSLATING

1. Write each sentence as an equation or inequality. Let x represent the unknown number.

  a. The quotient of 15 and a number is 4.

  b. Three subtracted from 12 is a number.

  c. Four times a number, added to 17, is not equal to 21.

  d. Triple a number is less than 48.

2. Write each sentence as an equation. Let x represent the unknown number.

  a. The difference of 12 and a number is -45.

  b. The product of 12 and a number is -45.

  c. A number less 10 is twice the number.

3. Rajiv Puri invested part of his $20,000 inheritance in a mutual funds account that pays 7% simple interest yearly and the rest in a certificate of deposit that pays 9% simple interest yearly. At the end of one year, Rajiv's investments earned $1550. Find the amount he invested at each rate.

4. The number of nonbusiness bankruptcies has decreased in recent years. In 2010, the number of nonbusiness bankruptcies was 621,069 less than twice the number in 2014. If the total of nonbusiness bankruptcies for these two years was 2,270,148, find the number of nonbusiness bankruptcies for each year. (*Source:* uscourts.gov)

5. Graph $x - 3y = 6$ by finding and plotting intercepts.

6. Find the slope of the line whose equation is $7x + 2y = 9$.

7. Use the product rule to simplify each expression.

  a. $4^2 \cdot 4^5$ **b.** $x^4 \cdot x^6$

  c. $y^3 \cdot y$ **d.** $y^3 \cdot y^2 \cdot y^7$

  e. $(-5)^7 \cdot (-5)^8$ **f.** $a^2 \cdot b^2$

8. Simplify.

  a. $\dfrac{x^9}{x^7}$ **b.** $\dfrac{x^{19}y^5}{xy}$

  c. $(x^5y^2)^3$ **d.** $(-3a^2b)(5a^3b)$

9. Subtract $(5z - 7)$ from the sum of $(8z + 11)$ and $(9z - 2)$.

10. Subtract $(9x^2 - 6x + 2)$ from $(x + 1)$.

11. Multiply: $(3a + b)^3$

12. Multiply: $(2x + 1)(5x^2 - x + 2)$

13. Use a special product to square each binomial.

  a. $(t + 2)^2$

  b. $(p - q)^2$

  c. $(2x + 5)^2$

  d. $(x^2 - 7y)^2$

14. Multiply.

  a. $(x + 9)^2$

  b. $(2x + 1)(2x - 1)$

  c. $8x(x^2 + 1)(x^2 - 1)$

15. Simplify each expression. Write results using positive exponents only.

  a. $\dfrac{1}{x^{-3}}$ **b.** $\dfrac{1}{3^{-4}}$

  c. $\dfrac{p^{-4}}{q^{-9}}$ **d.** $\dfrac{5^{-3}}{2^{-5}}$

16. Simplify. Write results with positive exponents.

  a. 5^{-3} **b.** $\dfrac{9}{x^{-7}}$ **c.** $\dfrac{11^{-1}}{7^{-2}}$

17. Divide: $\dfrac{4x^2 + 7 + 8x^3}{2x + 3}$

18. Divide $(4x^3 - 9x + 2)$ by $(x - 4)$.

19. Find the GCF of each list of numbers.

  a. 28 and 40

  b. 55 and 21

  c. 15, 18, and 66

20. Find the GCF of $9x^2$, $6x^3$, and $21x^5$.

Factor.

21. $-9a^5 + 18a^2 - 3a$

22. $7x^6 - 7x^5 + 7x^4$

23. $3m^2 - 24m - 60$

24. $-2a^2 + 10a + 12$

25. $3x^2 + 11x + 6$

26. $10m^2 - 7m + 1$

27. $x^2 + 12x + 36$

28. $4x^2 + 12x + 9$

29. $x^2 + 4$

30. $x^2 - 4$

31. $x^3 + 8$

32. $27y^3 - 1$

33. $2x^3 + 3x^2 - 2x - 3$

34. $3x^3 + 5x^2 - 12x - 20$

35. $12m^2 - 3n^2$

36. $x^5 - x$

37. Solve: $x(2x - 7) = 4$

38. Solve: $3x^2 + 5x = 2$

39. Find the x-intercepts of the graph of $y = x^2 - 5x + 4$.

40. Find the x-intercepts of the graph of $y = x^2 - x - 6$.

41. The height of a triangular sail is 2 meters less than twice the length of the base. If the sail has an area of 30 square meters, find the length of its base and the height.

42. The height of a parallelogram is 5 feet more than three times its base. If the area of the parallelogram is 182 square feet, find the length of its base and height.

43. Simplify: $\dfrac{5x - 5}{x^3 - x^2}$

44. Simplify: $\dfrac{2x^2 - 50}{4x^4 - 20x^3}$

45. Divide: $\dfrac{6x + 2}{x^2 - 1} \div \dfrac{3x^2 + x}{x - 1}$

46. Multiply: $\dfrac{6x^2 - 18x}{3x^2 - 2x} \cdot \dfrac{15x - 10}{x^2 - 9}$

47. Simplify: $\dfrac{\dfrac{x + 1}{y}}{\dfrac{x}{y} + 2}$

48. Simplify: $\dfrac{\dfrac{m}{3} + \dfrac{n}{6}}{\dfrac{m + n}{12}}$

Roots and Radicals

CHECK YOUR PROGRESS

Vocabulary Check
Chapter Highlights
Chapter Review
Getting Ready for the Test
Chapter Test
Cumulative Review

Having spent the last chapter studying equations, we return now to algebraic expressions. We expand on our skills of operating on expressions—adding, subtracting, multiplying, dividing, and raising to powers—to include finding roots. Finding roots is defined by raising to powers. As we master finding roots, we will work with equations that contain roots and solve problems that can be modeled by such equations.

Is it Soccer or Football?

Soccer, or football as it is known to the rest of the world, is a sport played between two teams of eleven players with a spherical ball. This game is played in over 200 countries and is the most popular sport in the world. The men's FIFA World Cup takes place only every four years. It is said that over 715 million television viewers watched the final match of the 2014 World Cup. Below is a graph of the stadiums that held games for the 2014 World Cup.

In Exercise 43, page 546, we explore the dimensions of a standard competition soccer ball.

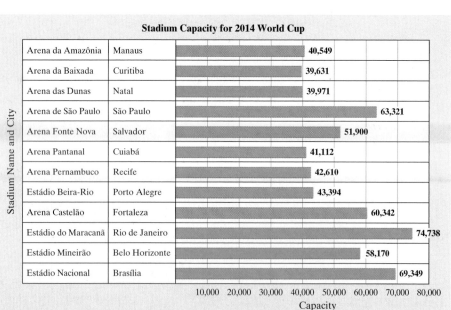

Stadium Capacity for 2014 World Cup

Stadium Name	City	Capacity
Arena da Amazônia	Manaus	40,549
Arena da Baixada	Curitiba	39,631
Arena das Dunas	Natal	39,971
Arena de São Paulo	São Paulo	63,321
Arena Fonte Nova	Salvador	51,900
Arena Pantanal	Cuiabá	41,112
Arena Pernambuco	Recife	42,610
Estádio Beira-Rio	Porto Alegre	43,394
Arena Castelão	Fortaleza	60,342
Estádio do Maracanã	Rio de Janeiro	74,738
Estádio Mineirão	Belo Horizonte	58,170
Estádio Nacional	Brasília	69,349

8.1 | Introduction to Radicals

OBJECTIVES

1 Find Square Roots.
2 Find Cube Roots.
3 Find *n*th Roots.
4 Approximate Square Roots.
5 Simplify Radicals Containing Variables.

OBJECTIVE

1   Finding Square Roots

In this section, we define finding the **root** of a number by its reverse operation, raising a number to a power. We begin with squares and square roots.

$$\text{The } square \text{ of } 5 \text{ is } 5^2 = 25.$$
$$\text{The } square \text{ of } -5 \text{ is } (-5)^2 = 25.$$
$$\text{The } square \text{ of } \frac{1}{2} \text{ is } \left(\frac{1}{2}\right)^2 = \frac{1}{4}.$$

The reverse operation of squaring a number is finding the **square root** of a number. For example,

$$\text{A } square\ root \text{ of } 25 \text{ is } 5 \text{ because } 5^2 = 25.$$
$$\text{A } square\ root \text{ of } 25 \text{ is also } -5 \text{ because } (-5)^2 = 25.$$
$$\text{A } square\ root \text{ of } \frac{1}{4} \text{ is } \frac{1}{2} \text{ because } \left(\frac{1}{2}\right)^2 = \frac{1}{4}.$$

> **In general, a number *b* is a square root of a number *a* if $b^2 = a$.**

Notice that both 5 and −5 are square roots of 25. The symbol $\sqrt{}$ denotes the **positive** or **principal square root** of a number. For example,

$$\sqrt{25} = 5 \text{ since } 5^2 = 25 \text{ and } 5 \text{ is positive.}$$

The symbol $-\sqrt{}$ denotes the **negative square root.** For example,

$$-\sqrt{25} = -5$$

The symbol $\sqrt{}$ is called a **radical** or **radical sign.** The expression within or under a radical sign is called the **radicand.** An expression containing a radical is called a **radical expression.**

$$\overset{\text{radical sign}}{\sqrt{a}}_{\text{radicand}}$$

Square Root

If *a* is a positive number, then

$\sqrt{a}$ is the **positive square root** of *a* and

$-\sqrt{a}$ is the **negative square root** of *a*.

$$\sqrt{a} = b \quad \text{only if} \quad b^2 = a \text{ and } b > 0$$

Also, $\sqrt{0} = 0$.

EXAMPLE 1   Find each square root.

a. $\sqrt{36}$ **b.** $-\sqrt{16}$ **c.** $\sqrt{\dfrac{9}{100}}$ **d.** $\sqrt{0}$ **e.** $\sqrt{0.64}$

Solution

a. $\sqrt{36} = 6$ because $6^2 = 36$ and 6 is positive.

b. $-\sqrt{16} = -4$. The negative sign in front of the radical indicates the negative square root of 16.

(Continued on next page)

c. $\sqrt{\dfrac{9}{100}} = \dfrac{3}{10}$ because $\left(\dfrac{3}{10}\right)^2 = \dfrac{9}{100}$ and $\dfrac{3}{10}$ is positive.

d. $\sqrt{0} = 0$ because $0^2 = 0$.

e. $\sqrt{0.64} = 0.8$ because $(0.8)^2 = 0.64$ and 0.8 is positive. □

PRACTICE

1 Find each square root.

a. $\sqrt{\dfrac{4}{81}}$ **b.** $-\sqrt{25}$ **c.** $\sqrt{144}$ **d.** $\sqrt{0.49}$ **e.** $-\sqrt{1}$ ■

Is the square root of a negative number a real number? For example, is $\sqrt{-4}$ a real number? To answer this question, we ask ourselves, is there a real number whose square is -4? Since there is no real number whose square is -4, we say that $\sqrt{-4}$ is not a real number. In general,

> A square root of a negative number is not a real number.

Study the following table to make sure you understand the differences discussed earlier.

Number	Square Roots of Number	$\sqrt{number}$	$-\sqrt{number}$
25	$-5, 5$	$\sqrt{25} = 5$ only	$-\sqrt{25} = -5$
$\dfrac{1}{4}$	$-\dfrac{1}{2}, \dfrac{1}{2}$	$\sqrt{\dfrac{1}{4}} = \dfrac{1}{2}$ only	$-\sqrt{\dfrac{1}{4}} = -\dfrac{1}{2}$
-4	No real square roots.	$\sqrt{-4}$ is not a real number.	

We will discuss numbers such as $\sqrt{-4}$ further in Chapter 9.

OBJECTIVE

2 Finding Cube Roots

We can find roots other than square roots. For example, since $2^3 = 8$, we call 2 the **cube root** of 8. In symbols, we write

$$\sqrt[3]{8} = 2 \qquad \text{The number 3 is called the \textbf{index.}}$$

Also,

$$\sqrt[3]{27} = 3 \quad \text{Since } 3^3 = 27$$
$$\sqrt[3]{-64} = -4 \quad \text{Since } (-4)^3 = -64$$

Notice that unlike the square root of a negative number, the cube root of a negative number is a real number. This is so because although we cannot find a real number whose **square** is negative, we **can** find a real number whose **cube** is negative. In fact, the cube of a negative number is a negative number. Therefore, the cube root of a negative number is a negative number.

EXAMPLE 2 Find each cube root.

a. $\sqrt[3]{1}$ **b.** $\sqrt[3]{-27}$ **c.** $\sqrt[3]{\dfrac{1}{125}}$

Solution

a. $\sqrt[3]{1} = 1$ because $1^3 = 1$.

b. $\sqrt[3]{-27} = -3$ because $(-3)^3 = -27$.

c. $\sqrt[3]{\dfrac{1}{125}} = \dfrac{1}{5}$ because $\left(\dfrac{1}{5}\right)^3 = \dfrac{1}{125}$.

PRACTICE
2   Find each cube root.

a. $\sqrt[3]{0}$ b. $\sqrt[3]{-64}$ c. $\sqrt[3]{\dfrac{1}{8}}$

OBJECTIVE
3   Finding *n*th Roots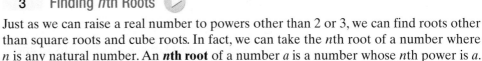

Just as we can raise a real number to powers other than 2 or 3, we can find roots other than square roots and cube roots. In fact, we can take the *n*th root of a number where *n* is any natural number. An ***n*th root** of a number *a* is a number whose *n*th power is *a*. The natural number *n* is called the **index.**

In symbols, the *n*th root of *a* is written as $\sqrt[n]{a}$. The index 2 is usually omitted for square roots.

> **Helpful Hint**
>
> If the index is even, such as $\sqrt{}, \sqrt[4]{}, \sqrt[6]{}$, and so on, the radicand must be nonnegative for the root to be a real number. For example,
>
> $\sqrt[4]{16} = 2$ but $\sqrt[4]{-16}$ is not a real number
>
> $\sqrt[6]{64} = 2$ but $\sqrt[6]{-64}$ is not a real number

✔ **CONCEPT CHECK**
Which of the following is a real number?

a. $\sqrt{-64}$ b. $\sqrt[4]{-64}$ c. $\sqrt[5]{-64}$ d. $\sqrt[6]{-64}$

EXAMPLE 3   Find each root.

a. $\sqrt[4]{16}$ ▶ b. $\sqrt[5]{-32}$ c. $-\sqrt[3]{8}$ ▶ d. $\sqrt[4]{-81}$

Solution

a. $\sqrt[4]{16} = 2$ because $2^4 = 16$ and 2 is positive.

b. $\sqrt[5]{-32} = -2$ because $(-2)^5 = -32$.

c. $-\sqrt[3]{8} = -2$ since $\sqrt[3]{8} = 2$.

d. $\sqrt[4]{-81}$ is not a real number since the index 4 is even and the radicand -81 is negative.

PRACTICE
3   Find each root.

a. $\sqrt[4]{81}$ b. $\sqrt[5]{100,000}$ c. $\sqrt[6]{-64}$ d. $\sqrt[3]{-125}$

OBJECTIVE
4   Approximating Square Roots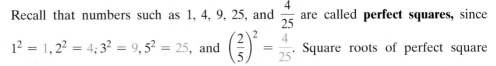

Recall that numbers such as 1, 4, 9, 25, and $\dfrac{4}{25}$ are called **perfect squares,** since

$1^2 = 1, 2^2 = 4; 3^2 = 9, 5^2 = 25$, and $\left(\dfrac{2}{5}\right)^2 = \dfrac{4}{25}$. Square roots of perfect square radicands simplify to rational numbers. What happens when we try to simplify a root such as $\sqrt{3}$? Since 3 is not a perfect square, $\sqrt{3}$ is not a rational number. It cannot be written as a quotient of integers. It is called an **irrational number** and we can find a decimal **approximation** of it. To find decimal approximations, use a calculator or an appendix. (For calculator help, see the box on the next page.)

EXAMPLE 4 Use a calculator or an appendix to approximate $\sqrt{3}$ to three decimal places.

Solution We may use an appendix or a calculator to approximate $\sqrt{3}$. To use a calculator, find the square root key $\boxed{\sqrt{}}$.

$$\sqrt{3} \approx 1.732050808$$

To three decimal places, $\sqrt{3} \approx 1.732$. □

PRACTICE
4 Use a calculator or an appendix to approximate $\sqrt{17}$ to three decimal places. ■

OBJECTIVE
5 Simplifying Radicals Containing Variables ▶

Radicals can also contain variables. To simplify radicals containing variables, special care must be taken. To see how we simplify $\sqrt{x^2}$, let's look at a few examples in this form.

$$\text{If } x = 3, \text{ we have } \sqrt{3^2} = \sqrt{9} = 3, \text{ or } x.$$
$$\text{If } x \text{ is } 5, \text{ we have } \sqrt{5^2} = \sqrt{25} = 5, \text{ or } x.$$

From these two examples, you may think that $\sqrt{x^2}$ simplifies to x. Let's now look at an example where x is a negative number. If $x = -3$, we have $\sqrt{(-3)^2} = \sqrt{9} = 3$, not -3, our original x. To make sure that $\sqrt{x^2}$ simplifies to a nonnegative number, we have the following.

> For any real number a,
> $$\sqrt{a^2} = |a|.$$

Thus,

$$\sqrt{x^2} = |x|,$$
$$\sqrt{(-8)^2} = |-8| = 8$$
$$\sqrt{(7y)^2} = |7y|, \quad \text{and so on.}$$

To avoid this, for the rest of the chapter we assume that **if a variable appears in the radicand of a radical expression, it represents positive numbers only.** Then

$$\sqrt{x^2} = |x| = x \text{ since } x \text{ is a positive number.}$$

$$\sqrt{y^2} = y \qquad \text{Because } (y)^2 = y^2$$
$$\sqrt{x^8} = x^4 \qquad \text{Because } (x^4)^2 = x^8$$
$$\sqrt{9x^2} = 3x \qquad \text{Because } (3x)^2 = 9x^2$$
$$\sqrt[3]{8z^{12}} = 2z^4 \qquad \text{Because } (2z^4)^3 = 8z^{12}$$

EXAMPLE 5 Simplify each expression. Assume that all variables represent positive numbers.

a. $\sqrt{z^2}$ **b.** $\sqrt{x^6}$ **c.** $\sqrt[3]{27y^6}$ **d.** $\sqrt{16x^{16}}$ **e.** $\sqrt{\dfrac{x^4}{25}}$ **f.** $\sqrt[3]{-125a^{12}b^{15}}$

Solution

a. $\sqrt{z^2} = z$ because $(z)^2 = z^2$.

b. $\sqrt{x^6} = x^3$ because $(x^3)^2 = x^6$.

c. $\sqrt[3]{27y^6} = 3y^2$ because $(3y^2)^3 = 27y^6$.

d. $\sqrt{16x^{16}} = 4x^8$ because $(4x^8)^2 = 16x^{16}$.

e. $\sqrt{\dfrac{x^4}{25}} = \dfrac{x^2}{5}$ because $\left(\dfrac{x^2}{5}\right)^2 = \dfrac{x^4}{25}$.

f. $\sqrt[3]{-125a^{12}b^{15}} = -5a^4b^5$ because $(-5a^4b^5)^3 = -125a^{12}b^{15}$.   □

PRACTICE
5   Simplify each expression. Assume that all variables represent positive numbers.

a. $\sqrt{x^{10}}$ b. $\sqrt{y^{14}}$ c. $\sqrt[3]{125z^9}$ d. $\sqrt{49x^2}$ e. $\sqrt{\dfrac{z^4}{36}}$ f. $\sqrt[3]{-8a^6b^{12}}$

Calculator Explorations

To simplify or approximate square roots using a calculator, locate the key marked $\boxed{\sqrt{}}$. To simplify $\sqrt{25}$ using a scientific calculator, press $\boxed{25}$ $\boxed{\sqrt{}}$. The display should read $\boxed{5}$. To simplify $\sqrt{25}$ using a graphing calculator, press $\boxed{\sqrt{}}$ $\boxed{25}$ $\boxed{\text{ENTER}}$.

To approximate $\sqrt{30}$, press $\boxed{30}$ $\boxed{\sqrt{}}$ (or $\boxed{\sqrt{}}$ $\boxed{30}$ $\boxed{\text{ENTER}}$). The display should read $\boxed{5.4772256}$. This is an approximation for $\sqrt{30}$. A three-decimal-place approximation is

$$\sqrt{30} \approx 5.477$$

Is this answer reasonable? Since 30 is between perfect squares 25 and 36, $\sqrt{30}$ is between $\sqrt{25} = 5$ and $\sqrt{36} = 6$. The calculator result is then reasonable since 5.4772256 is between 5 and 6.

Use a calculator to approximate each expression to three decimal places. Decide whether each result is reasonable.

1. $\sqrt{7}$ 2. $\sqrt{14}$ 3. $\sqrt{11}$

4. $\sqrt{200}$ 5. $\sqrt{82}$ 6. $\sqrt{46}$

Many scientific calculators have a key, such as $\boxed{\sqrt[x]{y}}$, that can be used to approximate roots other than square roots. To approximate these roots using a graphing calculator, look under the $\boxed{\text{MATH}}$ menu or consult your manual.

Use a calculator to approximate each expression to three decimal places. Decide whether each result is reasonable.

7. $\sqrt[3]{40}$ 8. $\sqrt[3]{71}$ 9. $\sqrt[4]{20}$

10. $\sqrt[4]{15}$ 11. $\sqrt[5]{18}$ 12. $\sqrt[6]{2}$

✔ Vocabulary, Readiness & Video Check

Use the choices below to fill in each blank.

principal   radical sign   index   radicand

1. In the expression $\sqrt[4]{16}$, the number 4 is called the _____, the number 16 is called the _____, and $\sqrt{}$ is called the _____.

2. The symbol $\sqrt{}$ is used to denote the positive, or _____, square root.

Answer each exercise true or false.

3. $\sqrt{-16}$ simplifies to a real number.

4. $\sqrt{64} = 8$, while $\sqrt[3]{64} = 4$.

5. The number 9 has two square roots.

6. $\sqrt{0} = 0$ and $\sqrt{1} = 1$.

7. If x is a positive number, $\sqrt{x^{10}} = x^5$.

8. If x is a positive number, $\sqrt{x^{16}} = x^4$.

Martin-Gay Interactive Videos

See Video 8.1

Watch the section lecture video and answer the following questions.

OBJECTIVE
1

9. Explain the differences between ▥ Examples 1 and 2, including how you know which one simplifies to a positive number and which one to a negative number.

OBJECTIVE
2

10. From ▥ Example 11, what is an important difference between the square root and the cube root of a negative number?

OBJECTIVE
3

11. From ▥ Examples 12–15, given a negative radicand, what kind of index must you have to have a real number?

OBJECTIVE
4

12. From ▥ Example 16, how do you determine if an approximate answer is reasonable?

OBJECTIVE
5

13. As explained in ▥ Example 19, when simplifying radicals containing variables, what is a shortcut you can use when dealing with exponents?

8.1 Exercise Set MyMathLab® ▶

Find each square root. See Example 1.

1. $\sqrt{16}$

2. $\sqrt{64}$

3. $\sqrt{\dfrac{1}{25}}$

4. $\sqrt{\dfrac{1}{64}}$

5. $-\sqrt{100}$

6. $-\sqrt{36}$

7. $\sqrt{-4}$

8. $\sqrt{-25}$

9. $-\sqrt{121}$

10. $-\sqrt{49}$

11. $\sqrt{\dfrac{9}{25}}$

12. $\sqrt{\dfrac{25}{36}}$

13. $\sqrt{900}$

14. $\sqrt{400}$

15. $\sqrt{144}$

16. $\sqrt{169}$

17. $\sqrt{\dfrac{1}{100}}$

18. $\sqrt{\dfrac{1}{121}}$

19. $\sqrt{0.25}$

20. $\sqrt{0.04}$

Find each cube root. See Example 2.

21. $\sqrt[3]{125}$

22. $\sqrt[3]{64}$

23. $\sqrt[3]{-64}$

24. $\sqrt[3]{-27}$

25. $-\sqrt[3]{8}$

26. $-\sqrt[3]{27}$

27. $\sqrt[3]{\dfrac{1}{8}}$

28. $\sqrt[3]{\dfrac{1}{64}}$

29. $\sqrt[3]{-125}$

30. $\sqrt[3]{-1}$

MIXED PRACTICE

Find each root. See Examples 1 through 3.

31. $\sqrt[5]{32}$

32. $\sqrt[4]{81}$

33. $\sqrt{81}$

34. $\sqrt{49}$

35. $\sqrt[4]{-16}$

36. $\sqrt{-9}$

37. $\sqrt[3]{-\dfrac{27}{64}}$

38. $\sqrt[3]{-\dfrac{8}{27}}$

39. $-\sqrt[4]{625}$

40. $-\sqrt[5]{32}$

41. $\sqrt[6]{1}$

42. $\sqrt[5]{1}$

Approximate each square root to three decimal places. See Example 4.

43. $\sqrt{7}$

44. $\sqrt{10}$

45. $\sqrt{37}$

46. $\sqrt{27}$

47. $\sqrt{136}$

48. $\sqrt{8}$

49. A standard baseball diamond is a square with 90-foot sides connecting the bases. The distance from home plate to second base is $90 \cdot \sqrt{2}$ feet. Approximate $\sqrt{2}$ to two decimal places and use your result to approximate the distance $90 \cdot \sqrt{2}$ feet.

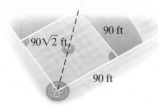

50. The roof of the warehouse shown needs to be shingled. The total area of the roof is exactly $240 \cdot \sqrt{41}$ square feet. Approximate $\sqrt{41}$ to two decimal places and use your result to approximate the area $240 \cdot \sqrt{41}$ square feet. Approximate this area to the nearest whole number.

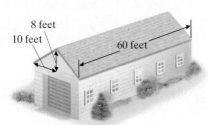

Find each root. Assume that all variables represent positive numbers. See Example 5.

51. $\sqrt{m^2}$ **52.** $\sqrt{y^{10}}$

53. $\sqrt{x^4}$ **54.** $\sqrt{z^8}$

55. $\sqrt{9x^8}$ **56.** $\sqrt{36x^{12}}$

57. $\sqrt{81x^2}$ **58.** $\sqrt{100z^4}$

59. $\sqrt{a^2b^4}$ **60.** $\sqrt{x^{12}y^{20}}$

61. $\sqrt{16a^6b^4}$ **62.** $\sqrt{4m^{14}n^2}$

63. $\sqrt[3]{a^6b^{18}}$ **64.** $\sqrt[3]{x^{12}y^{18}}$

65. $\sqrt[3]{-8x^3y^{27}}$ **66.** $\sqrt[3]{-27a^6b^{30}}$

67. $\sqrt{\dfrac{x^6}{36}}$ **68.** $\sqrt{\dfrac{y^8}{49}}$

69. $\sqrt{\dfrac{25y^2}{9}}$ **70.** $\sqrt{\dfrac{4x^2}{81}}$

REVIEW AND PREVIEW

Write each integer as a product of two integers such that one of the factors is a perfect square. For example, we can write $18 = 9 \cdot 2$, where 9 is a perfect square.

71. 50   **72.** 8   **73.** 32

74. 75   **75.** 28   **76.** 44

77. 27   **78.** 90

CONCEPT EXTENSIONS

Solve. See the Concept Check in this section.

79. Which of the following is a real number?

    a. $\sqrt{-1}$ **b.** $\sqrt[3]{-125}$ **c.** $\sqrt[6]{-128}$ **d.** $\sqrt[8]{-1}$

80. Which of the following is a real number?

    a. $\sqrt{-1}$ **b.** $\sqrt[3]{-1}$ **c.** $\sqrt[4]{-1}$ **d.** $\sqrt[5]{-1}$

The length of a side of a square is given by the expression $\sqrt{A}$, where A is the square's area. Use this expression for Exercises 81 through 84. Be sure to attach the appropriate units.

△ **81.** The area of a square is 49 square miles. Find the length of a side of the square.

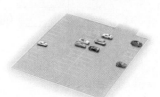

△ **82.** The area of a square is $\dfrac{1}{81}$ square meter. Find the length of a side of the square.

△ **83.** Sony currently makes the smallest portable mini disc player. It is approximately in the shape of a square with top area of 9.61 square inches. Find the length of a side. (*Source:* SONY)

△ **84.** A parking lot is in the shape of a square with area 2500 square yards. Find the length of a side.

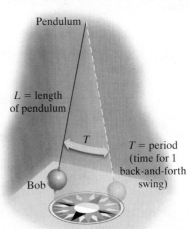

85. Simplify $\sqrt{\sqrt{81}}$.   **86.** Simplify $\sqrt[3]{\sqrt[3]{1}}$.

87. Simplify $\sqrt{\sqrt{10{,}000}}$.   **88.** Simplify

                                   $\sqrt{\sqrt{1{,}600{,}000{,}000}}$.

For each square root below, give two whole numbers that the square root lies between. For example, since $\sqrt{11}$ is between $\sqrt{9}$ and $\sqrt{16}$, $\sqrt{11}$ is between 3 and 4.

89. $\sqrt{18}$ **90.** $\sqrt{28}$

91. $\sqrt{80}$ **92.** $\sqrt{98}$

93. The formula for calculating the period (time for one back-and-forth swing) of a pendulum is $T = 2\pi\sqrt{\dfrac{L}{g}}$, where T is the period of the swing, L is the length of the pendulum, and g is the acceleration of gravity. Suppose there is a Foucault's pendulum with length = 30 ft and $g = 32$ ft/sec². Using $\pi \approx 3.14$, find the period of this pendulum. Round to the nearest tenth of a second.

(***Note:*** In 1851, French physicist Léon Foucault used a pendulum to demonstrate that the earth rotates on its axis.)

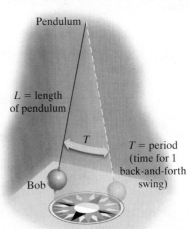

94. If the amount of gold discovered by humankind could be assembled in one location, it is estimated that it would be a cube with a volume of 19,683 cubic yards. Each side of the cube would be $\sqrt[3]{19,683}$ yards long. How long would one side of the cube be? (*Source:* howstuffworks.com)

95. Explain why the square root of a negative number is not a real number.

96. Explain why the cube root of a negative number is a real number.

97. Graph $y = \sqrt{x}$. (Complete the table below, plot the ordered pair solutions, and draw a smooth curve through the points. Remember that since the radicand cannot be negative, this particular graph begins at the point with coordinates $(0, 0)$.)

x	y	
0	0	
1		
3		(approximate)
4		
9		

98. Graph $y = \sqrt[3]{x}$. (Complete the table below, plot the ordered pair solutions, and draw a smooth curve through the points.)

x	y	
-8		
-2		(approximate)
-1		
0		
1		
2		(approximate)
8		

Recall from this section that $\sqrt{a^2} = |a|$ for any real number a. Simplify the following given that x represents any real number.

99. $\sqrt{x^2}$

100. $\sqrt{4x^2}$

101. $\sqrt{(x+2)^2}$

102. $\sqrt{x^2 + 6x + 9}$

(*Hint:* First factor $x^2 + 6x + 9$.)

Use a graphing calculator and graph each function. Observe the graph from left to right and give the ordered pair that corresponds to the "beginning" of the graph. Then tell why the graph starts at that point.

103. $y = \sqrt{x - 2}$

104. $y = \sqrt{x + 3}$

105. $y = \sqrt{x + 4}$

106. $y = \sqrt{x - 5}$

8.2 | Simplifying Radicals

OBJECTIVES

1 Use the Product Rule to Simplify Square Roots.

2 Use the Quotient Rule to Simplify Square Roots.

3 Simplify Radicals Containing Variables.

4 Simplify Higher Roots.

OBJECTIVE

1 Simplifying Radicals Using the Product Rule

A square root is simplified when the radicand contains no perfect square factors (other than 1). For example, $\sqrt{20}$ is not simplified because $\sqrt{20} = \sqrt{4 \cdot 5}$ and 4 is a perfect square.

To begin simplifying square roots, we notice the following pattern.

$$\sqrt{9 \cdot 16} = \sqrt{144} = 12$$
$$\sqrt{9} \cdot \sqrt{16} = 3 \cdot 4 = 12$$

Since both expressions simplify to 12, we can write

$$\sqrt{9 \cdot 16} = \sqrt{9} \cdot \sqrt{16}$$

This suggests the following product rule for square roots.

> **Product Rule for Square Roots**
>
> If $\sqrt{a}$ and $\sqrt{b}$ are real numbers, then
>
> $$\sqrt{a \cdot b} = \sqrt{a} \cdot \sqrt{b}$$

In other words, the square root of a product is equal to the product of the square roots.

To simplify $\sqrt{45}$, for example, we factor 45 so that one of its factors is a perfect square factor.

$$\sqrt{45} = \sqrt{9 \cdot 5} \qquad \text{Factor 45.}$$
$$= \sqrt{9} \cdot \sqrt{5} \qquad \text{Use the product rule.}$$
$$= 3\sqrt{5} \qquad \text{Write } \sqrt{9} \text{ as 3.}$$

> **Helpful Hint**
> Remember, the notation
> $3\sqrt{5}$ means $3 \cdot \sqrt{5}$.

The notation $3\sqrt{5}$ means $3 \cdot \sqrt{5}$. Since the radicand 5 has no perfect square factor other than 1, the expression $3\sqrt{5}$ is in simplest form.

> **Helpful Hint**
> A radical expression in simplest form *does not mean* a decimal approximation. The simplest form of a radical expression is an exact form and may still contain a radical.
> $$\underbrace{\sqrt{45} = 3\sqrt{5}}_{\text{exact}} \qquad \underbrace{\sqrt{45} \approx 6.71}_{\text{decimal approximation}}$$

EXAMPLE 1 Simplify.

    a. $\sqrt{54}$ **b.** $\sqrt{12}$ **c.** $\sqrt{200}$ **d.** $\sqrt{35}$

Solution

a. Try to factor 54 so that at least one of the factors is a perfect square. Since 9 is a perfect square and $54 = 9 \cdot 6$,

$$\sqrt{54} = \sqrt{9 \cdot 6} \qquad \text{Factor 54 so that one factor is a perfect square.}$$
$$= \sqrt{9} \cdot \sqrt{6} \qquad \text{Apply the product rule.}$$
$$= 3\sqrt{6} \qquad \text{Write } \sqrt{9} \text{ as 3.}$$

b.
$$\sqrt{12} = \sqrt{4 \cdot 3} \qquad \text{Factor 12 so that one factor is a perfect square.}$$
$$= \sqrt{4} \cdot \sqrt{3} \qquad \text{Apply the product rule.}$$
$$= 2\sqrt{3} \qquad \text{Write } \sqrt{4} \text{ as 2.}$$

c.
$$\sqrt{200} = \sqrt{100 \cdot 2} \qquad \text{Factor 200 so that one factor is a perfect square.}$$
$$= \sqrt{100} \cdot \sqrt{2} \qquad \text{Apply the product rule.}$$
$$= 10\sqrt{2} \qquad \text{Write } \sqrt{100} \text{ as 10.}$$

d. The radicand 35 contains no perfect square factors other than 1. Thus $\sqrt{35}$ is in simplest form. □

PRACTICE
1 Simplify.

    a. $\sqrt{24}$ **b.** $\sqrt{60}$ **c.** $\sqrt{42}$ **d.** $\sqrt{300}$ ■

In Example 1(c), 100 is the largest perfect square factor of 200. What happens if we don't use the largest perfect square factor? Although using the largest perfect square factor saves time, the result is the same no matter what perfect square factor is used. For example, it is also true that $200 = 4 \cdot 50$. Then

$$\sqrt{200} = \sqrt{4} \cdot \sqrt{50}$$
$$= 2 \cdot \sqrt{50}$$

Since $\sqrt{50}$ is not in simplest form, we continue.

$$\sqrt{200} = 2 \cdot \sqrt{50}$$
$$= 2 \cdot \sqrt{25 \cdot 2}$$
$$= 2 \cdot \sqrt{25} \cdot \sqrt{2}$$
$$= 2 \cdot 5 \cdot \sqrt{2}$$
$$= 10\sqrt{2}$$

EXAMPLE 2 Simplify: $3\sqrt{8}$

Solution Remember that $3\sqrt{8}$ means $3 \cdot \sqrt{8}$.

$$3 \cdot \sqrt{8} = 3 \cdot \sqrt{4 \cdot 2} \qquad \text{Factor 8 so that one factor is a perfect square.}$$
$$= 3 \cdot \sqrt{4} \cdot \sqrt{2} \qquad \text{Use the product rule.}$$
$$= 3 \cdot 2 \cdot \sqrt{2} \qquad \text{Write } \sqrt{4} \text{ as 2.}$$
$$= 6 \cdot \sqrt{2} \text{ or } 6\sqrt{2} \qquad \text{Write } 3 \cdot 2 \text{ as 6.} \qquad \square$$

PRACTICE
2 Simplify $5\sqrt{40}$. ∎

OBJECTIVE

2 Simplifying Radicals Using the Quotient Rule ▷

Next, let's examine the square root of a quotient.

$$\sqrt{\frac{16}{4}} = \sqrt{4} = 2$$

Also,

$$\frac{\sqrt{16}}{\sqrt{4}} = \frac{4}{2} = 2$$

Since both expressions equal 2, we can write

$$\sqrt{\frac{16}{4}} = \frac{\sqrt{16}}{\sqrt{4}}$$

This suggests the following quotient rule.

Quotient Rule for Square Roots

If $\sqrt{a}$ and $\sqrt{b}$ are real numbers and $b \neq 0$, then

$$\sqrt{\frac{a}{b}} = \frac{\sqrt{a}}{\sqrt{b}}$$

In other words, the square root of a quotient is equal to the quotient of the square roots.

EXAMPLE 3 Simplify.

a. $\sqrt{\dfrac{25}{36}}$ 　　 **b.** $\sqrt{\dfrac{3}{64}}$ 　　 **c.** $\sqrt{\dfrac{40}{81}}$

Use the quotient rule.

Solution

a. $\sqrt{\dfrac{25}{36}} = \dfrac{\sqrt{25}}{\sqrt{36}} = \dfrac{5}{6}$

b. $\sqrt{\dfrac{3}{64}} = \dfrac{\sqrt{3}}{\sqrt{64}} = \dfrac{\sqrt{3}}{8}$

c. $\sqrt{\dfrac{40}{81}} = \dfrac{\sqrt{40}}{\sqrt{81}}$ 　　 Use the quotient rule.

$$= \frac{\sqrt{4} \cdot \sqrt{10}}{9} \qquad \text{Apply the product rule and write } \sqrt{81} \text{ as 9.}$$

$$= \frac{2\sqrt{10}}{9} \qquad \text{Write } \sqrt{4} \text{ as 2.} \qquad \square$$

PRACTICE

3 Simplify.

a. $\sqrt{\dfrac{5}{49}}$

b. $\sqrt{\dfrac{9}{100}}$

c. $\sqrt{\dfrac{18}{25}}$ ■

OBJECTIVE

3 Simplifying Radicals Containing Variables

Recall that $\sqrt{x^6} = x^3$ because $(x^3)^2 = x^6$. If an odd exponent occurs, we write the exponential expression so that one factor is the greatest even power contained in the expression. Then we use the product rule to simplify.

EXAMPLE 4 Simplify. Assume that all variables represent positive numbers.

a. $\sqrt{x^5}$ b. $\sqrt{8y^2}$ c. $\sqrt{\dfrac{45}{x^6}}$ d. $\sqrt{\dfrac{5p^3}{9}}$

Solution

a. $\sqrt{x^5} = \sqrt{x^4 \cdot x} = \sqrt{x^4} \cdot \sqrt{x} = x^2\sqrt{x}$

b. $\sqrt{8y^2} = \sqrt{4 \cdot 2 \cdot y^2} = \sqrt{4y^2 \cdot 2} = \sqrt{4y^2} \cdot \sqrt{2} = 2y\sqrt{2}$

c. $\sqrt{\dfrac{45}{x^6}} = \dfrac{\sqrt{45}}{\sqrt{x^6}} = \dfrac{\sqrt{9 \cdot 5}}{x^3} = \dfrac{\sqrt{9} \cdot \sqrt{5}}{x^3} = \dfrac{3\sqrt{5}}{x^3}$

d. $\sqrt{\dfrac{5p^3}{9}} = \dfrac{\sqrt{5p^3}}{\sqrt{9}} = \dfrac{\sqrt{p^2 \cdot 5p}}{3} = \dfrac{\sqrt{p^2} \cdot \sqrt{5p}}{3} = \dfrac{p\sqrt{5p}}{3}$ □

PRACTICE

4 Simplify. Assume that all variables represent positive numbers.

a. $\sqrt{x^7}$ b. $\sqrt{12a^4}$ c. $\sqrt{\dfrac{98}{z^8}}$ d. $\sqrt{\dfrac{11y^9}{49}}$ ■

OBJECTIVE

4 Simplifying Higher Roots

The product and quotient rules also apply to roots other than square roots. In general, we have the following product and quotient rules for radicals.

Product Rule for Radicals

If $\sqrt[n]{a}$ and $\sqrt[n]{b}$ are real numbers, then

$$\sqrt[n]{a \cdot b} = \sqrt[n]{a} \cdot \sqrt[n]{b}$$

Quotient Rule for Radicals

If $\sqrt[n]{a}$ and $\sqrt[n]{b}$ are real numbers and $b \neq 0$, then

$$\sqrt[n]{\dfrac{a}{b}} = \dfrac{\sqrt[n]{a}}{\sqrt[n]{b}}$$

To simplify cube roots, look for perfect cube factors of the radicand. For example, 8 is a perfect cube, since $2^3 = 8$.

To simplify $\sqrt[3]{48}$, factor 48 as $8 \cdot 6$.

$\sqrt[3]{48} = \sqrt[3]{8 \cdot 6}$ Factor 48.

$\phantom{\sqrt[3]{48}} = \sqrt[3]{8} \cdot \sqrt[3]{6}$ Apply the product rule.

$\phantom{\sqrt[3]{48}} = 2\sqrt[3]{6}$ Write $\sqrt[3]{8}$ as 2.

$2\sqrt[3]{6}$ is in simplest form since the radicand 6 contains no perfect cube factors other than 1.

EXAMPLE 5   Simplify.

a. $\sqrt[3]{54}$ b. $\sqrt[3]{18}$ c. $\sqrt[3]{\dfrac{7}{8}}$ d. $\sqrt[3]{\dfrac{40}{27}}$

Solution

a. $\sqrt[3]{54} = \sqrt[3]{27 \cdot 2} = \sqrt[3]{27} \cdot \sqrt[3]{2} = 3\sqrt[3]{2}$

b. The number 18 contains no perfect cube factors, so $\sqrt[3]{18}$ cannot be simplified further.

c. $\sqrt[3]{\dfrac{7}{8}} = \dfrac{\sqrt[3]{7}}{\sqrt[3]{8}} = \dfrac{\sqrt[3]{7}}{2}$

d. $\sqrt[3]{\dfrac{40}{27}} = \dfrac{\sqrt[3]{40}}{\sqrt[3]{27}} = \dfrac{\sqrt[3]{8 \cdot 5}}{3} = \dfrac{\sqrt[3]{8} \cdot \sqrt[3]{5}}{3} = \dfrac{2\sqrt[3]{5}}{3}$ □

PRACTICE
5   Simplify.

a. $\sqrt[3]{24}$ b. $\sqrt[3]{38}$ c. $\sqrt[3]{\dfrac{5}{27}}$ d. $\sqrt[3]{\dfrac{15}{64}}$ ■

To simplify fourth roots, look for perfect fourth powers of the radicand. For example, 16 is a perfect fourth power since $2^4 = 16$.

To simplify $\sqrt[4]{32}$, factor 32 as $16 \cdot 2$.

$$\sqrt[4]{32} = \sqrt[4]{16 \cdot 2} \qquad \text{Factor 32.}$$
$$= \sqrt[4]{16} \cdot \sqrt[4]{2} \qquad \text{Apply the product rule.}$$
$$= 2\sqrt[4]{2} \qquad \text{Write } \sqrt[4]{16} \text{ as 2.}$$

EXAMPLE 6   Simplify.

a. $\sqrt[4]{243}$ b. $\sqrt[4]{\dfrac{3}{16}}$ c. $\sqrt[5]{64}$

Solution

a. $\sqrt[4]{243} = \sqrt[4]{81 \cdot 3} = \sqrt[4]{81} \cdot \sqrt[4]{3} = 3\sqrt[4]{3}$

b. $\sqrt[4]{\dfrac{3}{16}} = \dfrac{\sqrt[4]{3}}{\sqrt[4]{16}} = \dfrac{\sqrt[4]{3}}{2}$

c. $\sqrt[5]{64} = \sqrt[5]{32 \cdot 2} = \sqrt[5]{32} \cdot \sqrt[5]{2} = 2\sqrt[5]{2}$ □

PRACTICE
6   Simplify.

a. $\sqrt[4]{80}$ b. $\sqrt[4]{\dfrac{5}{81}}$ c. $\sqrt[5]{96}$ ■

✔ **Vocabulary, Readiness & Video Check**

Use the choices below to fill in the blanks. Not all choices will be used.

$a \cdot b$ $\dfrac{a}{b}$ $\dfrac{\sqrt{a}}{\sqrt{b}}$ $\sqrt{a} \cdot \sqrt{b}$

1. If $\sqrt{a}$ and $\sqrt{b}$ are real numbers, then $\sqrt{a \cdot b} =$ _____ .

2. If $\sqrt{a}$ and $\sqrt{b}$ are real numbers, then $\sqrt{\dfrac{a}{b}} =$ _____ .

For Exercises 3 and 4, fill in the blanks using the example: $\sqrt{4 \cdot 9} = \sqrt{\underline{4}} \cdot \sqrt{\underline{9}} = \underline{2} \cdot \underline{3} = \underline{6}$.

3. $\sqrt{16 \cdot 25} = \sqrt{\underline{}} \cdot \sqrt{\underline{}} = \underline{} \cdot \underline{} = \underline{}$

4. $\sqrt{36 \cdot 3} = \sqrt{\underline{}} \cdot \sqrt{\underline{}} = \underline{} \cdot \sqrt{\underline{}} = \underline{}$

Martin-Gay Interactive Videos

See Video 8.2 🍎

Watch the section lecture video and answer the following questions.

OBJECTIVE 1
5. From ▦ Example 3, if you have trouble finding a perfect square factor in the radicand, what is recommended?

OBJECTIVE 2
6. Based on the lecture before ▦ Example 5, complete the following statement. In words, the quotient rule for square roots says that the square root of a quotient is equal to the square root of the _____ over the square root of the _____.

OBJECTIVE 3
7. From ▦ Examples 6–8, we know that even powers of a variable are perfect square factors of the variable. Therefore, what must be true about the power of any variable left in the radicand of a simplified square root? Explain.

OBJECTIVE 4
8. From ▦ Example 9, how does factoring the radicand as a product of primes help simplify higher roots also?

8.2 Exercise Set MyMathLab® ▷

Use the product rule to simplify each radical. See Examples 1 and 2.

1. $\sqrt{20}$ **2.** $\sqrt{44}$

3. $\sqrt{50}$ **4.** $\sqrt{28}$

5. $\sqrt{33}$ **6.** $\sqrt{21}$

7. $\sqrt{98}$ **8.** $\sqrt{125}$

9. $\sqrt{60}$ **10.** $\sqrt{90}$

11. $\sqrt{180}$ **12.** $\sqrt{150}$

13. $\sqrt{52}$ **14.** $\sqrt{75}$

15. $3\sqrt{25}$ **16.** $9\sqrt{36}$

17. $7\sqrt{63}$ **18.** $11\sqrt{99}$

19. $-5\sqrt{27}$ **20.** $-6\sqrt{75}$

Use the quotient rule and the product rule to simplify each radical. See Example 3.

21. $\sqrt{\dfrac{8}{25}}$ **22.** $\sqrt{\dfrac{63}{16}}$

23. $\sqrt{\dfrac{27}{121}}$ **24.** $\sqrt{\dfrac{24}{169}}$

25. $\sqrt{\dfrac{9}{4}}$ **26.** $\sqrt{\dfrac{100}{49}}$

27. $\sqrt{\dfrac{125}{9}}$ **28.** $\sqrt{\dfrac{27}{100}}$

29. $\sqrt{\dfrac{11}{36}}$ **30.** $\sqrt{\dfrac{30}{49}}$

31. $-\sqrt{\dfrac{27}{144}}$ **32.** $-\sqrt{\dfrac{84}{121}}$

Simplify each radical. Assume that all variables represent positive numbers. See Example 4.

33. $\sqrt{x^7}$ **34.** $\sqrt{y^3}$

35. $\sqrt{x^{13}}$ **36.** $\sqrt{y^{17}}$

37. $\sqrt{36a^3}$ **38.** $\sqrt{81b^5}$

39. $\sqrt{96x^4}$ **40.** $\sqrt{40y^{10}}$

41. $\sqrt{\dfrac{12}{m^2}}$ **42.** $\sqrt{\dfrac{63}{p^2}}$

43. $\sqrt{\dfrac{9x}{y^{10}}}$ **44.** $\sqrt{\dfrac{6y^2}{z^{16}}}$

45. $\sqrt{\dfrac{88}{x^{12}}}$ **46.** $\sqrt{\dfrac{500}{y^{22}}}$

MIXED PRACTICE

Simplify each radical. See Examples 1 through 4.

47. $8\sqrt{4}$ **48.** $6\sqrt{49}$

49. $\sqrt{\dfrac{36}{121}}$ **50.** $\sqrt{\dfrac{25}{144}}$

51. $\sqrt{175}$ **52.** $\sqrt{700}$

53. $\sqrt{\dfrac{20}{9}}$ **54.** $\sqrt{\dfrac{45}{64}}$

55. $\sqrt{24m^7}$ **56.** $\sqrt{50n^{13}}$

57. $\sqrt{\dfrac{23y^3}{4x^6}}$ **58.** $\sqrt{\dfrac{41x^5}{9y^8}}$

Simplify each radical. See Example 5.

59. $\sqrt[3]{24}$ **60.** $\sqrt[3]{81}$

61. $\sqrt[3]{250}$ **62.** $\sqrt[3]{56}$

63. $\sqrt[3]{\dfrac{5}{64}}$ **64.** $\sqrt[3]{\dfrac{32}{125}}$

65. $\sqrt[3]{\dfrac{23}{8}}$ **66.** $\sqrt[3]{\dfrac{37}{27}}$

67. $\sqrt[3]{\dfrac{15}{64}}$ **68.** $\sqrt[3]{\dfrac{4}{27}}$

69. $\sqrt[3]{80}$ **70.** $\sqrt[3]{108}$

Simplify. See Example 6.

71. $\sqrt[4]{48}$ **72.** $\sqrt[4]{405}$

73. $\sqrt[4]{\dfrac{8}{81}}$ **74.** $\sqrt[4]{\dfrac{25}{256}}$

75. $\sqrt[5]{96}$ **76.** $\sqrt[5]{128}$

77. $\sqrt[5]{\dfrac{5}{32}}$ **78.** $\sqrt[5]{\dfrac{16}{243}}$

REVIEW AND PREVIEW

Perform the following operations. See Sections 5.2 and 5.3.

79. $6x + 8x$ **80.** $(6x)(8x)$

81. $(2x + 3)(x - 5)$ **82.** $(2x + 3) + (x - 5)$

83. $9y^2 - 9y^2$ **84.** $(9y^2)(-8y^2)$

CONCEPT EXTENSIONS

Simplify each radical. Assume that all variables represent positive numbers.

85. $\sqrt{x^6y^3}$ **86.** $\sqrt{a^{13}b^{14}}$

87. $\sqrt{98x^5y^4}$ **88.** $\sqrt{27x^8y^{11}}$

89. $\sqrt[3]{-8x^6}$ **90.** $\sqrt[3]{27x^{12}}$

Simplify.

△ **91.** If a cube is to have a volume of 80 cubic inches, then each side must be $\sqrt[3]{80}$ inches long. Simplify the radical representing the side length.

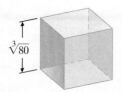

△ **92.** Jeannie Boswell is swimming across a 40-foot-wide river, trying to head straight across to the opposite shore. However, the current is strong enough to move her downstream 100 feet by the time she reaches land. (See the figure.) Because of the current, the actual distance she swam is $\sqrt{11,600}$ feet. Simplify this radical.

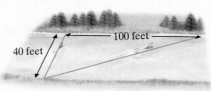

100 feet

40 feet

93. By using replacement values for a and b, show that $\sqrt{a^2 + b^2}$ does not equal $a + b$.

94. By using replacement values for a and b, show that $\sqrt{a + b}$ does not equal $\sqrt{a} + \sqrt{b}$.

The length of a side of a cube is given by the expression $\sqrt{\dfrac{A}{6}}$ *units where A square units is the cube's surface area. Use this expression for Exercises 95 through 98. Be sure to attach the appropriate units.*

$\sqrt{A/6}$

△ **95.** The surface area of a cube is 120 square inches. Find the exact length of a side of the cube.

△ **96.** The surface area of a cube is 594 square feet. Find the exact length of a side of the cube.

97. Rubik's cube, named after its inventor, Erno Rubik, was first imagined by him in 1974 and, by 1980, was a worldwide phenomenon. A standard Rubik's cube has a surface area of 30.375 square inches. Find the length of one side of a Rubik's cube. (A few world records are listed below. *Source: Guinness World Records*)

Fastest time to solve 1 Rubik's cube: 5.27 sec by Sam Zhixiao Wang (China) in 2011.

World Record for fastest average time: 8.18 sec by Feliks Zemdegs (Australia) at Rubik's World Championship in 2013.

△ **98.** The Borg spaceship on *Star Trek: The Next Generation* is in the shape of a cube. Suppose a model of this ship has a surface area of 121 square inches. Find the length of a side of the ship.

The cost *C* in dollars per day to operate a small delivery service is given by $C = 100\sqrt[3]{n} + 700$, where *n* is the number of deliveries per day.

99. Find the cost if the number of deliveries is 1000.

100. Approximate the cost if the number of deliveries is 500.

The Mosteller formula for calculating body surface area is $B = \sqrt{\dfrac{hw}{3600}}$, where B is an individual's body surface area in square meters, h is the individual's height in centimeters, and w is the individual's weight in kilograms. Use this formula in Exercises 101 and 102. Round answers to the nearest tenth.

101. Approximate the body surface area of a person who is 170 cm tall and weighs 64 kilograms.

102. Approximate the body surface area of a person who is 183 cm tall and weighs 85 kilograms.

8.3 Adding and Subtracting Radicals ▷

OBJECTIVES

1 Add or Subtract Like Radicals. ▷

2 Simplify Radical Expressions and Then Add or Subtract Any Like Radicals. ▷

OBJECTIVE

1   Adding and Subtracting Like Radicals ▷

To combine like terms, we use the distributive property.

$$5x + 3x = (5 + 3)x = 8x$$

The distributive property can also be applied to expressions containing radicals. For example,

$$5\sqrt{2} + 3\sqrt{2} = (5 + 3)\sqrt{2} = 8\sqrt{2}$$

Also,

$$9\sqrt{5} - 6\sqrt{5} = (9 - 6)\sqrt{5} = 3\sqrt{5}$$

Radical terms $5\sqrt{2}$ and $3\sqrt{2}$ are **like radicals,** as are $9\sqrt{5}$ and $6\sqrt{5}$.

Like Radicals

Like radicals are radical expressions that have the same index and the same radicand.

From the examples above, we can see that **only like radicals can be combined** in this way. For example, the expression $2\sqrt{3} + 3\sqrt{2}$ cannot be simplified further since the radicals are not like radicals. Also, the expression $4\sqrt{7} + 4\sqrt[3]{7}$ cannot be simplified further because the radicals are not like radicals since the indices are different.

EXAMPLE 1 Simplify by combining like radical terms.

a. $4\sqrt{5} + 3\sqrt{5}$ **b.** $\sqrt{10} - 6\sqrt{10}$ **c.** $\sqrt[3]{7} + \sqrt[3]{7} - 4\sqrt[3]{5}$ **d.** $2\sqrt{6} + 2\sqrt[3]{6}$

Solution

a. $4\sqrt{5} + 3\sqrt{5} = (4 + 3)\sqrt{5} = 7\sqrt{5}$

b. $\sqrt{10} - 6\sqrt{10} = 1\sqrt{10} - 6\sqrt{10} = (1 - 6)\sqrt{10} = -5\sqrt{10}$

c. $\sqrt[3]{7} + \sqrt[3]{7} - 4\sqrt[3]{5} = 1\sqrt[3]{7} + 1\sqrt[3]{7} - 4\sqrt[3]{5} = (1 + 1)\sqrt[3]{7} - 4\sqrt[3]{5} = 2\sqrt[3]{7} - 4\sqrt[3]{5}$
   This expression cannot be simplified further since the radicands are not the same.

d. $2\sqrt{6} + 2\sqrt[3]{6}$ cannot be simplified further since the indices are not the same. ☐

PRACTICE

1 Simplify by combining like radical terms.

a. $3\sqrt{2} + 5\sqrt{2}$ **b.** $\sqrt{6} - 8\sqrt{6}$

c. $6\sqrt[4]{5} - 2\sqrt[4]{5} + 11\sqrt[4]{7}$ **d.** $4\sqrt[3]{13} - 5\sqrt[3]{13}$ ■

✔ **CONCEPT CHECK**

Which is true?

a. $2 + 3\sqrt{5} = 5\sqrt{5}$ **b.** $2\sqrt{3} + 2\sqrt{7} = 2\sqrt{10}$ **c.** $\sqrt{3} + \sqrt{5} = \sqrt{8}$

d. $\sqrt{3} + \sqrt{3} = 3$ **e.** None of the above is true.

OBJECTIVE

2 Simplifying Radicals, Then Adding or Subtracting

At first glance, it appears that the expression $\sqrt{50} + \sqrt{8}$ cannot be simplified further because the radicands are different. However, the product rule can be used to simplify each radical, and then further simplification might be possible.

EXAMPLE 2 Add or subtract by first simplifying each radical.

a. $\sqrt{50} + \sqrt{8}$ **b.** $7\sqrt{12} - \sqrt{75}$ **c.** $\sqrt{25} - \sqrt{27} - 2\sqrt{18} - \sqrt{16}$

Solution

a. First simplify each radical.

$$\sqrt{50} + \sqrt{8} = \sqrt{25 \cdot 2} + \sqrt{4 \cdot 2} \qquad \text{Factor radicands.}$$
$$= \sqrt{25} \cdot \sqrt{2} + \sqrt{4} \cdot \sqrt{2} \qquad \text{Apply the product rule.}$$
$$= 5\sqrt{2} + 2\sqrt{2} \qquad \text{Simplify } \sqrt{25} \text{ and } \sqrt{4}.$$
$$= 7\sqrt{2} \qquad \text{Add like radicals.}$$

b. $7\sqrt{12} - \sqrt{75} = 7\sqrt{4 \cdot 3} - \sqrt{25 \cdot 3} \qquad \text{Factor radicands.}$
$$= 7\sqrt{4} \cdot \sqrt{3} - \sqrt{25} \cdot \sqrt{3} \qquad \text{Apply the product rule.}$$
$$= 7 \cdot 2\sqrt{3} - 5\sqrt{3} \qquad \text{Simplify } \sqrt{4} \text{ and } \sqrt{25}.$$
$$= 14\sqrt{3} - 5\sqrt{3} \qquad \text{Multiply.}$$
$$= 9\sqrt{3} \qquad \text{Subtract like radicals.}$$

c. $\sqrt{25} - \sqrt{27} - 2\sqrt{18} - \sqrt{16}$
$$= 5 - \sqrt{9 \cdot 3} - 2\sqrt{9 \cdot 2} - 4 \qquad \text{Factor radicands.}$$
$$= 5 - \sqrt{9} \cdot \sqrt{3} - 2\sqrt{9} \cdot \sqrt{2} - 4 \qquad \text{Apply the product rule.}$$
$$= 5 - 3\sqrt{3} - 2 \cdot 3\sqrt{2} - 4 \qquad \text{Simplify.}$$
$$= 1 - 3\sqrt{3} - 6\sqrt{2} \qquad \text{Write } 5 - 4 \text{ as 1 and}$$
$$\qquad 2 \cdot 3 \text{ as 6.} \qquad ☐$$

Answer to Concept Check:
e (a, b, and c are not true since each left side cannot be simplified further. For d, $\sqrt{3} + \sqrt{3} = 2\sqrt{3}$.)

PRACTICE
2   Add or subtract by first simplifying each radical.

a. $\sqrt{45} + \sqrt{20}$ **b.** $\sqrt{36} + 3\sqrt{24} - \sqrt{40} - \sqrt{150}$

c. $\sqrt{98} - 5\sqrt{8}$

If radical expressions contain variables, we proceed in a similar way. Simplify radicals using the product and quotient rules. Then add or subtract any like radicals.

EXAMPLE 3   Simplify $2\sqrt{x^2} - \sqrt{25x^5} + \sqrt{x^5}$. Assume variables represent positive numbers.

Solution $2\sqrt{x^2} - \sqrt{25x^5} + \sqrt{x^5}$

$= 2x - \sqrt{25x^4 \cdot x} + \sqrt{x^4 \cdot x}$ Factor radicands so that one factor is a perfect square. Simplify $\sqrt{x^2}$.

$= 2x - \sqrt{25x^4} \cdot \sqrt{x} + \sqrt{x^4} \cdot \sqrt{x}$ Use the product rule.

$= 2x - 5x^2\sqrt{x} + x^2\sqrt{x}$ Write $\sqrt{25x^4}$ as $5x^2$ and $\sqrt{x^4}$ as x^2.

$= 2x - 4x^2\sqrt{x}$ Add like radicals.

PRACTICE
3   Simplify $\sqrt{x^3} - 8x\sqrt{x} + 3\sqrt{x^2}$. Assume variables represent positive numbers.

EXAMPLE 4   Simplify the radical expression $5\sqrt[3]{16x^3} - \sqrt[3]{54x^3}$.

Solution $5\sqrt[3]{16x^3} - \sqrt[3]{54x^3}$

$= 5\sqrt[3]{8x^3 \cdot 2} - \sqrt[3]{27x^3 \cdot 2}$ Factor radicands so that one factor is a perfect cube.

$= 5 \cdot \sqrt[3]{8x^3} \cdot \sqrt[3]{2} - \sqrt[3]{27x^3} \cdot \sqrt[3]{2}$ Use the product rule.

$= 5 \cdot 2x \cdot \sqrt[3]{2} - 3x \cdot \sqrt[3]{2}$ Write $\sqrt[3]{8x^3}$ as $2x$ and $\sqrt[3]{27x^3}$ as $3x$.

$= 10x\sqrt[3]{2} - 3x\sqrt[3]{2}$ Write $5 \cdot 2x$ as $10x$.

$= 7x\sqrt[3]{2}$ Subtract like radicals.

PRACTICE
4   Simplify the radical expression $4\sqrt[3]{81x^6} - \sqrt[3]{24x^6}$.

✓ Vocabulary, Readiness & Video Check

Fill in each blank.

1. Radicals that have the same index and same radicand are called _____.

2. The expressions $7\sqrt[3]{2x}$ and $-\sqrt[3]{2x}$ are called _____.

3. $11\sqrt{2} + 6\sqrt{2} = $ _____.
   a. $66\sqrt{2}$ **b.** $17\sqrt{2}$ **c.** $17\sqrt{4}$

4. $\sqrt{5}$ is the same as _____.
   a. $0\sqrt{5}$ **b.** $1\sqrt{5}$ **c.** $5\sqrt{5}$

5. $\sqrt{5} + \sqrt{5} = $ _____
   a. $\sqrt{10}$ **b.** 5 **c.** $2\sqrt{5}$

6. $9\sqrt{7} - \sqrt{7} = $ _____
   a. $8\sqrt{7}$ **b.** 9 **c.** 0

Martin-Gay Interactive Videos

See Video 8.3

Watch the section lecture video and answer the following questions.

OBJECTIVE
1   **7.** From Examples 1–4, how is combining like radicals similar to combining like terms?

OBJECTIVE
2   **8.** From Example 5, why should you always check to see if all radical terms in your expression are simplified before attempting to add or subtract the radicals?

8.3   Exercise Set   MyMathLab®

Simplify each expression by combining like radicals where possible. See Example 1.

1. $4\sqrt{3} - 8\sqrt{3}$

2. $2\sqrt{5} - 9\sqrt{5}$

3. $3\sqrt{6} + 8\sqrt{6} - 2\sqrt{6} - 5$

4. $12\sqrt{2} - 3\sqrt{2} + 8\sqrt{2} + 10$

5. $\sqrt{11} + \sqrt{11} + 11$

6. $\sqrt{13} + 13 + \sqrt{13}$

7. $6\sqrt{5} - 5\sqrt{5} + \sqrt{2}$

8. $4\sqrt{3} + \sqrt{5} - 3\sqrt{3}$

9. $\sqrt[3]{18} + \sqrt[3]{18} - 4\sqrt[3]{18}$

10. $\sqrt[3]{49} - 8\sqrt[3]{49} + \sqrt[3]{49}$

11. $2\sqrt[3]{3} + 5\sqrt[3]{3} - \sqrt{3}$

12. $8\sqrt[3]{5} + 2\sqrt[3]{5} + \sqrt{5}$

13. $2\sqrt[3]{2} - 7\sqrt[3]{2} - 6$

14. $5\sqrt[3]{9} + 2 - 11\sqrt[3]{9}$

MIXED PRACTICE

Add or subtract by first simplifying each radical and then combining any like radical terms. Assume that all variables represent positive real numbers. See Examples 2 and 3.

15. $\sqrt{12} + \sqrt{27}$

16. $\sqrt{50} + \sqrt{18}$

17. $\sqrt{45} + 3\sqrt{20}$

18. $\sqrt{28} + \sqrt{63}$

19. $2\sqrt{54} - \sqrt{20} + \sqrt{45} - \sqrt{24}$

20. $2\sqrt{8} - \sqrt{128} + \sqrt{48} + \sqrt{18}$

21. $4x - 3\sqrt{x^2} + \sqrt{x}$

22. $x - 6\sqrt{x^2} + 2\sqrt{x}$

23. $\sqrt{25x} + \sqrt{36x} - 11\sqrt{x}$

24. $3\sqrt{x^3} - x\sqrt{4x}$

25. $\sqrt{16x} - \sqrt{x^3}$

26. $\sqrt{8x^3} - \sqrt{x^2}$

27. $12\sqrt{5} - \sqrt{5} - 4\sqrt{5}$

28. $7\sqrt{3} + 2\sqrt{3} - 13\sqrt{3}$

29. $\sqrt{5} + \sqrt[3]{5}$

30. $\sqrt{5} + \sqrt{5}$

31. $4 + 8\sqrt{2} - 9$

32. $6 - 2\sqrt{3} - \sqrt{3}$

33. $8 - \sqrt{2} - 5\sqrt{2}$

34. $\sqrt{75} + \sqrt{48}$

35. $5\sqrt{32} - \sqrt{72}$

36. $2\sqrt{80} - \sqrt{45}$

37. $\sqrt{8} + \sqrt{9} + \sqrt{18} + \sqrt{81}$

38. $\sqrt{6} + \sqrt{16} + \sqrt{24} + \sqrt{25}$

39. $\sqrt{\dfrac{5}{9}} + \sqrt{\dfrac{5}{81}}$

40. $\sqrt{\dfrac{3}{64}} + \sqrt{\dfrac{3}{16}}$

41. $\sqrt{\dfrac{3}{4}} - \sqrt{\dfrac{3}{64}}$

42. $\sqrt{\dfrac{7}{25}} - \sqrt{\dfrac{7}{100}}$

43. $2\sqrt{45} - 2\sqrt{20}$

44. $5\sqrt{18} + 2\sqrt{32}$

45. $\sqrt{35} - \sqrt{140}$

46. $\sqrt{6} - \sqrt{600}$

47. $5\sqrt{2x} + \sqrt{98x}$

48. $3\sqrt{9x} + 2\sqrt{x}$

49. $5\sqrt{x} + 4\sqrt{4x} - 13\sqrt{x}$

50. $\sqrt{9x} + \sqrt{81x} - 11\sqrt{x}$

51. $\sqrt{3x^3} + 3x\sqrt{x}$

52. $x\sqrt{4x} + \sqrt{9x^3}$

Add or subtract by first simplifying each radical and then combining any like radical terms. Assume that all variables represent positive real numbers. See Example 4.

53. $\sqrt[3]{81} + \sqrt[3]{24}$

54. $\sqrt[3]{32} - \sqrt[3]{4}$

55. $4\sqrt[3]{9} - \sqrt[3]{243}$

56. $7\sqrt[3]{6} - \sqrt[3]{48}$

▶ **57.** $\sqrt[3]{8} + \sqrt[3]{54} - 5$

58. $\sqrt[3]{64} + \sqrt[3]{14} - 9$

59. $\sqrt{32x^2} + \sqrt[3]{32} + \sqrt{4x^2}$

60. $\sqrt{18x^2} + \sqrt[3]{24} + \sqrt{2x^2}$

61. $2\sqrt[3]{8x^3} + 2\sqrt[3]{16x^3}$

62. $3\sqrt[3]{27z^3} + 3\sqrt[3]{81z^3}$

63. $12\sqrt[3]{y^7} - y^2\sqrt[3]{8y}$

64. $19\sqrt[3]{z^{11}} - z^3\sqrt[3]{125z^2}$

65. $\sqrt{40x} + \sqrt[3]{40} - 2\sqrt{10x} - \sqrt[3]{5}$

66. $\sqrt{72x^2} + \sqrt[3]{54} - x\sqrt{50} - 3\sqrt[3]{2}$

REVIEW AND PREVIEW

Square each binomial. See Section 5.4.

67. $(x + 6)^2$

68. $(3x + 2)^2$

69. $(2x - 1)^2$

70. $(x - 5)^2$

CONCEPT EXTENSIONS

71. In your own words, describe like radicals.

72. In the expression $\sqrt{5} + 2 - 3\sqrt{5}$, explain why 2 and -3 cannot be combined.

73. Find the perimeter of the rectangular picture frame.

$\sqrt{5}$ inches

$3\sqrt{5}$ inches

74. Find the perimeter of the plot of land.

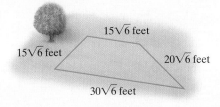

15$\sqrt{6}$ feet

15$\sqrt{6}$ feet

20$\sqrt{6}$ feet

30$\sqrt{6}$ feet

75. An 8-foot-long water trough is to be made of wood. Each of the two triangular end pieces has an area of $\dfrac{3\sqrt{27}}{4}$ square feet. The two side panels are both rectangular. In simplest radical form, find the total area of the wood needed.

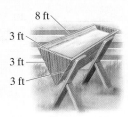

8 ft

3 ft

3 ft

3 ft

76. Eight wooden braces are to be attached along the diagonals of the vertical sides of a storage bin. Each of four of these diagonals has a length of $\sqrt{52}$ feet, while each of the other four has a length of $\sqrt{80}$ feet. In simplest radical form, find the total length of the wood needed for these braces.

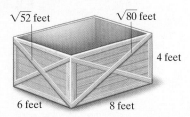

$\sqrt{52}$ feet $\sqrt{80}$ feet

4 feet

6 feet   8 feet

Determine whether each expression can be simplified. If yes, then simplify. See the Concept Check in this section.

77. $4\sqrt{2} + 3\sqrt{2}$

78. $3\sqrt{7} + 3\sqrt{6}$

79. $6 + 7\sqrt{6}$

80. $5x\sqrt{2} + 8x\sqrt{2}$

81. $\sqrt{7} + \sqrt{7} + \sqrt{7}$

82. $6\sqrt{5} - \sqrt{5}$

Simplify.

83. $\sqrt{\dfrac{x^3}{16}} - x\sqrt{\dfrac{9x}{25}} + \dfrac{\sqrt{81x^3}}{2}$

84. $7\sqrt{x^{11}y^7} - x^2y\sqrt{25x^7y^5} + \sqrt{8x^8y^2}$

8.4 Multiplying and Dividing Radicals

OBJECTIVES

1 Multiply Radicals.
2 Divide Radicals.
3 Rationalize Denominators.
4 Rationalize Using Conjugates.

OBJECTIVE

1 Multiplying Radicals

In Section 8.2, we used the product and quotient rules for radicals to help us simplify radicals. In this section, we use these rules to simplify products and quotients of radicals.

> **Product Rule for Radicals**
>
> If $\sqrt[n]{a}$ and $\sqrt[n]{b}$ are real numbers, then
>
> $$\sqrt[n]{a} \cdot \sqrt[n]{b} = \sqrt[n]{a \cdot b}$$

This property says that the product of the nth roots of two numbers is the nth root of the product of the two numbers. For example,

$$\sqrt{3} \cdot \sqrt{2} = \sqrt{3 \cdot 2} = \sqrt{6} \quad \text{Also,} \quad \sqrt[3]{5} \cdot \sqrt[3]{7} = \sqrt[3]{5 \cdot 7} = \sqrt[3]{35}$$

EXAMPLE 1 Multiply. Then simplify if possible.

a. $\sqrt{7} \cdot \sqrt{3}$ **b.** $\sqrt{3} \cdot \sqrt{3}$ **c.** $\sqrt{3} \cdot \sqrt{15}$ **d.** $2\sqrt{3} \cdot 5\sqrt{2}$ **e.** $\sqrt{2x^3} \cdot \sqrt{6x}$

Solution

a. $\sqrt{7} \cdot \sqrt{3} = \sqrt{7 \cdot 3} = \sqrt{21}$

b. $\sqrt{3} \cdot \sqrt{3} = \sqrt{3 \cdot 3} = \sqrt{9} = 3$

c. $\sqrt{3} \cdot \sqrt{15} = \sqrt{45}$. Next, simplify $\sqrt{45}$.
$$\sqrt{45} = \sqrt{9 \cdot 5} = \sqrt{9} \cdot \sqrt{5} = 3\sqrt{5}$$

d. $2\sqrt{3} \cdot 5\sqrt{2} = 2 \cdot 5\sqrt{3 \cdot 2} = 10\sqrt{6}$

e. $\sqrt{2x^3} \cdot \sqrt{6x} = \sqrt{2x^3 \cdot 6x}$ Use the product rule.
$\qquad\qquad\quad = \sqrt{12x^4}$ Multiply.
$\qquad\qquad\quad = \sqrt{4x^4 \cdot 3}$ Write $12x^4$ so that one factor is a perfect square.
$\qquad\qquad\quad = \sqrt{4x^4} \cdot \sqrt{3}$ Use the product rule.
$\qquad\qquad\quad = 2x^2\sqrt{3}$ Simplify. $\qquad$ □

PRACTICE

1 Multiply. Then simplify if possible.

a. $\sqrt{11} \cdot \sqrt{7}$ **b.** $9\sqrt{10} \cdot 8\sqrt{3}$ **c.** $\sqrt{5} \cdot \sqrt{10}$
d. $\sqrt{17} \cdot \sqrt{17}$ **e.** $\sqrt{15y} \cdot \sqrt{5y^3}$

From Example 1(b), we found that

$$\sqrt{3} \cdot \sqrt{3} = 3 \quad \text{or} \quad (\sqrt{3})^2 = 3$$

This is true in general.

> If a is a positive number,
>
> $$\sqrt{a} \cdot \sqrt{a} = a \quad \text{or} \quad (\sqrt{a})^2 = a$$

✔ **CONCEPT CHECK**

Identify the true statement(s).

a. $\sqrt{7} \cdot \sqrt{7} = 7$ **b.** $\sqrt{2} \cdot \sqrt{3} = 6$
c. $(\sqrt{131})^2 = 131$ **d.** $\sqrt{5x} \cdot \sqrt{5x} = 5x$ (Here, x is a positive number.)

Answer to Concept Check:
a, c, d

EXAMPLE 2   Find: $(3\sqrt{2})^2$

Solution $(3\sqrt{2})^2 = 3^2 \cdot (\sqrt{2})^2 = 9 \cdot 2 = 18$

PRACTICE
2   Find $(2\sqrt{7})^2$.

EXAMPLE 3   Multiply $\sqrt[3]{4} \cdot \sqrt[3]{18}$. Then simplify if possible.

Solution $\sqrt[3]{4} \cdot \sqrt[3]{18} = \sqrt[3]{4 \cdot 18} = \sqrt[3]{4 \cdot 2 \cdot 9} = \sqrt[3]{8 \cdot 9} = \sqrt[3]{8} \cdot \sqrt[3]{9} = 2\sqrt[3]{9}$

PRACTICE
3   Multiply $\sqrt[3]{10} \cdot \sqrt[3]{50}$. Then simplify if possible.

When multiplying radical expressions containing more than one term, use the same techniques we use to multiply other algebraic expressions with more than one term.

EXAMPLE 4   Multiply. Then simplify if possible.
  a. $\sqrt{5}(\sqrt{5} - \sqrt{2})$ **b.** $\sqrt{3x}(\sqrt{x} - 5\sqrt{3})$
  c. $(\sqrt{x} + \sqrt{2})(\sqrt{3} - \sqrt{2})$

Solution

a. Using the distributive property, we have

$$\sqrt{5}(\sqrt{5} - \sqrt{2}) = \sqrt{5} \cdot \sqrt{5} - \sqrt{5} \cdot \sqrt{2}$$
$$= 5 - \sqrt{10} \qquad \text{Since } \sqrt{5} \cdot \sqrt{5} = 5 \text{ and } \sqrt{5} \cdot \sqrt{2} = \sqrt{10}$$

b. $\sqrt{3x}(\sqrt{x} - 5\sqrt{3}) = \sqrt{3x} \cdot \sqrt{x} - \sqrt{3x} \cdot 5\sqrt{3}$ Use the distributive property.
$$= \sqrt{3x \cdot x} - 5\sqrt{3x \cdot 3} \qquad \text{Use the product rule.}$$
$$= \sqrt{3 \cdot x^2} - 5\sqrt{9 \cdot x} \qquad \text{Factor each radicand so that one factor is a perfect square.}$$
$$= \sqrt{3} \cdot \sqrt{x^2} - 5 \cdot \sqrt{9} \cdot \sqrt{x} \qquad \text{Use the product rule.}$$
$$= x\sqrt{3} - 5 \cdot 3 \cdot \sqrt{x} \qquad \text{Simplify.}$$
$$= x\sqrt{3} - 15\sqrt{x} \qquad \text{Simplify.}$$

c. Use the FOIL method of multiplication.

$$(\sqrt{x} + \sqrt{2})(\sqrt{3} - \sqrt{2}) = \overset{\text{F}}{\sqrt{x} \cdot \sqrt{3}} - \overset{\text{O}}{\sqrt{x} \cdot \sqrt{2}} + \overset{\text{I}}{\sqrt{2} \cdot \sqrt{3}} - \overset{\text{L}}{\sqrt{2} \cdot \sqrt{2}}$$
$$= \sqrt{3x} - \sqrt{2x} + \sqrt{6} - \sqrt{4} \qquad \text{Apply the product rule.}$$
$$= \sqrt{3x} - \sqrt{2x} + \sqrt{6} - 2 \qquad \text{Simplify.}$$

PRACTICE
4   Multiply. Then simplify if possible.
  a. $\sqrt{3}(\sqrt{3} - \sqrt{5})$ **b.** $\sqrt{2z}(\sqrt{z} + 7\sqrt{2})$
  c. $(\sqrt{x} - \sqrt{7})(\sqrt{x} + \sqrt{2})$

The special product formulas can be used to multiply expressions containing radicals.

EXAMPLE 5 Multiply. Then simplify if possible.

    a. $(\sqrt{5} - 7)(\sqrt{5} + 7)$ **b.** $(\sqrt{7x} + 2)^2$

Solution

    a. Recall from Chapter 5 that $(a - b)(a + b) = a^2 - b^2$. Then

$$(\sqrt{5} - 7)(\sqrt{5} + 7) = (\sqrt{5})^2 - 7^2$$
$$= 5 - 49$$
$$= -44$$

    b. Recall that $(a + b)^2 = a^2 + 2ab + b^2$. Then

$$(\sqrt{7x} + 2)^2 = (\sqrt{7x})^2 + 2(\sqrt{7x})(2) + (2)^2$$
$$= 7x + 4\sqrt{7x} + 4$$

PRACTICE
5 Multiply. Then simplify if possible.

    a. $(\sqrt{7} + 4)(\sqrt{7} - 4)$ **b.** $(\sqrt{3x} - 5)^2$

OBJECTIVE
2 Dividing Radicals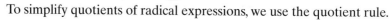

To simplify quotients of radical expressions, we use the quotient rule.

Quotient Rule for Radicals

If $\sqrt[n]{a}$ and $\sqrt[n]{b}$ are real numbers and $b \neq 0$, then

$$\frac{\sqrt[n]{a}}{\sqrt[n]{b}} = \sqrt[n]{\frac{a}{b}}, \text{ providing } b \neq 0$$

EXAMPLE 6 Divide. Then simplify if possible.

    a. $\dfrac{\sqrt{14}}{\sqrt{2}}$ **b.** $\dfrac{\sqrt{100}}{\sqrt{5}}$ **c.** $\dfrac{\sqrt{12x^3}}{\sqrt{3x}}$

Solution Use the quotient rule and then simplify the resulting radicand.

    a. $\dfrac{\sqrt{14}}{\sqrt{2}} = \sqrt{\dfrac{14}{2}} = \sqrt{7}$

    b. $\dfrac{\sqrt{100}}{\sqrt{5}} = \sqrt{\dfrac{100}{5}} = \sqrt{20} = \sqrt{4 \cdot 5} = \sqrt{4} \cdot \sqrt{5} = 2\sqrt{5}$

    c. $\dfrac{\sqrt{12x^3}}{\sqrt{3x}} = \sqrt{\dfrac{12x^3}{3x}} = \sqrt{4x^2} = 2x$

PRACTICE
6 Divide. Then simplify if possible.

    a. $\dfrac{\sqrt{21}}{\sqrt{7}}$ **b.** $\dfrac{\sqrt{48}}{\sqrt{6}}$ **c.** $\dfrac{\sqrt{45y^5}}{\sqrt{5y}}$

EXAMPLE 7 Divide $\dfrac{\sqrt[3]{32}}{\sqrt[3]{4}}$. Then simplify if possible.

Solution $\dfrac{\sqrt[3]{32}}{\sqrt[3]{4}} = \sqrt[3]{\dfrac{32}{4}} = \sqrt[3]{8} = 2$

PRACTICE
7 Divide $\dfrac{\sqrt[3]{625}}{\sqrt[3]{5}}$. Then simplify if possible.

OBJECTIVE

3   Rationalizing Denominators

It is sometimes easier to work with radical expressions if the denominator does not contain a radical. To rewrite the expression so that the denominator does not contain a radical expression, we use the fact that we can multiply the numerator and the denominator of a fraction by the same nonzero number without changing the value of the expression. This is the same as multiplying the fraction by 1. For example, to get rid of

the radical in the denominator of $\dfrac{\sqrt{5}}{\sqrt{2}}$, we multiply by 1 in the form of $\dfrac{\sqrt{2}}{\sqrt{2}}$. Then

$$\frac{\sqrt{5}}{\sqrt{2}} = \frac{\sqrt{5}}{\sqrt{2}} \cdot 1 = \frac{\sqrt{5}}{\sqrt{2}} \cdot \frac{\sqrt{2}}{\sqrt{2}} = \frac{\sqrt{5}}{\sqrt{2}} \cdot \frac{\sqrt{2}}{\sqrt{2}} = \frac{\sqrt{10}}{2}$$

This process is called **rationalizing** the denominator.

EXAMPLE 8   Rationalize each denominator.

a. $\dfrac{2}{\sqrt{7}}$ b. $\dfrac{\sqrt{5}}{\sqrt{12}}$ c. $\sqrt{\dfrac{1}{18x}}$

Solution

a. To rewrite $\dfrac{2}{\sqrt{7}}$ so that there is no radical in the denominator, we multiply by 1 in the form of $\dfrac{\sqrt{7}}{\sqrt{7}}$.

$$\frac{2}{\sqrt{7}} = \frac{2}{\sqrt{7}} \cdot \frac{\sqrt{7}}{\sqrt{7}} = \frac{2 \cdot \sqrt{7}}{\sqrt{7} \cdot \sqrt{7}} = \frac{2\sqrt{7}}{7}$$

b. We can multiply by $\dfrac{\sqrt{12}}{\sqrt{12}}$, but see what happens if we simplify first.

$$\frac{\sqrt{5}}{\sqrt{12}} = \frac{\sqrt{5}}{\sqrt{4 \cdot 3}} = \frac{\sqrt{5}}{2\sqrt{3}}$$

To rationalize the denominator now, we multiply by $\dfrac{\sqrt{3}}{\sqrt{3}}$.

$$\frac{\sqrt{5}}{2\sqrt{3}} = \frac{\sqrt{5}}{2\sqrt{3}} \cdot \frac{\sqrt{3}}{\sqrt{3}} = \frac{\sqrt{5} \cdot \sqrt{3}}{2\sqrt{3} \cdot \sqrt{3}} = \frac{\sqrt{15}}{2 \cdot 3} = \frac{\sqrt{15}}{6}$$

c. First we simplify.

$$\sqrt{\frac{1}{18x}} = \frac{\sqrt{1}}{\sqrt{18x}} = \frac{1}{\sqrt{9} \cdot \sqrt{2x}} = \frac{1}{3\sqrt{2x}}$$

Now to rationalize the denominator, we multiply by $\dfrac{\sqrt{2x}}{\sqrt{2x}}$.

$$\frac{1}{3\sqrt{2x}} = \frac{1}{3\sqrt{2x}} \cdot \frac{\sqrt{2x}}{\sqrt{2x}} = \frac{1 \cdot \sqrt{2x}}{3\sqrt{2x} \cdot \sqrt{2x}} = \frac{\sqrt{2x}}{3 \cdot 2x} = \frac{\sqrt{2x}}{6x}$$

PRACTICE

8   Rationalize each denominator.

a. $\dfrac{4}{\sqrt{5}}$ b. $\dfrac{\sqrt{3}}{\sqrt{18}}$ c. $\sqrt{\dfrac{3}{14x}}$

As a general rule, simplify a radical expression first and then rationalize the denominator.

EXAMPLE 9 Rationalize each denominator.

a. $\dfrac{5}{\sqrt[3]{4}}$ b. $\dfrac{\sqrt[3]{7}}{\sqrt[3]{3}}$

Solution

a. Since the denominator contains a cube root, we multiply the numerator and the denominator by a factor that gives the **cube root of a perfect cube** in the denominator. Recall that $\sqrt[3]{8} = 2$ and that the denominator $\sqrt[3]{4}$ multiplied by $\sqrt[3]{2}$ is $\sqrt[3]{4 \cdot 2}$ or $\sqrt[3]{8}$.

$$\dfrac{5}{\sqrt[3]{4}} = \dfrac{5 \cdot \sqrt[3]{2}}{\sqrt[3]{4} \cdot \sqrt[3]{2}} = \dfrac{5\sqrt[3]{2}}{\sqrt[3]{8}} = \dfrac{5\sqrt[3]{2}}{2}$$

b. Recall that $\sqrt[3]{27} = 3$. Multiply the denominator $\sqrt[3]{3}$ by $\sqrt[3]{9}$ and the result is $\sqrt[3]{3 \cdot 9}$ or $\sqrt[3]{27}$.

$$\dfrac{\sqrt[3]{7}}{\sqrt[3]{3}} = \dfrac{\sqrt[3]{7} \cdot \sqrt[3]{9}}{\sqrt[3]{3} \cdot \sqrt[3]{9}} = \dfrac{\sqrt[3]{63}}{\sqrt[3]{27}} = \dfrac{\sqrt[3]{63}}{3}$$

PRACTICE
9   Rationalize each denominator.

a. $\dfrac{3}{\sqrt[3]{25}}$ b. $\dfrac{\sqrt[3]{6}}{\sqrt[3]{5}}$

OBJECTIVE
4   Rationalizing Denominators Using Conjugates ▶

To rationalize a denominator that is a sum, such as the denominator in

$$\dfrac{2}{4 + \sqrt{3}}$$

we multiply the numerator and the denominator by $4 - \sqrt{3}$. The expressions $4 + \sqrt{3}$ and $4 - \sqrt{3}$ are called **conjugates** of each other. When a radical expression such as $4 + \sqrt{3}$ is multiplied by its conjugate, $4 - \sqrt{3}$, the product simplifies to an expression that contains no radicals.

$$(a + b)(a - b) = a^2 - b^2$$
$$(4 + \sqrt{3})(4 - \sqrt{3}) = 4^2 - (\sqrt{3})^2 = 16 - 3 = 13$$

Then

$$\dfrac{2}{4 + \sqrt{3}} = \dfrac{2(4 - \sqrt{3})}{(4 + \sqrt{3})(4 - \sqrt{3})} = \dfrac{2(4 - \sqrt{3})}{13}$$

EXAMPLE 10 Rationalize each denominator and simplify.

a. $\dfrac{2}{1 + \sqrt{3}}$ b. $\dfrac{\sqrt{5} + 4}{\sqrt{5} - 1}$ c. $\dfrac{3}{1 + \sqrt{x}}$

Solution

a. Multiply the numerator and the denominator of this fraction by the conjugate of $1 + \sqrt{3}$, that is, by $1 - \sqrt{3}$.

$$\frac{2}{1 + \sqrt{3}} = \frac{2(1 - \sqrt{3})}{(1 + \sqrt{3})(1 - \sqrt{3})}$$

$$= \frac{2(1 - \sqrt{3})}{1^2 - (\sqrt{3})^2}$$

> **Helpful Hint**
> Don't forget that $(\sqrt{3})^2 = 3$.

$$= \frac{2(1 - \sqrt{3})}{1 - 3}$$

$$= \frac{2(1 - \sqrt{3})}{-2}$$

$$= -\frac{2(1 - \sqrt{3})}{2} \qquad \frac{a}{-b} = -\frac{a}{b}$$

$$= -1(1 - \sqrt{3}) \qquad \text{Simplify.}$$

$$= -1 + \sqrt{3} \qquad \text{Multiply.}$$

b. $\dfrac{\sqrt{5} + 4}{\sqrt{5} - 1} = \dfrac{(\sqrt{5} + 4)(\sqrt{5} + 1)}{(\sqrt{5} - 1)(\sqrt{5} + 1)}$ Multiply the numerator and denominator by $\sqrt{5} + 1$, the conjugate of $\sqrt{5} - 1$.

$$= \frac{5 + \sqrt{5} + 4\sqrt{5} + 4}{5 - 1} \qquad \text{Multiply.}$$

$$= \frac{9 + 5\sqrt{5}}{4} \qquad \text{Simplify.}$$

c. $\dfrac{3}{1 + \sqrt{x}} = \dfrac{3(1 - \sqrt{x})}{(1 + \sqrt{x})(1 - \sqrt{x})}$ Multiply the numerator and denominator by $1 - \sqrt{x}$, the conjugate of $1 + \sqrt{x}$.

$$= \frac{3(1 - \sqrt{x})}{1 - x}$$

□

PRACTICE
10   Rationalize each denominator and simplify.

a. $\dfrac{4}{1 + \sqrt{5}}$ **b.** $\dfrac{\sqrt{3} + 2}{\sqrt{3} - 1}$ **c.** $\dfrac{8}{5 - \sqrt{x}}$ ▪

EXAMPLE 11   Simplify: $\dfrac{12 - \sqrt{18}}{9}$

Solution First simplify $\sqrt{18}$.

$$\frac{12 - \sqrt{18}}{9} = \frac{12 - \sqrt{9 \cdot 2}}{9} = \frac{12 - 3\sqrt{2}}{9}$$

Next, factor out a common factor of 3 from the terms in the numerator and the denominator and simplify.

$$\frac{12 - 3\sqrt{2}}{9} = \frac{3(4 - \sqrt{2})}{3 \cdot 3} = \frac{4 - \sqrt{2}}{3}$$

□

PRACTICE
11   Simplify $\dfrac{14 - \sqrt{28}}{6}$.   ▪

✔ Vocabulary, Readiness & Video Check

Fill in each blank.

1. $\sqrt{7} \cdot \sqrt{3} =$ _____

2. $\sqrt{10} \cdot \sqrt{10} =$ _____

3. $\dfrac{\sqrt{15}}{\sqrt{3}} =$ _____

4. The process of eliminating the radical in the denominator of a radical expression is called _____ _____.

5. The conjugate of $2 + \sqrt{3}$ is _____.

Martin-Gay Interactive Videos

See Video 8.4 🔘

Watch the section lecture video and answer the following questions.

OBJECTIVE 1
6. In ▦ Examples 1 and 3, the product rule for radicals is applied twice, but in different ways. Explain.

OBJECTIVE 1
7. Starting with ▦ Example 2, what important reminder is made repeatedly about the square root of a positive number that is squared?

OBJECTIVE 2
8. From ▦ Examples 6 and 7, when you're looking at a quotient of two radicals, what would make you think to apply the quotient rule in order to simplify?

OBJECTIVE 3
9. From the lecture before ▦ Example 8, what is the goal of rationalizing a denominator?

OBJECTIVE 4
10. From ▦ Example 11, why will multiplying a denominator by its conjugate rationalize the denominator?

8.4 Exercise Set MyMathLab® ▶

Multiply and simplify. Assume that all variables represent positive real numbers. See Examples 1, 2, 4, and 5.

1. $\sqrt{8} \cdot \sqrt{2}$
2. $\sqrt{3} \cdot \sqrt{12}$
3. $\sqrt{10} \cdot \sqrt{5}$
4. $\sqrt{2} \cdot \sqrt{14}$
5. $(\sqrt{6})^2$
6. $(\sqrt{10})^2$
7. $\sqrt{2x} \cdot \sqrt{2x}$
8. $\sqrt{5y} \cdot \sqrt{5y}$
9. $(2\sqrt{5})^2$
10. $(3\sqrt{10})^2$
11. $(6\sqrt{x})^2$
12. $(8\sqrt{y})^2$
13. $\sqrt{3x^5} \cdot \sqrt{6x}$
14. $\sqrt{21y^7} \cdot \sqrt{3y}$
15. $\sqrt{2xy^2} \cdot \sqrt{8xy}$
16. $\sqrt{18x^2y^2} \cdot \sqrt{2x^2y}$
17. $\sqrt{6}(\sqrt{5} + \sqrt{7})$
18. $\sqrt{10}(\sqrt{3} - \sqrt{7})$
19. $\sqrt{10}(\sqrt{2} + \sqrt{5})$
20. $\sqrt{6}(\sqrt{3} + \sqrt{2})$
21. $\sqrt{7y}(\sqrt{y} - 2\sqrt{7})$
22. $\sqrt{5b}(2\sqrt{b} + \sqrt{5})$
23. $(\sqrt{3} + 6)(\sqrt{3} - 6)$
24. $(\sqrt{5} + 2)(\sqrt{5} - 2)$
25. $(\sqrt{3} + \sqrt{5})(\sqrt{2} - \sqrt{5})$
26. $(\sqrt{7} + \sqrt{5})(\sqrt{2} - \sqrt{5})$
27. $(2\sqrt{11} + 1)(\sqrt{11} - 6)$
28. $(5\sqrt{3} + 2)(\sqrt{3} - 1)$
29. $(\sqrt{x} + 6)(\sqrt{x} - 6)$
30. $(\sqrt{y} + 5)(\sqrt{y} - 5)$
31. $(\sqrt{x} - 7)^2$
32. $(\sqrt{x} + 4)^2$
33. $(\sqrt{6y} + 1)^2$
34. $(\sqrt{3y} - 2)^2$

Divide and simplify. Assume that all variables represent positive real numbers. See Example 6.

35. $\dfrac{\sqrt{32}}{\sqrt{2}}$
36. $\dfrac{\sqrt{40}}{\sqrt{10}}$
37. $\dfrac{\sqrt{21}}{\sqrt{3}}$
38. $\dfrac{\sqrt{55}}{\sqrt{5}}$
39. $\dfrac{\sqrt{90}}{\sqrt{5}}$
40. $\dfrac{\sqrt{96}}{\sqrt{8}}$
41. $\dfrac{\sqrt{75y^5}}{\sqrt{3y}}$
42. $\dfrac{\sqrt{24x^7}}{\sqrt{6x}}$
43. $\dfrac{\sqrt{150}}{\sqrt{2}}$
44. $\dfrac{\sqrt{120}}{\sqrt{3}}$
45. $\dfrac{\sqrt{72y^5}}{\sqrt{3y^3}}$
46. $\dfrac{\sqrt{54x^3}}{\sqrt{2x}}$
47. $\dfrac{\sqrt{24x^3y^4}}{\sqrt{2xy}}$
48. $\dfrac{\sqrt{96x^5y^3}}{\sqrt{3x^2y}}$

Rationalize each denominator and simplify. Assume that all variables represent positive real numbers. See Example 8.

49. $\dfrac{\sqrt{3}}{\sqrt{5}}$ **50.** $\dfrac{\sqrt{2}}{\sqrt{3}}$ **51.** $\dfrac{7}{\sqrt{2}}$

52. $\dfrac{8}{\sqrt{11}}$ **53.** $\dfrac{1}{\sqrt{6y}}$ **54.** $\dfrac{1}{\sqrt{10z}}$

55. $\sqrt{\dfrac{3}{x}}$ **56.** $\sqrt{\dfrac{5}{x}}$ **57.** $\sqrt{\dfrac{1}{8}}$

58. $\sqrt{\dfrac{1}{27}}$ **59.** $\sqrt{\dfrac{2}{15}}$ **60.** $\sqrt{\dfrac{11}{14}}$

61. $\dfrac{8y}{\sqrt{5}}$ **62.** $\dfrac{7x}{\sqrt{2}}$ **63.** $\sqrt{\dfrac{y}{12x}}$

64. $\sqrt{\dfrac{x}{20y}}$

Rationalize each denominator and simplify. Assume that all variables represent positive real numbers. See Example 10.

65. $\dfrac{3}{\sqrt{2}+1}$ **66.** $\dfrac{6}{\sqrt{5}+2}$

67. $\dfrac{\sqrt{5}+1}{\sqrt{6}-\sqrt{5}}$ **68.** $\dfrac{\sqrt{3}+1}{\sqrt{3}-\sqrt{2}}$

69. $\dfrac{3}{\sqrt{x}-4}$ **70.** $\dfrac{4}{\sqrt{x}-1}$

MIXED PRACTICE

Rationalize each denominator and simplify.

71. $\sqrt{\dfrac{3}{20}}$ **72.** $\sqrt{\dfrac{3}{50}}$

73. $\dfrac{4}{2-\sqrt{5}}$ **74.** $\dfrac{2}{1-\sqrt{2}}$

75. $\dfrac{3x}{\sqrt{2x}}$ **76.** $\dfrac{5y}{\sqrt{3y}}$

77. $\dfrac{5}{2+\sqrt{x}}$ **78.** $\dfrac{9}{3+\sqrt{x}}$

Simplify the following. See Example 11.

79. $\dfrac{6+2\sqrt{3}}{2}$ **80.** $\dfrac{9+6\sqrt{2}}{3}$

81. $\dfrac{18-12\sqrt{5}}{6}$ **82.** $\dfrac{8-20\sqrt{3}}{4}$

83. $\dfrac{15\sqrt{3}+5}{5}$ **84.** $\dfrac{8+16\sqrt{2}}{8}$

Multiply or divide as indicated. See Examples 3 and 7.

85. $\sqrt[3]{12}\cdot\sqrt[3]{4}$ **86.** $\sqrt[3]{9}\cdot\sqrt[3]{6}$

87. $2\sqrt[3]{5}\cdot6\sqrt[3]{2}$ **88.** $8\sqrt[3]{4}\cdot7\sqrt[3]{7}$

89. $\sqrt[3]{15}\cdot\sqrt[3]{25}$ **90.** $\sqrt[3]{4}\cdot\sqrt[3]{4}$

91. $\dfrac{\sqrt[3]{54}}{\sqrt[3]{2}}$ **92.** $\dfrac{\sqrt[3]{80}}{\sqrt[3]{10}}$

93. $\dfrac{\sqrt[3]{120}}{\sqrt[3]{5}}$ **94.** $\dfrac{\sqrt[3]{270}}{\sqrt[3]{5}}$

Rationalize each denominator. See Example 9.

95. $\sqrt[3]{\dfrac{5}{4}}$ **96.** $\sqrt[3]{\dfrac{7}{9}}$

97. $\dfrac{6}{\sqrt[3]{2}}$ **98.** $\dfrac{3}{\sqrt[3]{5}}$

99. $\sqrt[3]{\dfrac{1}{9}}$ **100.** $\sqrt[3]{\dfrac{8}{11}}$

101. $\sqrt[3]{\dfrac{2}{9}}$ **102.** $\sqrt[3]{\dfrac{3}{4}}$

REVIEW AND PREVIEW

Solve each equation. See Sections 2.4 and 5.3.

103. $x+5=7^2$ **104.** $2y-1=3^2$

105. $4z^2+6z-12=(2z)^2$

106. $16x^2+x+9=(4x)^2$

107. $9x^2+5x+4=(3x+1)^2$

108. $x^2+3x+4=(x+2)^2$

CONCEPT EXTENSIONS

△ **109.** Find the area of a rectangle whose length is $13\sqrt{2}$ meters and width is $5\sqrt{6}$ meters.

$5\sqrt{6}$ meters

$13\sqrt{2}$ meters

△ **110.** Find the volume of a box whose length is $\sqrt{3}$ feet, width is $\sqrt{2}$ feet, and height is $\sqrt{2}$ feet.

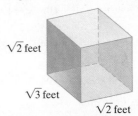

$\sqrt{2}$ feet

$\sqrt{3}$ feet

$\sqrt{2}$ feet

△ **111.** If a circle has area A, then the formula for the radius r of the circle is

$$r=\sqrt{\dfrac{A}{\pi}}$$

Simplify this expression by rationalizing the denominator.

△ **112.** If a round ball has volume V, then the formula for the radius r of the ball is

$$r=\sqrt[3]{\dfrac{3V}{4\pi}}$$

Simplify this expression by rationalizing the denominator.

Identify each statement as true or false. See the Concept Check in this section.

113. $\sqrt{5} \cdot \sqrt{5} = 5$

114. $\sqrt{5} \cdot \sqrt{3} = 15$

115. $\sqrt{3x} \cdot \sqrt{3x} = 2\sqrt{3x}$

116. $\sqrt{3x} + \sqrt{3x} = 2\sqrt{3x}$

117. $\sqrt{11} + \sqrt{2} = \sqrt{13}$

118. $\sqrt{11} \cdot \sqrt{2} = \sqrt{22}$

119. When rationalizing the denominator of $\dfrac{\sqrt{2}}{\sqrt{3}}$, explain why both the numerator and the denominator must be multiplied by $\sqrt{3}$.

120. In your own words, explain why $\sqrt{6} + \sqrt{2}$ cannot be simplified further, but $\sqrt{6} \cdot \sqrt{2}$ can be.

121. When rationalizing the denominator of $\dfrac{\sqrt[3]{2}}{\sqrt[3]{3}}$, explain why both the numerator and the denominator must be multiplied by $\sqrt[3]{9}$.

122. When rationalizing the denominator of $\dfrac{5}{1 + \sqrt{2}}$, explain why multiplying by $\dfrac{\sqrt{2}}{\sqrt{2}}$ will not accomplish this, but multiplying by $\dfrac{1 - \sqrt{2}}{1 - \sqrt{2}}$ will.

It is often more convenient to work with a radical expression whose numerator is rationalized. Rationalize the numerator of each expression by multiplying the numerator and denominator by the conjugate of the numerator.

123. $\dfrac{\sqrt{3} + 1}{\sqrt{2} - 1}$

124. $\dfrac{\sqrt{2} - 2}{2 - \sqrt{3}}$

Integrated Review Simplifying Radicals

Sections 8.1–8.4

Simplify. Assume that all variables represent positive numbers.

1. $\sqrt{36}$ **2.** $\sqrt{48}$ **3.** $\sqrt{x^4}$ **4.** $\sqrt{y^7}$

5. $\sqrt{16x^2}$ **6.** $\sqrt{18x^{11}}$ **7.** $\sqrt[3]{8}$ **8.** $\sqrt[4]{81}$

9. $\sqrt[3]{-27}$ **10.** $\sqrt{-4}$ **11.** $\sqrt{\dfrac{11}{9}}$ **12.** $\sqrt[3]{\dfrac{7}{64}}$

13. $-\sqrt{16}$ **14.** $-\sqrt{25}$ **15.** $\sqrt{\dfrac{9}{49}}$ **16.** $\sqrt{\dfrac{1}{64}}$

17. $\sqrt{a^8 b^2}$ **18.** $\sqrt{x^{10} y^{20}}$ **19.** $\sqrt{25m^6}$ **20.** $\sqrt{9n^{16}}$

Add or subtract as indicated.

21. $5\sqrt{7} + \sqrt{7}$ **22.** $\sqrt{50} - \sqrt{8}$

23. $5\sqrt{2} - 5\sqrt{3}$ **24.** $2\sqrt{x} + \sqrt{25x} - \sqrt{36x} + 3x$

Multiply and simplify if possible.

25. $\sqrt{2} \cdot \sqrt{15}$ **26.** $\sqrt{3} \cdot \sqrt{3}$ **27.** $(2\sqrt{7})^2$

28. $(3\sqrt{5})^2$ **29.** $\sqrt{3}(\sqrt{11} + 1)$ **30.** $\sqrt{6}(\sqrt{3} - 2)$

31. $\sqrt{8y} \cdot \sqrt{2y}$ **32.** $\sqrt{15x^2} \cdot \sqrt{3x^2}$ **33.** $(\sqrt{x} - 5)(\sqrt{x} + 2)$

34. $(3 + \sqrt{2})^2$

Divide and simplify if possible.

35. $\dfrac{\sqrt{8}}{\sqrt{2}}$ **36.** $\dfrac{\sqrt{45}}{\sqrt{15}}$ **37.** $\dfrac{\sqrt{24x^5}}{\sqrt{2x}}$ **38.** $\dfrac{\sqrt{75a^4 b^5}}{\sqrt{5ab}}$

Rationalize each denominator.

39. $\sqrt{\dfrac{1}{6}}$ **40.** $\dfrac{x}{\sqrt{20}}$ **41.** $\dfrac{4}{\sqrt{6} + 1}$ **42.** $\dfrac{\sqrt{2} + 1}{\sqrt{x} - 5}$

43. A standard tournament soccer ball must weigh between 410 and 450 grams, and has specified circumference and air pressure ranges. If a tournament soccer ball has a volume of 5310 cu centimeters, what is the radius of the ball? Use the formula $r = \sqrt[3]{\dfrac{3V}{4\pi}}$. Round to the nearest centimeter.

Chapter 8 Vocabulary Check

Fill in each blank with one of the words or phrases listed below. Not all choices will be used.

index	radicand	like radicals
rationalizing the denominator	conjugate	leg
principal square root	radical	hypotenuse

1. The expressions $5\sqrt{x}$ and $7\sqrt{x}$ are examples of _____.

2. In the expression $\sqrt[3]{45}$, the number 3 is the _____, the number 45 is the _____, and $\sqrt{}$ is called the _____ sign.

3. The _____ of $a + b$ is $a - b$.

4. The _____ of 25 is 5.

5. The process of eliminating the radical in the denominator of a radical expression is called _____.

6. The Pythagorean theorem states that for a right triangle, $(\text{leg})^2 + (\text{leg})^2 = ($_____$)^2$.

Chapter 8 Highlights

DEFINITIONS AND CONCEPTS	EXAMPLES
Section 8.1 Introduction to Radicals	
The **positive** or **principal square root** of a positive number a is written as $\sqrt{a}$. The **negative square root** of a is written as $-\sqrt{a}$. $\sqrt{a} = b$ only if $b^2 = a$ and $b > 0$.	$\sqrt{25} = 5 \qquad \sqrt{100} = 10$ $-\sqrt{9} = -3 \qquad \sqrt{\dfrac{4}{49}} = \dfrac{2}{7}$

DEFINITIONS AND CONCEPTS	EXAMPLES

Section 8.1   Introduction to Radicals (continued)

A square root of a negative number is not a real number.

The **cube root** of a real number a is written as $\sqrt[3]{a}$ and $\sqrt[3]{a} = b$ only if $b^3 = a$.

The **nth root** of a number a is written as $\sqrt[n]{a}$ and $\sqrt[n]{a} = b$ only if $b^n = a$.

In $\sqrt[n]{a}$, the natural number n is called the **index,** the symbol $\sqrt{}$ is called a **radical,** and the expression within the radical is called the **radicand.**

(*Note:* If the index is even, the radicand must be nonnegative for the root to be a real number.)

$\sqrt{-4}$ is not a real number.

$\sqrt[3]{64} = 4 \qquad \sqrt[3]{-8} = -2$

$\sqrt[4]{81} = 3 \qquad \sqrt[5]{-32} = -2$

$$\text{index} \atop \downarrow$$
$$\sqrt[n]{a}$$
$$\nwarrow$$
$$\text{radicand}$$

Section 8.2   Simplifying Radicals

Product Rule for Radicals

If $\sqrt[n]{a}$ and $\sqrt[n]{b}$ are real numbers, then $\sqrt[n]{a} \cdot \sqrt[n]{b} = \sqrt[n]{a \cdot b}$.

A square root is in **simplified form** if the radicand contains no perfect square factors other than 1. To simplify a square root, factor the radicand so that one of its factors is a perfect square factor.

To simplify cube roots, factor the radicand so that one of its factors is a perfect cube.

Quotient Rule for Radicals

If $\sqrt[n]{a}$ and $\sqrt[n]{b}$ are real numbers and $b \neq 0$, then

$$\sqrt[n]{\frac{a}{b}} = \frac{\sqrt[n]{a}}{\sqrt[n]{b}}$$

$\sqrt{2} \cdot \sqrt{3} = \sqrt{6}$

$\sqrt[3]{7} \cdot \sqrt[3]{2} = \sqrt[3]{14}$

$\sqrt{45} = \sqrt{9 \cdot 5}$

$\qquad = \sqrt{9} \cdot \sqrt{5}$

$\qquad = 3\sqrt{5} \qquad$ in simplest form.

$\sqrt[3]{48} = \sqrt[3]{8 \cdot 6}$

$\qquad = \sqrt[3]{8} \cdot \sqrt[3]{6}$

$\qquad = 2\sqrt[3]{6}$

$\sqrt{\dfrac{18}{x^6}} = \dfrac{\sqrt{9 \cdot 2}}{\sqrt{x^6}} = \dfrac{\sqrt{9} \cdot \sqrt{2}}{x^3} = \dfrac{3\sqrt{2}}{x^3}$

$\sqrt[3]{\dfrac{18}{x^6}} = \dfrac{\sqrt[3]{18}}{\sqrt[3]{x^6}} = \dfrac{\sqrt[3]{18}}{x^2}$

Section 8.3   Adding and Subtracting Radicals

Like radicals are radical expressions that have the same index and the same radicand.

To combine like radicals, use the distributive property.

Like Radicals

$5\sqrt{2}, -7\sqrt{2}, \sqrt{2}$ Also, $-\sqrt[3]{11}, 3\sqrt[3]{11}$

$2\sqrt{7} - 13\sqrt{7} = (2 - 13)\sqrt{7} = -11\sqrt{7}$

$\sqrt[3]{24} + \sqrt[3]{8} + \sqrt[3]{81}$

$\qquad = \sqrt[3]{8 \cdot 3} + 2 + \sqrt[3]{27 \cdot 3}$

$\qquad = \sqrt[3]{8} \cdot \sqrt[3]{3} + 2 + \sqrt[3]{27} \cdot \sqrt[3]{3}$

$\qquad = 2\sqrt[3]{3} + 2 + 3\sqrt[3]{3}$

$\qquad = (2 + 3)\sqrt[3]{3} + 2$

$\qquad = 5\sqrt[3]{3} + 2$

DEFINITIONS AND CONCEPTS	EXAMPLES

Section 8.4   Multiplying and Dividing Radicals

The product and quotient rules for radicals may be used to simplify products and quotients of radicals.	Perform the indicated operations and simplify. $$\sqrt{3} \cdot \sqrt{11} = \sqrt{33}$$ $$(2\sqrt{5})^2 = 2^2 \cdot (\sqrt{5})^2 = 4 \cdot 5 = 20$$ Multiply. $$(\sqrt{3x} + 1)(\sqrt{5} - \sqrt{3})$$ $$= \sqrt{15x} - \sqrt{9x} + \sqrt{5} - \sqrt{3}$$ $$= \sqrt{15x} - 3\sqrt{x} + \sqrt{5} - \sqrt{3}$$ $$\frac{\sqrt[3]{56x^4}}{\sqrt[3]{7x}} = \sqrt[3]{\frac{56x^4}{7x}} = \sqrt[3]{8x^3} = 2x$$
The process of eliminating the radical in the denominator of a radical expression is called **rationalizing the denominator.**	Rationalize the denominator. $$\frac{5}{\sqrt{11}} = \frac{5 \cdot \sqrt{11}}{\sqrt{11} \cdot \sqrt{11}} = \frac{5\sqrt{11}}{11}$$
The **conjugate** of $a + b$ is $a - b$.	The conjugate of $2 + \sqrt{3}$ is $2 - \sqrt{3}$.
To rationalize a denominator that is a sum or difference of radicals, multiply the numerator and the denominator by the conjugate of the denominator.	Rationalize the denominator. $$\frac{5}{6 - \sqrt{5}} = \frac{5(6 + \sqrt{5})}{(6 - \sqrt{5})(6 + \sqrt{5})}$$ $$= \frac{5(6 + \sqrt{5})}{36 + 6\sqrt{5} - 6\sqrt{5} - 5}$$ $$= \frac{5(6 + \sqrt{5})}{31}$$

(8.1) *Find the root.*

1. $\sqrt{81}$

2. $-\sqrt{49}$

3. $\sqrt[3]{27}$

4. $\sqrt[4]{16}$

5. $-\sqrt{\dfrac{9}{64}}$

6. $\sqrt{\dfrac{36}{81}}$

7. $\sqrt[4]{\dfrac{16}{81}}$

8. $\sqrt[3]{-\dfrac{27}{64}}$

9. Which radical(s) is not a real number?

    a. $\sqrt{4}$ **b.** $-\sqrt{4}$ **c.** $\sqrt{-4}$ **d.** $\sqrt[3]{-4}$

10. Which radical(s) is not a real number?

    a. $\sqrt{-5}$ **b.** $\sqrt[3]{-5}$ **c.** $\sqrt[4]{-5}$ **d.** $\sqrt[5]{-5}$

Find the following roots. Assume that variables represent positive numbers only.

11. $\sqrt{x^{12}}$

12. $\sqrt{x^8}$

13. $\sqrt{9x^6}$

14. $\sqrt{25x^4}$

15. $\sqrt{\dfrac{16}{y^{10}}}$

16. $\sqrt{\dfrac{y^{12}}{49}}$

(8.2) *Simplify each expression using the product rule. Assume that variables represent nonnegative real numbers.*

17. $\sqrt{54}$

18. $\sqrt{88}$

19. $\sqrt{150x^3}$

20. $\sqrt{92y^5}$

21. $\sqrt[3]{54}$

22. $\sqrt[3]{88}$

23. $\sqrt[4]{48}$

24. $\sqrt[4]{162}$

Simplify each expression using the quotient rule. Assume that variables represent positive real numbers.

25. $\sqrt{\dfrac{18}{25}}$

26. $\sqrt{\dfrac{75}{64}}$

27. $\sqrt{\dfrac{45y^2}{4x^4}}$

28. $\sqrt{\dfrac{20x^5}{9x^2}}$

29. $\sqrt[4]{\dfrac{9}{16}}$

30. $\sqrt[3]{\dfrac{40}{27}}$

31. $\sqrt[3]{\dfrac{3}{8}}$

32. $\sqrt[4]{\dfrac{5}{81}}$

65. $\dfrac{3}{\sqrt{5}-2}$

66. $\dfrac{8}{\sqrt{10}-3}$

67. $\dfrac{\sqrt{2}+1}{\sqrt{3}-1}$

68. $\dfrac{\sqrt{3}-2}{\sqrt{5}+2}$

69. $\dfrac{10}{\sqrt{x}+5}$

70. $\dfrac{8}{\sqrt{x}-1}$

71. $\sqrt[3]{\dfrac{7}{9}}$

72. $\sqrt[3]{\dfrac{3}{4}}$

73. $\sqrt[3]{\dfrac{3}{2}}$

74. $\sqrt[3]{\dfrac{5}{4}}$

(8.3) *Add or subtract by combining like radicals.*

33. $3\sqrt[3]{2} + 2\sqrt[3]{3} - 4\sqrt[3]{2}$

34. $5\sqrt{2} + 2\sqrt[3]{2} - 8\sqrt{2}$

35. $\sqrt{6} + 2\sqrt[3]{6} - 4\sqrt[3]{6} + 5\sqrt{6}$

36. $3\sqrt{5} - \sqrt[3]{5} - 2\sqrt{5} + 3\sqrt[3]{5}$

Add or subtract by simplifying each radical and then combining like terms. Assume that variables represent nonnegative real numbers.

37. $\sqrt{28x} + \sqrt{63x} + \sqrt[3]{56}$

38. $\sqrt{75y} + \sqrt{48y} - \sqrt[4]{16}$

39. $\sqrt{\dfrac{5}{9}} - \sqrt{\dfrac{5}{36}}$

40. $\sqrt{\dfrac{11}{25}} + \sqrt{\dfrac{11}{16}}$

41. $2\sqrt[3]{125} - 5\sqrt[3]{8}$

42. $3\sqrt[3]{16} - 2\sqrt[3]{2}$

(8.4) *Find the product and simplify if possible.*

43. $3\sqrt{10} \cdot 2\sqrt{5}$

44. $2\sqrt[3]{4} \cdot 5\sqrt[3]{6}$

45. $\sqrt{3}(2\sqrt{6} - 3\sqrt{12})$

46. $4\sqrt{5}(2\sqrt{10} - 5\sqrt{5})$

47. $(\sqrt{3} + 2)(\sqrt{6} - 5)$

48. $(2\sqrt{5} + 1)(4\sqrt{5} - 3)$

49. $(\sqrt{x} - 2)^2$

50. $(\sqrt{y} + 4)^2$

Divide and simplify if possible. Assume that all variables represent positive numbers.

51. $\dfrac{\sqrt{27}}{\sqrt{3}}$

52. $\dfrac{\sqrt{20}}{\sqrt{5}}$

53. $\dfrac{\sqrt{160}}{\sqrt{8}}$

54. $\dfrac{\sqrt{96}}{\sqrt{3}}$

55. $\dfrac{\sqrt{30x^6}}{\sqrt{2x^3}}$

56. $\dfrac{\sqrt{54x^5y^2}}{\sqrt{3xy^2}}$

Rationalize each denominator and simplify.

57. $\dfrac{\sqrt{2}}{\sqrt{11}}$

58. $\dfrac{\sqrt{3}}{\sqrt{13}}$

59. $\sqrt{\dfrac{5}{6}}$

60. $\sqrt{\dfrac{7}{10}}$

61. $\dfrac{1}{\sqrt{5x}}$

62. $\dfrac{5}{\sqrt{3y}}$

63. $\sqrt{\dfrac{3}{x}}$

64. $\sqrt{\dfrac{6}{y}}$

lc

Chapter 8 Getting Ready for the Test

MULTIPLE CHOICE *Select the correct choice.*

▶ 1. Choose the expression that simplifies to -4.

    A. $\sqrt{-16}$ **B.** $-\sqrt{16}$ **C.** $\sqrt[3]{8}$ **D.** $\sqrt[3]{-8}$

▶ 2. $7\sqrt{3} - \sqrt{3} =$

    A. 7   **B.** 6   **C.** $6\sqrt{3}$ **D.** cannot be simplified

▶ 3. $7\sqrt{3} \cdot \sqrt{2} =$

    A. 35   **B.** $7\sqrt{6}$ **C.** 42   **D.** $8\sqrt{6}$ **E.** cannot be simplified

▶ 4. $(4\sqrt{5})^2 =$

    A. 40   **B.** 80   **C.** $8\sqrt{5}$ **D.** $16\sqrt{5}$ **E.** cannot be simplified

5. Simplify: $\sqrt{18x^{16}}$

A. $9x^8$ **B.** $9x^4$ **C.** $3x^4\sqrt{2}$ **D.** $3x^8\sqrt{2}$

6. Simplify: $\sqrt[3]{x^{27}}$

A. x^3 **B.** x^9 **C.** $x^{13}\sqrt[3]{x}$ **D.** cannot be simplified

7. To rationalize the denominator of $\dfrac{\sqrt{5}}{\sqrt{2}}$, we multiply by:

A. $\dfrac{\sqrt{5}}{\sqrt{2}}$ **B.** $\dfrac{\sqrt{10}}{\sqrt{10}}$ **C.** $\dfrac{\sqrt{2}}{\sqrt{2}}$ **D.** $\dfrac{\sqrt{5}}{\sqrt{5}}$

8. Square both sides of the equation $x + 1 = \sqrt{9x - 9}$. The result is:

A. $x^2 + 2x + 1 = 9x - 9$ **B.** $x^2 + 1 = 9x - 9$ **C.** $x^2 + x + 1 = 9x - 9$ **D.** $x + 1 = 9x - 9$

9. Simplify: $36^{1/2}$

A. 18   **B.** 9   **C.** 6   **D.** none of these

10. Simplify: $36^{-1/2}$

A. -18 **B.** -9 **C.** -6 **D.** $\dfrac{1}{18}$ **E.** $\dfrac{1}{9}$ **F.** $\dfrac{1}{6}$

11. Which expression(s) simplify to $x^{2/3}$?

A. $x^{1/3} \cdot x^2$ **B.** $(x^{1/3})^2$ **C.** both A and B   **D.** none of these

Chapter 8 Test   MyMathLab®   You Tube

Simplify the following. Indicate if the expression is not a real number.

1. $\sqrt{16}$

2. $\sqrt[3]{-125}$

3. $16^{3/4}$

4. $\left(\dfrac{9}{16}\right)^{1/2}$

5. $\sqrt[4]{-81}$

6. $27^{-2/3}$

Simplify each radical expression. Assume that variables represent positive numbers only.

7. $\sqrt{54}$ **8.** $\sqrt{92}$

9. $\sqrt{3x^6}$ **10.** $\sqrt{8x^4y^7}$

11. $\sqrt{9x^9}$ **12.** $\sqrt[3]{8}$

13. $\sqrt[3]{40}$ **14.** $\sqrt{x^{10}}$

15. $\sqrt{y^7}$ **16.** $\sqrt{\dfrac{5}{16}}$

17. $\sqrt{\dfrac{y^3}{25}}$ **18.** $\sqrt[3]{\dfrac{2}{27}}$

19. $3\sqrt{8x}$

Perform each indicated operation. Assume that all variables represent positive numbers.

20. $\sqrt{13} + \sqrt{13} - 4\sqrt{13}$

21. $\sqrt{12} - 2\sqrt{75}$

22. $\sqrt{2x^2} + \sqrt[3]{54} - x\sqrt{18}$

23. $\sqrt{\dfrac{3}{4}} + \sqrt{\dfrac{3}{25}}$

24. $\sqrt{7} \cdot \sqrt{14}$

25. $\sqrt{2}(\sqrt{6} - \sqrt{5})$

26. $(\sqrt{x} + 2)(\sqrt{x} - 3)$

27. $\dfrac{\sqrt{50}}{\sqrt{10}}$

28. $\dfrac{\sqrt{40x^4}}{\sqrt{2x}}$

Rationalize the denominator.

29. $\sqrt{\dfrac{2}{3}}$ **30.** $\sqrt[3]{\dfrac{5}{9}}$

31. $\sqrt{\dfrac{5}{12x^2}}$ **32.** $\dfrac{2\sqrt{3}}{\sqrt{3} - 3}$

Solve each of the following radical equations.

33. $\sqrt{x} + 8 = 11$

34. $\sqrt{3x - 6} = \sqrt{x + 4}$

35. $\sqrt{2x - 2} = x - 5$

36. Find the length of the unknown leg of a right triangle if the other leg is 8 inches long and the hypotenuse is 12 inches long.

37. Find the distance between $(-3, 6)$ and $(-2, 8)$.

Simplify each expression using positive exponents only.

38. $16^{-3/4} \cdot 16^{-1/4}$

39. $\left(\dfrac{x^{2/3}}{y^{2/5}}\right)^5$

Chapter 8 Cumulative Review

1. Simplify each expression.

a. $\dfrac{(-12)(-3) + 3}{-7 - (-2)}$ **b.** $\dfrac{2(-3)^2 - 20}{-5 + 4}$

2. Simplify each expression.

a. $\dfrac{4(-3) - (-6)}{-8 + 4}$ **b.** $\dfrac{3 + (-3)(-2)^3}{-1 - (-4)}$

3. Solve: $2x + 3x - 5 + 7 = 10x + 3 - 6x - 4$

4. Solve: $6y - 11 + 4 + 2y = 8 + 15y - 8y$

5. Complete the table for the equation $y = 3x$.

x	y
-1	
0	
	-9

6. Complete the table for the equation $2x + y = 6$.

x	y
0	
	-2
3	

7. Find an equation of the line with y-intercept $(0, -3)$ and slope $\dfrac{1}{4}$.

8. Find an equation of a line with y-intercept $(0, 4)$ and slope -2.

9. Find an equation of the line parallel to the line $y = 5$ and passing through $(-2, -3)$.

10. Find an equation of the line perpendicular to $y = 4$ and passing through $(1, 5)$.

11. Decide whether the equation describes a function.

a. $y = x$

b. $y = 2x + 1$

c. $y = 5$

d. $x = -1$

12. Decide whether the equation describes a function.

a. $2x + 3 = y$

b. $x + 4 = 0$

c. $\dfrac{1}{2}y = 2x$

d. $y = 0$

13. Determine whether $(12, 6)$ is a solution of the given system.

$$\begin{cases} 2x - 3y = 6 \\ x = 2y \end{cases}$$

14. Determine whether the following ordered pairs are solutions of the given system.

$$\begin{cases} 2x + y = 4 \\ x + y = 2 \end{cases}$$

a. $(1, 1)$ **b.** $(2, 0)$

15. Solve the system.

$$\begin{cases} 2x + y = 10 \\ x = y + 2 \end{cases}$$

16. Solve the system.

$$\begin{cases} 3y = x + 10 \\ 2x + 5y = 24 \end{cases}$$

17. Solve the system.

$$\begin{cases} -x - \dfrac{y}{2} = \dfrac{5}{2} \\ \dfrac{x}{6} - \dfrac{y}{2} = 0 \end{cases}$$

18. Solve the system.

$$\begin{cases} \dfrac{x}{2} + y = \dfrac{5}{6} \\ 2x - y = \dfrac{5}{6} \end{cases}$$

19. A chemistry teaching assistant needs 10 liters of a 20% saline solution (salt water) for his 2 p.m. laboratory class. Unfortunately, the only mixtures on hand are a 5% saline solution and a 25% saline solution. How much of each solution should he mix to produce the 20% solution?

20. Two streetcars are 11 miles apart and traveling toward each other on parallel tracks. They meet in 12 minutes. Find the speed of each streetcar if one travels 15 miles per hour faster than the other.

21. Graph the solution of the system.

$$\begin{cases} 3x \geq y \\ x + 2y \leq 8 \end{cases}$$

22. Graph the solution of the system.

$$\begin{cases} x + y \leq 1 \\ 2x - y \geq 2 \end{cases}$$

23. Combine like terms to simplify $-9x^2 + 3xy - 5y^2 + 7yx$.

24. Combine like terms to simplify.

$$4a^2 + 3a - 2a^2 + 7a - 5$$

25. Factor: $x^2 + 7xy + 6y^2$

26. Factor: $3x^2 + 15x + 18$

27. Simplify: $\dfrac{4 - x^2}{3x^2 - 5x - 2}$

28. Simplify: $\dfrac{2x^2 + 7x + 3}{x^2 - 9}$

29. Divide: $\dfrac{3x^3 y^7}{40} \div \dfrac{4x^3}{y^2}$

30. Divide: $\dfrac{12x^2 y^3}{5} \div \dfrac{3y^3}{x}$

31. Subtract: $\dfrac{2y}{2y - 7} - \dfrac{7}{2y - 7}$

32. Subtract: $\dfrac{-4x^2}{x + 1} - \dfrac{4x}{x + 1}$

33. Add: $\dfrac{2x}{x^2 + 2x + 1} + \dfrac{x}{x^2 - 1}$

34. Add: $\dfrac{3x}{x^2 + 5x + 6} + \dfrac{1}{x^2 + 2x - 3}$

35. Solve: $\dfrac{x}{2} + \dfrac{8}{3} = \dfrac{1}{6}$

36. Solve: $\dfrac{1}{21} + \dfrac{x}{7} = \dfrac{5}{3}$

37. If the following two triangles are similar, find the unknown length x.

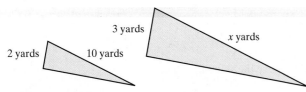

38. If the following two triangles are similar, find the unknown length.

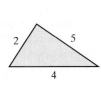 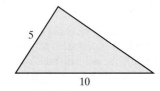

39. Simplify: $\dfrac{\dfrac{1}{z} - \dfrac{1}{2}}{\dfrac{1}{3} - \dfrac{z}{6}}$

40. Simplify: $\dfrac{x + 3}{\dfrac{1}{x} + \dfrac{1}{3}}$

41. Simplify.
   a. $\sqrt{54}$ **b.** $\sqrt{12}$
   c. $\sqrt{200}$ **d.** $\sqrt{35}$

42. Simplify.
   a. $\sqrt{40}$ **b.** $\sqrt{500}$
   c. $\sqrt{63}$ **d.** $\sqrt{169}$

43. Multiply. Then simplify if possible.
   a. $(\sqrt{5} - 7)(\sqrt{5} + 7)$
   b. $(\sqrt{7x} + 2)^2$

44. Multiply. Then simplify if possible.
   a. $(\sqrt{6} + 2)^2$
   b. $(\sqrt{x} + 5)(\sqrt{x} - 5)$

45. Solve: $\sqrt{x} + 6 = 4$

46. Solve: $\sqrt{x + 4} = \sqrt{3x - 1}$

47. Find the length of the hypotenuse of a right triangle whose legs are 6 inches and 8 inches long.

48. Find the length of the unknown leg of a right triangle whose other leg is 9 and whose hypotenuse is 13.

49. Simplify each expression.
   a. $4^{3/2}$ **b.** $27^{2/3}$ **c.** $-16^{3/4}$

50. Simplify each expression.
   a. $9^{5/2}$ **b.** $-81^{1/4}$ **c.** $64^{2/3}$

Appendix E

Tables

E.1 Table of Squares and Square Roots

n	n^2	$\sqrt{n}$	n	n^2	$\sqrt{n}$
1	1	1.000	51	2601	7.141
2	4	1.414	52	2704	7.211
3	9	1.732	53	2809	7.280
4	16	2.000	54	2916	7.348
5	25	2.236	55	3025	7.416
6	36	2.449	56	3136	7.483
7	49	2.646	57	3249	7.550
8	64	2.828	58	3364	7.616
9	81	3.000	59	3481	7.681
10	100	3.162	60	3600	7.746
11	121	3.317	61	3721	7.810
12	144	3.464	62	3844	7.874
13	169	3.606	63	3969	7.937
14	196	3.742	64	4096	8.000
15	225	3.873	65	4225	8.062
16	256	4.000	66	4356	8.124
17	289	4.123	67	4489	8.185
18	324	4.243	68	4624	8.246
19	361	4.359	69	4761	8.307
20	400	4.472	70	4900	8.367
21	441	4.583	71	5041	8.426
22	484	4.690	72	5184	8.485
23	529	4.796	73	5329	8.544
24	576	4.899	74	5476	8.602
25	625	5.000	75	5625	8.660
26	676	5.099	76	5776	8.718
27	729	5.196	77	5929	8.775
28	784	5.292	78	6084	8.832
29	841	5.385	79	6241	8.888
30	900	5.477	80	6400	8.944
31	961	5.568	81	6561	9.000
32	1024	5.657	82	6724	9.055
33	1089	5.745	83	6889	9.110
34	1156	5.831	84	7056	9.165
35	1225	5.916	85	7225	9.220
36	1296	6.000	86	7396	9.274
37	1369	6.083	87	7569	9.327
38	1444	6.164	88	7744	9.381
39	1521	6.245	89	7921	9.434
40	1600	6.325	90	8100	9.487
41	1681	6.403	91	8281	9.539
42	1764	6.481	92	8464	9.592
43	1849	6.557	93	8649	9.644
44	1936	6.633	94	8836	9.695
45	2025	6.708	95	9025	9.747
46	2116	6.782	96	9216	9.798
47	2209	6.856	97	9409	9.849
48	2304	6.928	98	9604	9.899
49	2401	7.000	99	9801	9.950
50	2500	7.071	100	10,000	10.000

E.2 Table of Percent, Decimal, and Fraction Equivalents

	Percent, Decimal, and Fraction Equivalents	
Percent	*Decimal*	*Fraction*
1%	0.01	$\frac{1}{100}$
5%	0.05	$\frac{1}{20}$
10%	0.1	$\frac{1}{10}$
12.5% or $12\frac{1}{2}$%	0.125	$\frac{1}{8}$
$16.\bar{6}$% or $16\frac{2}{3}$%	$0.1\bar{6}$	$\frac{1}{6}$
20%	0.2	$\frac{1}{5}$
25%	0.25	$\frac{1}{4}$
30%	0.3	$\frac{3}{10}$
$33.\bar{3}$% or $33\frac{1}{3}$%	$0.\bar{3}$	$\frac{1}{3}$
37.5% or $37\frac{1}{2}$%	0.375	$\frac{3}{8}$
40%	0.4	$\frac{2}{5}$
50%	0.5	$\frac{1}{2}$
60%	0.6	$\frac{3}{5}$
62.5% or $62\frac{1}{2}$%	0.625	$\frac{5}{8}$
$66.\bar{6}$% or $66\frac{2}{3}$%	$0.\bar{6}$	$\frac{2}{3}$
70%	0.7	$\frac{7}{10}$
75%	0.75	$\frac{3}{4}$
80%	0.8	$\frac{4}{5}$
$83.\bar{3}$% or $83\frac{1}{3}$%	$0.8\bar{3}$	$\frac{5}{6}$
87.5% or $87\frac{1}{2}$%	0.875	$\frac{7}{8}$
90%	0.9	$\frac{9}{10}$
100%	1.0	1
110%	1.1	$1\frac{1}{10}$
125%	1.25	$1\frac{1}{4}$
$133.\bar{3}$% or $133\frac{1}{3}$%	$1.\bar{3}$	$1\frac{1}{3}$
150%	1.5	$1\frac{1}{2}$
$166.\bar{6}$% or $166\frac{2}{3}$%	$1.\bar{6}$	$1\frac{2}{3}$
175%	1.75	$1\frac{3}{4}$
200%	2.0	2

Contents of Student Resources

Study Skills Builders

Attitude and Study Tips:
1. Have You Decided to Complete This Course Successfully?
2. Tips for Studying for an Exam
3. What to Do the Day of an Exam
4. Are You Satisfied with Your Performance on a Particular Quiz or Exam?
5. How Are You Doing?
6. Are You Preparing for Your Final Exam?

Organizing Your Work:
7. Learning New Terms
8. Are You Organized?
9. Organizing a Notebook
10. How Are Your Homework Assignments Going?

MyMathLab and MathXL:
11. Tips for Turning In Your Homework on Time
12. Tips for Doing Your Homework Online
13. Organizing Your Work
14. Getting Help with Your Homework Assignments
15. Tips for Preparing for an Exam
16. How Well Do You Know the Resources Available to You in MyMathLab?

Additional Help Inside and Outside Your Textbook:
17. How Well Do You Know Your Textbook?
18. Are You Familiar with Your Textbook Supplements?
19. Are You Getting All the Mathematics Help That You Need?

Bigger Picture—Study Guide Outline

Practice Final Exam

Answers to Selected Exercises

Student Resources

Attitude and Study Tips

Study Skills Builder 1

Have You Decided to Complete This Course Successfully?

Ask yourself if one of your current goals is to complete this course successfully.

If it is not a goal of yours, ask yourself why. One common reason is fear of failure. Amazingly enough, fear of failure alone can be strong enough to keep many of us from doing our best in any endeavor.

Another common reason is that you simply haven't taken the time to think about or write down your goals for this course. To help accomplish this, answer the questions below.

Exercises

1. Write down your goal(s) for this course.

2. Now list steps you will take to make sure your goal(s) in Exercise 1 are accomplished.

3. Rate your commitment to this course with a number between 1 and 5. Use the diagram below to help.

High Commitment		Average Commitment		Not Commited at All
5	4	3	2	1

4. If you have rated your personal commitment level (from the exercise above) as a 1, 2, or 3, list the reasons why this is so. Then determine whether it is possible to increase your commitment level to a 4 or 5.

Good luck, and don't forget that a positive attitude will make a big difference.

Study Skills Builder 2

Tips for Studying for an Exam

To prepare for an exam, try the following study techniques:

- Start the study process days before your exam.
- Make sure that you are up-to-date on your assignments.
- If there is a topic that you are unsure of, use one of the many resources that are available to you. For example,

  See your instructor.

  View a lecture video on the topic.

  Visit a learning resource center on campus.

  Read the textbook material and examples on the topic.

- Reread your notes and carefully review the Chapter Highlights at the end of any chapter.
- Work the review exercises at the end of the chapter.
- Find a quiet place to take the Chapter Test found at the end of the chapter. Do not use any resources when taking this sample test. This way, you will have a clear indication of how prepared you are for your exam. Check your answers and use the Chapter Test Prep Videos to make sure that you correct any missed exercises.

Good luck, and keep a positive attitude.

Exercises

Let's see how you did on your last exam.

1. How many days before your last exam did you start studying for that exam?

2. Were you up-to-date on your assignments at that time or did you need to catch up on assignments?

3. List the most helpful text supplement (if you used one).

4. List the most helpful campus supplement (if you used one).

5. List your process for preparing for a mathematics test.

6. Was this process helpful? In other words, were you satisfied with your performance on your exam?

7. If not, what changes can you make in your process that will make it more helpful to you?

Study Skills Builder 3

What to Do the Day of an Exam

Your first exam may be soon. On the day of an exam, don't forget to try the following:

- Allow yourself plenty of time to arrive.
- Read the directions on the test carefully.
- Read each problem carefully as you take your test. Make sure that you answer the question asked.
- Watch your time and pace yourself so that you may attempt each problem on your test.
- Check your work and answers.
- *Do not turn your test in early.* If you have extra time, spend it double-checking your work.

Good luck!

Exercises

Answer the following questions based on your most recent mathematics exam, whenever that was.

1. How soon before class did you arrive?
2. Did you read the directions on the test carefully?
3. Did you make sure you answered the question asked for each problem on the exam?
4. Were you able to attempt each problem on your exam?
5. If your answer to Exercise 4 is no, list reasons why.
6. Did you have extra time on your exam?
7. If your answer to Exercise 6 is yes, describe how you spent that extra time.

Study Skills Builder 4

Are You Satisfied with Your Performance on a Particular Quiz or Exam?

If not, don't forget to analyze your quiz or exam and look for common errors. Were most of your errors a result of:

- *Carelessness?* Did you turn in your quiz or exam before the allotted time expired? If so, resolve to use any extra time to check your work.
- *Running out of time?* Answer the questions you are sure of first. Then attempt the questions you are unsure of, and delay checking your work until all questions have been answered.
- *Not understanding a concept?* If so, review that concept and correct your work so that you make sure you understand it before the next quiz or the final exam.
- *Test conditions?* When studying for a quiz or exam, make sure you place yourself in conditions similar to test conditions. For example, before your next quiz or exam, take a sample test without the aid of your notes or text.

(For a sample test, see your instructor or use the Chapter Test at the end of each chapter.)

Exercises

1. Have you corrected all your previous quizzes and exams?
2. List any errors you have found common to two or more of your graded papers.
3. Is one of your common errors not understanding a concept? If so, are you making sure you understand all the concepts for the next quiz or exam?
4. Is one of your common errors making careless mistakes? If so, are you now taking all the time allotted to check over your work so that you can minimize the number of careless mistakes?
5. Are you satisfied with your grades thus far on quizzes and tests?
6. If your answer to Exercise 5 is no, are there any more suggestions you can make to your instructor or yourself to help? If so, list them here and share these with your instructor.

Study Skills Builder 5

How Are You Doing?

If you haven't done so yet, take a few moments and think about how you are doing in this course. Are you working toward your goal of successfully completing this course? Is your performance on homework, quizzes, and tests satisfactory? If not, you might want to see your instructor to see if he/she has any suggestions on how you can improve your performance. Reread Section 1.1 for ideas on places to get help with your mathematics course.

Exercises

Answer the following.

1. List any textbook supplements you are using to help you through this course.
2. List any campus resources you are using to help you through this course.
3. Write a short paragraph describing how you are doing in your mathematics course.
4. If improvement is needed, list ways that you can work toward improving your situation as described in Exercise 3.

Study Skills Builder 6

Are You Preparing for Your Final Exam?

To prepare for your final exam, try the following study techniques:

- Review the material that you will be responsible for on your exam. This includes material from your textbook, your notebook, and any handouts from your instructor.
- Review any formulas that you may need to memorize.
- Check to see if your instructor or mathematics department will be conducting a final exam review.
- Check with your instructor to see whether final exams from previous semesters/quarters are available to students for review.

- Use your previously taken exams as a practice final exam. To do so, rewrite the test questions in mixed order on blank sheets of paper. This will help you prepare for exam conditions.
- If you are unsure of a few concepts, see your instructor or visit a learning lab for assistance. Also, view the video segment of any troublesome sections.
- If you need further exercises to work, try the Cumulative Reviews at the end of the chapters.

Once again, good luck! I hope you are enjoying this textbook and your mathematics course.

Organizing Your Work

Study Skills Builder 7

Learning New Terms

Many of the terms used in this text may be new to you. It will be helpful to make a list of new mathematical terms and symbols as you encounter them and to review them frequently. Placing these new terms (including page references) on 3×5 index cards might help you later when you're preparing for a quiz.

Exercises

1. Name one way you might place a word and its definition on a 3×5 card.
2. How do new terms stand out in this text so that they can be found?

44. $(4a - 7b)^2$ **45.** $(5p - 7q)^2$ **46.** $(7x + 3y)(x + 3y)$ **47.** $(5 - 2y)(25 + 10y + 4y^2)$ **48.** $(4x + 3)(16x^2 - 12x + 9)$
49. $-(x - 5)(x + 6)$ **50.** $-(x - 2)(x - 4)$ **51.** $(7 - x)(2 + x)$ **52.** $(3 + x)(1 - x)$ **53.** $3x^2y(x + 6)(x - 4)$ **54.** $2xy(x + 5y)(x - y)$
55. $5xy^2(x - 7y)(x - y)$ **56.** $4x^2y(x - 5)(x + 3)$ **57.** $3xy(4x^2 + 81)$ **58.** $2xy^2(3x^2 + 4)$ **59.** $(2 + x)(2 - x)$ **60.** $(3 + y)(3 - y)$
61. $(s + 4)(3r - 1)$ **62.** $(x - 2)(x^2 + 3)$ **63.** $(4x - 3)(x - 2y)$ **64.** $(2x - y)(2x + 7z)$ **65.** $6(x + 2y)(x + y)$
66. $2(x + 4y)(6x - y)$ **67.** $(x + 3)(y + 2)(y - 2)$ **68.** $(y + 3)(y - 3)(x^2 + 3)$ **69.** $(5 + x)(x + y)$ **70.** $(x - y)(7 + y)$
71. $(7t - 1)(2t - 1)$ **72.** prime   **73.** $(3x + 5)(x - 1)$ **74.** $(7x - 2)(x + 3)$ **75.** $(x + 12y)(x - 3y)$ **76.** $(3x - 2y)(x + 4y)$
77. $(1 - 10ab)(1 + 2ab)$ **78.** $(1 + 5ab)(1 - 12ab)$ **79.** $(3 + x)(3 - x)(1 + x)(1 - x)$ **80.** $(3 + x)(3 - x)(2 + x)(2 - x)$
81. $(x + 4)(x - 4)(x^2 + 2)$ **82.** $(x + 5)(x - 5)(x^2 + 3)$ **83.** $(x - 15)(x - 8)$ **84.** $(y + 16)(y + 6)$ **85.** $2x(3x - 2)(x - 4)$
86. $2y(3y + 5)(y - 3)$ **87.** $(3x - 5y)(9x^2 + 15xy + 25y^2)$ **88.** $(6y - z)(36y^2 + 6yz + z^2)$ **89.** $(xy + 2z)(x^2y^2 - 2xyz + 4z^2)$
90. $(3ab + 2)(9a^2b^2 - 6ab + 4)$ **91.** $2xy(1 + 6x)(1 - 6x)$ **92.** $2x(x + 3)(x - 3)$ **93.** $(x + 2)(x - 2)(x + 6)$
94. $(x - 2)(x + 6)(x - 6)$ **95.** $2a^2(3a + 5)$ **96.** $2n(2n - 3)$ **97.** $(a^2 + 2)(a + 2)$ **98.** $(a - b)(1 + x)$ **99.** $(x + 2)(x - 2)(x + 7)$
100. $(a + 3)(a - 3)(a + 5)$ **101.** $(x - y + z)(x - y - z)$ **102.** $(x + 2y + 3)(x + 2y - 3)$ **103.** $(9 + 5x + 1)(9 - 5x - 1)$
104. $(b + 4a + c)(b - 4a - c)$ **105.** answers may vary   **106.** yes; $9(x^2 + 9y^2)$ **107.** a, c   **108.** b, c

Section 6.6

Practice Exercises

1. $-4, 5$ **2.** $-\dfrac{3}{4}, 12$ **3.** $0, \dfrac{6}{7}$ **4.** $-4, 12$ **5.** $\dfrac{4}{3}$ **6.** $-3, \dfrac{2}{3}$ **7.** $-6, 4$ **8.** $-3, 0, 3$ **9.** $\dfrac{2}{3}, \dfrac{3}{2}, 5$ **10.** $-3, 0, 2$
11. The x-intercepts are $(2, 0)$ and $(4, 0)$.

Calculator Explorations 6.6

1. $-0.9, 2.2$ **3.** no real solution   **5.** $-1.8, 2.8$

Vocabulary, Readiness & Video Check 6.6

1. quadratic   **3.** $3, -5$ **5.** One side of the equation must be a factored polynomial and the other side must be zero.   **7.** To find the x-intercepts
of any graph in two variables, we let $y = 0$. Doing this with our quadratic equation gives us an equation $= 0$, which we can try to solve by factoring.

Exercise Set 6.6

1. $6, 7$ **3.** $2, -1$ **5.** $-9, -17$ **7.** $0, -6$ **9.** $0, 8$ **11.** $-\dfrac{3}{2}, \dfrac{5}{4}$ **13.** $\dfrac{7}{2}, -\dfrac{2}{7}$ **15.** $\dfrac{1}{2}, -\dfrac{1}{3}$ **17.** $-0.2, -1.5$ **19.** $9, 4$ **21.** $-4, 2$

23. $0, 7$ **25.** $8, -4$ **27.** $4, -4$ **29.** $-3, 12$ **31.** $\dfrac{7}{3}, -2$ **33.** $-5, 5$ **35.** $-2, \dfrac{1}{6}$ **37.** $0, 4, 8$ **39.** $\dfrac{3}{4}$ **41.** $-\dfrac{1}{2}, 0, \dfrac{1}{2}$ **43.** $-\dfrac{3}{8}, 0, \dfrac{1}{2}$

45. $-3, 2$ **47.** $-20, 0$ **49.** $\dfrac{17}{2}$ **51.** $-\dfrac{1}{2}, \dfrac{1}{2}$ **53.** $-\dfrac{3}{2}, -\dfrac{1}{2}, 3$ **55.** $-5, 3$ **57.** $-\dfrac{5}{6}, \dfrac{6}{5}$ **59.** $2, -\dfrac{4}{5}$ **61.** $-\dfrac{4}{3}, 5$ **63.** $-4, 3$

65. $\dfrac{8}{3}, -9, 0$ **67.** -7 **69.** $0, \dfrac{3}{2}$ **71.** $0, 1, -1$ **73.** $-6, \dfrac{4}{3}$ **75.** $\dfrac{6}{7}, 1$ **77.** $\left(-\dfrac{4}{3}, 0\right), (1, 0)$ **79.** $(-2, 0), (5, 0)$ **81.** $(-6, 0), \left(\dfrac{1}{2}, 0\right)$

83. E   **85.** B   **87.** C   **89.** $\dfrac{47}{45}$ **91.** $\dfrac{17}{60}$ **93.** $\dfrac{15}{8}$ **95.** $\dfrac{7}{10}$ **97.** didn't write equation in standard form; should be $x = 4$ or $x = -2$

99. answers may vary; for example $(x - 6)(x + 1) = 0$ **101.** answers may vary; for example, $x^2 - 12x + 35 = 0$ **103. a.** $300; 304; 276; 216;$

$124; 0; -156$ **b.** 5 sec   **c.** 304 ft   **d.**
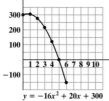
$y = -16x^2 + 20x + 300$

105. $0, \dfrac{1}{2}$ **107.** $0, -15$

Chapter 6 Vocabulary Check

1. quadratic equation　**2.** Factoring　**3.** greatest common factor　**4.** perfect square trinomial　**5.** difference of two squares　**6.** difference of two cubes　**7.** sum of two cubes　**8.** 0　**9.** hypotenuse　**10.** leg　**11.** hypotenuse

Chapter 6 Review

1. $2x - 5$　**3.** $4x(5x + 3)$　**5.** $(2x + 3)(3x - 5)$　**7.** $(x - 1)(3x + 2)$　**9.** $(2a + b)(5a + 7b)$　**11.** $(x + 4)(x + 2)$　**13.** prime
15. $(x + 6y)(x - 2y)$　**17.** $2(3 - x)(12 + x)$　**19.** $10a(a - 1)(a - 10)$　**21.** $-48, 2$　**23.** $(2x + 1)(x + 6)$　**25.** $(3x + 4y)(2x - y)$
27. $5y(2y - 3)(y + 4)$　**29.** $2(3x - 5)^2$　**31.** $(2x + 3)(2x - 3)$　**33.** prime　**35.** $(2x + 3)(4x^2 - 6x + 9)$　**37.** $2(3 - xy)(9 + 3xy + x^2y^2)$
39. $(4x^2 + 1)(2x + 1)(2x - 1)$　**41.** $-6, 2$　**43.** $-\dfrac{1}{5}, -3$　**45.** $-4, 6$　**47.** $2, 8$　**49.** $-\dfrac{2}{7}, \dfrac{3}{8}$　**51.** $-\dfrac{2}{5}$　**53.** 3　**55.** $0, -\dfrac{7}{4}, 3$
57. c　**59.** 9 units　**61.** width: 20 in.; length: 25 in.　**63.** 19 and 20　**65. a.** 17.5 sec and 10 sec; The rocket reaches a height of 2800 ft on its way up and on its way back down.　**b.** 27.5 sec　**67.** $7(x - 9)$　**69.** $\left(m + \dfrac{2}{5}\right)\left(m - \dfrac{2}{5}\right)$　**71.** $(y + 2)(x - 1)$　**73.** $3x(x - 9)(x - 1)$
75. $2(x + 3)(x - 3)$　**77.** $5(x + 2)^2$　**79.** $2xy(2x - 3y)$　**81.** $3(8x^2 - x - 6)$　**83.** $(x + 3)(x + 2)(x - 2)$
85. $5x^2 - 9x - 2; (5x + 1)(x - 2)$　**87.** $-\dfrac{7}{2}, 4$　**89.** $0, -7, -4$　**91.** $0, 16$　**93.** length: 6 in.; width: 2 in.　**95.** $28x^2 - \pi x^2; x^2(28 - \pi)$

Chapter 6 Getting Ready for the Test

1. B　**2.** D　**3.** A　**4.** A　**5.** B　**6.** B　**7.** B　**8.** A　**9.** C

Chapter 6 Test

1. $(x + 7)(x + 4)$　**2.** $(7 - m)(7 + m)$　**3.** $(y + 11)^2$　**4.** $(a + 3)(4 - y)$　**5.** prime　**6.** $(y - 12)(y + 4)$　**7.** prime
8. $3x(3x + 1)(x + 4)$　**9.** $(3a - 7)(a + b)$　**10.** $(3x - 2)(x - 1)$　**11.** $(x + 12y)(x + 2y)$　**12.** $5(6 + x)(6 - x)$
13. $(6t + 5)(t - 1)$　**14.** $(y + 2)(y - 2)(x - 7)$　**15.** $x(1 + x^2)(1 + x)(1 - x)$　**16.** $-xy(y^2 + x^2)$　**17.** $(4x - 1)(16x^2 + 4x + 1)$
18. $8(y - 2)(y^2 + 2y + 4)$　**19.** $-9, 3$　**20.** $-7, 2$　**21.** $-7, 1$　**22.** $0, \dfrac{3}{2}, -\dfrac{4}{3}$　**23.** $0, 3, -3$　**24.** $-3, 5$　**25.** $0, \dfrac{5}{2}$　**26.** 17 ft
27. 8 and 9　**28.** 7 sec　**29.** hypotenuse: 25 cm; legs: 15 cm, 20 cm

Chapter 6 Cumulative Review

1. a. $9 \leq 11$　**b.** $8 > 1$　**c.** $3 \neq 4$; Sec. 1.2, Ex. 3　**3. a.** $\dfrac{6}{7}$　**b.** $\dfrac{11}{27}$　**c.** $\dfrac{22}{5}$; Sec. 1.3, Ex. 2　**5.** $\dfrac{14}{3}$; Sec. 1.4, Ex. 5　**7. a.** -12
b. -1; Sec. 1.5, Ex. 7　**9. a.** -32　**b.** -14　**c.** 90; Sec. 1.7, Ex. 1　**11. a.** $4x$　**b.** $11y^2$　**c.** $8x^2 - x$;　**d.** $5n^2$; Sec. 2.1, Ex. 3
13. -4; Sec. 2.2, Ex. 7　**15.** -11; Sec. 2.3, Ex. 2　**17.** $\dfrac{16}{3}$; Sec. 2.4, Ex. 2　**19.** shorter: 12 in.; longer: 36 in.; Sec. 2.5, Ex. 3
21.

; Sec. 3.2, Ex. 5　**23.** $m = \dfrac{3}{4}$; y-intercept: $(0, -1)$; Sec. 3.4, Ex. 5　**25. a.** 250　**b.** 1; Sec. 5.1, Ex. 2　**27. a.** 2　**b.** 5
c. 0; Sec. 5.2, Ex. 1　**29.** $9x^2 - 6x - 1$; Sec. 5.2, Ex. 13　**31.** $6x^2 - 11x - 10$; Sec. 5.3, Ex. 5
33. $9y^2 + 6y + 1$; Sec. 5.4, Ex. 4　**35. a.** $\dfrac{1}{9}$　**b.** $\dfrac{2}{x^3}$　**c.** $\dfrac{3}{4}$　**d.** $\dfrac{1}{16}$　**e.** $\dfrac{1}{y^4}$; Sec. 5.5, Ex. 1
37. a. 3.67×10^8　**b.** 3.0×10^{-6}　**c.** 2.052×10^{10}　**d.** 8.5×10^{-4}; Sec. 5.5, Ex. 5　**39.** $x + 4$; Sec. 5.6, Ex. 4
41. a. x^3　**b.** y; Sec. 6.1, Ex. 2　**43.** $(x + 3)(x + 4)$; Sec. 6.2, Ex. 1　**45.** $(4x - 1)(2x - 5)$; Sec. 6.3, Ex. 2　**47.** $(5a + 3b)(5a - 3b)$;
Sec. 6.5, Ex. 2b　**49.** $3, -1$; Sec. 6.6, Ex. 1

CHAPTER 7 RATIONAL EXPRESSIONS

Section 7.1

Practice Exercises

1. a. $\dfrac{9}{7}$　**b.** $-\dfrac{3}{11}$　**2. a.** $x = -6$　**b.** none　**c.** $x = -2$ or $x = -4$　**d.** none　**3.** $\dfrac{x^5}{6}$　**4.** $\dfrac{x + 1}{x - 2}$　**5.** $\dfrac{x^2}{x + 9}$　**6.** $\dfrac{1}{x + 7}$
7. a. -1　**b.** 1　**8.** $-\dfrac{2x + 3}{x + 4}$ or $\dfrac{-2x - 3}{x + 4}$　**9.** $\dfrac{-(x + 3)}{6x - 11}, \dfrac{-x - 3}{6x - 11}, \dfrac{x + 3}{-(6x - 11)}, \dfrac{x + 3}{-6x + 11}, \dfrac{x + 3}{11 - 6x}$

Vocabulary, Readiness & Video Check 7.1

1. rational expression　**3.** -1　**5.** 2　**7.** $\dfrac{-a}{b}; \dfrac{a}{-b}$　**9.** Rational expressions are fractions and are therefore undefined if the denominator is zero; if a denominator contains variables, set it equal to zero and solve.　**11.** You would need to write parentheses around the numerator or denominator if it had more than one term because the negative sign needs to apply to the entire numerator or denominator.

Exercise Set 7.1

1. $\dfrac{7}{4}$　**3.** 3　**5.** $-\dfrac{8}{3}$　**7.** $-\dfrac{11}{2}$　**9.** $x = 0$　**11.** $x = -2$　**13.** $x = \dfrac{5}{2}$　**15.** none　**17.** $x = 6, x = -1$　**19.** none
21. $x = -2, x = -\dfrac{7}{3}$　**23.** $\dfrac{-(x - 10)}{x + 8}, \dfrac{-x + 10}{x + 8}, \dfrac{x - 10}{-(x + 8)}, \dfrac{x - 10}{-x - 8}$　**25.** $\dfrac{-(5y - 3)}{y - 12}, \dfrac{-5y + 3}{y - 12}, \dfrac{5y - 3}{-(y - 12)}, \dfrac{5y - 3}{-y + 12}$　**27.** 1　**29.** -1

31. $\dfrac{1}{4(x+2)}$ **33.** $\dfrac{1}{x+2}$ **35.** can't simplify **37.** -5 **39.** $\dfrac{7}{x}$ **41.** $\dfrac{1}{x-9}$ **43.** $5x+1$ **45.** $\dfrac{x^2}{x-2}$ **47.** $7x$ **49.** $\dfrac{x+5}{x-5}$

51. $\dfrac{x+2}{x+4}$ **53.** $\dfrac{x+2}{2}$ **55.** $-(x+2)$ or $-x-2$ **57.** $\dfrac{x+1}{x-1}$ **59.** $\dfrac{m-3}{m+2}$ **61.** $\dfrac{11x}{6}$ **63.** $x+y$ **65.** $\dfrac{5-y}{2}$ **67.** x^2-2x+4

69. $-x^2-x-1$ **71.** $\dfrac{2y+5}{3y+4}$ **73.** correct **75.** correct **77.** $\dfrac{3}{11}$ **79.** $\dfrac{4}{3}$ **81.** $\dfrac{117}{40}$ **83.** correct **85.** incorrect; $\dfrac{1+2}{1+3}=\dfrac{3}{4}$

87. no **89.** yes **91.** answers may vary **93.** answers may vary **95. a.** \$37.5 million **b.** $\approx$\$85.7 million **c.** $\approx$\$48.2 million

97. 400 mg **99.** $C=78.125$; medium **101.** 0.581 **103.** **105.**

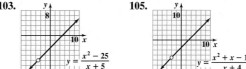

Section 7.2

Practice Exercises

1. a. $\dfrac{12a}{5b^2}$ **b.** $-\dfrac{2q}{3}$ **2.** $\dfrac{3}{x+1}$ **3.** $-\dfrac{3x-5}{2x(x+2)}$ **4.** $\dfrac{b^2}{8a^2}$ **5.** $\dfrac{3(x-5)}{4}$ **6.** $\dfrac{2}{x(x-3)}$ **7.** 1 **8. a.** $\dfrac{(y+9)^2}{16x^2}$ **b.** $\dfrac{1}{4x}$

c. $-\dfrac{7(x-2)}{x+4}$ **9.** 2 sq ft **10.** 504 sq in. **11.** 549,000 sq ft **12.** 70.0 miles per hour

Vocabulary, Readiness & Video Check 7.2

1. reciprocals **3.** $\dfrac{a\cdot d}{b\cdot c}$ or $\dfrac{ad}{bc}$ **5.** $\dfrac{6}{7}$ **7.** fractions; reciprocal **9.** The units in the unit fraction consist of $\dfrac{\text{units converting to}}{\text{original units}}$.

Exercise Set 7.2

1. $\dfrac{21}{4y}$ **3.** x^4 **5.** $-\dfrac{b^2}{6}$ **7.** $\dfrac{x^2}{10}$ **9.** $\dfrac{1}{3}$ **11.** $\dfrac{m+n}{m-n}$ **13.** $\dfrac{x+5}{x}$ **15.** $\dfrac{(x+2)(x-3)}{(x-4)(x+4)}$ **17.** $\dfrac{2x^4}{3}$ **19.** $\dfrac{12}{y^6}$ **21.** $x(x+4)$

23. $\dfrac{3(x+1)}{x^3(x-1)}$ **25.** m^2-n^2 **27.** $-\dfrac{x+2}{x-3}$ **29.** $\dfrac{x+2}{x-3}$ **31.** $\dfrac{5}{6}$ **33.** $\dfrac{3x}{8}$ **35.** $\dfrac{3}{2}$ **37.** $\dfrac{3x+4y}{2(x+2y)}$ **39.** $\dfrac{2(x+2)}{x-2}$ **41.** $-\dfrac{y(x+2)}{4}$

43. $\dfrac{(a+5)(a+3)}{(a+2)(a+1)}$ **45.** $\dfrac{5}{x}$ **47.** $\dfrac{2(n-8)}{3n-1}$ **49.** $4x^3(x-3)$ **51.** $\dfrac{(a+b)^2}{a-b}$ **53.** $\dfrac{3x+5}{x^2+4}$ **55.** $\dfrac{4}{x-2}$ **57.** $\dfrac{a-b}{6(a^2+ab+b^2)}$

59. 1440 **61.** 5 **63.** 81 **65.** 73 **67.** 56.7 **69.** 1,201,500 sq ft **71.** 270.5 miles/hour **73.** 1 **75.** $-\dfrac{10}{9}$ **77.** $-\dfrac{1}{5}$

79. **81.** true **83.** false; $\dfrac{x^2+3x}{20}$ **85.** $\dfrac{2}{9(x-5)}$ sq ft **87.** $\dfrac{x}{2}$ **89.** $\dfrac{5a(2a+b)(3a-2b)}{b^2(a-b)(a+2b)}$ **91.** answers may vary

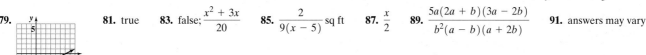

Chapter 7 Vocabulary Check

1. rational expression   **2.** complex fraction   **3.** $\dfrac{-a}{b}; \dfrac{a}{-b}$ **4.** denominator   **5.** simplifying   **6.** reciprocals   **7.** least common denominator

8. ratio   **9.** proportion   **10.** cross products   **11.** inverse variation   **12.** direct variation

Chapter 7 Review

1. $x = 2, x = -2$ **3.** $\dfrac{4}{3}$ **5.** $\dfrac{2}{x}$ **7.** $\dfrac{1}{x-5}$ **9.** $\dfrac{x(x-2)}{x+1}$ **11.** $\dfrac{x-3}{x-5}$ **13.** $\dfrac{x+a}{x-c}$ **15.** $-\dfrac{1}{x^2+4x+16}$ **17.** $\dfrac{3x^2}{y}$ **19.** $\dfrac{x-3}{x+2}$

21. $\dfrac{x+3}{x-4}$ **23.** $(x-6)(x-3)$ **25.** $\dfrac{1}{2}$ **27.** $-\dfrac{2(2x+3)}{y-2}$ **29.** $\dfrac{1}{x+2}$ **31.** $\dfrac{2x-10}{3x^2}$ **33.** $14x$ **35.** $\dfrac{10x^2y}{14x^3y}$

37. $\dfrac{x^2-3x-10}{(x+2)(x-5)(x+9)}$ **39.** $\dfrac{4y-30x^2}{5x^2y}$ **41.** $\dfrac{-2x-2}{x+3}$ **43.** $\dfrac{x-4}{3x}$ **45.** $\dfrac{x^2+2x+4}{4x}; \dfrac{x+2}{32}$ **47.** 30   **49.** no solution

51. $\dfrac{9}{7}$ **53.** $b = \dfrac{4A}{5x^2}$ **55.** $x = 6$ **57.** $x = 9$ **59.** 675 parts   **61.** 3   **63.** fast car speed: 30 mph; slow car speed: 20 mph   **65.** $17\dfrac{1}{2}$ hr

67. $x = 15$ **69.** $y = 110$ **71.** $y = \dfrac{100}{27}$ **73.** 3960 **75.** $-\dfrac{7}{18y}$ **77.** $\dfrac{3y-1}{2y-1}$ **79.** $\dfrac{1}{2x}$ **81.** $\dfrac{x-4}{x+4}$ **83.** $\dfrac{1}{x-6}$

85. $\dfrac{2}{(x+3)(x-2)}$ **87.** $\dfrac{1}{2}$ **89.** 1   **91.** $x = 6$ **93.** $\dfrac{3}{10}$ **95.** 16.2

Chapter 7 Getting Ready for the Test

1. B   **2.** C   **3.** D   **4.** D   **5.** A   **6.** D   **7.** A   **8.** B   **9.** B   **10.** A   **11.** C   **12.** A

Chapter 7 Test

1. $x = -1, x = -3$ **2. a.** \$115   **b.** \$103   **3.** $\dfrac{3}{5}$ **4.** $\dfrac{1}{x+6}$ **5.** $\dfrac{1}{x^2-3x+9}$ **6.** $\dfrac{2m(m+2)}{m-2}$ **7.** $\dfrac{a+2}{a+5}$ **8.** $-\dfrac{1}{x+y}$ **9.** 15

10. $\dfrac{y-2}{4}$ **11.** $\dfrac{19x-6}{2x+5}$ **12.** $\dfrac{3a-4}{(a-3)(a+2)}$ **13.** $\dfrac{3}{x-1}$ **14.** $\dfrac{2(x+5)}{x(y+5)}$ **15.** $\dfrac{x^2+2x+35}{(x+9)(x+2)(x-5)}$ **16.** $\dfrac{30}{11}$ **17.** -6

18. no solution   **19.** $-2, 5$ **20.** no solution   **21.** $\dfrac{xz}{2y}$ **22.** $\dfrac{5y^2-1}{y+2}$ **23.** $b - a$ **24.** 28   **25.** $\dfrac{8}{9}$ **26.** 18 bulbs   **27.** 5 or 1

28. 30 mph   **29.** $6\dfrac{2}{3}$ hr   **30.** $x = 12$

Chapter 7 Cumulative Review

1. a. $\dfrac{15}{x} = 4$ **b.** $12 - 3 = x$ **c.** $4x + 17 \neq 21$ **d.** $3x < 48$; Sec. 1.4, Ex. 9   **3.** amount at 7%: \$12,500; amount at 9%: \$7500; Sec. 2.8, Ex. 4

5. 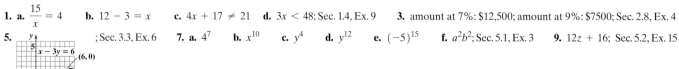 ; Sec. 3.3, Ex. 6   **7. a.** 4^7 **b.** x^{10} **c.** y^4 **d.** y^{12} **e.** $(-5)^{15}$ **f.** a^2b^2; Sec. 5.1, Ex. 3   **9.** $12z + 16$; Sec. 5.2, Ex. 15

11. $27a^3 + 27a^2b + 9ab^2 + b^3$; Sec. 5.3, Ex. 8   **13. a.** $t^2 + 4t + 4$ **b.** $p^2 - 2pq + q^2$ **c.** $4x^2 + 20x + 25$ **d.** $x^4 - 14x^2y + 49y^2$; Sec. 5.4, Ex. 5

15. a. x^3 **b.** 81   **c.** $\dfrac{q^9}{p^4}$ **d.** $\dfrac{32}{125}$; Sec. 5.5, Ex. 2   **17.** $4x^2 - 4x + 6 + \dfrac{-11}{2x+3}$; Sec. 5.6, Ex. 6   **19. a.** 4   **b.** 1   **c.** 3; Sec. 6.1, Ex. 1

21. $-3a(3a^4 - 6a + 1)$; Sec. 6.1, Ex. 5   **23.** $3(m+2)(m-10)$; Sec. 6.2, Ex. 9   **25.** $(3x+2)(x+3)$; Sec. 6.3, Ex. 1   **27.** $(x+6)^2$; Sec. 6.3, Ex. 8

29. prime polynomial; Sec. 6.5, Ex. 4b   **31.** $(x+2)(x^2-2x+4)$; Sec. 6.5, Ex. 8   **33.** $(2x+3)(x+1)(x-1)$; Ch. 6 Int. Rev., Ex. 2

35. $3(2m+n)(2m-n)$; Ch. 6 Int. Rev., Ex. 3   **37.** $-\dfrac{1}{2}, 4$; Sec. 6.6, Ex. 6   **39.** $(1,0), (4,0)$; Sec. 6.6, Ex. 11   **41.** base: 6 m; height: 10 m; Sec. 6.7, Ex. 3

43. $\dfrac{5}{x^2}$; Sec. 7.1, Ex. 3   **45.** $\dfrac{2}{x(x+1)}$; Sec. 7.2, Ex. 6   **47.** $\dfrac{x+1}{x+2y}$; Sec. 7.8, Ex. 5

CHAPTER 8 ROOTS AND RADICALS

Section 8.1

Practice Exercises

1. a. $\dfrac{2}{9}$ **b.** -5 **c.** 12   **d.** 0.7   **e.** -1 **2. a.** 0   **b.** -4 **c.** $\dfrac{1}{2}$ **3. a.** 3   **b.** 10   **c.** not a real number   **d.** -5 **4.** 4.123

5. a. x^5 **b.** y^7 **c.** $5z^3$ **d.** $7x$ **e.** $\dfrac{z^2}{6}$ **f.** $-2a^2b^4$

Calculator Explorations 8.1

1. 2.646; yes   **3.** 3.317; yes   **5.** 9.055; yes   **7.** 3.420; yes   **9.** 2.115; yes   **11.** 1.783; yes

Vocabulary, Readiness & Video Check 8.1

1. index; radicand; radical sign   **3.** false   **5.** true   **7.** true   **9.** The radical sign, $\sqrt{}$, indicates a positive square root only. A negative sign before the radical sign, $-\sqrt{}$, indicates a negative square root.   **11.** an odd-numbered index   **13.** Divide the index into each exponent in the radicand.

Exercise Set 8.1

1. 4   **3.** $\dfrac{1}{5}$ **5.** −10   **7.** not a real number   **9.** −11   **11.** $\dfrac{3}{5}$ **13.** 30   **15.** 12   **17.** $\dfrac{1}{10}$ **19.** 0.5   **21.** 5   **23.** −4   **25.** −2

27. $\dfrac{1}{2}$ **29.** −5   **31.** 2   **33.** 9   **35.** not a real number   **37.** $-\dfrac{3}{4}$ **39.** −5   **41.** 1   **43.** 2.646   **45.** 6.083   **47.** 11.662

49. $\sqrt{2} \approx 1.41$; 126.90 ft   **51.** m **53.** x^2 **55.** $3x^4$ **57.** $9x$ **59.** ab^2 **61.** $4a^3b^2$ **63.** a^2b^6 **65.** $-2xy^9$ **67.** $\dfrac{x^3}{6}$ **69.** $\dfrac{5y}{3}$

71. $25 \cdot 2$ **73.** $16 \cdot 2$ or $4 \cdot 8$ **75.** $4 \cdot 7$ **77.** $9 \cdot 3$ **79.** a, b   **81.** 7 mi   **83.** 3.1 in.   **85.** 3   **87.** 10   **89.** 4, 5   **91.** 8, 9   **93.** 6.1 sec

95. answers may vary   **97.** 1; 1.7; 2; 3   **99.** $|x|$ **101.** $|x + 2|$ **103.** $(2, 0)$; answers may vary   **105.** $(-4, 0)$; answers may vary

Section 8.2

Practice Exercises

1. a. $2\sqrt{6}$ **b.** $2\sqrt{15}$ **c.** $\sqrt{42}$ **d.** $10\sqrt{3}$ **2.** $10\sqrt{10}$ **3. a.** $\dfrac{\sqrt{5}}{7}$ **b.** $\dfrac{3}{10}$ **c.** $\dfrac{3\sqrt{2}}{5}$ **4. a.** $x^3\sqrt{x}$ **b.** $2a^2\sqrt{3}$ **c.** $\dfrac{7\sqrt{2}}{z^4}$

d. $\dfrac{y^4\sqrt{11y}}{7}$ **5. a.** $2\sqrt[3]{3}$ **b.** $\sqrt[3]{38}$ **c.** $\dfrac{\sqrt[3]{5}}{3}$ **d.** $\dfrac{\sqrt[3]{15}}{4}$ **6. a.** $2\sqrt[4]{5}$ **b.** $\dfrac{\sqrt[4]{5}}{3}$ **c.** $2\sqrt[5]{3}$

Vocabulary, Readiness & Video Check 8.2

1. $\sqrt{a} \cdot \sqrt{b}$ **3.** 16; 25; 4; 5; 20   **5.** Factor until you have a product of primes. A repeated prime factor means a perfect square—if more than one factor is repeated you can multiply all the repeated factors together to get one larger perfect square factor.   **7.** The power must be 1. Any even power is a perfect square and can be simplified; any higher odd power is the product of an even power times the variable with a power of 1.

Exercise Set 8.2

1. $2\sqrt{5}$ **3.** $5\sqrt{2}$ **5.** $\sqrt{33}$ **7.** $7\sqrt{2}$ **9.** $2\sqrt{15}$ **11.** $6\sqrt{5}$ **13.** $2\sqrt{13}$ **15.** 15   **17.** $21\sqrt{7}$ **19.** $-15\sqrt{3}$ **21.** $\dfrac{2\sqrt{2}}{5}$

23. $\dfrac{3\sqrt{3}}{11}$ **25.** $\dfrac{3}{2}$ **27.** $\dfrac{5\sqrt{5}}{3}$ **29.** $\dfrac{\sqrt{11}}{6}$ **31.** $-\dfrac{\sqrt{3}}{4}$ **33.** $x^3\sqrt{x}$ **35.** $x^6\sqrt{x}$ **37.** $6a\sqrt{a}$ **39.** $4x^2\sqrt{6}$ **41.** $\dfrac{2\sqrt{3}}{m}$ **43.** $\dfrac{3\sqrt{x}}{y^5}$

45. $\dfrac{2\sqrt{22}}{x^6}$ **47.** 16   **49.** $\dfrac{6}{11}$ **51.** $5\sqrt{7}$ **53.** $\dfrac{2\sqrt{5}}{3}$ **55.** $2m^3\sqrt{6m}$ **57.** $\dfrac{y\sqrt{23y}}{2x^3}$ **59.** $2\sqrt[3]{3}$ **61.** $5\sqrt[3]{2}$ **63.** $\dfrac{\sqrt[3]{5}}{4}$ **65.** $\dfrac{\sqrt[3]{23}}{2}$

67. $\dfrac{\sqrt[3]{15}}{4}$ **69.** $2\sqrt[3]{10}$ **71.** $2\sqrt[4]{3}$ **73.** $\dfrac{\sqrt[4]{8}}{3}$ **75.** $2\sqrt[5]{3}$ **77.** $\dfrac{\sqrt[5]{5}}{2}$ **79.** $14x$ **81.** $2x^2 - 7x - 15$ **83.** 0   **85.** $x^3y\sqrt{y}$

87. $7x^2y^2\sqrt{2x}$ **89.** $-2x^2$ **91.** $2\sqrt[3]{10}$ **93.** answers may vary   **95.** $2\sqrt{5}$ in.   **97.** 2.25 in.   **99.** \$1700   **101.** 1.7 sq m

Section 8.3

Practice Exercises

1. a. $8\sqrt{2}$ **b.** $-7\sqrt{6}$ **c.** $4\sqrt[4]{5} + 11\sqrt[4]{7}$ **d.** $4\sqrt{13} - 5\sqrt[3]{13}$ **2. a.** $5\sqrt{5}$ **b.** $6 - 2\sqrt{10} + \sqrt{6}$ **c.** $-3\sqrt{2}$ **3.** $-7x\sqrt{x} + 3x$ **4.** $10x^2\sqrt[3]{3}$

Vocabulary, Readiness & Video Check 8.3

1. like radicals   **3. b.** $17\sqrt{2}$ **5. c.** $2\sqrt{5}$ **7.** Both like terms and like radicals are combined using the distributive property; also only like (vs. unlike) terms can be combined, as with like radicals (same index and same radical).

Exercise Set 8.3

1. $-4\sqrt{3}$ **3.** $9\sqrt{6} - 5$ **5.** $2\sqrt{11} + 11$ **7.** $\sqrt{5} + \sqrt{2}$ **9.** $-2\sqrt[3]{18}$ **11.** $7\sqrt[3]{3} - \sqrt{3}$ **13.** $-5\sqrt[3]{2} - 6$ **15.** $5\sqrt{3}$ **17.** $9\sqrt{5}$
19. $4\sqrt{6} + \sqrt{5}$ **21.** $x + \sqrt{x}$ **23.** 0   **25.** $4\sqrt{x} - x\sqrt{x}$ **27.** $7\sqrt{5}$ **29.** $\sqrt{5} + \sqrt[3]{5}$ **31.** $-5 + 8\sqrt{2}$ **33.** $8 - 6\sqrt{2}$ **35.** $14\sqrt{2}$

37. $5\sqrt{2} + 12$ **39.** $\dfrac{4\sqrt{5}}{9}$ **41.** $\dfrac{3\sqrt{3}}{8}$ **43.** $2\sqrt{5}$ **45.** $-\sqrt{35}$ **47.** $12\sqrt{2x}$ **49.** 0   **51.** $x\sqrt{3x} + 3x\sqrt{x}$ **53.** $5\sqrt[3]{3}$ **55.** $\sqrt[3]{9}$

57. $-3 + 3\sqrt[3]{2}$ **59.** $4x\sqrt{2} + 2\sqrt[3]{4} + 2x$ **61.** $4x + 4x\sqrt[3]{2}$ **63.** $10y^2\sqrt[3]{y}$ **65.** $\sqrt[3]{5}$ **67.** $x^2 + 12x + 36$ **69.** $4x^2 - 4x + 1$

71. answers may vary   **73.** $8\sqrt{5}$ in.   **75.** $\left(48 + \dfrac{9\sqrt{3}}{2}\right)$ sq ft   **77.** yes; $7\sqrt{2}$ **79.** no   **81.** yes; $3\sqrt{7}$ **83.** $\dfrac{83x\sqrt{x}}{20}$

Section 8.4

Practice Exercises

1. a. $\sqrt{77}$ **b.** $72\sqrt{30}$ **c.** $5\sqrt{2}$ **d.** 17   **e.** $5y^2\sqrt{3}$ **2.** 28   **3.** $5\sqrt[3]{4}$ **4. a.** $3 - \sqrt{15}$ **b.** $z\sqrt{2} + 14\sqrt{z}$

c. $x + \sqrt{2x} - \sqrt{7x} - \sqrt{14}$ **5. a.** −9   **b.** $3x - 10\sqrt{3x} + 25$ **6. a.** $\sqrt{3}$ **b.** $2\sqrt{2}$ **c.** $3y^2$ **7.** 5   **8. a.** $\dfrac{4\sqrt{5}}{5}$ **b.** $\dfrac{\sqrt{6}}{6}$ **c.** $\dfrac{\sqrt{42x}}{14x}$

9. a. $\dfrac{3\sqrt[3]{5}}{5}$ **b.** $\dfrac{\sqrt[3]{150}}{5}$ **10. a.** $-1 + \sqrt{5}$ **b.** $\dfrac{5 + 3\sqrt{3}}{2}$ **c.** $\dfrac{8(5 + \sqrt{x})}{25 - x}$ **11.** $\dfrac{7 - \sqrt{7}}{3}$

Vocabulary, Readiness & Video Check 8.4

1. $\sqrt{21}$ **3.** $\sqrt{\dfrac{15}{3}}$ or $\sqrt{5}$ **5.** $2 - \sqrt{3}$ **7.** The square root of a positive number times the square root of the same positive number (or the square root of a positive number squared) is that positive number.   **9.** To write an equivalent expression without a radical in the denominator.

Exercise Set 8.4

1. 4 **3.** $5\sqrt{2}$ **5.** 6 **7.** $2x$ **9.** 20 **11.** $36x$ **13.** $3x^3\sqrt{2}$ **15.** $4xy\sqrt{y}$ **17.** $\sqrt{30} + \sqrt{42}$ **19.** $2\sqrt{5} + 5\sqrt{2}$
21. $y\sqrt{7} - 14\sqrt{y}$ **23.** -33 **25.** $\sqrt{6} - \sqrt{15} + \sqrt{10} - 5$ **27.** $16 - 11\sqrt{11}$ **29.** $x - 36$ **31.** $x - 14\sqrt{x} + 49$

33. $6y + 2\sqrt{6y} + 1$ **35.** 4 **37.** $\sqrt{7}$ **39.** $3\sqrt{2}$ **41.** $5y^2$ **43.** $5\sqrt{3}$ **45.** $2y\sqrt{6}$ **47.** $2xy\sqrt{3y}$ **49.** $\dfrac{\sqrt{15}}{5}$ **51.** $\dfrac{7\sqrt{2}}{2}$

53. $\dfrac{\sqrt{6y}}{6y}$ **55.** $\dfrac{\sqrt{3x}}{x}$ **57.** $\dfrac{\sqrt{2}}{4}$ **59.** $\dfrac{\sqrt{30}}{15}$ **61.** $\dfrac{8y\sqrt{5}}{5}$ **63.** $\dfrac{\sqrt{3xy}}{6x}$ **65.** $3\sqrt{2} - 3$ **67.** $\sqrt{30} + 5 + \sqrt{6} + \sqrt{5}$

69. $\dfrac{3\sqrt{x} + 12}{x - 16}$ **71.** $\dfrac{\sqrt{15}}{10}$ **73.** $-8 - 4\sqrt{5}$ **75.** $\dfrac{3\sqrt{2x}}{2}$ **77.** $\dfrac{10 - 5\sqrt{x}}{4 - x}$ **79.** $3 + \sqrt{3}$ **81.** $3 - 2\sqrt{5}$ **83.** $3\sqrt{3} + 1$

85. $2\sqrt[3]{6}$ **87.** $12\sqrt[3]{10}$ **89.** $5\sqrt[3]{3}$ **91.** 3 **93.** $2\sqrt[3]{3}$ **95.** $\dfrac{\sqrt[3]{10}}{2}$ **97.** $3\sqrt[3]{4}$ **99.** $\dfrac{\sqrt[3]{3}}{3}$ **101.** $\dfrac{\sqrt[3]{6}}{3}$ **103.** 44 **105.** 2

107. 3 **109.** $130\sqrt{3}$ sq m **111.** $\dfrac{\sqrt{A\pi}}{\pi}$ **113.** true **115.** false **117.** false **119.** answers may vary **121.** answers may vary

123. $\dfrac{2}{\sqrt{6} - \sqrt{2} - \sqrt{3} + 1}$

Integrated Review

1. 6 **2.** $4\sqrt{3}$ **3.** x^2 **4.** $y^3\sqrt{y}$ **5.** $4x$ **6.** $3x^5\sqrt{2x}$ **7.** 2 **8.** 3 **9.** -3 **10.** not a real number **11.** $\dfrac{\sqrt{11}}{3}$ **12.** $\dfrac{\sqrt[3]{7}}{4}$

13. -4 **14.** -5 **15.** $\dfrac{3}{7}$ **16.** $\dfrac{1}{8}$ **17.** a^4b **18.** x^5y^{10} **19.** $5m^3$ **20.** $3n^8$ **21.** $6\sqrt{7}$ **22.** $3\sqrt{2}$ **23.** cannot be simplified

24. $\sqrt{x} + 3x$ **25.** $\sqrt{30}$ **26.** 3 **27.** 28 **28.** 45 **29.** $\sqrt{33} + \sqrt{3}$ **30.** $3\sqrt{2} - 2\sqrt{6}$ **31.** $4y$ **32.** $3x^2\sqrt{5}$ **33.** $x - 3\sqrt{x} - 10$

34. $11 + 6\sqrt{2}$ **35.** 2 **36.** $\sqrt{3}$ **37.** $2x^2\sqrt{3}$ **38.** $ab^2\sqrt{15a}$ **39.** $\dfrac{\sqrt{6}}{6}$ **40.** $\dfrac{x\sqrt{5}}{10}$ **41.** $\dfrac{4\sqrt{6} - 4}{5}$ **42.** $\dfrac{\sqrt{2x} + 5\sqrt{2} + \sqrt{x} + 5}{x - 25}$

43. 11 cm

Chapter 8 Vocabulary Check

1. like radicals   **2.** index; radicand; radical   **3.** conjugate   **4.** principal square root   **5.** rationalizing the denominator   **6.** hypotenuse

Chapter 8 Review

1. 9   **3.** 3   **5.** $-\dfrac{3}{8}$ **7.** $\dfrac{2}{3}$ **9.** c   **11.** x^6 **13.** $3x^3$ **15.** $\dfrac{4}{y^5}$ **17.** $3\sqrt{6}$ **19.** $5x\sqrt{6x}$ **21.** $3\sqrt[3]{2}$ **23.** $2\sqrt[4]{3}$ **25.** $\dfrac{3\sqrt{2}}{5}$

27. $\dfrac{3y\sqrt{5}}{2x^2}$ **29.** $\dfrac{\sqrt[4]{9}}{2}$ **31.** $\dfrac{\sqrt[3]{3}}{2}$ **33.** $2\sqrt[3]{3}-\sqrt[3]{2}$ **35.** $6\sqrt{6}-2\sqrt[3]{6}$ **37.** $5\sqrt{7x}+2\sqrt[3]{7}$ **39.** $\dfrac{\sqrt{5}}{6}$ **41.** 0   **43.** $30\sqrt{2}$

45. $6\sqrt{2}-18$ **47.** $3\sqrt{2}-5\sqrt{3}+2\sqrt{6}-10$ **49.** $x-4\sqrt{x}+4$ **51.** 3   **53.** $2\sqrt{5}$ **55.** $x\sqrt{15x}$ **57.** $\dfrac{\sqrt{22}}{11}$ **59.** $\dfrac{\sqrt{30}}{6}$

61. $\dfrac{\sqrt{5x}}{5x}$ **63.** $\dfrac{\sqrt{3x}}{x}$ **65.** $3\sqrt{5}+6$ **67.** $\dfrac{\sqrt{6}+\sqrt{2}+\sqrt{3}+1}{2}$ **69.** $\dfrac{10\sqrt{x}-50}{x-25}$ **71.** $\dfrac{\sqrt[3]{21}}{3}$ **73.** $\dfrac{\sqrt[3]{12}}{2}$ **75.** 18   **77.** 25

79. 12   **81.** 1   **83.** $3\sqrt{13}$; 10.82   **85.** $4\sqrt{34}$ ft; 23.32 ft   **87.** $\sqrt{130}$ **89.** 2.4 in.   **91.** $a^{5/2}$ **93.** $x^{5/2}$ **95.** 4   **97.** -2

99. -512 **101.** $\dfrac{8}{27}$ **103.** 32   **105.** $\dfrac{1}{3^{2/3}}$ **107.** $\dfrac{1}{x^2}$ **109.** 12   **111.** $4x^8$ **113.** $3x^3\sqrt{2x}$ **115.** $\dfrac{1}{5}$ **117.** $\dfrac{y^2}{9}$ **119.** $7\sqrt{3}$

121. $-\dfrac{\sqrt{3}}{4}$ **123.** $7\sqrt{2}$ **125.** $\sqrt{10}-\sqrt{2}+4\sqrt{5}-4$ **127.** $2\sqrt{6}$ **129.** $\dfrac{\sqrt{14}}{7}$ **131.** $\dfrac{3\sqrt{x}+18}{x-36}$ **133.** 1   **135.** 14

137. $\sqrt{58}$; 7.62   **139.** 32 ft

Chapter 8 Getting Ready for the Test

1. B   **2.** C   **3.** B   **4.** B   **5.** D   **6.** B   **7.** C   **8.** A   **9.** C   **10.** F   **11.** B

Chapter 8 Test

1. 4   **2.** -5 **3.** 8   **4.** $\dfrac{3}{4}$ **5.** not a real number   **6.** $\dfrac{1}{9}$ **7.** $3\sqrt{6}$ **8.** $2\sqrt{23}$ **9.** $x^3\sqrt{3}$ **10.** $2x^2y^3\sqrt{2y}$ **11.** $3x^4\sqrt{x}$

12. 2   **13.** $2\sqrt[3]{5}$ **14.** x^5 **15.** $y^3\sqrt{y}$ **16.** $\dfrac{\sqrt{5}}{4}$ **17.** $\dfrac{y\sqrt{y}}{5}$ **18.** $\dfrac{\sqrt[3]{2}}{3}$ **19.** $6\sqrt{2x}$ **20.** $-2\sqrt{13}$ **21.** $-8\sqrt{3}$ **22.** $3\sqrt[3]{2}-2x\sqrt{2}$

23. $\dfrac{7\sqrt{3}}{10}$ **24.** $7\sqrt{2}$ **25.** $2\sqrt{3}-\sqrt{10}$ **26.** $x-\sqrt{x}-6$ **27.** $\sqrt{5}$ **28.** $2x\sqrt{5x}$ **29.** $\dfrac{\sqrt{6}}{3}$ **30.** $\dfrac{\sqrt[3]{15}}{3}$ **31.** $\dfrac{\sqrt{15}}{6x}$

32. $-1-\sqrt{3}$ **33.** 9   **34.** 5   **35.** 9   **36.** $4\sqrt{5}$ in.   **37.** $\sqrt{5}$ **38.** $\dfrac{1}{16}$ **39.** $\dfrac{x^{10/3}}{y^2}$

Chapter 8 Cumulative Review

1. a. $-\dfrac{39}{5}$ **b.** 2; Sec. 1.7, Ex. 9   **3.** -3; Sec. 2.2, Ex. 5

5.

x	y
-1	-3
0	0
-3	-9; Sec. 3.1, Ex. 7

7. $y=\dfrac{1}{4}x-3$; Sec. 3.5, Ex. 3   **9.** $y=-3$; Sec. 3.5, Ex. 7   **11. a.** function   **b.** function   **c.** function   **d.** not a function; Sec. 3.6, Ex. 5   **13.** yes; Sec. 4.1, Ex. 1   **15.** $(4,2)$; Sec. 4.2, Ex. 1   **17.** $\left(-\dfrac{15}{7},-\dfrac{5}{7}\right)$; Sec. 4.3, Ex. 6   **19.** 5% saline solution: 2.5 L; 25% saline solution: 7.5 L; Sec. 4.4, Ex. 4

21. 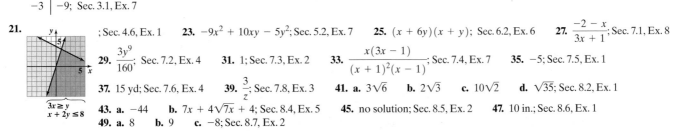 ; Sec. 4.6, Ex. 1   **23.** $-9x^2+10xy-5y^2$; Sec. 5.2, Ex. 7   **25.** $(x+6y)(x+y)$; Sec. 6.2, Ex. 6   **27.** $\dfrac{-2-x}{3x+1}$; Sec. 7.1, Ex. 8

29. $\dfrac{3y^9}{160}$; Sec. 7.2, Ex. 4   **31.** 1; Sec. 7.3, Ex. 2   **33.** $\dfrac{x(3x-1)}{(x+1)^2(x-1)}$; Sec. 7.4, Ex. 7   **35.** -5; Sec. 7.5, Ex. 1

37. 15 yd; Sec. 7.6, Ex. 4   **39.** $\dfrac{3}{z}$; Sec. 7.8, Ex. 3   **41. a.** $3\sqrt{6}$ **b.** $2\sqrt{3}$ **c.** $10\sqrt{2}$ **d.** $\sqrt{35}$; Sec. 8.2, Ex. 1

43. a. -44 **b.** $7x+4\sqrt{7x}+4$; Sec. 8.4, Ex. 5   **45.** no solution; Sec. 8.5, Ex. 2   **47.** 10 in.; Sec. 8.6, Ex. 1

49. a. 8   **b.** 9   **c.** -8; Sec. 8.7, Ex. 2

PRACTICE FINAL EXAM

1. -81 **2.** $\dfrac{1}{64}$ **3.** -48 **4.** $-3x^3 + 5x^2 + 4x + 5$ **5.** $16x^2 - 16x + 4$ **6.** $3x^3 + 22x^2 + 41x + 14$ **7.** $(y - 12)(y + 4)$

8. $3x(3x + 1)(x + 4)$ **9.** $5(6 + x)(6 - x)$ **10.** $(3a - 7)(a + b)$ **11.** $8(y - 2)(y^2 + 2y + 4)$ **12.** $\dfrac{y^{14}}{x^2}$ **13.** $\dfrac{5y^2 - 1}{y + 2}$ **14.** $\dfrac{2(x + 5)}{x(y + 5)}$

15. $\dfrac{3a - 4}{(a - 3)(a + 2)}$ **16.** 8 **17.** $-7, 1$ **18.** $(-\infty, -2]$ **19.** $\dfrac{3 \pm \sqrt{7}}{2}$ **20.** $\dfrac{30}{11}$ **21.** -6 **22.** no solution   **23.** 9

24.   **25.**   **26.** 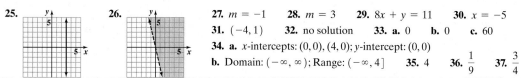   **27.** $m = -1$ **28.** $m = 3$ **29.** $8x + y = 11$ **30.** $x = -5$

31. $(-4, 1)$ **32.** no solution   **33. a.** 0 **b.** 0 **c.** 60

34. a. x-intercepts: $(0, 0), (4, 0)$; y-intercept: $(0, 0)$

b. Domain: $(-\infty, \infty)$; Range: $(-\infty, 4]$ **35.** 4 **36.** $\dfrac{1}{9}$ **37.** $\dfrac{3}{4}$

38. $3\sqrt{6}$ **39.** $3x^4\sqrt{x}$ **40.** $-8\sqrt{3}$ **41.** $2x\sqrt{5x}$ **42.** $2\sqrt{3} - \sqrt{10}$ **43.** $\dfrac{\sqrt{15}}{6x}$ **44.** $-1 - \sqrt{3}$ **45.** 5 or 1 **46.** $401, 802$

47. $2\dfrac{1}{2}$ hr   **48.** 120 cc

Graphing Answer Section

CHAPTER 1 REVIEW OF REAL NUMBERS

Practice Exercises 1.5

1.    2. 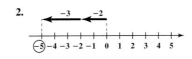   4.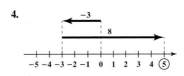

CHAPTER 2 EQUATIONS, INEQUALITIES, AND PROBLEM SOLVING

Exercise Set 2.9

1. $, x \geq 2$ 2. $, x > -3$ 3. $, x < -5$ 4. $, x \leq 4$ 5. $, (-\infty, -1]$

6. $, (-\infty, 0)$ 7. $, (-\infty, \frac{1}{2})$ 8. $, (-\infty, -\frac{2}{3})$ 9. $, [5, \infty)$ 10. $, (3, \infty)$

11. $, (-\infty, -3)$ 12. $, (-3, \infty)$ 13. $, [-5, \infty)$ 14. $, (-\infty, -3]$

15. $, [-2, \infty)$ 16. $, (-4, \infty)$ 17. $, (-3, \infty)$ 18. $, [7, \infty)$

19. $, (-\infty, 1]$ 20. $, (-\infty, -3)$ 21. $, (-5, \infty)$ 22. $, [7, \infty)$

23. $, (-\infty, -2]$ 24. $, (-\infty, -2)$ 25. $, (-\infty, -8]$ 26. $, (-\infty, \frac{4}{3}]$

27. $, (4, \infty)$ 28. $, (-\infty, -\frac{9}{2}]$ 29. $, [20, \infty)$ 30. $, (-\infty, -3)$ 31. $, (16, \infty)$

32. $, (-\infty, 5]$ 33. $, (-3, \infty)$ 34. $, (-\infty, 2]$ 35. $, (-\infty, -\frac{2}{3}]$ 36. $, (\frac{4}{11}, \infty)$

37. $, (\frac{8}{3}, \infty)$ 38. $, [-\frac{48}{5}, \infty)$ 39. $, (-13, \infty)$ 40. $, (\frac{8}{3}, \infty)$ 41. $, (-\infty, 0)$

42. $, (-\infty, 0]$ 43. $, (-\infty, 0]$ 44. $, (\frac{14}{3}, \infty)$ 45. $, (3, \infty)$ 46. $, (-\infty, \frac{5}{4}]$

47.   48. $, (-\infty, \frac{14}{3})$ 49. $, (-1, 3)$ 50. $, [2, 3]$ 51. $, [0, 2)$

52. $, [-1, 4]$ 53. $, (-1, 2)$ 54. $, (-\frac{5}{2}, -1)$ 55. $, [4, 5]$ 56. $, [2, 5]$

57. $, (1, 5)$ 58. $, (-5, -3]$ 59. $, (1, 4)$ 60. $, (-\frac{3}{2}, \frac{3}{2}]$ 61. $, (0, \frac{14}{3}]$

62. $, [-\frac{13}{2}, 0)$ 95. $, (1, \infty)$ 96. $, [-4, \infty)$ 97. $, (-\infty, \frac{5}{8})$ 98. $, (\frac{2}{3}, \infty)$

Chapter 2 Review

89.   90.   91.   92.   93.   94.

95.   96.   97.   98.   99.   100.

115.   116.   117.

Chapter 2 Test

17.   18.   19.   20.

Chapter 2 Cumulative Review

45.   46.

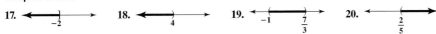

CHAPTER 3 GRAPHING

Section 3.1

Practice Exercises

3.
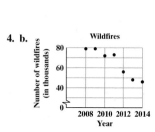

4. b.

Exercise Set 3.1

17.
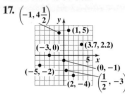

18.
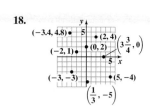

33. c.
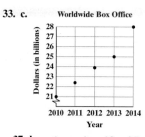

34. c.
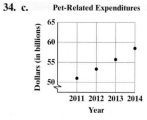

35. c.
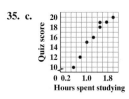

36. c.
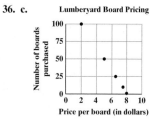

37. b.
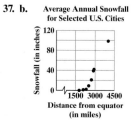

38. b.
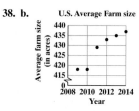

61.
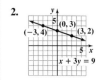

62.
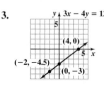

63.

64.
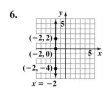

Section 3.2

Practice Exercises

2.

3.

4.

5.

6.

7.
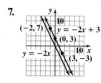

8. a.
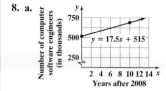

Calculator Explorations 3.2

1.
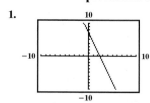

2.
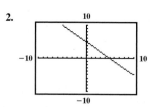

3.
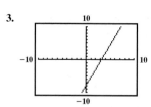

4. 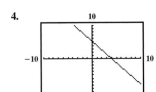   **5.** 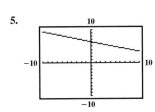   **6.**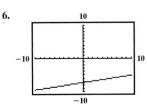

Exercise Set 3.2

9.   **10.**   **11.**   **12.** 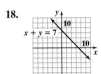   **13.** 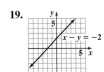   **14.**

15. 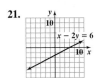   **16.**   **17.**   **18.** 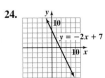   **19.**   **20.**

21.   **22.**   **23.**   **24.**   **25.** 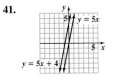   **26.**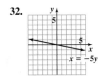

27. 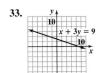   **28.**   **29.** 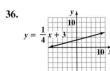   **30.** 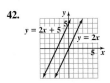   **31.** 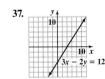   **32.**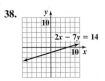

33. 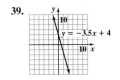   **34.** 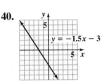   **35.** 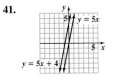   **36.** 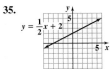   **37.** 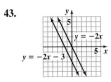   **38.**

39. 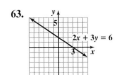   **40.** 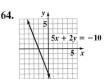   **41.** 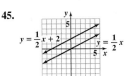   **42.** 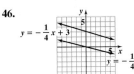   **43.**

44. 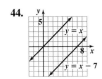   **45.** 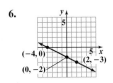   **46.**   **61.**   **62.**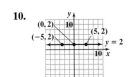

63. 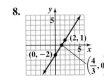   **64.** 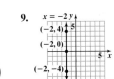   **69.**   **70.**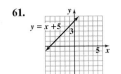

Section 3.3

Practice Exercises

6.   **7.**   **8.**   **9.**   **10.**

Calculator Explorations 3.3

1.
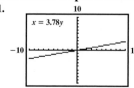

2.
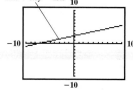

3.
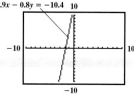

4.
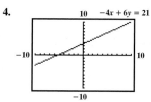

5. $-2.2x + 6.8y = 15.5$
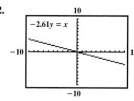

6. $5.9x - 0.8y = -10.4$
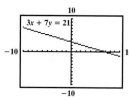

Exercise Set 3.3

13.

14.

15.

16.

17.

18.

19.

20.

21.

22.

23.

24.

25.

26.

27.

28.

29.

30.

31.

32.

33.

34.
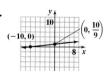

35.

36.

37.

38.

39.

40.

41.

42.

43.

44.

45.

46.

47.
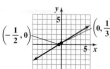

48.
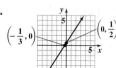

Section 3.4
Calculator Explorations

1.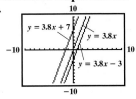

2.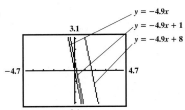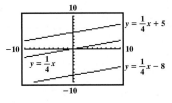

3.

4.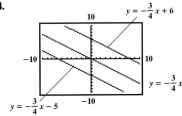

Integrated Review

5.

6.

7.

8.

9.

10.

11.

12.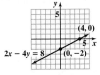

Chapter 3 Review

1.
(−7, 0)

2.
$\left(0, 4\frac{4}{5}\right)$
4

3.
(−2, −5)

4.
(1, −3)

5.
(0.7, 0.7)

6.
(−6, 4)

7. b.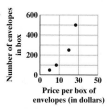

8. b.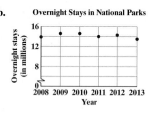
Overnight Stays in National Parks

15.
(1, 3) (9, 9)
(−3, 0)

16.
(10, 5)
(0, 0)
(−10, −5)

19.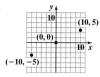
$x - y = 1$

20.
$x + y = 6$

21.
$x - 3y = 12$

22.
$5x - y = -8$

23.
$x = 3y$

24.
$y = -2x$

25.
$2x - 3y = 6$

26.
$4x - 3y = 12$

31.
$x - 3y = 12$
(12, 0)
(0, −4)

32.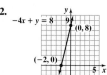
$-4x + y = 8$ (0, 8)
(−2, 0)

33.
$y = -3$
(0, −3)

34.
$x = 5$
(5, 0)

35.
$y = -3x$
(0, 0)

36.
(0, 0) $x = 5y$

37.
$x - 2 = 0$
(2, 0)

38.
$y + 6 = 0$ (0, −6)

63.
(0, −1)
$y = 3x - 1$

64.
$y = -3x$
(0, 0)

65.
(3, 0)
(0, −5) $5x - 3y = 15$

66.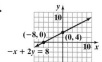
(−8, 0) (0, 4)
$-x + 2y = 8$

109.
(10, 0)
$x - 5y = 10$
(0, −2)

110.
(0, 4)
(4, 0)
$x + y = 4$

111.
$y = -4x$
(0, 0)
(1, −4)

112.
(−3, 0) $2x + 3y = -6$
(0, −2)

113.
$x = 3$
(3, 0)

114.
(0, −2)
$y = -2$

Chapter 3 Test

1.
$y = \frac{1}{2}x$

2.
$2x + y = 8$ 7
3

3.
$5x - 7y = 10$

4.
$y = -1$

5.
$x - 3 = 0$

30. b.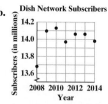
Dish Network Subscribers

Chapter 3 Cumulative Review

32.
$y = -3x + 5$

33.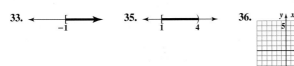

35.

36.

CHAPTER 5 EXPONENTS AND POLYNOMIALS

Chapter 5 Cumulative Review

28.

31.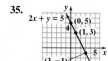

35.

37.

41.

CHAPTER 6 FACTORING POLYNOMIALS

Section 6.6

Exercise Set 6.6

103. d.

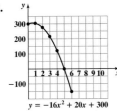

$y = -16x^2 + 20x + 300$

104. d.

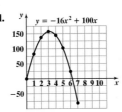

$y = -16x^2 + 100x$

Chapter 6 Cumulative Review

21.

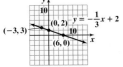

$y = -\frac{1}{3}x + 2$

$(0, 2)$

$(-3, 3)$

$(6, 0)$

CHAPTER 7 RATIONAL EXPRESSIONS

Exercise Set 7.1

103.

$y = \frac{x^2 - 25}{x + 5}$

104.

$y = \frac{x^2 - 16}{x - 4}$

105.

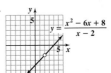

$y = \frac{x^2 + x - 12}{x + 4}$

106.

$y = \frac{x^2 - 6x + 8}{x - 2}$

Exercise Set 7.2

79.

$x - 2y = 6$

80.

$5x - y = 10$

Chapter 7 Cumulative Review

5.

$x - 3y = 6$

$(6, 0)$

$(0, -2)$

CHAPTER 8 ROOTS AND RADICALS

Exercise Set 8.1

97.

98.

Chapter 8 Cumulative Review

21.

$$3x \geq y$$
$$x + 2y \leq 8$$

22.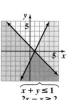

$$x + y \leq 1$$
$$2x - y \geq 2$$

Practice Final Exam

24.

25.

26.

Video Answer Section

CHAPTER 1 REVIEW OF REAL NUMBERS

Section 1.2
9. To form a true statement: $0 < 7$. **10.** Five is greater than or equal to four; $5 \geq 4$ **11.** 0 belongs to the whole numbers, the integers, the rational numbers, and the real numbers; since 0 is a rational number, it cannot also be an irrational number. **12.** absolute value

Section 1.3
8. 5, Fundamental Principle of Fractions **9.** The division operation changes to multiplication and the second fraction $\frac{1}{20}$ changes to its reciprocal $\frac{20}{1}$.
10. Find the LCD; two fractions must have the same or common denominator before you can subtract (or add). **11.** The number $4\frac{7}{6}$ is not in proper mixed number form as the fraction part, $\frac{7}{6}$, should not be an improper fraction.

Section 1.4
8. The order in which we perform operations does matter! We came up with an order of operations to avoid getting more than one answer when evaluating an expression. **9.** The replacement value for z is not used because it's not needed—there is no variable z in the given algebraic expression.
10. No; the variable was replaced with 0 in the equation to see if a true statement occurred, and it did not. **11.** We translate phrases to mathematical expressions and sentences to mathematical equations.

Section 1.5
5. absolute values **6.** Negative; when you add two numbers with different signs, the sign of the sum is the same as the sign of the number with the larger absolute value and -8.4 has a larger absolute value than 6.3. **7.** Negative temperatures; the high temperature for the day was $-6°$F.
8. Example 13 is an example of the opposite of the *absolute value* of $-a$, not the opposite of $-a$. The absolute value of $-a$ is positive, so its opposite is negative, therefore the answers to Examples 12 and 13 have different signs.

Section 1.6
9. addition, opposite **10.** $-10 + (8) + (-4) + (-20)$; it's rewritten to change the subtraction operations to addition and turn the problem into an addition of real numbers problem **11.** There's a minus sign in the numerator and the replacement value is negative (notice parentheses are used around the replacement value), and it's always good to be careful when working with negative signs. **12.** This means that the overall vertical altitude change of the jet is actually a decrease in altitude from when the Example started. **13.** In Example 9, you have two supplementary angles and know the measure of one of them. From the definition, you know that the two supplementary angles must sum to 180°. Therefore you can subtract the known angle measure from 180° to get the measure of the other angle.

Section 1.7
9. The parentheses, or lack of them, determine the base of the expression. In Example 6, $(-2)^4$, the base is -2 and all of -2 is raised to the fourth power.
In Example 7, -2^4, the base is 2 and only 2 is raised to the fourth power. **10.** Remember, the product of a number and its reciprocal is 1, *not*
-1. $\frac{2}{3} \cdot \frac{3}{2} = 1$, as needed. **11.** Yes; because division of real numbers is defined in terms of multiplication. **12.** The replacement values are negative and both will be squared. Therefore they must be placed in parentheses so the entire value, including the negative, is squared. **13.** The football team lost 4 yards on each play and a loss of yardage is represented by a negative number.

Section 1.8
8. order; grouping **9.** 2 is outside the parentheses, so the point is made that you should only distribute the -9 to the terms within the parentheses and not also to the 2. **10.** 0; 0; 1; 1.

CHAPTER 2 EQUATIONS, INEQUALITIES, AND PROBLEM SOLVING

Section 2.1
7. Although these terms have exactly the same variables, the exponents on each are not exactly the same—the exponents on x differ in each term.
8. distributive property **9.** -1 **10.** The sum of 5 times a number and -2, added to 7 times the number; $5x + (-2) + 7x$; because there are like terms

Section 2.2
7. both sides **8.** To confirm our solution, we replace the variable with the solution in the original equation to make sure we have a true statement.
9. $\frac{1}{7}x$

Section 2.3
5. same **6.** addition property; multiplication property; answers may vary **7.** $(x + 1) + (x + 3) = 2x + 4$

Section 2.4

9. 3; distributive property, addition property of equality, multiplication property of equality   **10.** Because both sides have more than one term, you need to apply the distributive property to make sure you multiply every single term in the equation by the LCD.   **11.** The number of decimal places in each number helps you determine the least power of 10 you can multiply through by so you are no longer dealing with decimals.   **12. a.** all real numbers as a   **b.** no

Section 2.5

7. in the statement of the application   **8.** The original application asks for the measure of two supplementary angles. The solution of $x = 43$ only gives us the measure of one of the angles.   **9.** That the 3 angle measures are consecutive even integers and that they sum to $180°$.

Section 2.6

1. relationships   **2.** This is a distance, rate, and time problem. The distance is given in miles and the time is given in hours, so the rate that we are finding must be in miles per hour (mph).   **3.** To show that the process of solving this equation for x—dividing both sides by 5, the coefficient of x—is the same process used to solve a formula for a specific variable. Treat whatever is multiplied by that specific variable as the coefficient—the coefficient is all the factors except that specific variable.

Section 2.9

7. The graph of Example 1 is shaded from $-\infty$ to and including -1, as indicated by a bracket. To write interval notation, you write down what is shaded for the inequality from left to right. A parenthesis is always used with $-\infty$, so from the graph, the interval notation is $(-\infty, -1]$.   **8.** Step 5 is where you apply the multiplication property of inequality. If a negative number is multiplied or divided when applying this property, you need to make sure you remember to reverse the direction of the inequality symbol.   **9.** You would divide the left, middle, and right by -3 instead of 3, which would reverse the directions of both inequality symbols.   **10.** no greater than; $\leq$

CHAPTER 3 GRAPHING

Section 3.1

7. horizontal: top tourist destinations vertical: number of arrivals (in millions) to these destinations   **8.** origin; left or right; up or down   **9.** Data occurring in pairs of numbers can be written as ordered pairs, called paired data, and then graphed on a coordinate system.   **10.** $(7, 0)$ and $(0, 7)$; since one of these points is a solution and one is not, it shows that it is very important to remember that the first number is the x-value and the second number is the y-value and not to mix them up.   **11.** a linear equation in one variable

Section 3.2

1. In the definition, x and y both have an understood power of 1. Example 3 shows an equation where y has a power of 2, so it is not a linear equation in two variables.   **2.** Find 3 points in order to check your work. Make sure the points lie along one straight line—if not, an algebraic mistake was probably made.   **3.** An infinite number of points make up the line and each point corresponds to an ordered pair that is a solution of the linear equation in two variables.

Section 3.3

9. Because x-intercepts lie on the x-axis; because y-intercepts lie on the y-axis.   **10.** Using a third point as a check that your points lie along a straight line is always good practice.   **11.** For a horizontal line, the coefficient of x will be 0; for a vertical line, the coefficient of y will be 0.

Section 3.4

8. Whatever y-value you decide to start with in the numerator, you *must* start with the corresponding x-value in the denominator.   **9.** solve the equation for y; the slope is the coefficient of x.   **10.** Zero slope indicates $m = 0$ and a horizontal line; undefined slope indicates m is undefined and a vertical line; no slope refers to an undefined slope.   **11.** slope-intercept form; this form makes the slope easy to see, and you need to compare slopes to determine if two lines are parallel or perpendicular.   **12.** Step 4: INTERPRET the results.

CHAPTER 5 EXPONENTS AND POLYNOMIALS

Section 5.1

7. Example 4 can be written as $-4^2 = -1 \cdot 4^2$, which is similar to Example 7, $4 \cdot 3^2$, and shows why the negative sign should not be considered part of the base when there are no parentheses. **8.** The properties allow us to reorder and regroup factors and put those with common bases together, making it easier to apply the product rule; yes, in Example 13. **9.** Be careful not to confuse the power rule with the product rule. The power rule involves a power raised to a power (exponents are multiplied), and the product rule involves a product (exponents are added). **10.** Remember to raise the -2 (or any number) to the power along with the variables. **11.** the quotient rule **12.** No, Example 30 is a fraction and does not use the quotient rule.

Section 5.2

7. The degree of the polynomial is the greatest degree of any of its terms, so we need to find the degree of each term first. **8.** the replacement value for the variables **9.** simplifying it **10.** Addition; no, we subtract in Examples 9–11. To subtract, we change the signs of the polynomial being subtracted and then add.

Section 5.3

5. No. The monomials are unlike terms. **6.** distributive property, product rule **7.** Yes. The parentheses have been removed for the vertical format, but every term in the first polynomial is still distributed to every term in the second polynomial.

Section 5.4

5. a binomial times a binomial   **6.** FOIL order for multiplication, distributive property   **7.** Multiplying gives you four terms, and the two like terms will always subtract out.   **8.** The FOIL method is only used for multiplying a binomial and a binomial and that is not the case for this example.

Section 5.5

5. A negative exponent has nothing to do with the sign of the simplified result.   **6.** power of a product rule, power rule for exponents, negative exponent definition, quotient rule for exponents   **7.** When you move the decimal point to the left, the sign of the exponent will be positive; when you move the decimal point to the right, the sign of the exponent will be negative.   **8.** the exponent on 10   **9.** the quotient rule

Section 5.6

7. the common denominator   **8.** Filling in missing powers helps you keep like terms lined up and your work clear and neat.

CHAPTER 6 FACTORING POLYNOMIALS

Section 6.1

7. The GCF of a list of numbers is the largest number that is a factor of all numbers in the list.   **8.** The GCF of common variable factors is the variable raised to the smallest exponent.   **9.** When factoring out a GCF, the number of terms in the other factor should have the same number of terms as your original polynomial.   **10.** Look for a GCF other than 1 or −1; if you have a simplified four-term polynomial.

Section 6.2

11. 15 is positive, so its factors would have to either be both positive or both negative. Since the factors need to sum to −8, both factors must be negative.   **12.** Since the sum of the factors is 3, the factors are −2 and 5, (−2 + 5 = 3). If you accidentally choose factors whose sum is −3, simply "switch" the signs of the factors.

Section 6.3

7. Consider the factors of the first and last terms and the signs of the trinomial. Continue to check by multiplying until you get the middle term of the trinomial.   **8.** If the GCF has been factored out, then neither binomial can contain a common factor other than 1 or −1. This helps limit your choice of factors for one or both binomials since you cannot choose factors that would give the terms in either binomial a common factor.   **9.** The first and last terms are squares, a^2 and b^2, and the middle term is $2 \cdot a \cdot b$ or $-2 \cdot a \cdot b$.

Section 6.4

5. This gives us a four-term polynomial, which may be factored by grouping.

Section 6.5

9. In order to recognize the binomial as a difference of squares and also to identify the terms to use in the special factoring formula.   **10.** A prime polynomial is one that can't be factored further.   **11.** First rewrite the original binomial with terms written as cubes. Answers will then vary depending on your interpretation.

Section 6.6

5. One side of the equation must be a factored polynomial and the other side must be zero.   **6.** Because no matter how many factors you have in a multiplication problem, it's still true that for a zero product, at least one of the factors must be zero.   **7.** To find the x-intercepts of any graph in two variables, we let $y = 0$. Doing this with our quadratic equation gives us an equation = 0, which we can try to solve by factoring.

CHAPTER 7 RATIONAL EXPRESSIONS

Section 7.1

8. replacement values for the variables; by evaluating the expression for different replacement values—variables are replaced with these values and the expression is simplified   **9.** Rational expressions are fractions and are therefore undefined if the denominator is zero; if a denominator contains variables, set it equal to zero and solve.   **10.** Although x is a factor in the numerator, it is not a factor in the denominator—factor means write as a product and the denominator is a difference, not a product.   **11.** You would need to write parentheses around the numerator or denominator if it had more than one term because the negative sign needs to apply to the entire numerator or denominator.

Section 7.2

6. Yes, multiplying and simplifying rational expressions often requires polynomial factoring. Example 2 alone involves factoring out a GCF, factoring a trinomial with $a \neq 1$, and factoring a difference of squares.   **7.** fractions; reciprocal   **8.** Multiplication and division of rational expressions are performed similarly—both involve multiplication—but there are important differences. Note the operation first to see whether you multiply by the reciprocal or not.   **9.** The units in the unit fraction consist of $\frac{\text{units converting to}}{\text{original units}}$.

CHAPTER 8 ROOTS AND RADICALS

Section 8.1
9. The radical sign, $\sqrt{\ }$, indicates a positive square root only. A negative sign before the radical sign, $-\sqrt{\ }$, indicates a negative square root.
10. A square root of a negative number is not a real number, but the cube root of a negative number is a real number.   **11.** an odd-numbered index
12. Take the two integers that your answer falls between and square them, then check to make sure that the radicand falls between these two squares.
13. Divide the index into each exponent in the radicand.

Section 8.2
5. Factor until you have a product of primes. A repeated prime factor means a perfect square—if more than one factor is repeated you can multiply all the repeated factors together to get one larger perfect square factor.   **6.** numerator; denominator   **7.** The power must be 1. Any even power is a perfect square and can be simplified; any higher odd power is the product of an even power times the variable with a power of 1.   **8.** If a factor is repeated the same number of times as the index, then you have a perfect root, and the product rule can be applied.

Section 8.3
7. Both like terms and like radicals are combined using the distributive property; also only like (vs. unlike) terms can be combined, as with like radicals (same index and same radical).   **8.** Sometimes you can't see that there are like radicals to combine until you simplify, so you may incorrectly think you cannot add or subtract if you don't simplify first.

Section 8.4
6. In each example, the product rule is first used to multiply the radicals and then later used to simplify the radicals.   **7.** The square root of a positive number times the square root of the same positive number (or the square root of a positive number squared) is that positive number.   **8.** If you notice that some simplifying can be done to the fraction if both radicands are under one radical.   **9.** To write an equivalent expression without a radical in the denominator.   **10.** Using the FOIL order to multiply, the Outer product and the Inner product are the only terms with radicals and they will subtract out.

Index

Photo Credits

Cover Sgursolzlu/Fotolia